Globe Fearon Mathematics . . .

Chapters are organized in the sequence mathematics teachers asked for.

Contents of the Teacher's Edition

Consultants

Michelle Tiberio,
Middle School Teacher,
Gloucester, VA

Carol Pitkewicz, Neil Zarcone,
Michael Zafonte,
Bayport-Blue Point High School, NY

Rochelle Gilbert,
Monroe City School District, LA

Don Busenbark,
High School Teacher,
Roosevelt, UT

Susan Youngblood,
Middle School Teacher,
Macon, GA

Judy Roe,
Middle School Teacher,
Fort Bragg, NC

Gladys H. Pugh,
Mathematics Teacher and
Tutor Center Coordinator,
Scranton, PA

Printed in the United States of America

2 3 4 5 6 7 8 9 10   04 03 02 01 00

ISBN: 0-130-23407-9 (Student Edition)
ISBN: 0-130-23406-0 (Annotated Teacher's Edition)
Formerly titled *Globe High School Mathematics*

Globe
Fearon

Annotated Teacher's Edition

Globe Fearon

MATHEMATICS

REVISED EDITION

Globe
Fearon

Upper Saddle River, New Jersey
www.globefearon.com

. . . reaches every student

The Teacher's Resource Binder includes 258 pages of reproducible worksheets, 184 pages of tests, and 9 pages of teaching aids.

Here is everything you need to teach, conveniently organized.

The completely annotated Teacher's Edition has extra-wide side margins, containing practical suggestions for teaching each lesson.

The Student's Edition contains 496 pages, with 56 pages of extra practice, emphasizing solid skills development, problem solving, and critical thinking.

The revised editions of *Mathematics Workshop: Basic Skills 1 and 2,* also available from Globe Fearon, provide additional practice in skills development and problem solving. The sequence of topics matches that of *Globe Fearon Mathematics.*

Set the stage . . .

Chapter Openers

Motivating two-page chapter openers introduce the chapter concepts.

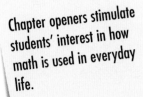
Chapter openers stimulate students' interest in how math is used in everyday life.

Each spread opens with a list of ways students can use the skills they learn in the chapter in everyday life. Also featured is a discussion question which encourages the class to talk about other real-life applications.

The career feature introduces students to a career that uses some of the skills covered in the chapter. Each one provides a brief description of the career, personality traits that lend themselves to a career in that field, and some aspects of the job itself. Also included is an overview of the experience and education recommended and other careers related to the Chapter Skills.

Each Portfolio Project encourages students to use the skills from the chapter and apply them in a real-life situation.

. . . for active learning

Background Lessons

Most chapters begin with a background lesson to orient students to the chapter.

A real-life situation related to the chapter concepts is presented.

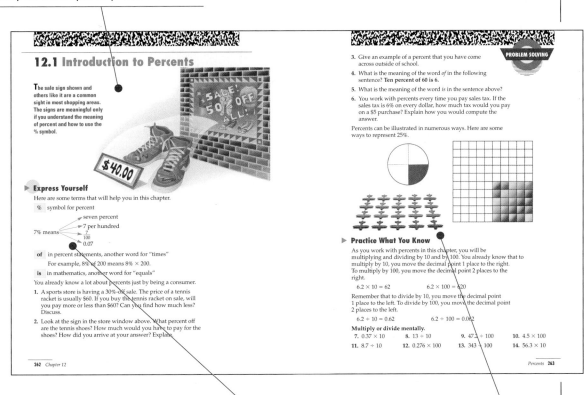

12.1 Introduction to Percents

The sale sign shown and others like it are a common sight in most shopping areas. The signs are meaningful only if you understand the meaning of percent and how to use the % symbol.

▶ **Express Yourself**

Here are some terms that will help you in this chapter.

% symbol for percent

7% means — seven percent
— 7 per hundred
— $\frac{7}{100}$
— 0.07

of in percent statements, another word for "times"
For example, 8% of 200 means 8% × 200.

is in mathematics, another word for "equals"

You already know a lot about percents just by being a consumer.

1. A sports store is having a 30%-off sale. The price of a tennis racket is usually $60. If you buy the tennis racket on sale, will you pay more or less than $60? Can you find how much less? Discuss.

2. Look at the sign in the store window above. What percent off are the tennis shoes? How much would you have to pay for the shoes? How did you arrive at your answer? Explain.

262 Chapter 12

PROBLEM SOLVING

3. Give an example of a percent that you have come across outside of school.

4. What is the meaning of the word *of* in the following sentence? **Ten percent of 60 is 6.**

5. What is the meaning of the word *is* in the sentence above?

6. You work with percents every time you pay sales tax. If the sales tax is 6% on every dollar, how much tax would you pay on a $5 purchase? Explain how you would compute the answer.

Percents can be illustrated in numerous ways. Here are some ways to represent 25%.

▶ **Practice What You Know**

As you work with percents in this chapter, you will be multiplying and dividing by 10 and by 100. You already know that to multiply by 10, you move the decimal point 1 place to the right. To multiply by 100, you move the decimal point 2 places to the right.

6.2 × 10 = 62   6.2 × 100 = 620

Remember that to divide by 10, you move the decimal point 1 place to the left. To divide by 100, you move the decimal point 2 places to the left.

6.2 ÷ 10 = 0.62   6.2 ÷ 100 = 0.062

Multiply or divide mentally.

7. 0.37 × 10   8. 13 ÷ 10   9. 47.1 ÷ 100   10. 4.5 × 100

11. 8.7 ÷ 10   12. 0.276 × 100   13. 343 ÷ 100   14. 56.3 × 10

Percents 263

Mathematical terms are highlighted and defined.

Students practice previously taught skills that they will use in the chapter.

Build understanding . . .

Skills Lessons

Skills instruction and practice are carefully paced, step by step.

Skills lessons begin with an interesting question or situation that gives students a reason for learning.

The blue box contains clear examples.

Skills lessons are two pages long and delightfully readable.

Think and Discuss questions provide practice in the lesson skills and lead students to think critically.

12.2 Decimals and Percents

Weekly ratings reports tell us about television viewing. Such a report is shown here. Each rating point is equivalent to 1% of the television sets in the United States. You can express the rating of each program as a percent or as a decimal.

SPORTS ON TV

Ratings for network sports events for the week ending Nov. 2

Event	Rating
1. Monday Night Football	17.5
2. Sunday NFL Game 1	14.1
3. Sunday NFL Game 2	12.4
4. Sunday NFL Game 3	11.7

Examples

To write a decimal as a percent, multiply the decimal by 100 and write a percent sign after it.

To write a percent as a decimal, divide the percent by 100 and omit the percent sign.

A Write 0.375 as a percent.

$0.375 = 0.37.5$ Move the decimal point two places to the right.
$\quad\quad = \textbf{37.5\%}$ Write a % sign.

B Write 4% as a decimal.

$4\% = .04.$ Move the decimal point two places to the left.
$\quad\ = \textbf{0.04}$ Add zeros as placeholders and omit the percent sign.

▶ **Think and Discuss**

1. Write 13% as a decimal. How many places and in what direction did you move the decimal point?

2. Refer to the introduction to this lesson. Write the rating of the fourth-rated program as a percent and as a decimal.

3. Write 67.3 as a percent.

264   *Chapter 12*

. . . for active learning

Background Lessons

Most chapters begin with a background lesson to orient students to the chapter.

A real-life situation related to the chapter concepts is presented.

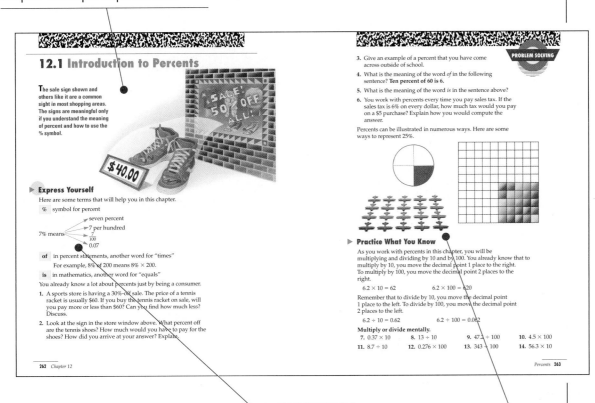

12.1 Introduction to Percents

The sale sign shown and others like it are a common sight in most shopping areas. The signs are meaningful only if you understand the meaning of percent and how to use the % symbol.

$40.00

▶ **Express Yourself**

Here are some terms that will help you in this chapter.

% symbol for percent

7% means
— seven percent
— 7 per hundred
— $\frac{7}{100}$
— 0.07

of in percent statements, another word for "times"
For example, 8% of 200 means 8% × 200.

is in mathematics, another word for "equals"

You already know a lot about percents just by being a consumer.

1. A sports store is having a 30%-off sale. The price of a tennis racket is usually $60. If you buy the tennis racket on sale, will you pay more or less than $60? Can you find how much less? Discuss.

2. Look at the sign in the store window above. What percent off are the tennis shoes? How much would you have to pay for the shoes? How did you arrive at your answer? Explain.

262 *Chapter 12*

PROBLEM SOLVING

3. Give an example of a percent that you have come across outside of school.

4. What is the meaning of the word *of* in the following sentence? **Ten percent of 60 is 6.**

5. What is the meaning of the word *is* in the sentence above?

6. You work with percents every time you pay sales tax. If the sales tax is 6% on every dollar, how much tax would you pay on a $5 purchase? Explain how you would compute the answer.

Percents can be illustrated in numerous ways. Here are some ways to represent 25%.

▶ **Practice What You Know**

As you work with percents in this chapter, you will be multiplying and dividing by 10 and by 100. You already know that to multiply by 10, you move the decimal point 1 place to the right. To multiply by 100, you move the decimal point 2 places to the right.

$6.2 \times 10 = 62$ $\qquad$ $6.2 \times 100 = 620$

Remember that to divide by 10, you move the decimal point 1 place to the left. To divide by 100, you move the decimal point 2 places to the left.

$6.2 \div 10 = 0.62$ $\qquad$ $6.2 \div 100 = 0.062$

Multiply or divide mentally.

7. 0.37×10 $\quad$ 8. $13 \div 10$ $\quad$ 9. $47.1 \div 100$ $\quad$ 10. 4.5×100

11. $8.7 \div 10$ $\quad$ 12. 0.276×100 $\quad$ 13. $343 \div 100$ $\quad$ 14. 56.3×10

Percents **263**

Mathematical terms are highlighted and defined.

Students practice previously taught skills that they will use in the chapter.

Build understanding . . .

Skills Lessons

Skills instruction and practice are carefully paced, step by step.

Skills lessons begin with an interesting question or situation that gives students a reason for learning.

The blue box contains clear examples.

Skills lessons are two pages long and delightfully readable.

Think and Discuss questions provide practice in the lesson skills and lead students to think critically.

12.2 Decimals and Percents

SPORTS ON TV

Ratings for network sports events for the week ending Nov. 2

Event	Rating
1. Monday Night Football	17.5
2. Sunday NFL Game 1	14.1
3. Sunday NFL Game 2	12.4
4. Sunday NFL Game 3	11.7

●Weekly ratings reports tell us about television viewing. Such a report is shown here. Each rating point is equivalent to 1% of the television sets in the United States. You can express the rating of each program as a percent or as a decimal.

Examples

To write a decimal as a percent, multiply the decimal by 100 and write a percent sign after it.

To write a percent as a decimal, divide the percent by 100 and omit the percent sign.

A Write 0.375 as a percent.

0.375 = 0.37.5   Move the decimal point two places to the right.
= **37.5%**   Write a % sign.

B Write 4% as a decimal.

4% = .04.   Move the decimal point two places to the left.
= **0.04**   Add zeros as placeholders and omit the percent sign.

▶ **Think and Discuss**

1. Write 13% as a decimal. How many places and in what direction did you move the decimal point?

2. Refer to the introduction to this lesson. Write the rating of the fourth-rated program as a percent and as a decimal.

3. Write 67.3 as a percent.

264 *Chapter 12*

Knowing the Score – Reviews and Tests

On the job and in learning, checking your performance is important. It helps you learn where to concentrate your efforts.

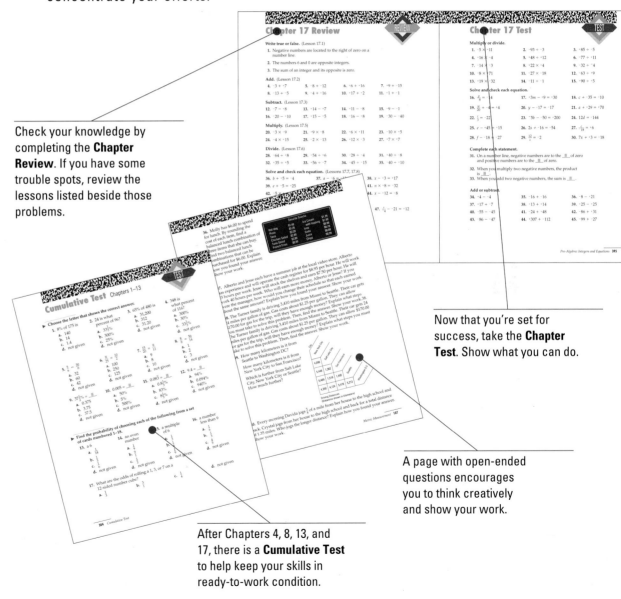

Check your knowledge by completing the **Chapter Review**. If you have some trouble spots, review the lessons listed beside those problems.

Now that you're set for success, take the **Chapter Test**. Show what you can do.

A page with open-ended questions encourages you to think creatively and show your work.

After Chapters 4, 8, 13, and 17, there is a **Cumulative Test** to help keep your skills in ready-to-work condition.

Keep your knowledge of problem-solving strategies fresh by completing the **Review** section at the end of each lesson. The more you practice these strategies, the easier it becomes for you to use them.

PROBLEM SOLVING

Questions	Answers
5. What operations must I carry out?	Addition, division, subtraction, multiplication
6. In what order should I do the operations?	Follow the sequence under Plan for Question 4.

...planning how to solve a problem ...lem before. Ask ...problem

Another poin...
is whether y...
yourself if a...
can be used...

▶ Think a...

1. Solve t...

2. As yo...
this p...
Pa...
5...
t...

3. C...

4.7 Using a Table to Find Information

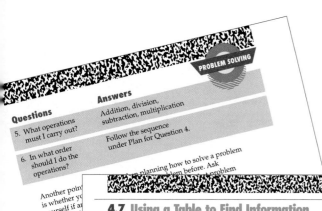

AUSTRALIA

- Cairns
- Alice Springs
- Perth
- Adelaide
- Sydney
- Melbourne

	Adelaide	Alice Springs	Cairns	Melbourne	Perth	Sydney
	1693	2436				
	2845	2436				
	755	2488	3501			
	2713	3772	4727	3468		
	1422	2960	2853	893	4135	

Before you even open the envelope, you could start mentally planning your trip with the help of a map and a kilometer table.

Use the kilometer table to answer the following questions.
1. How far is it from Alice Springs to Perth? Look down the column from Alice Springs until you come to the row that goes across to Perth.

2. Which city is 2853 kilometers from Sydney? Find 2853 in the row that goes across to Sydney, and see which city is at the head of that column.

3. Which two cities are 755 kilometers apart? Find 755 in the table, and read the cities for that column and row.

For part of your trip, you plan to take trains. Below is a train schedule for four cities. Each train is named after one of the special animals of Australia.

Train	Arrives at Sydney	Arrives at Wollongong	Arrives at Canberra	Arrives at Melbourne
Kangaroo	8:30 a.m.	10:00 a.m.	11:50 a.m.	4:30 p.m.
Wallaby	12:00 noon	1:40 p.m.	3:45 p.m.	8:45 p.m.
Koala	4:00 p.m.	5:30 p.m.	7:15 p.m.	11:30 p.m.

Use the train schedule to answer the following questions.
4. What time does the Wallaby arrive at Canberra?

5. About how long is the trip from Sydney to Wollongong? Is it the same for all three trains?

6. It is 11:00 a.m. in Canberra. How long will it be until the next train to Melbourne leaves?

7. The trip from Canberra to Melbourne is about 500 kilometers. Use the schedule to find how long the trip on the Koala takes. Then estimate how fast the train travels.

For another part of your trip, you plan to rent a car. The table below shows how far you can go, in kilometers, on a single tank of gasoline, depending on the size of the car's gas tank and the car's kilometer-per-liter rating.

Size of Tank	Maximum Distance (per tank of gas)			
	5.9 km/L	7.8 km/L	9.9 km/L	13.7 km/L
32 L	188.8	249.6	316.8	438.4
40 L	236	312	396	548
50 L	295	390	495	685
65 L	383.5	507	643.5	890.5

Use the table above to answer the following questions.
8. What is the greatest distance you can travel on one tank of gasoline if your tank holds 40 liters and your car averages 7.8 kilometers per liter?

9. On one tank, how far could you go in a car with a 32-liter tank that averages 5.9 kilometers per liter? How much farther could you go in a car with a 65-liter tank that averages 13.7 kilometers per liter?

▶ **Review** (Lesson 3.8)
10. Each section of a theater seats 175 people. There are 8 sections. What operation would you use to find how many seats are in the theater? How many seats are there?

Problem-Solving Lessons
Provide Winning Strategies

The main reason for learning math skills is to apply them to the mathematical problems that are a part of daily life. **Problem-Solving Lessons** introduce you to plans and strategies for dealing with those problems.

PROBLEM SOLVING

Problem-Solving Lessons have the Problem-Solving logo in the corner.

Four problem-solving lessons present information about using a **4-Step Problem-Solving Process.** Look for the **Read**, **Plan**, **Do**, and **Check** logo in these lessons.

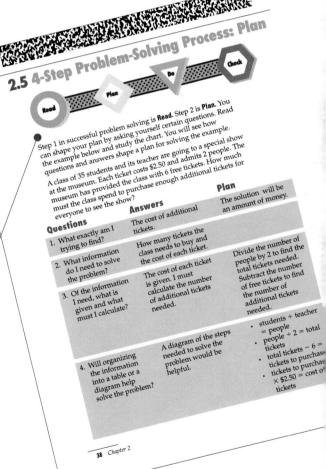

2.5 4-Step Problem-Solving Process: Plan

Read   Plan   Do   Check

Step 1 in successful problem solving is **Read**. Step 2 is **Plan**. You can shape your plan by asking yourself certain questions. Read the example below and study the chart. You will see how questions and answers shape a plan for solving the example.

A class of 35 students and its teacher are going to a special show at the museum. Each ticket costs $2.50 and admits 2 people. The museum has provided the class with 6 free tickets. How much must the class spend to purchase enough additional tickets for everyone to see the show?

Questions	Answers	Plan
	The cost of additional tickets.	The solution will be an amount of money.
1. What exactly am I trying to find?		
2. What information do I need to solve the problem?	How many tickets the class needs to buy and the cost of each ticket.	Divide the number of people by 2 to find the total tickets needed. Subtract the number of free tickets to find the number of additional tickets needed.
3. Of the information I need, what is given and what must I calculate?	The cost of each ticket is given. I must calculate the number of additional tickets needed.	
4. Will organizing the information into a table or a diagram help solve the problem?	A diagram of the steps needed to solve the problem would be helpful.	• students + teacher = people • people ÷ 2 = total tickets • total tickets − 6 = tickets to purchas • tickets to purchas × $2.50 = cost o tickets

38 Chapter 2

The first exercise sets are matched with the examples. Because the lesson always appears on two facing pages, it's easy to look back to the examples for help.

SKILLS

2. Convert 5 miles to feet.

3. Refer to the introduction to this lesson. Which roller coaster drops farther?

4. It takes Jan 8 minutes to run a mile. How many feet does she run in 1 minute?

5. Convert 5.1 feet to inches in two ways. First, round to the nearest foot and then convert. Second, convert and then round to the nearest inch. Which answer is a better estimate? Why?

6. Explain how you would order 35 yards, 1392 inches, and 114 feet from shortest to longest.

Exercises

Convert each measure. (See Example A.)

7. 4 ft. to in.
8. 25 yd. to ft.
9. 2 mi. to ft.
10. 7 yd. to in.
11. 20 ft. to in.
12. 3 yd. to ft.
13. 10 yd. to in.
14. 9 mi. to ft.

Convert each measure. (See Example B.)

15. 561 ft. to yd.
16. 540 in. to yd.
17. 15,840 ft. to mi.
18. 228 in. to ft.
19. 7040 yd. to mi.
20. 36,960 ft. to mi.

▶ **Mixed Practice** (For more practice, see page 425.)

Convert each measure.

21. 5 ft. to in.
22. 108 in. to yd.
23. 297 ft. to yd.
24. 10 ft. to in.
25. 1800 in. to ft.
26. 21,600 in. to yd.

Mixed Practice is more challenging. You must decide which example to follow.

If you need **Extra Practice**, check the page reference for additional practice problems in the back of the book.

▶ **Applications**

27. A marathon can be 26 miles 385 yards long. How many yards is that?

28. Bill told his mother he was going to race in the 440 this weekend. "Don't you usually run the $\frac{1}{4}$-mile race?" she asked. Was Bill running in a different race than usual? Explain.

Applications give you a chance to apply what you've learned to real-life situations.

▶ **Review** (Lessons 7.1, 7.3, 7.4)

Add.

29. $\begin{array}{r} \frac{1}{6} \\ + \frac{5}{6} \end{array}$
30. $\begin{array}{r} 2\frac{1}{2} \\ + 1\frac{3}{4} \end{array}$
31. $\begin{array}{r} \frac{3}{10} \\ + \frac{1}{4} \end{array}$
32. $\frac{4}{5} + \frac{1}{2}$
33. $2\frac{2}{3} + 6\frac{1}{3}$

Customary Measurement **177**

Every lesson ends with a **Review** of a past lesson or lessons. Often the skill reviewed will be needed in the next lesson.

Skills Lessons Direct You Step-by-Step

About three-fourths of the lessons in *Globe Fearon Mathematics* are **Skills Lessons.** These lessons present step-by-step directions and practice problems.

Skills lessons have the Skills logo in the corner.

Each lesson starts with clear examples of the skills needed in the exercises. Important new terms are shown in heavy type.

Important steps in examples are shown. The answers to examples are shown in heavy type.

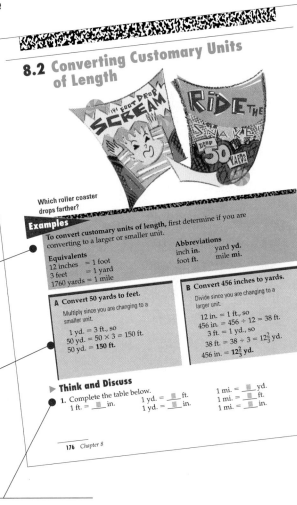

8.2 Converting Customary Units of Length

Which roller coaster drops farther?

Examples

To convert customary units of length, first determine if you are converting to a larger or smaller unit.

Equivalents
12 inches = 1 foot
3 feet = 1 yard
1760 yards = 1 mile

Abbreviations
inch **in.**   yard **yd.**
foot **ft.**   mile **mi.**

A Convert 50 yards to feet.

Multiply since you are changing to a smaller unit.

1 yd. = 3 ft., so
50 yd. = 50 × 3 = 150 ft.
50 yd. = **150 ft.**

B Convert 456 inches to yards.

Divide since you are changing to a larger unit.

12 in. = 1 ft., so
456 in. = 456 ÷ 12 = 38 ft.
3 ft. = 1 yd., so
38 ft. = 38 ÷ 3 = $12\frac{2}{3}$ yd.
456 in. = **$12\frac{2}{3}$ yd.**

▶ **Think and Discuss**

1. Complete the table below.
1 ft. = ▨ in.   1 yd. = ▨ ft.   1 mi. = ▨ yd.
                  1 yd. = ▨ in.   1 mi. = ▨ ft.
                                    1 mi. = ▨ in.

Working through the **Think and Discuss** questions gives you a chance to check your understanding. This is the time to get more help if you need it.

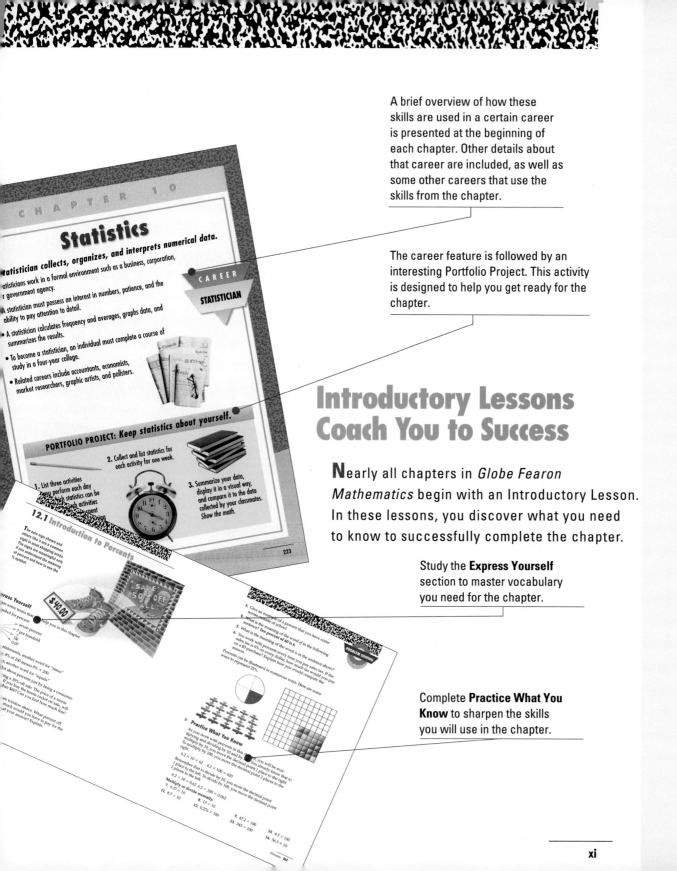

A brief overview of how these skills are used in a certain career is presented at the beginning of each chapter. Other details about that career are included, as well as some other careers that use the skills from the chapter.

The career feature is followed by an interesting Portfolio Project. This activity is designed to help you get ready for the chapter.

Introductory Lessons Coach You to Success

Nearly all chapters in *Globe Fearon Mathematics* begin with an Introductory Lesson. In these lessons, you discover what you need to know to successfully complete the chapter.

Study the **Express Yourself** section to master vocabulary you need for the chapter.

Complete **Practice What You Know** to sharpen the skills you will use in the chapter.

Be Comfortable with Math

Math is everywhere! You can hardly make it through a day without dealing with mathematics. Many people use math every day in their careers, too! So, the more thorough your understanding of math, the more comfortable you will be handling math situations in daily life and in your future job. *Globe Fearon Mathematics* can help.

Use statistics to describe

- how classmates spend their free time.
- the win-lose record of a school team and players' performances.
- average test scores in a class.
- the favorite television programs, movies, or books of friends.

What are some other ways to use statistics?

Each chapter is introduced by a photograph of a student using math skills in a real-life situation.

Chapter 16 Pre-Algebra: Expressions and Sentences

Chapter 17 Pre-Algebra: Integers and Equations

Chapter 13 Probability

Chapter 14 Geometry: Perimeter and Area

Chapter 15 Geometry: Surface Area and Volume

*Problem-solving lessons
are shown in blue.*

Chapter 10 Statistics

Chapter 11 Ratio and Proportion

Chapter 12 Percents

Chapter 8   Customary Measurement

Chapter 9   Graphs

*Problem-solving lessons
are shown in blue.*

Chapter 5   Introducing Fractions and Mixed Numbers

Chapter 6   Multiplying and Dividing Fractions and Mixed Numbers

Chapter 7   Adding and Subtracting Fractions and Mixed Numbers

Chapter 3   Dividing Whole Numbers and Decimals

Chapter 4   Metric Measurement

*Problem-solving lessons
are shown in blue.*

Contents

*Problem-solving lessons
are shown in blue.*

Consultants

Michelle Tiberio,
Middle School Teacher,
Gloucester, VA

Carol Pitkewicz, Neil Zarcone,
Michael Zafonte,
Bayport-Blue Point High School, NY

Rochelle Gilbert,
Monroe City School District, LA

Don Busenbark,
High School Teacher,
Roosevelt, UT

Susan Youngblood,
Middle School Teacher,
Macon, GA

Judy Roe,
Middle School Teacher,
Fort Bragg, NC

Gladys H. Pugh,
Mathematics Teacher and
Tutor Center Coordinator,
Scranton, PA

Printed in the United States of America

2 3 4 5 6 7 8 9 10   04 03 02 01 00

ISBN: 0-130-23407-9 (Student Edition)
ISBN: 0-130-23406-0 (Annotated Teacher's Edition)
Formerly titled *Globe High School Mathematics*

Globe Fearon

MATHEMATICS

REVISED EDITION

$8291 \div 151 = 54.907284 \quad C = 2\pi r \quad 0.263 + 0.938 = 1.201$

$1760 \text{ yards} = 1 \text{ mile} \quad 4500 lb. = 2T \ 500 \text{ lb.} \quad V = Bh$

Globe
Fearon

Upper Saddle River, New Jersey
www.globefearon.com

Pacing Chart

Chapter/Title	Lesson Days	Review and Test Days	Cumulative Number of Days
1 Adding and Subtracting Whole Numbers and Decimals	12	2	14
2 Multiplying Whole Numbers and Decimals	11	2	27
3 Dividing Whole Numbers and Decimals	13	2	42
4 Metric Measurement	8	2	52
Cumulative Review and Test		2	54
5 Introducing Fractions and Mixed Numbers	8	2	64
6 Multiplying and Dividing Fractions and Mixed Numbers	8	2	74
7 Adding and Subtracting Fractions and Mixed Numbers	10	2	86 (about one-half year—85 class days)
8 Customary Measurement	10	2	98
Cumulative Review and Test		2	100
9 Graphs	9	2	111
10 Statistics	7	2	120
11 Ratio and Proportion	8	2	130
12 Percents	11	2	143
13 Probability	7	2	152
Cumulative Review and Test		2	154
14 Geometry: Perimeter and Area	9	2	165 (about 1 year—170 class days)
15 Geometry: Surface Area and Volume	8	2	(175)
16 Pre-Algebra: Expressions and Sentences	8	2	(185)
17 Pre-Algebra: Integers and Equations	11	2	(198)
Cumulative Review and Test		2	(200)

but allows for spontaneous classroom activities, a cumulative record of days lets the teacher monitor and manage the pacing of the class, keep track of its accomplishments, and still make spontaneous changes when classes need more or fewer days on a topic.

Varying the Classroom Activities

Group work and other activities can vary classroom routine and inject new energy into students. Many activities in the problem-solving lessons are especially appropriate for students working in pairs or small groups, and most teachers regularly use at least some of these varied groupings:

1. Small groups. Groups can develop methods to solve a problem, and a representative of each group can present its method to the class. Also, students can work in groups to check each other's work.
2. Board work. Several students write out their solutions to problems at the chalkboard and then present them to the class.
3. Unit teaching. One or more students can be assigned to prepare a new lesson or review a prior one; those students present their lessons to the entire class.

One of the special benefits of these varied activities comes when a student develops a method different from the one presented by the teacher or the text. Students can show great pride in developing and explaining their own methods. And it sometimes seems that students may put more energy into learning a student-generated method than a teacher-presented one. In fact, very exciting discussions can often follow the question, "Did anybody do it a different way?"

Globe Fearon Mathematics can be adapted for any general math class.

Managing and Pacing the *Globe Fearon Mathematics* Program

Globe Fearon Mathematics is designed for consistent lessons and flexible use. For consistency, the lessons, reviews, and tests are each designed to be completed in one class period.

The second feature—flexibility—allows schools to use *Globe Fearon Mathematics* for several categories of students: students going on into a standard sequence of algebra and geometry classes, students taking *Globe Fearon Mathematics* as a terminal high school mathematics class, and students who have previously been unable to succeed on many of these same mathematical topics. Teachers can organize the *Globe Fearon Mathematics* lessons, review, and tests to present courses appropriate for each of these student categories.

One way to organize the course is to go directly through the lessons of the text. As shown in the chart on page Txxxii under "Cumulative Number of Days," this plan covers all the material on operations, fractions, measurement, ratio and proportion, graphs, statistics, probability, and perimeter and area. This straightforward plan would be appropriate for students taking *Globe Fearon Mathematics* as their terminal mathematics class.

If the program is geared to students going on to algebra and geometry classes, the teacher may want to change the order for some of the later chapters. For example, the geometry chapters (Chapters 14 and 15) can be covered anytime after Chapter 8, the chapter on customary measurement. The pre-algebra chapters (Chapters 16 and 17) can be presented anytime after Chapter 7, the chapter on adding and subtracting fractions and mixed numbers. For these students, teachers may find they can combine some pairs of lessons in Chapters 1–4, thereby leaving more days for lessons in the later chapters.

Another way to cover the text is to skip selected lessons that do not affect the hierarchy of mathematics skills and procedures. Using this method, a teacher could tailor an appropriate course for any given mathematics class.

Teachers can make up their own charts to plan the lessons, reviews, and tests and regularly compare their planned numbers of days with the actual numbers. Like a daily lesson plan that organizes content

Globe Fearon Mathematics is designed for consistency and flexibility.

English as a Second Language

Many of the learning difficulties of ESL students relate to the assumptions made by native speakers as they use their own language. For example, a simple phrase that is misinterpreted may create confusion when ESL students encounter word problems. The teacher can help students working in a new language in the following ways:

1. Explain special terms. Students should discuss mathematical terms that have nonmathematical meanings, such as product, times, order, and many others. Also, classes should read aloud and discuss instructions and mathematical explanations.
2. Allow translation time. While many ESL students will be familiar with the numerals 1, 2, 3, and so forth, the spoken words for the numerals may be unfamiliar. A student may need a moment to translate the spoken words five and eight to, say, *cinco* and *ocho* before being able to write down 5 and 8.
3. Discuss cultural references. Students should take special time to talk about proper names and other culture-specific references in the text. For example, the class should clarify rules, proper names, and procedures when discussing topics from sports, geography, politics, and so on.

Listening to Student Language

The teacher skill of using students' language to learn what they do and do not understand can be very useful. The language that students use will be different from the language of textbooks and teachers. For example, Lesson 2.10, "Multiplying Decimals by Decimals" (student text pages 48–49), has the sentence, "Add the number of decimal places in the multipliers to get the number of decimal places in the product." A student might express this as follows: "Start at the right of the first number, and count until you get to the point. Then count the same way on the second number. Add those two, and that's where the point should be in the bottom number." In this case the student language is very specific, telling *what* you do, and *where*, and uses only the most basic mathematical terms. If you were to try to get the student to express this in the terminology of the book, it might cause the students to become confused.

Listening to student language and using it judiciously can be useful to teachers. It reveals what students understand mathematics to be and aids teachers in posing questions that help students learn.

Teaching Students with Special Needs

The overriding goal of *Globe Fearon Mathematics* is a mathematics program appropriate for each of its students. For some groups of students, such as those with learning disabilities (LD) or those for whom English is a second language (ESL), there are strategies that can help overcome common constraints.

Special education teachers and school counselors are often available to help assess individual needs and perhaps even work with particular students. The classroom mathematics teacher should also know about the learning problems common to these students.

Learning Disabled Students

Specific sensory and motor skill problems can add difficulty for LD students.

1. Auditory skills. Many LD students have difficulty discriminating between certain pairs of sounds and distinguishing between similar-sounding words. This may affect their ability to remember spoken information and instructions.
2. Visual skills. Some LD students have difficulty discriminating between letters and similar-looking words, and this may affect their ability to recall written information. Problems with spatial conceptualization often add further difficulties in "seeing" mathematical and geometric relationships.
3. Language skills. Some LD students may have problems internalizing spoken or written language or may have problems expressing themselves verbally.
4. Motor skills. Other LD students may have difficulty with writing and drawing skills.

Many LD students learn to compensate for these constraints. The teacher can help by providing repetition and detailed instructions. For example, providing frequent summaries of previous material, presenting information in both spoken and written form, and offering extra practice opportunities can provide the repetition students may need to help them digest information. Moreover, providing detailed instruction by showing step-by-step solutions to sample problems, highlighting central ideas in charts and tables, and breaking complex assignments into discrete, individual tasks can also help students achieve at their full potential, which frequently will prove to be at the average or above-average level.

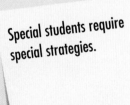

Special students require special strategies.

mathematics for planning and record keeping. Regular shopping for food and clothing and special shopping for appliances and furniture involve describing options and deciding among choices, and mathematics is often helpful in making those decisions. Simple home projects such as painting rooms and building shelves and complex projects such as remodeling and building additions involve many topics from arithmetic and geometry. Other topics can be found in school subjects such as science, industrial arts, drawing, music, and many others.

Nonschool Activities as a Source

Another source for expanding and enriching mathematics topics is nonschool activities. Many student activities outside school involve mathematics, and these can provide additional opportunities to investigate math.

Newspapers and the Internet

Newspaper and Internet coverage of elections, budgets, public works projects, and other topics are good opportunities to expand the study of topics such as proportions, percents, and statistics and to enrich experiences with basic operations on whole numbers and decimals. For some students, business and stock market pages can motivate and enrich the study of fractions and mixed numbers.

Personal Finances

Some students may find they are comparing service charges for different types of bank accounts or are trying to estimate net wages based on taxes and other deductions. These students could present their own findings to the entire class.

As students study how all these activities can relate directly to the mathematics topics they study, they can begin to bring in their own examples. Holiday trips, family reunions, community projects, and social group activities all provide opportunities to use mathematics, and an awareness of those uses expands and enriches students' mathematics skills. A teacher who helps students open up to these opportunities is helping them learn to use and recognize their own mathematics skills.

Other ideas for enrichment activities come from both school and nonschool sources.

Expanding and Enriching the *Globe Fearon Mathematics Program*

In this Teacher's Edition there are notes on when to use the program's ancillary materials. Teachers can use the **Extra Practice & Mixed Review** worksheets, **Enrichment** worksheets, **Problem Solving** worksheets, **Decision Making** worksheets, and chapter and cumulative tests to expand and enrich the *Globe Fearon Mathematics* program.

Other Classes as a Source

Another way for teachers to enhance their students' mathematical awareness and skills is to direct students to investigate how their other classes apply to mathematics topics. Some examples follow:

Geography and Social Studies

Students can calculate the average number of people who live in each square mile of their own towns and cities. These calculations of population density make for interesting comparisons with other towns, cities, and nations. Graphs and charts, percents and proportions, and statistics can be used to summarize information and compare the agricultural, manufacturing, and service industries of their own region with those of other regions and countries. Other tables and charts can describe their own region in terms of climate, natural resources, and other characteristics.

Physical Education

Many popular sports use geometric shapes. Playing fields are rectangular (football, soccer), diamond shaped (baseball infield), or combinations of lines and curves (running tracks), and rulebooks for these sports often specify exact measurements for these fields. Also, sports equipment often has geometric shapes: circular wheels for cyclists, parallel bars for gymnasts, and many others. Coaches and athletes in these sports have to be familiar with these measurements and shapes.

Competitive sports such as swimming, diving, skating, and many others use scoring procedures involving different kinds of calculations. Students who are active in any of these activities could present their special knowledge to the entire mathematics class.

Home Economics

Running a household is a rich source for mathematics applications. The important considerations of budgets, income, and financing require

The Teacher's Edition contains cross-references to enrichment material in the Teacher's Resource Binder.

Using Alternative Assessment

Alternative Assessment can be used in addition to the traditional paper and pencil assessment to provide a complete picture of student achievement. Alternative Assessment includes a performance task, an answer or possible answer, and items for the scoring rubric found on page 161 of the Teacher's Resource Binder.

Making Portfolios

A student's portfolio is a collection of his or her work over a year. The portfolio provides a long-term record of the student's best efforts, progress, and achievement. Some suggested items to be included in a portfolio are:

1. Table of Contents
2. Letter explaining the contents to the reviewer
3. Math autobiography
4. Paper/pencil tests with student corrections of math errors
5. Performance assessments
6. Homework samples
7. Journal notes
8. Projects
9. Teacher/student observations

Using the Rubric

The rubric is found on page 161 of the Teacher's Resource Binder. It is designed for use with any activity that needs to be assessed with a numerical score. It is based on a five-point scale that can be converted to a percentile or letter grade. For example, a score of 5 is 100%, 4 is 85%, 3 is 70%, 2 is 55%, and 1 is 40%. Or you can customize the rubic to fit your own teaching needs.

The first eight criteria in the rubric are generic. The last two criteria are left blank, so that the rubric can be customized. These criteria should be based on specific tasks, which are provided along with each Portfolio Project on Chapter Opener pages.

To use the rubric, copy the blank master on page 161 of the Teacher's Resource Binder once. Write two specific criteria into the last spaces. Copy this customized version, making one for each student or group of students. When the activity is complete, evaluate how well each criterion was met. Add the points and convert to the preferred grading system.

Another way to use the rubric is to have students grade themselves. They can exchange papers with a teammate or grade their own. Once they've seen the rubric, students may find they have a better understanding of what is required.

Models and Manipulatives

An important part of mathematics instruction, particularly in the primary grades, is to manipulate objects to investigate the operations of addition, subtraction, multiplication, and division. Also, students manipulate objects such as balances and number lines to investigate ideas such as equivalence, direction, and movement.

Manipulatives are seen less frequently in the upper grades, but they are still important, especially when students are introduced to new topics. For example, in Chapter 13 of *Globe Fearon Mathematics*, students manipulate coins, number cubes, and spinners to investigate probability. In Chapter 14, they use a string to compare the circumferences of circular objects and cardboard shapes to compare the areas of polygons.

As students develop their mathematical skills they can use pictures and symbols to represent the results of manipulating objects. When pictures and symbols replace manipulatives, those pictures and symbols are called "models." In *Globe Fearon Mathematics*, students use models such as graphs (Chapter 9), scale drawings (Chapter 11), tree diagrams (Chapter 13), and geometric figures (Chapters 14 and 15).

Teachers can use models to organize information efficiently. For example, consider this diagram:

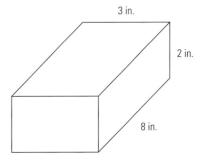

The diagram presents the same information as the sentence, "A brick is 2 inches high, 3 inches wide, and 8 inches long." The diagram is compact and efficient and is especially useful for questions like "What is the total surface area of the brick?" and "What is the total length of all the edges?"

Manipulatives are introduced at appropriate points.

Models advance learning to a new level.

proaches to a problem and to check work demonstrates a grasp of underlying concepts. The ability to evaluate results obtained with a calculator demonstrates a knowledge of basic facts and skills in estimation.

Mental Mathematics Applications

Here are two mental mathematical methods that students can use outside the classroom.

Making Correct Change

A customer gives you a five-dollar bill for a 28-cent purchase. The quickest way to make change is to "count up" rather than to subtract. Just pick up the appropriate coins or bills as you say to yourself, "2 pennies makes 30¢, and 2 dimes is 50¢, and 2 quarters is $1; then 4 more dollars is $5."

Leaving a Fair Tip

A fair tip in a restaurant is often figured to be 15%. A quick way to calculate 15% is to first find 10% by moving the decimal point one place. Then find half of that, and add the two amounts. As an example, 15% of $32 is 10%, or $3.20, plus half that, which is $1.60, for a tip of $4.80.

In some areas where the tax on restaurant food is 7%, 7$1/2$%, or 8%, an even faster way to calculate a fair tip is simply to double the tax!

Calculator Applications

Here are two ways to check when you use your calculator.

Estimating

The method presented in Lessons 1.12, "Estimating Sums and Differences" (student text pages 24–25), 2.6, "Estimating Products" (pages 40–41), and 3.4, "Estimating Quotients" (pages 62–63), can be used to check calculator results. In this method you round each number, perform the operations, and then compare your estimated result with the calculated result.

Calculating a Range

Another method is to calculate a range for the result. Replace each number with one that would give you a smaller result and then with one that would give you a larger result. Perform the operations on each set of numbers; the original calculated result should lie between the two new values.

Choosing the Best Computation Method

Globe Fearon Mathematics lessons help students develop skills at three types of computation: paper-and-pencil methods, mental math, and using a calculator. Here are several common misconceptions about the different computation methods.

Misconception Number 1: You should prefer one method in all situations over the other two.

Globe Fearon Mathematics shows that each of the three methods is useful. For example, Lesson 2.3, "Multiplying by Powers and Multiples of 10" (student text pages 34–35), uses mental mathematics to find the products 12×10 and 9×400. Lesson 3.5, "Dividing by 2-Digit Divisors" (pages 64–65), shows a detailed paper-and-pencil procedure for dividing by a 2-digit number, while Lesson 3.6, "Dividing by 3-Digit Divisors" (pages 66–67), shows how to divide by a 3-digit number by using a calculator or pencil and paper. These and other examples emphasize to students that each method has its special strengths and its own importance in mathematics.

Misconception Number 2: You only need to write down the answer when you use mental mathematics or a calculator.

Students should be taught to keep a complete written record of the steps. For a mental mathematics problem like 9 times 400, that record might be the mathematical sentence

$$9 \times 400 = 3600$$

For a calculator problem, the written record might be

$$8291 \div 151 = 54.907284$$

Urge students to write down intermediate steps when there are several steps.

Misconception Number 3: Mental mathematics is tricks and a calculator is a tool—neither one is real mathematics.

Clearly, being able to work out a paper-and-pencil calculation shows a certain type of mathematical skill, but the other two methods also show mathematical skill. The ability to mentally explore various ap-

Critical Thinking

Critical thinking means using higher-order thinking skills. Critical thinking includes making generalizations, explaining why one procedure works or why another one does not, and analyzing possible options in order to make a decision. In *Globe Fearon Mathematics*, many features promote and develop critical thinking. The **Think and Discuss** questions in each skills lesson involve students in critical thinking. These activities extend the worked-through examples by providing guided practice and higher-order analytic thinking. Students answer questions about specific subskills needed to learn the lesson skill; other questions lead students to make generalizations about the skill. For example, in Lessons 3.12, "Dividing Decimals by Decimals" (student text pages 78–79), and 3.13, "Dividing Whole Numbers by Decimals" (pages 80–81), students divide by decimals. The first **Think and Discuss** questions in these lessons ask the students to repeat the process described in the examples. Then questions such as "What is the quotient?" and "How many places did you move the decimal point?" ask the students to interpret parts of the process. The last **Think and Discuss** questions ask students to explain or interpret the division procedure.

Lesson 7.5, "Subtracting Fractions with Unlike Denominators" (student text pages 158–159), is a good example of how *Globe Fearon Mathematics* develops critical thinking as well as checking skills and subskills. The first **Think and Discuss** question asks students to repeat the process shown in the examples. The second question is to get students to relate Example A to the questions asked in the introduction to the lesson. The third question focuses on one of the subskills for the process. The fourth question asks students to explain a common mistake that is made in subtracting two fractions.

In problem-solving lessons, critical thinking questions lead students to analyze their approach to solving problems. For instance, in Lesson 7.6, "Working with Fractions: An Alternative Strategy" (student text pages 160–161), students are introduced to an alternative strategy for adding and subtracting fractions and then, through a series of questions, are led to consider how this approach is different from the one they learned previously and when it makes sense to adopt this approach. As a result of the critical-thinking features, *Globe Fearon Mathematics* prepares students to think analytically and use mathematics outside the classroom.

Critical thinking is built into lessons.

Problem Solving

Globe Fearon Mathematics teaches students a four-step process to develop their problem-solving skills:

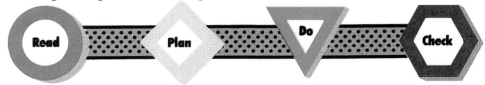

The steps are carefully developed early in the program. In Lesson 1.3, "A 4-Step Problem-Solving Process" (student text pages 6 – 7), students start to work with the four-step process, and in Lesson 1.4, "4-Step Problem-Solving Process: Read" (pages 8 – 9), they learn the active procedure of reading a mathematics problem. In Lesson 2.5, "4-Step Problem-Solving Process: Plan" (pages 38 – 39), students focus on planning how to solve a problem, and in Lesson 3.7, "4-Step Problem-Solving Process: Do and Check" (pages 68 – 69), they concentrate on solving and checking problems. Throughout the rest of the text, selected lessons return to problem-solving activities to give students practice.

Problem solving is not always a linear process. If the **Check** step shows that the answer is incorrect, the student should go back into the process. Depending on the results of the **Check** step, the student might **Read** the problem again for more information, go back and revise the **Plan,** or verify calculations in the **Do** step. Sometimes in the middle of one step the student may go back to a previous step. This sort of use of the four steps should be encouraged.

The problem-solving lessons throughout the chapters introduce students to various strategies. For example, Lessons 4.8, "Making a Table to Organize Information" (student text pages 100 – 101), and 8.5, "Using Tables to Solve Problems" (pages 182 – 183), show how to make a table to solve problems. Lesson 7.8, "Simplifying the Problem" (pages 164 – 165), shows how a simpler problem can help solve the original. Lessons 6.3, "Using Guess and Check to Solve Problems" (pages 134 – 135), and 16.5, "Using Guess and Check to Solve Equations" (pages 360 – 361), show how to use the Guess and Check strategy.

Students who develop strong problem-solving skills benefit twofold. First, by being able to solve and check problems, they are able to apply mathematics both inside and outside the classroom. Second, by experiencing success, they start to think of themselves as able mathematics students.

> Problem solving is taught as a four-step process.

The teaching circle serves the special needs of *Globe Fearon Mathematics* students in two main ways. First, students learn how to make generalizations by discussing examples and describing patterns. Second, students learn how and when to apply mathematics by using the patterns they describe. These two skills, generalizing and applying, are basic for all students as they go on in their mathematical studies and as they find opportunities to use mathematics outside the classroom.

Using the Review Feature of the Lessons

In the **Review** section of each lesson, students practice skills they have learned in previous lessons. Regular review, as part of daily mathematics activity, has at least three important purposes:

1. Regular review of previously learned skills helps students maintain their ability to use those skills.

2. Maintenance and review reinforce student's awareness that mathematics skills are connected to each other.

3. Students show less resistance to learning new materials when they know that today's topic will be needed in tomorrow's and next week's lessons.

Peer Teaching

When students work in pairs, taking turns teaching each other, reviewing previous work, or sharing their own mathematical methods and skills, both students can gain. Students being taught get one-on-one tutoring without fear of teacher evaluation. Also, they get mathematical ideas explained in their own language. Students doing the teaching often gain clearer, more in-depth understanding of the topic and almost always develop a longer retention of the material they get to teach.

There are several ways to make the most of peer-teaching activities. First, make sure the teaching students have clear instructions about what they are to focus on. Second, be sure to monitor peer-teaching activities, reminding the teaching students to give examples, discuss patterns, and ask questions like, "How did you get your answer?" With clear expectations and detailed instructions, both students in the pair benefit from the peer-teaching relationship.

Strategies for Successful Teaching

Presenting the Lessons

Globe Fearon Mathematics uses a plan that engages students in learning. This plan, which may be called the teaching circle, is implemented in four steps:

1. The lesson's motivational opener introduces a real-life situation.
2. The lesson develops additional examples, which are based on the first one.
3. Students discuss the pattern shown in the examples.
4. Students apply the pattern to other examples.

Each skills lesson in *Globe Fearon Mathematics* uses the teaching circle. A typical example is Lesson 2.4, "Multiplying by 2-Digit and 3-Digit Multipliers" (student text pages 36–37), which is developed in the following way:

1. A problem situation motivates the use of multiplication and leads to an instance calling for multiplication by a two-digit multiplier.
2. The examples show multiplying by two-digit and three-digit multipliers. The Teacher's Edition side column shows two alternative examples.
3. The last two **Think and Discuss** questions invite students to talk about the procedures.
4. In the three types of Exercises, students apply the process—first to exercises that are matched to the worked-through examples, then to **Mixed Practice** exercises, and finally to real-life applications.

Another typical example is Lesson 1.12, "Estimating Sums and Differences" (student text pages 24–25). This lesson is developed as follows:

1. The lesson opener presents a practical application of the skill of estimating.
2. The Examples show how to estimate a sum and estimate a difference. The Teacher's Edition side column provides alternative examples.
3. **Think and Discuss** exercises 3–5 ask students to discuss the methods they have learned.
4. Students apply those steps in the Exercises.

. . . additional materials

Enrichment worksheets in the TRB offer students new and interesting challenges.

Real-Life Application worksheets in the TRB help students develop decision-making skills for real-life situations involving mathematics.

The Teacher's Resource Binder enlarges and enriches your instructional resources.

9 **Enrichment** Page 2 of 2

Name _____
Class _____
Date _____ Score _____

4 **Real-Life Application**

Name _____
Class _____
Date _____ Score _____

3 **Vocabulary & Writing About Mathematics**

(Use after completing Chapter 3)

Name _____
Class _____
Date _____ Score _____

▶ **Vocabulary**

Before each description, write the letter for the matching term.

_____ 1. A process in arithmetic that is the inverse of multiplication.
_____ 2. In a division problem, the number that is divided by another number.
_____ 3. A set of rules used to find the value of an expression like 8 + 4 ÷ 3.

a. dividend
b. order of operations
c. divisor
d. quotient
e. remainder
f. division

Complete each sentence.

4. In the expression 37 ÷ 3, the divisor is _____ and the _____ is 37.

5. The answer to a division problem is called the _____ .

6. If you divide 7.9 by 2, the answer is 3.95. The answer is 4 if you _____ to the nearest whole number.

7. If you divide 37 by 3, the quotient is _____ and the _____ is 1.

▶ **Writing About Mathematics**

8. When you use the pencil-and-paper method to divide a whole number, you use a four-step process one or more times. In your own words, describe the four steps.

_____
_____

9. Suppose you want to estimate the answer to this problem: 753 ÷ 28. Describe how you would arrive at your estimate.

_____
_____

10. When you need to divide by a power of 10, you can find the quotient very quickly. Why is this?

_____
_____

Globe Fearon Mathematics 139

Vocabulary & Writing About Mathematics worksheets in the TRB allow students to check their understanding of key terms and to write about mathematics.

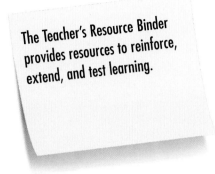

A wealth of . . .

Teacher's Resource Binder

The Teacher's Resource Binder offers over 400 reproducible pages.

For each chapter, the TRB contains two short answer tests and two multiple choice tests to give the teacher maximum flexibility.

Extra Practice & Mixed Review worksheets in the TRB provide practice of the skills taught in the lesson and mixed review of at least three previous lessons.

Problem-Solving worksheets in the TRB reinforce key strategies taught in the text.

10B Chapter Test Page 1 of 2
Multiple Choice: Form B, Chapter 10

Name _____
Class _____
Date _____ Score _____

Write the letter...

---

10 Problem Solving Page 1 of 2

Name _____
Class _____
Date _____ Score _____

(Use after completing Lesson 17.11, pp. 392–393)

▶ **Using a Formula**

To comp...

---

67 Extra Practice & Mixed Review

Name _____
Class _____
Date _____ Score _____

(Use after completing Lesson 8.9, pp. 190–191)

▶ **Extra Practice** (Lesson 8.9)

Solve each problem below.

1. Special Delivery tried to leave a package for Lauren at 10:13 a.m. and 3:28 p.m. How much time passed between the two attempts?

2. Lauren arrived home at 3:55 p.m. How much earlier would she have needed to be home to accept the package at 3:28 p.m.?

3. If Monica arrived home at 4:43 p.m. and Lauren asked her to make the 38-minute drive to the delivery office, could they get there before it closed at 5:15 p.m.?

4. At 4:50 p.m. Lauren called the delivery office and learned that they could deliver her package at 10:30 a.m. the next day. How long must Lauren wait for the package?

5. If Lauren could be at the delivery office by 8:15 a.m., how much sooner would she have the package than the 10:30 a.m. time?

6. Lauren opened her package at 10:37 a.m. If it took 40 minutes to play each of her two new CDs, when did she finish?

▶ **Mixed Review** (Lessons 6.8, 7.6)

Add or subtract. (Lesson 7.6)

7. $\frac{1}{2} + \frac{1}{3}$ _____ 8. $\frac{3}{4} - \frac{3}{8}$ _____ 9. $\frac{1}{3} - \frac{1}{4}$ _____ 10. $\frac{1}{2} + \frac{4}{9}$ _____

11. $\frac{2}{3} + \frac{2}{3}$ _____ 12. $\frac{9}{10} - \frac{7}{10}$ _____ 13. $\frac{1}{2} + \frac{5}{6} + \frac{3}{4}$ _____ 14. $\frac{2}{3} + \frac{1}{4} + \frac{2}{5}$ _____

15. $\frac{7}{8} - \frac{5}{8}$ _____ 16. $\frac{2}{3} + \frac{3}{4} + \frac{5}{8}$ _____ 17. $\frac{1}{2} + \frac{3}{8} + \frac{10}{16}$ _____ 18. $\frac{1}{2} + \frac{2}{3} - \frac{2}{4}$ _____

Use the table at the right to answer the questions. (Lesson 6.8)

19. The Booster Club is making school pennants to sell to students at the big game. Find the unit cost for 1 pennant.

20. The Booster Club decides on a profit of $\frac{1}{3}$ the cost of materials. What will be the amount they charge for each pennant?

Materials for 1 Pennant	Amount	Unit Cost
Red velour	$\frac{1}{8}$ yd.	3.69/yd.
White satin	$\frac{1}{12}$ yd.	$8.99/yd.
White thread	$\frac{1}{8}$ spool	$0.99/spool
Gold cord for trim	$1\frac{1}{2}$ yd.	$0.45/yd.
Gold thread	$\frac{1}{8}$ spool	$0.99/spool

Copyright © Globe Fearon, Inc. All rights reserved.   *Globe Fearon Mathematics* 67

. . . for teaching success

Answers appear on reproduced student page or in side column.

Error Alert identifies common student errors.

Information and ideas are right where teachers need them — next to the full-size lesson page.

Challenges, Puzzles, and **Projects** provide for student enrichment.

SKILLS

5. Refer to the introduction to this lesson. Did Jolene or Amy have the longer nail?

6. When converting metric units, how do you decide whether to multiply or divide?

Exercises

Convert each measure. (See Example A.)

7. 53 mm to cm
  5.3 cm
8. 77 mm to cm
  7.7 cm
9. 134 cm to m
  1.34 m
10. 280 cm to m
  2.80 m
11. 6384 m to km
  6.384 km
12. 915 m to km
  0.915 km

Convert each measure. (See Example B.)

13. 2.9 km to m
  2900 m
14. 6.1 km to m
  6100 m
15. 42 m to cm
  4200 cm
16. 0.15 m to cm
  15 cm
17. 8.4 cm to mm
  84 mm
18. 27 cm to mm
  270 mm

Convert each measure. (See Example C.)

19. 9 mm to m
  0.009 m
20. 431 mm to m
  0.431 m
21. 5364 cm to km
  0.05364 km
22. 0.8 cm to m
  80,000 cm
23. 0.0052 m to mm
  5.2 mm
24. 12 km to mm
  12,000,000 mm

▶ **Mixed Practice** (For more practice, see page 413.)

Convert each measure.

25. 3100 m to km
  3.1 km
26. 3.6 cm to mm
  36 mm
27. 5.8 m to cm
  580 cm
28. 3470 mm to m
  3.470 m
29. 1.9 m to mm
  1900 mm
30. 115 mm to cm
  11.5 cm
31. 3.2 km to m
  3200 m
32. 0.73 km to cm
  73,000 cm
33. 629 cm to km
  0.00629 km

▶ **Applications**

34. List the trails shown in the diagram at the right in order from shortest to longest.
  Mirror Lake, Blue Heron, Marsh
35. The Blue Heron Trail is how many meters longer than the Mirror Lake Trail? 2200 m

▶ **Review** (Lessons 3.10, 3.11, 3.12)

Divide. Round the quotient to the nearest tenth.

36. 6.8 ÷ 3.2 2.1
37. 44.731 ÷ 9 5.0
38. 0.2695 ÷ 0.05 5.4
39. 684.5 ÷ 4 171.1
40. 3.91 ÷ 17 0.2
41. 3.575 ÷ 6.5 0.6
42. 87.55 ÷ 25 3.5
43. 0.897 ÷ 0.3 3.0

Metric Measurement **89**

▶ **Think and Discuss Answers**

1. 0.00063 km
2. 600,000 cm
3. Move the decimal point to the right to multiply; move the decimal point to the left to divide.
4. Divide by 1,000,000 (move the decimal point 6 places to the left).
5. Jolene
6. When converting to a smaller unit, multiply; when converting to a larger unit, divide.

★ **Error Alert**

Errors may indicate that students are not dividing to change to a larger unit and are not multiplying to change to a smaller unit.

Reinforcement
Extra Practice, page 413
EP/MR Worksheet 33, TRB, page 33

Challenge
A map has a scale of 1:1,000,000 where 1 centimeter on the map equals 1,000,000 centimeters on the ground. Find out how many kilometers apart the following cities are, using the map distances shown:

St. Louis–Kansas City 4.11 cm
Boston–New York 348 mm
Atlanta–New Orleans 0.0792 m
(answers: 41.1 km; 348 km; 79.2 km)

T89

Complete support . . .

Teacher's Edition

The Teacher's Edition is designed for quick reference as the lesson is taught.

Objectives state the lesson's goals.

Purpose helps teachers answer the question, "Why do we have to learn this?"

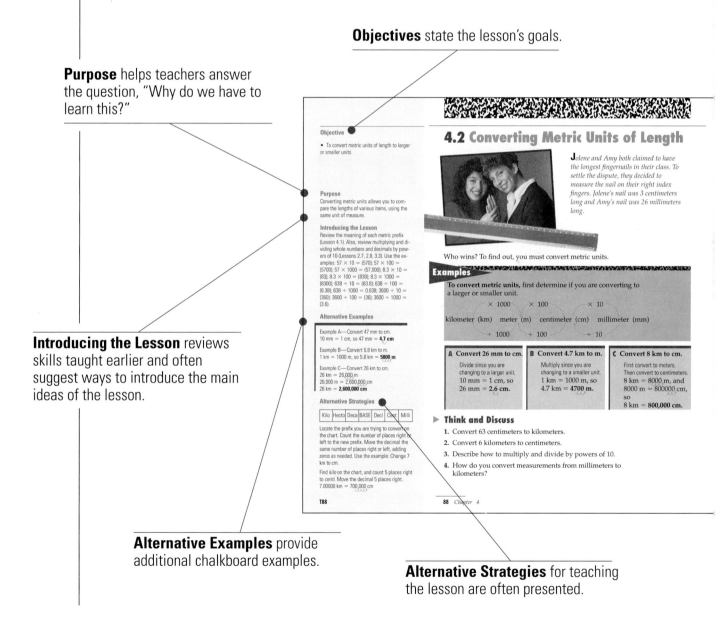

Objective

• To convert metric units of length to larger or smaller units

Purpose
Converting metric units allows you to compare the lengths of various items, using the same unit of measure.

Introducing the Lesson
Review the meaning of each metric prefix (Lesson 4.1). Also, review multiplying and dividing whole numbers and decimals by powers of 10 (Lessons 2.7, 2.8, 3.3). Use the examples: 57 × 10 = (570); 57 × 100 = (5700); 57 × 1000 = (57,000); 8.3 × 10 = (83); 8.3 × 100 = (830); 8.3 × 1000 = (8300); 638 ÷ 10 = (63.8); 638 ÷ 100 = (6.38); 638 ÷ 1000 = 0.638; 3600 ÷ 10 = (360); 3600 ÷ 100 = (36); 3600 ÷ 1000 = (3.6).

Alternative Examples

Example A—Convert 47 mm to cm.
10 mm = 1 cm, so 47 mm = **4.7 cm**

Example B—Convert 5.8 km to m.
1 km = 1000 m, so 5.8 km = **5800 m**

Example C—Convert 26 km to cm.
26 km = 26,000 m
26,000 m = 2,600,000 cm
26 km = **2,600,000 cm**

Alternative Strategies

Kilo	Hecto	Deca	BASE	Deci	Cent	Milli

Locate the prefix you are trying to convert on the chart. Count the number of places right or left to the new prefix. Move the decimal the same number of places right or left, adding zeros as needed. Use the example: Change 7 km to cm.

Find *kilo* on the chart, and count 5 places right to *centi*. Move the decimal 5 places right.
7.00000 km = 700,000 cm

T88

4.2 Converting Metric Units of Length

Jolene and Amy both claimed to have the longest fingernails in their class. To settle the dispute, they decided to measure the nail on their right index fingers. Jolene's nail was 3 centimeters long and Amy's nail was 26 millimeters long.

Who wins? To find out, you must convert metric units.

Examples

To convert metric units, first determine if you are converting to a larger or smaller unit.

$$\times\ 1000 \qquad \times\ 100 \qquad \times\ 10$$

kilometer (km)   meter (m)   centimeter (cm)   millimeter (mm)

$$\div\ 1000 \qquad \div\ 100 \qquad \div\ 10$$

A Convert 26 mm to cm.
Divide since you are changing to a larger unit.
10 mm = 1 cm, so
26 mm = **2.6 cm.**

B Convert 4.7 km to m.
Multiply since you are changing to a smaller unit.
1 km = 1000 m, so
4.7 km = **4700 m.**

C Convert 8 km to cm.
First convert to meters. Then convert to centimeters.
8 km = 8000 m, and
8000 m = 800000 cm, so
8 km = **800,000 cm.**

▶ **Think and Discuss**

1. Convert 63 centimeters to kilometers.
2. Convert 6 kilometers to centimeters.
3. Describe how to multiply and divide by powers of 10.
4. How do you convert measurements from millimeters to kilometers?

88 *Chapter 4*

Introducing the Lesson reviews skills taught earlier and often suggest ways to introduce the main ideas of the lesson.

Alternative Examples provide additional chalkboard examples.

Alternative Strategies for teaching the lesson are often presented.

. . . and create interest

Cumulative Test

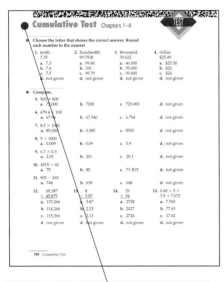

Three-page cumulative tests occur after every four or five chapters. The multiple-choice format prepares students for standardized testing.

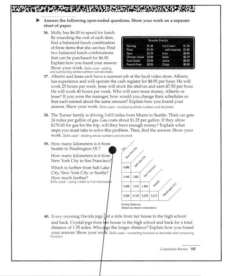

Open-ended questions give students the practice necessary to succeed on proficiency exams.

Cumulative tests help maintain skills from previous chapters.

Appendix

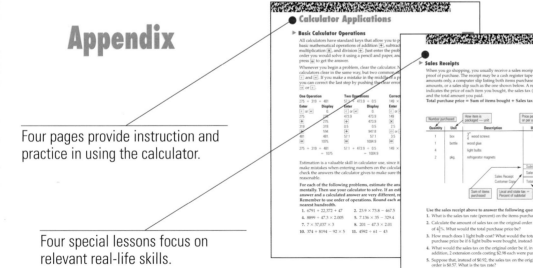

Four pages provide instruction and practice in using the calculator.

Four special lessons focus on relevant real-life skills.

Special lessons and reference materials at the back of the text are a useful resource.

. . . while developing skills

The logo indicates the lesson emphasis: development of skills.

Students benefit from a sound, consistent instructional design.

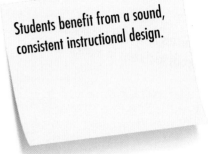

4. Refer to the introduction to this lesson. What percent of the television sets were not tuned to Monday Night Football? Explain how you found your answer.

5. What does 0% mean? How do you change it to a decimal?

6. Jason bought a used car for $1250 and had to pay 7% sales tax. He decided to figure the tax on his calculator, but it doesn't have a percent key. How would he write 7% as a decimal so that he could calculate the answer?

Exercises

Write each decimal as a percent. (See Example A.)

7. 0.65	8. 0.05	9. 0.5	10. 0.73	11. 1.00
12. 0.09	13. 0.215	14. 0.9	15. 0.075	16. 0.11

Exercises are carefully keyed to each example in the blue box.

Write each percent as a decimal. (See Example B.)

17. 8%	18. 32%	19. 11.4%	20. 15%	21. 13.5%
22. 25%	23. 44.5%	24. 81%	25. 66.5%	26. 100%

▶ **Mixed Practice** (For more practice, see page 87.)

Write each percent as a decimal and each decimal as a percent.

27. 0.2	28. 0.16	29. 75%	30. 1.25%	31. 16.5%
32. 0.08	33. 0.135	34. 9.6%	35. 0.505	36. 3.6%
37. 0.01	38. 99%	39. 78%	40. 0.12	41. 0.021

Mixed Practice exercises require students to decide how to solve each problem.

Extra Practice pages are provided at the end of the book.

▶ **Applications**

42. Outfielder Ted Williams, the "Splendid Splinter," hit 0.406 in 1941. Write his batting average as a percent.

43. A bank pays the interest advertised below. Write the interest rate as a decimal.

> 7.8% ON LONG TERM DEPOSITS

Applications require students to apply the lesson skills to solving word problems in a real-life setting.

▶ **Review** (Lesson 5.7)

Convert each fraction to a decimal.

44. $\frac{4}{5}$ 45. $\frac{1}{2}$ 46. $\frac{2}{3}$ 47. $\frac{15}{20}$ 48. $\frac{3}{4}$ 49. $\frac{7}{8}$

Convert each decimal to a fraction in lowest terms.

50. 0.4   51. 0.33   52. 0.95   53. 0.056   54. 0.04   55. 0.125

Review maintains previously taught skills.

Teach students . . .

Problem-Solving Lessons

Carefully paced problem-solving lessons help students succeed.

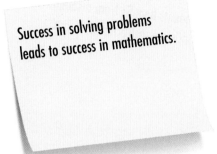

The logo indicates the lesson emphasis: problem solving.

Problem-solving lessons begin with an interesting situation to challenge students.

PROBLEM SOLVING

10.5 Investigating Averages

$13,600 $21,290

$14,090

Luisa just got a job. When she interviewed she was told that her division's average salary was a little over $21,290. Then a co-worker told her the average salary was $13,600. Luisa decided to do her own calculations. She found the average salary to be $14,090. Why do you think these figures are different?

Luisa's company consists of 3 managers and 12 clerks. Their salaries are shown below.

Salaries (in dollars)

50,000	50,000	50,000	15,325	15,060	15,000	14,125	14,090
14,000	13,750	13,600	13,600	13,600	13,600	13,600	

Find the mean salary.   Total payroll is $319,350.
   Mean = $319,350 ÷ 15 = $21,290

Find the median salary.   There are 15 salaries: 7 are greater than
   $14,090, 7 are less than $14,090.
   Median = $14,090

Find the mode of the salaries.   Five people earn $13,600.
   Mode = $13,600

The mean, median, and mode can be different numbers. Yet each is sometimes called an average, just as in the above case.

1. Find the median and the mean salaries of the 12 clerks. Discuss why the mean of this group of salaries is different from the mean of the original group of salaries.

2. Suppose two of the managers in Luisa's department leave their jobs. What are the mean, median, and mode salaries now? Explain how changing one or two figures can affect the mean, median, and mode differently.

232   Chapter 10

PROBLEM SOLVING

3. Now suppose one of the three managers earns $120,000 instead of $50,000. What are the mean, median, and mode salaries now? Discuss how each changes.

4. Which average—the mean, the median, or the mode—most accurately describes the typical salary in Luisa's division? Justify your answer.

5. Suppose you wanted to study average income in the United States as part of a history project. Would you use median or mean income in your study? Justify your choice.

Read the following example:

According to a recent study, half of Newark Community College's students are over 24 years old. The average age of the students is 29.

Based on the information in this lesson, use the word *mean* or *median* to complete each statement.

6. The ▨ age of Newark Community College students is 29.

7. The ▨ age of Newark Community College students is 24.

Sometimes finding the mean, median, or mode is not enough to help you understand a situation.

Planet	Approximate Length of a Day in Earth Hours
Mercury	1416
Venus	5832
Earth	24
Mars	24.6
Jupiter	9.9
Saturn	10.2
Uranus	22
Neptune	19
Pluto	144

8. What is the mean length of one day in our solar system?

9. What is the median length of one day in our solar system?

10. Is the use of mean or median helpful in understanding day length in our solar system? Discuss.

▶ **Review** (Lesson 9.4)

11. Use the following data to make a bar graph.
   National League Pennant Winners (through 1998)
   Cubs—4 years   Cardinals—1 year
   Tigers—10 years   Yankees—34 years

Statistics **233**

Exercises give practice with the lesson's problem-solving techniques and require the student to think mathematically.

Review maintains skills introduced in previous lessons.

... to think mathematically

Problem-solving process lessons help students master the steps of successful problem solving.

A diagram of the four steps of the problem-solving process reminds students to **Read, Plan, Do,** and **Check.**

Students apply what they have learned to new situations.

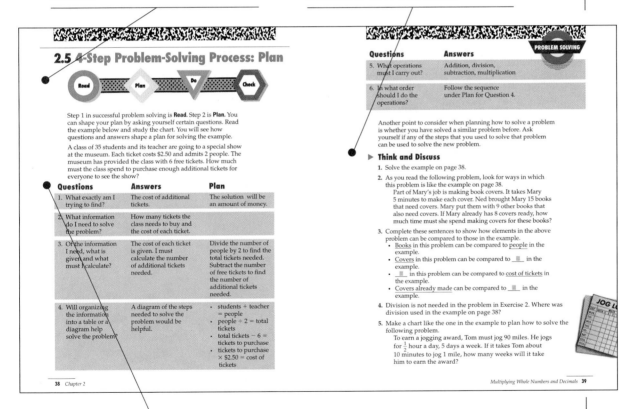

2.5 4-Step Problem-Solving Process: Plan

Read ▸ Plan ▸ Do ▸ Check

Step 1 in successful problem solving is **Read.** Step 2 is **Plan.** You can shape your plan by asking yourself certain questions. Read the example below and study the chart. You will see how questions and answers shape a plan for solving the example.

A class of 35 students and its teacher are going to a special show at the museum. Each ticket costs $2.50 and admits 2 people. The museum has provided the class with 6 free tickets. How much must the class spend to purchase enough additional tickets for everyone to see the show?

Questions	Answers	Plan
1. What exactly am I trying to find?	The cost of additional tickets.	The solution will be an amount of money.
2. What information do I need to solve the problem?	How many tickets the class needs to buy and the cost of each ticket.	
3. Of the information I need, what is given and what must I calculate?	The cost of each ticket is given. I must calculate the number of additional tickets needed.	Divide the number of people by 2 to find the total tickets needed. Subtract the number of free tickets to find the number of additional tickets needed.
4. Will organizing the information into a table or a diagram help solve the problem?	A diagram of the steps needed to solve the problem would be helpful.	• students + teacher = people • people ÷ 2 = total tickets • total tickets − 6 = tickets to purchase • tickets to purchase × $2.50 = cost of tickets

38 Chapter 2

Questions	Answers
5. What operations must I carry out?	Addition, division, subtraction, multiplication
6. In what order should I do the operations?	Follow the sequence under Plan for Question 4.

PROBLEM SOLVING

Another point to consider when planning how to solve a problem is whether you have solved a similar problem before. Ask yourself if any of the steps that you used to solve that problem can be used to solve the new problem.

▸ **Think and Discuss**

1. Solve the example on page 38.

2. As you read the following problem, look for ways in which this problem is like the example on page 38.
   Part of Mary's job is making book covers. It takes Mary 5 minutes to make each cover. Ned brought Mary 15 books that need covers. Mary put them with 9 other books that also need covers. If Mary already has 8 covers ready, how much time must she spend making covers for these books?

3. Complete these sentences to show how elements in the above problem can be compared to those in the example.
   • Books in this problem can be compared to people in the example.
   • Covers in this problem can be compared to ▢ in the example.
   • ▢ in this problem can be compared to cost of tickets in the example.
   • Covers already made can be compared to ▢ in the example.

4. Division is not needed in the problem in Exercise 2. Where was division used in the example on page 38?

5. Make a chart like the one in the example to plan how to solve the following problem.
   To earn a jogging award, Tom must jog 90 miles. He jogs for $\frac{1}{2}$ hour a day, 5 days a week. If it takes Tom about 10 minutes to jog 1 mile, how many weeks will it take him to earn the award?

JOG L

Multiplying Whole Numbers and Decimals **39**

Students learn that planning involves asking the right questions.

Review, evaluate, . . .

Chapter Review and Test

Review occurs in every lesson and at the end of every chapter. Each chapter concludes with a chapter test.

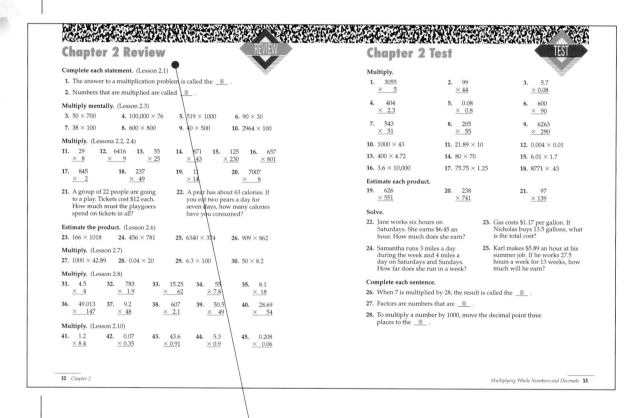

Chapter 2 Review · REVIEW

Complete each statement. (Lesson 2.1)

1. The answer to a multiplication problem is called the ▓ .
2. Numbers that are multiplied are called ▓ .

Multiply mentally. (Lesson 2.3)

3. 50×700 4. $100,000 \times 76$ 5. 519×1000 6. 90×30

7. 38×100 8. 600×800 9. 40×500 10. 2964×100

Multiply. (Lessons 2.2, 2.4)

11. 29×8 12. 6416×9 13. 55×25 14. 871×43 15. 125×230 16. 657×801

17. 845×2 18. 237×49 19. 11×14 20. 7007×8

21. A group of 22 people are going to a play. Tickets cost $12 each. How much must the playgoers spend on tickets in all?

22. A pear has about 63 calories. If you eat two pears a day for seven days, how many calories have you consumed?

Estimate the product. (Lesson 2.6)

23. 166×1018 24. 456×781 25. 6340×374 26. 909×862

Multiply. (Lesson 2.7)

27. 1000×42.89 28. 0.04×20 29. 6.3×100 30. 50×8.2

Multiply. (Lesson 2.8)

31. 4.5×4 32. 783×1.9 33. 15.25×62 34. 55×7.8 35. 8.1×18

36. 49.013×147 37. 9.2×48 38. 607×2.1 39. 50.5×49 40. 28.69×54

Multiply. (Lesson 2.10)

41. 1.2×8.4 42. 0.07×0.35 43. 43.6×0.91 44. 5.3×0.9 45. 0.208×0.06

Chapter 2 Test · TEST

Multiply.

1. 3055×5 2. 99×44 3. 5.7×0.08

4. 404×2.3 5. 0.08×0.8 6. 600×90

7. 543×51 8. 205×55 9. 6263×290

10. 1000×43 11. 21.89×10 12. 0.004×0.01

13. 400×4.72 14. 80×70 15. 6.01×1.7

16. $3.6 \times 10,000$ 17. 75.75×1.25 18. $8771 \times .43$

Estimate each product.

19. 626×551 20. 238×741 21. 97×139

Solve.

22. Jane works six hours on Saturdays. She earns $6.45 an hour. How much does she earn?

23. Gas costs $1.17 per gallon. If Nicholas buys 13.5 gallons, what is the total cost?

24. Samantha runs 3 miles a day during the week and 4 miles a day on Saturdays and Sundays. How far does she run in a week?

25. Karl makes $5.89 an hour at his summer job. If he works 27.5 hours a week for 13 weeks, how much will he earn?

Complete each sentence.

26. When 7 is multiplied by 28, the result is called the ▓ .

27. Factors are numbers that are ▓ .

28. To multiply a number by 1000, move the decimal point three places to the ▓ .

Each set of exercises is keyed to individual lessons for easy reference.

Call on the Reserves – Turn to the Appendix

When you need help, turn to the **Appendix**. You'll find a variety of information to help you succeed.

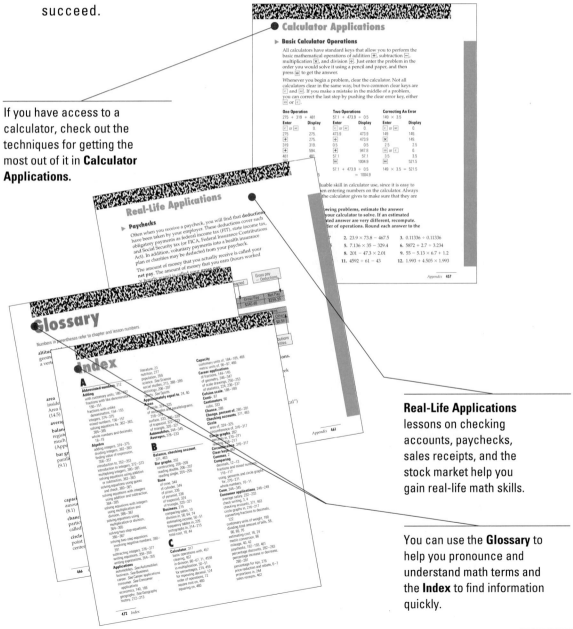

Calculator Applications

▶ Basic Calculator Operations

All calculators have standard keys that allow you to perform the basic mathematical operations of addition ⊞, subtraction ⊟, multiplication ⊠, and division ⊡. Just enter the problem in the order you would solve it using a pencil and paper, and then press ⊜ to get the answer.

Whenever you begin a problem, clear the calculator. Not all calculators clear in the same way, but two common clear keys are ⊂ and ⋅. If you make a mistake in the middle of a problem, you can correct the last step by pushing the clear error key, either ⋅ or ⊂.

One Operation		Two Operations		Correcting An Error	
275 + 319 + 481		57.1 + 473.9 ÷ 0.5		149 × 3.5	
Enter	**Display**	**Enter**	**Display**	**Enter**	**Display**
c or ac	0.	c or ac	0.	c or ac	0.
275	275.	473.9	473.9	149	149.
+	275.	+	473.9	×	149.
319	319.	0.5	0.5	2.5	2.5
+	594.	+	947.8	ce or c	0.
481	481.	57.1	57.1	3.5	3.5
		=	1004.9	=	521.5

57.1 + 473.9 ÷ 0.5 = 1004.9   149 × 3.5 = 521.5

...luable skill in calculator use, since it is easy to ...en entering numbers on the calculator. Always ...the calculator gives to make sure that they are

...wing problems, estimate the answer ...your calculator to solve. If an estimated ...ted answer are very different, recompute. ...der of operations. Round each answer to the

	2. 23.9 × 73.8 − 467.5	3. 0.11336 + 0.11336
	5. 7.136 × 35 − 329.4	6. 5872 + 2.7 + 3.234
	8. 201 − 47.3 × 2.01	9. 55 − 5.13 × 6.7 + 1.2
11. 4592 ÷ 61 − 43		12. 1.993 + 4.505 × 1.993

Appendix **457**

Real-Life Applications

▶ Paychecks

Often when you receive a paycheck, you will find that deductions have been taken by your employer. These deductions cover such obligatory payments as federal income tax (FIT), state income tax, and Social Security tax (or FICA, Federal Insurance Contributions Act). In addition, voluntary payments into a health insurance plan or charities may be deducted from your paycheck.

The amount of money that you actually receive is called your net pay. The amount of money that you earn (hours worked ...

Appendix **461**

Glossary

Numbers in parentheses refer to chapter and lesson numbers.

Index

A

Abbreviated numbers, 212
Adding
  with customary units, 186–187
  fractions with like denominators, 150–151
  fractions with unlike denominators, 154–155
  integers, 374–375
  mixed numbers, 158–157
  solving equations by, 362–363, 384–385
  whole numbers and decimals, 18–19
Algebra
  adding integers, 374–375
  dividing integers, 380–381
  finding value of expression, 356–357
  introduction to, 352–353
  introduction to integers, 380–381
  multiplying integers, 380–381
  solving equations using addition or subtraction, 362–363
  solving equations using guess and check, 360–361
  solving equations with integers using addition and subtraction, 384–385
  solving equations with integers using multiplication and division, 386–387
  solving equations using multiplication or division, 364–365
  solving two-step equations, 366–367
  solving two-step equations involving negative numbers, 390–391
  subtracting integers, 376–377
  writing equations, 358–359
  writing expressions, 354–355
Applications
  business. *See* Automobiles business. *See* Business career. *See* Career applications consumer. *See* Consumer applications
  economics, 140, 186
  geography. *See* Geography
  history, 212–213

B

Balance, checking account, 371, 463
Bar graphs, 208–209
  constructing, 208–209
  reading double, 206–207
  reading single, 204–205
Base
  of cone, 344
  of cylinder, 344
  of prism, 336
  of pyramid, 336
  of trapezoid, 324
  of triangle, 320–321
Business, 275
  comparing sales, 10
  division in, 58, 64, 74
  estimating income, 50–51
  frequency tables in, 276
  pictographs in, 214–215
  total cost, 18, 44

C

Calculator, 317
  basic operations with, 457
  clearing, 457
  in division, 66–67, 71, 456
  in multiplication, 274, 456
  for percentages, decimal, 124
  for repeating decimal, 124
  order of operations, 72
  square root on, 460
  squaring on, 460

... literature, 23
  nutrition, 277
  population, 359
  science. *See* Science
  social studies, 215, 388–389
  sports. *See* Sports
Approximately equal to, 24, 40
Areas
  of circle, 324–325
  of parallelograms, 318–319
  of rectangle, 320–321
  surface, 322–323
  of trapezoid, 324
  of triangle, 320–321
Automobiles, 186–189
Averages, 244, 278–233

Capacity
  customary units of, 184–185, 466
  metric units of, 96–97, 466
Career applications
  of fractions, 144–145
  of geometry, 346–347
  of scale drawings, 250–253
  of statistics, 224, 236–237
Celsius scale, 188–189
Centi-, 87
Centimeters, 90
  cubic, 333
Chance, 288
Change, percent of, 280–281
Checking accounts, 371, 463
Circle
  area of, 324–325
  circumference of, 316–317
Circle graphs, 202
  reading, 216–217
Circumference, of circle, 316–317
Clear keys, 457
Commas, 2
Comparing, 12–13
  fractions and mixed numbers, 116–117
  integers, 372–273
  using, percents and circle graphs, 270–271
  whole numbers, 10–11
Cone, 344–345
Consumer applications, 248–249
  average salary, 232–233
  check writing, 3, 4
  checking accounts, 371, 463
  circle graphs in, 216–217
  converting fractions to decimals, 122
  customary units of weight, 109
  dividing total amount of bills, 58, 66, 68, 76
  estimating cost, 16, 24
  metric conversion, 96
  mileage, 40, 42
  paychecks, 132–133, 461
  percentage discounts, 282–283
  percentage increase or decrease, 280–281
  percentage for tips, 276
  price reduction and rebate, 6–7
  proportions in, 244
  sales receipts, 462

Appendix **461**

466 *Index*

472 *Index*

Real-Life Applications lessons on checking accounts, paychecks, sales receipts, and the stock market help you gain real-life math skills.

If you have access to a calculator, check out the techniques for getting the most out of it in **Calculator Applications.**

You can use the **Glossary** to help you pronounce and understand math terms and the **Index** to find information quickly.

Career Focus Activity

Materials: invitations, thank-you notes, pens, stamps, decorations for a large hall, tables, and chairs

Procedure: Organize students into four groups. Each group will research a job for the job fair. They will create invitations and RSVPs. They will organize decorations, set-up, and clean up.

• Working with guidance counselors, one group of students sends invitations to local businesses, requesting they participate in a job fair. A specific date for the fair, a reply date, and a contact person, address, and phone number should be included in the invitation.

• Businesses to contact: banking, legal services, educational services, building industry, food industry, and health care professionals. Include other professionals whose jobs depend on the specific geographic location in which you live (farming, fishing, etc.).

• All students in the school should be invited to the job fair.

• A day before the fair, the second group decorates the room.

• The third group sets up tables and chairs for the number of attendees. Members of this group should also act as hosts to the visiting business representatives.

• All class members assist in clean up.

• After the successful job fair is over, the last group summarizes the findings and leads a class discussion. Members of the first group send thank-you notes within three days of the job fair to the businesses that participated.

• Each group then evaluates its experience and makes suggestions for future job fairs.

Add and subtract whole numbers and decimals to

• keep a budget.

• balance checking and savings accounts.

• estimate sums and differences.

• keep scores or times in sporting events.

What are some other ways to use adding and subtracting whole numbers and decimals?

Adding and Subtracting Whole Numbers and Decimals

A banker is an officer of a bank, a business that lends and invests money.

- Bankers work in banks and financial institutions and for the government and private companies.

- A banker should be good at figures and enjoy working with people.

- A banker makes decisions about loans and investments, creates financial plans, manages employees, and resolves customer problems.

- To become a banker, individuals study finance or work in a bank.

- Related careers include bank tellers, mortgage lenders or loan officers, investment counselors, and computer-entry personnel.

CAREER

BANKER

PORTFOLIO PROJECT: *Track your expenses for one month.*

1. Make an income and expense chart. Set up a two-column chart. Label one column *Income* and one column *Expenses*. List all of your income and expenses for a month.

2. At the end of the month, find out what your total monthly income and expenses were by adding each column. *Show the math.*

3. Subtract your total expenses from your total income. *Show the math.* If you have money left, identify two things you can do with it. You may want to put some in a bank!

About the Portfolio Project
Students should create an account book. One side of the page is for money earned; the other side is for expenditures. All math could be done in a format similar to a checkbook register, so students know the balance at each week's end, until the end of the month.

Assessment: The individual scoring rubric on page 161 of the Teacher's Resource Binder can be reproduced and used for assessment. Include the following information in the last two boxes. Students should have:
- listed all earned income and expenses in the correct columns.
- accurately figured all the math to obtain a correct balance.

1.1 Reading and Writing Whole Numbers

17115233 SOLD EVERY MONTH

Jeremy glanced quickly at a billboard and saw this ad.
He stopped to look more closely. "*How* many sold?" he thought.

Jeremy had to put in the missing commas to read this large number.

Examples

To read and write whole numbers correctly, you can use a place value chart. Each group of three digits has a name. A comma separates each group.

Billions	Hundred Millions	Ten Millions	Millions	Hundred Thousands	Ten Thousands	Thousands	Hundreds	Tens	Ones
	Millions			**Thousands**			**Ones**		

A **Find the place value of the 5 in the number 17,115,233.**

Count the number of places from the right. Find the column in the place value chart that is fourth from the right.

The 5 is in the **thousands place.**

B **Write 15 million, 37 as a standard numeral.**

Write each digit in the appropriate place. Write a zero where the place value is empty.

The standard numeral for 15 million, 37, is **15,000,037.**

C **Write 1,536,012 in words.**

1,536,012 is written as **one million, five hundred thirty-six thousand, twelve.**

Think and Discuss

1. Write two billion, three hundred forty-two thousand, sixty as a standard numeral.

2. Find the place value of the 5 in the number 256,006,902.

3. Write the largest standard numeral that can be made from the digits in the White House phone number, 202-456-1414.

4. How would you teach someone the correct way to write 3,065,000 in words?

SKILLS

Exercises

Find the place value of the 3 in each number. (See Example A.)

5. 947,342
Hundreds

6. 263,004
Thousands

7. 31,872,961
Ten millions

8. 1,322,654
Hundred thousands

9. 53,000,021
Millions

10. 198,536,724
Ten thousands

11. 57,231
Tens

12. 3,120,000,000
Billions

Write the standard numeral. (See Example B.)

13. 15 million, 312 thousand
15,312,000

14. 15 million, 312
15,000,312

15. 15 billion, 312 thousand
15,000,312,000

16. 402 thousand, 17
402,017

17. 402 million, 17
402,000,017

18. 402 billion, 17 million
402,017,000,000

19. 6 billion, 421 thousand, 92
6,000,421,092

20. 6 million, 421 thousand, 5
6,421,005

Write each number in words. (See Example C.)

21. 23,001

22. 30,001,412

23. 637,000,000

24. 3,791,060

25. 11,300,000,000

26. 4972

27. 3,433,012

28. 45,005

▶ Mixed Practice (For more practice, see page 400.)

29. Write the standard numeral for 63 thousand, 40.
63,040

30. What place value does the zero hold in 23,049?
Hundreds

31. Write 17,049,001 in words.
Seventeen million, forty-nine thousand, one

32. What digit is in the ten thousands place in 12,390,485?
9

▶ Applications

33. Georgia bought a used car for $999. When she wrote the check, she wrote the total amount in words. What did Georgia write?
Nine hundred ninety-nine dollars

34. Sal and Tom toss number cubes to see who can form the greater six-digit number. Sal rolls 1, 5, 6, 1, 2, and 5. Tom rolls 6, 3, 2, 4, 4, and 5. Who wins?
Sal, with 655,211

▶ Think and Discuss Answers

1. 2,000,342,060
2. ten millions place
3. 6,544,422,110
4. Read the numbers in each place value group and add the name of the group: 3 million, 65 thousand; in words, 3,065,000 is written as three million, sixty-five thousand.

★ Error Alert

Errors may occur when students ignore place value in the number. Make sure that they remain aware that each position has a value.

Answers

21. twenty-three thousand, one
22. thirty million, one thousand, four hundred twelve
23. six hundred thirty-seven million
24. three million, seven hundred ninety-one thousand, sixty
25. eleven billion, three hundred million
26. four thousand, nine hundred seventy-two
27. three million, four hundred thirty-three thousand, twelve
28. forty-five thousand, five

Reinforcement

Extra Practice, page 400
EP/MR Worksheet 1, TRB, page 1

Challenge

Write three thousand, four hundred two as a standard numeral. (3402) Also, write 3402 thousand as a standard numeral. (3,402,000) Which is greater? (the second number)

Objectives

- To identify place value to millionths
- To write decimals
- To write word names for decimals

Purpose

Whole numbers have place value; decimals have place value too. The idea of place value helps you understand parts of a whole. For example, dimes and pennies are parts of a dollar.

Introducing the Lesson

Have students write $1.00. Then ask them to write $1.25, $1.10, and $1.01. Now have students write the same amounts in words. Ask students to discuss how the cents amounts are related to the dollar. (Tenths of a dollar are dimes; hundredths of a dollar are pennies.)

Alternative Examples

Example A—Find the place value of the 5 in the decimal 0.0125.
The 5 is in the **ten-thousandths place.**

Example B—Write 42 thousandths as a decimal.
The decimal for 42 thousandths is **0.042.**

Example C—Write 2.067 in words.
2.067 is written as **two and sixty-seven thousandths.**

1.2 Reading and Writing Decimals

Helen was surprised when her September bank statement showed that her balance was $90 less than her check register balance. When she compared her canceled checks against her check register, she found her error. On check #1052, she had written $100.00, but in her check register, she had entered $10.00

This error taught Helen the importance of placing the decimal point accurately.

Examples

To read and write decimals, you can use a place value chart. A decimal point separates the ones place and the tenths place.

Hundreds	Tens	Ones	Tenths	Hundredths	Thousandths	Ten-thousandths	Hundred-thousandths	Millionths

A Find the place value of the 3 in the decimal 0.0013.

Count the number of places to the right of the decimal point.
Compare with the place value chart.

The 3 is in the **ten-thousandths place.**

B Write 65 thousandths as a decimal.

Write the digits so that they end in the thousandths place.
Write a zero for empty place values. When no whole number precedes the decimal point, write a zero in the ones place.

The decimal for 65 thousandths is **0.065.**

C Write 7.025 in words.

When the decimal point follows a whole number, you use the word *and*.

7.025 is written as **seven and twenty-five thousandths.**

▶ Think and Discuss

SKILLS

1. What is the place value of 5 in 17.456?

2. Write 0.033 in words.

3. With ten dimes in a dollar, 1 dime = 0.1 dollar, or one-tenth of a dollar. What part of a dollar is a penny?

4. Which would you rather have, 0.8 dollar or 8.0 dimes? Explain.

5. Write one hundred two thousandths and one hundred and two thousandths as decimals. Explain how they differ.

(handwritten: 1-14, 21-25)

Exercises

Find the place value of the 8 in each decimal. (See Example A.)

6. 0.08   **7.** 0.891   **8.** 0.1028   **9.** 176.8   **10.** 18.492

Write the decimal. (See Example B.)

11. 927 and 3 tenths   **12.** eleven thousandths

13. six hundred sixteen thousandths   **14.** 18 thousand and 18 thousandths

Write each decimal in words. (See Example C.)

15. 4.03   **16.** 0.019   **17.** 27.204   **18.** 2000.2   **19.** 729.07   **20.** 20.501

▶ Mixed Practice (For more practice, see page 400.)

21. What digit is in the hundredths place in 3768.425?
2

22. Write the decimal for 4 thousand 93 and 42 thousandths.
4093.042

23. Write 500.025 in words.
Five hundred and twenty-five thousandths

▶ Applications

24. Airmail paper is one thousand seven hundred fifty-five millionths of an inch thick. Write as a decimal.
0.001755 inch

25. Manuel received a paycheck for $169.65. Write the amount of the check in words.
One hundred sixty-nine dollars and sixty-five cents

▶ Review (Lesson 1.1)

Find the place value of the underlined digit.   *29*

26. 5601
Thousands

27. 18,964
Tens

28. 437,289
Ones

28. 99,754
Hundreds

30. 28,700
Thousands

31. 302,401
Tens

32. 782,050
Ten thousands

33. 4,062,893
Millions

34. 913,662
Thousands

35. 256,238
Hundred thousands

▶ Think and Discuss Answers

1. hundredths place
2. thirty-three thousandths
3. $0.01, or one hundredth of a dollar
4. It wouldn't matter since they are the same amount.
5. 0.102; 100.002; the first number is less than one; the second is more than one

★ Error Alert

Errors may occur when students misinterpret place value to the right of the decimal point. For example, they might express three thousandths as 0.3000.

Answers

6. hundredths
7. tenths
8. ten-thousandths
9. tenths
10. ones
11. 927.3
12. 0.011
13. 0.616
14. 18,000.018
15. four and three hundredths
16. nineteen thousandths
17. twenty-seven and two hundred four thousandths
18. two thousand and two tenths
19. seven hundred twenty-nine and seven hundredths
20. twenty and five hundred one thousandths

Reinforcement

Extra Practice, page 400
EP/MR Worksheet 2, TRB, page 2

Challenge

Write 3.402 million as a standard numeral. (3,402,000) Also, write 0.402 million as a standard numeral. (402,000) How much greater is the first number? (3 million)

Adding and Subtracting Whole Numbers and Decimals **5**

T5

1.3 A 4-Step Problem-Solving Process

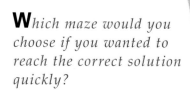

Which maze would you choose if you wanted to reach the correct solution quickly?

The guidesigns in the second maze keep you on track. They help you move quickly toward the solution and avoid errors.

In much the same way, word problems also contain guidesigns that lead you to the correct solution. Following the 4-step problem-solving process will help you learn to recognize and understand the guidesigns in word problems.

Read the problem below.

It took Maria weeks to save enough money to buy the $178 mountain bicycle she wanted. When she went to buy it, she found the price reduced by $25. As the clerk wrote up the sale, he told Maria that the bike had a $10 manufacturer's rebate. How much did the bike cost Maria?

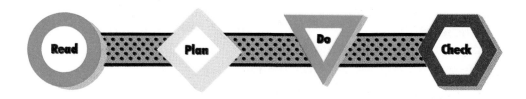

The 4-step problem-solving process is introduced briefly in the left column on the next page. See Lessons 1.4, 2.5, and 3.7 for more detailed information on each step. As you read each step, look in the right column to see how you can solve the problem about Maria's bicycle.

▶ 4-Step Problem-Solving Process

PROBLEM SOLVING

• **Step 1:**

Read the problem.

Decide what you need to find.

Examine the facts.

Look up any unfamiliar words.

Your Thinking

After reading the problem, think, "*I have to find what the final price of the bicycle is. I know 'price reduced' means Maria had to pay less money.*" You might have to look up *rebate* in a dictionary. It means *return of part of a payment*. Thus, getting a rebate also means paying less money.

• **Step 2:**

Organize your information.

Determine if you need more information.

Choose a strategy to solve the problem.

You find that you have all the information you need. You plan to add the price reduction and the rebate together and then subtract the sum from the original price.

• **Step 3:**

Carry out your plan.

Compute.

Reduction + rebate = total reduction.
$$\$25 + \$10 = \$35$$
Price − total reduction = final price
$$\$178 − \$35 = \$143$$

• **Step 4:**

Decide if your answer is reasonable.

Check your calculations—recompute if necessary.

The answer seems reasonable. It is less than the original price. Check the calculations.

▶ Think and Discuss

1. You used addition then subtraction in your plan. Can you think of another plan to solve the problem about Maria's bicycle?

2. How would you have to change your plan if, instead of a rebate of $10, the clerk told Maria she must pay a registration fee of $10? Would Maria pay the same amount?

3. How might using the 4-step problem-solving process help you solve problems that are not mathematical? Discuss.

▶ Think and Discuss Answers

1. Subtract twice; subtract price reduction to get sale price and then subtract rebate amount.

2. Add $10 to sale price of bike instead of subtracting $10. No, Maria would pay $163.

3. Answers may include applying **Read, Plan, Do,** and **Check** to the problem in a nonmathematical way; using a step-by-step approach to solving a problem.

★ Error Alert

Errors may occur when students do not realize that they sometimes must repeat steps to work out the best solution to a problem.

Reinforcement

EP/MR Worksheet 3, TRB, page 3

Project

Find and record the same five number facts for each of two members within a group. For example, list *area, population, elevation, electoral votes,* and *number of counties* for two states; or list *weight, height, length of tail, life span,* and *average number of newborn* for two animals, such as tigers and elephants. Create three word problems based on the facts you have found. Use the Read step to help you write each problem so that other students can understand it. Then exchange problems with another student. Complete steps 1–4 in the 4-step problem-solving process for the three problems you have. (Answers may vary. Check to make sure that students have written understandable problems and that they have carried out steps 1–4.)

1.4 4-Step Problem-Solving Process: Read

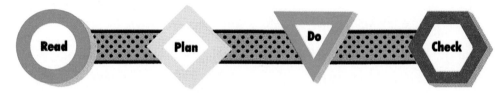

1. Take this test. Try to finish in 3 minutes or less.

> (1) Record the time you are starting the test.
>
> (2) Read through the whole test before computing.
>
> (3) Add the number of pages in this book to the number of pages in Chapter 8.
>
> (4) Subtract the number of pages in Chapter 16 from the answer to Step 3.
>
> (5) Add the number of pages in Chapters 11 and 2. Subtract the sum from the answer to Step 4.
>
> (6) Skip steps 3, 4, and 5.
>
> (7) Record the time you finish the test.

2. How long did the test take? Did you compute anything?

Step 1 in the 4-step problem-solving process is **Read**. If you followed the directions in Step 2, you quickly realized that you needed to read the problems, but did not need to work them.

If you read through the problems and did not compute anything, you practiced the main rule of the **Read** step: Always keep reading until you fully understand the problem and have all the information you need to solve it. If you are not absolutely certain of a word's meaning, look it up in a glossary or a dictionary.

The following chart shows you how asking certain questions helps you decide when you are ready to move on to Step 2 in the problem-solving process, **Plan**.

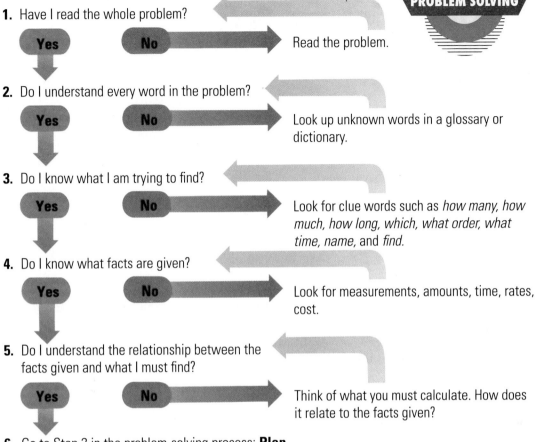

1. Have I read the whole problem?

Yes / No → Read the problem.

2. Do I understand every word in the problem?

Yes / No → Look up unknown words in a glossary or dictionary.

3. Do I know what I am trying to find?

Yes / No → Look for clue words such as *how many, how much, how long, which, what order, what time, name,* and *find.*

4. Do I know what facts are given?

Yes / No → Look for measurements, amounts, time, rates, cost.

5. Do I understand the relationship between the facts given and what I must find?

Yes / No → Think of what you must calculate. How does it relate to the facts given?

6. Go to Step 2 in the problem-solving process: **Plan**.

Read the problem and answer the questions.

How much fuel is burned in 8 hours by a motorcycle that consumes 2 liters of gasoline per hour?

1. What term is used to mean the same thing as *fuel*?

2. What term is used to mean the same thing as *burned*?

3. What other meanings does *consume* have?

4. What facts are given in the problem?

5. What are you supposed to find? Name some clue words.

Discuss how you would work through the chart to solve the following problem.

6. The toll to cross a certain bridge is 40¢. Denise drives across the bridge each day on her way to and from work. How much money does she spend on bridge tolls for 5 days?

★ **Error Alert**

Errors may occur if students read only the numbers in the problem and not the supporting prose information about the numbers. For example, they might not convert the terms "to and from work" to two trips per day.

Answers
1. gasoline
2. consumes
3. use up, burn, eat
4. A motorcycle uses 2 liters of gasoline per hour.
5. how much fuel is used in 8 hours; possible answers: how much, how many, how long
6. Read the whole problem. Look up any words that are unfamiliar. Look for clue words, such as *how much*. Know the facts. In this problem the facts are that the toll for one bridge crossing is 40¢ and Denise crosses the bridge two times in one day. You must calculate how much money she spends in 5 days for tolls.

Reinforcement
EP/MR Worksheet 4, TRB, page 4

Challenge
Work in groups of five. Make a list of ten number facts about your text book. You might include such facts as the number of pages, chapters, lessons, letters in title, and year of publication. Use these facts to write clues for a puzzle patterned after a crossword puzzle. On the puzzle, some numbers should overlap. Draw your puzzle without the answers. Make 2 columns of clues—one set for numbers going across and another set for numbers going down. Exchange puzzles with another group and solve. (Answers may vary but can resemble the puzzle shown below.)

¹3	8	5		²1	³2	0	
					4		
					8		

Adding and Subtracting Whole Numbers and Decimals **9**

T9

Objectives

- To compare two whole numbers
- To order three or more whole numbers

Purpose

Comparing and ordering whole numbers helps you to compare amounts, especially when the numbers have similar digits, or are close in value. For example, you might compare which of two people made more money, or which of two dances had more people.

Introducing the Lesson

Bring to class a clear plastic container filled with different-shaped and colored beans. Place it on a desk in front of the students. Ask for estimates on how many beans are in the bowl. Write the guesses on the chalkboard. Compare them. Ask students which is the greatest estimate, which is the second greatest, and so on until all the guesses are ranked.

Alternative Examples

Example A—Compare. 2389 ▮ 2398
2389 < 2398

Example B—Order 2389, 2398, 3298, 839 from greatest to least.
3298 > 2398 > 2389 > 839

▶ **Think and Discuss Answers**

1. 5702 > 5207
2. 609 > 396 > 369
3. Marlee
4. Sample answers may include: finding the fastest times in a race; the best scores in a sports tournament; the results of an election; or arranging items by size.

1.5 Comparing and Ordering Whole Numbers

Four seniors were competing to see who could sell the most popcorn at the home basketball games. Randy sold 1260 bags, Todd sold 1206 bags, Marlee sold 1602 bags, and Antonia sold 620 bags.

Who sold the most popcorn?

Examples

To compare whole numbers, align the ones places and work from left to right. Compare digits within a column. Use $>$ for "is greater than," $<$ for "is less than," and $=$ for "is equal to."

A Compare. 1260 ▮ 1206

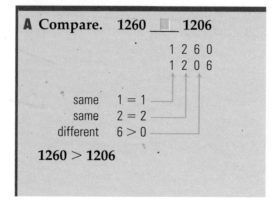

```
        1 2 6 0
        1 2 0 6
```

same $1 = 1$
same $2 = 2$
different $6 > 0$

1260 > 1206

B Order 1260, 1206, 1602, and 620 from greatest to least.

In Example A we saw that 1260 > 1206. Now compare 1602 with 1260 and 1206, using the same procedure.

$1602 > 1260 > 1206$

Finally, compare 620 with these three numbers.

$1602 > 1260 > 1206 > 620$

▶ ## Think and Discuss

1. Compare the numbers 5702 and 5207. Use $>$, $<$, or $=$.
2. Order the numbers 396, 609, and 369 from greatest to least.
3. Refer to the introduction to this lesson. Who sold the most popcorn?
4. Describe 3 situations for which you might need to order numbers.

Exercises

Compare. Use >, <, or =. (See Example A.)

5. 78 ▦ 65 >

6. 88 ▦ 92 <

7. 230 ▦ 302 <

8. 637 ▦ 736 <

9. 76 ▦ 74 >

10. 803 ▦ 803 =

11. 4239 ▦ 5293 <

12. 6013 ▦ 6103 <

13. 7887 ▦ 7787 >

14. 53,772 ▦ 53,227 >

15. 362,109 ▦ 354,109 >

16. 188,889 ▦ 188,888 >

Order from greatest to least. (See Example B.)

17. 75,581   57,851   75,851
75,851 > 75,581 > 57,851

18. 246   2464   266
2464 > 266 > 246

19. 828,331   882,313   282,313
882,313 > 828,331 > 282,313

20. 467   476   475   645
645 > 476 > 475 > 467

21. 409,320   49,320   490,230   409,230
490,230 > 409,320 > 409,230 > 49,320

22. 71,003   711,003   71,030   73,003   713,030
713,030 > 711,003 > 73,003 > 71,030 > 71,003

▶ **Mixed Practice** (For more practice, see page 401.)

Compare. Use >, <, or =.

23. 309 ▦ 409 <   **24.** 586 ▦ 585 >

25. 5421 ▦ 4421 >   **26.** 264 ▦ 245 >

Order from greatest to least.

27. 1,437,911,200   1,437,901,200   1,437,912,100
1,437,912,100 > 1,437,911,200 > 1,437,901,200

28. 4,693,233   4,393,233   493,633   469,333   4,693,333
4,693,333 > 4,693,233 > 4,393,233 > 493,633 > 469,333

29. 355,779   335,797   355,797   353,779   355,997
355,997 > 355,797 > 355,779 > 353,779 > 335,797

▶ **Applications**

30. Richard and Hideo just completed a community fund-raising drive. Richard raised $36,940. Hideo raised $34,247. Who raised more money? Richard

31. The top basketball scorers are: Carr, 1106; McGill, 1009; Maravich, 1381, Selvy, 1209; Williams, 1010. List the players' names in order of points scored, from greatest to least.
Maravich, Selvy, Carr, Williams, McGill

▶ **Review** (Lessons 1.1, 1.2)

Write each number in words.

32. 4083

33. 28,607

34. 39.4

35. 7.052

36. 309,866

37. 0.974

38. 4.002

39. 5.67

Answers

32. four thousand, eighty-three
33. twenty-eight thousand, six hundred seven
34. thirty-nine and four tenths
35. seven and fifty-two thousandths
36. three hundred nine thousand, eight hundred sixty-six
37. nine hundred seventy-four thousandths
38. four and two thousandths
39. five and sixty-seven hundredths

Reinforcement
Extra Practice, page 401
EP/MR Worksheet 5, TRB, page 5

Challenge
Anne traveled a total of 356 miles on a business trip. Included in that total were 3 trips out of her way: 50 miles to visit a friend, 107 miles to see some relatives, and 45 miles to see some sights. Her associate, Ray, took a similar trip. However, he traveled only 202 miles. As part of the 202 miles, he went 36 miles out of his way when he got lost, and 12 miles out of his way to visit friends.

Read the following statements and write a mathematical expression to compare the two trips.

1. Compare the total mileage of Anne's trip to that of Ray's trip. (356 > 202)
2. Compare the number of miles Anne went out of her way to the number of miles Ray went out of his way. (202 > 48)
3. Compare the number of miles each would have gone if they had not gone out of the way. (154 = 154)

Objectives

- To compare two decimals
- To order three or more decimals

Purpose

Comparing and ordering decimals helps you to understand and interpret scientific and technical information, which is often expressed in decimals.

Introducing the Lesson

Review the procedure for comparing and ordering whole numbers (Lesson 1.5). Write the numbers 264 and 265 on the chalkboard and have the students compare the two numbers. (264 < 265) Then, tell them to think of numbers between 264 and 265. Write those numbers on the chalkboard. (sample answers: 264.33; 264.136; 264.99; 264.5) Refer students to the place value chart in Lesson 1.2.

Alternative Examples

Example A—Compare. 10.01 ▓ 10.02
10.01 < 10.02

Example B—Order 25.6, 25.4, and 25.46 from least to greatest.
25.4 < 25.46 < 25.6

▶ **Think and Discuss Answers**

1. 1462.86 > 1426.86
2. 20.95 < 200.95 < 205.9 < 205.95
3. Tomás
4. Answers may range from 8.011 to 8.019 if only 3 decimal places are used.

1.6 Comparing and Ordering Decimals

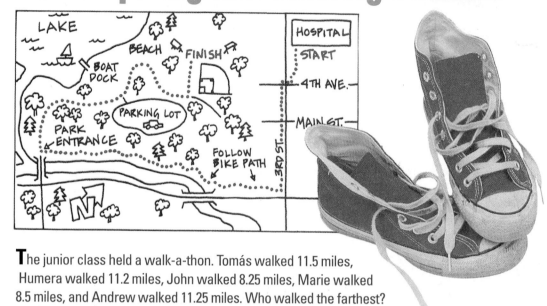

The junior class held a walk-a-thon. Tomás walked 11.5 miles, Humera walked 11.2 miles, John walked 8.25 miles, Marie walked 8.5 miles, and Andrew walked 11.25 miles. Who walked the farthest?

Examples

To compare decimals, align the ones places and work from left to right. Compare digits within a column. Use >, <, or =.

A Compare.   20.11 ▓ 20.12.

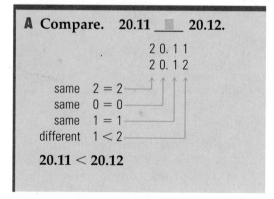

    2 0 . 1 1
    2 0 . 1 2

same	2 = 2	
same	0 = 0	
same	1 = 1	
different	1 < 2	

20.11 < 20.12

B Order 11.5, 11.2, and 11.25 from least to greatest.

Use Example A as a model.
Compare 11.5 and 11.2.
11.2 < 11.5
Compare 11.2 and 11.25.
11.20 < 11.25
Compare 11.25 and 11.5.
11.25 < 11.5
11.2 < 11.25 < 11.5

▶ **Think and Discuss**

1. Compare 1462.86 and 1426.86. Use >, <, or =.

2. Order 200.95, 205.9, 20.95, and 205.95 from least to greatest.

3. Refer to the introduction to this lesson. Who walked the farthest?

4. Find two numbers between 8.01 and 8.02.

Exercises

Compare. Use >, <, or =. (See Example A.)

5. 0.3 ▦ 0.4 <   **6.** 0.7 ▦ 0.8 <   **7.** 0.12 ▦ 0.21 <

8. 0.312 ▦ 0.313 <   **9.** 1.4 ▦ 1.7 <   **10.** 3.013 ▦ 3.013 =

11. 5.0117 ▦ 5.011 >   **12.** 20.080018 ▦ 20.080008 >

Order from least to greatest. (See Example B.)

13. 0.1006   0.1060   0.6001   0.0601
0.0601 < 0.1006 < 0.1060 < 0.6001
14. 1.771107   1.770117   17.71017   1.771017   1.777101
1.770117 < 1.771017 < 1.771107 < 1.777101 < 17.71017
15. 36.991132   36.901132   3.6911329   369.01132   36.091132
3.6911329 < 36.091132 < 36.901132 < 36.991132 < 369.01132

▶ **Mixed Practice** (For more practice, see page 401.)

Compare. Use >, <, or =.

16. 0.5 ▦ 0.50 =   **17.** 43.56 ▦ 44.65 <

18. 414.111 ▦ 414.11 >   **19.** 10.03003 ▦ 10.30303 <

20. 46.09119 ▦ 460.9119 <   **21.** 371.371 ▦ 371.371 =

Order from least to greatest.

22. 3.72   3.702   3.7   3.07
3.07 < 3.7 < 3.702 < 3.72
23. 0.98   0.098   0.908   9.09   0.89
0.098 < 0.89 < 0.908 < 0.98 < 9.09
24. 0.0025   0.0205   0.05
0.0025 < 0.0205 < 0.05
25. 5.73   5.75   5.37   5.57   5.35
5.35 < 5.37 < 5.57 < 5.73 < 5.75

▶ **Applications**

26. Claudia ran three hundred-meter heats at the Saturday track meet. Her times were 15.36 seconds, 15.32 seconds, and 15.26 seconds. In which heat did Claudia run fastest?
The third, 15.26 seconds

27. In baseball, ERA stands for Earned Run Average. In general, the lower an ERA is, the better that pitcher is. A team's starting pitchers had the ERAs shown here. Which pitcher had the best ERA? The second, Satherson, W.

TEAM ERA	
Pitchers	**ERA**
McMoore, J.	4.27
Satherson, W.	3.13
Winsom, T.	3.19
Adlers, G.	4.61
Dempke, P.	4.40
Andrews, A.	4.56
Dickens, R.	3.72
Stark, E.	4.10
Mathews, R.	3.70

▶ **Review** (Lesson 1.5)

Compare. Use >, <, or =.

28. 3792 ▦ 2792 >   **29.** 92 ▦ 920 <   **30.** 430 ▦ 430 =

Order from least to greatest.

31. 79,433   79,344   74,337
74,337 < 79,344 < 79,433
32. 802   892   908   1802
802 < 892 < 908 < 1802
33. 9008   8009   19,090   998
998 < 8009 < 9008 < 19,090
34. 243   422   244   234   423
234 < 243 < 244 < 422 < 423

Reinforcement
Extra Practice, page 401.
EP/MR Worksheet 6, TRB, page 6

Challenge
Seven girls participated in a downhill ski race. The girls decided to use their math skills and compare their times. Order the seven girls from fastest to slowest: Angela—62.5 sec.; Sandra—67.3 sec.; Liz—63.11 sec.; Antonia—67.35 sec.; Sue—63.325 sec.; Tanya—65.21 sec.; Claire—65.57 sec. (Angela, Liz, Sue, Tanya, Claire, Sandra, Antonia) Who has the slowest time? (Antonia) Who has the fastest? (Angela) Who in this group has the fourth best time? (Tanya)

Objective

• To round whole numbers to the nearest 10, 100, and 1000

Purpose

Rounding numbers helps you to estimate answers to problems and to estimate costs. You can decide if an answer is reasonable or if you can afford to buy something.

Introducing the Lesson

Review the place value chart in Lesson 1.1. Write the following numbers on the chalkboard and for each number, ask students to identify the numbers in these places: *tens, hundreds, thousands, ten thousands.* 653 (tens, 5; hundreds, 6); 9786 (tens, 8; hundreds, 7; thousands, 9); 13,267 (tens, 6; hundreds, 2; thousands, 3; ten thousands, 1); 1,736,025 (tens, 2; hundreds, 0; thousands, 6; ten thousands, 3)

Alternative Examples

Example A—Round to the nearest 10.
26,742
Round down to **26,740.**

Example B—Round to the nearest 100.
26,742
Round down to **26,700.**

Example C—Round to the nearest 1000.
26,742
Round up to **27,000.**

1.7 Rounding Whole Numbers

19,538 Cram Into Sealy Park

Huskies Win—Martin Belts 500-ft. Homer

Fans Roast as Temps Hit 101°

Read the numbers in the headlines. Which of the numbers do you think are actual counts? Which are close to the actual count? Numbers that are close to an actual count are called estimates. The examples below show how to estimate numbers by rounding.

Examples

To round whole numbers, determine the place value you will round to. Then examine the digit to the right.
Use the Rule of Rounding:
Round down if the digit is less than 5.
Round up if the digit is 5 or greater.

A Round to the nearest 10.

19,538
  ‌⌐ tens place

Since the digit to the right of the tens place is 5 or greater, 38 is closer to 40 than 30.

Round up to **19,540.**

B Round to the nearest 100.

19,538
  ‌⌐hundreds place

Since the digit to the right of the hundreds place is less than 5, 538 is closer to 500 than 600.

Round down to **19,500.**

C Round to the nearest 1000.

19,538
  ‌⌐thousands place

The digit to the right of the thousands place is 5.

Round up to **20,000.**

▶ **Think and Discuss**

1. Round $68,869 to the nearest ten thousand dollars.

2. When rounding 869,500 to the nearest thousand, do you round up or down? Why? What is 869,500 to the nearest thousand?

SKILLS

3. Refer to the introduction to this lesson. Why did some of the headlines use an actual count? Why did some use an estimated number? Explain.

4. You are buying a number of items at the store and want to be sure that you have enough money. Should you round up or down before adding the prices? Explain.

Exercises

Round to the nearest ten. (See Example A.)

5. 125
130
6. 179
180
7. 384
380
8. 403
400
9. 798
800
10. 6215
6220
11. 8491
8490
12. 10,322
10,320
13. 17,008
17,010
14. 20,212
20,210

Round to the nearest hundred. (See Example B.)

15. 983
1000
16. 829
800
17. 4055
4100
18. 10,775
10,800
19. 13,228
13,200
20. 6314
6300
21. 2864
2900
22. 9008
9000
23. 8330
8300
24. 6741
6700
25. 17,929
17,900
26. 4998
5000

Round to the nearest thousand. (See Example C.)

27. 9261
9000
28. 8590
9000
29. 4801
5000
30. 975
1000
31. 12,334
12,000
32. 19,730
20,000
33. 17,512
18,000
34. 62,000
62,000
35. 67,750
68,000
36. 40,001
40,000
37. 39,808
40,000
38. 1499
1000

▶ Mixed Practice (For more practice, see page 402.)

Round $64,508 to the nearest

39. ten dollars.
$64,510
40. hundred dollars.
$64,500
41. thousand dollars.
$65,000

Round 72,287 to the nearest

42. ten.
72,290
43. thousand.
72,000
44. ten thousand.
70,000

Round 25,019 to the nearest

45. ten.
25,020
46. hundred.
25,000
47. thousand.
25,000

▶ Applications

48. The seating capacity of Wrigley Field in Chicago is 37,272. To the nearest thousand, how many seats are in Wrigley Field? 37,000 seats

49. There were 17,000 fans at Monday's game, rounded to the nearest thousand. What is the least number of fans that might have been at the game? 16,500 fans

▶ Review (Lessons 1.5, 1.6)

Order from least to greatest.

50. 875 80 807 87 857
80 < 87 < 807 < 857 < 875

51. 46.2 46.02 4.602 462.2
4.602 < 46.02 < 46.2 < 462.2

▶ **Think and Discuss Answers**
1. $70,000
2. You round up; you round up because the digit to the right of the thousands place is 5 or greater; 870,000.
3. Actual counts are used when the number itself is important; estimated counts are used when the actual count is not important.
4. Round up because then the estimated total will be more than the actual total.

★ **Error Alert**
Mistakes may occur when students try to round numbers such as 49,950 to the thousands place, because more than one number changes.

Reinforcement
Extra Practice, page 402
EP/MR Worksheet 7, TRB, page 7

Challenge
For each number below, identify all the numbers than can be rounded *up* or *down* to get that number.

860 Round to the nearest ten. (855—864)
1500 Round to the nearest hundred. (1450—1549)
75,000 Round to the nearest thousand. (74,500—75,499)
6,280,000 Round to the nearest ten thousand. (6,275,000—6,284,999)
76,000,000 Round to the nearest million. (75,500,000—76,499,999)

Objectives

- To round decimals to the nearest whole number (and dollar)
- To round decimals to the nearest tenth and hundredth

Purpose
Rounding decimals allows you to quickly estimate costs when you shop or when you need to add or subtract money amounts.

Introducing the Lesson
Review comparing decimals (Lesson 1.6). Use the example: Compare—24.10 (<) 24.87. Then write the following numbers on the chalkboard: 24.87; 10.13; 0.85. Ask students to give a whole number that is greater and less than each. Discuss which whole number the decimal number is closer to. Ask how they decided. (sample answers: 24.87—25, 24, closer to 25; 10.13—11, 10, closer to 10; 0.85—1, 0, closer to 1)

Alternative Examples

Example A—Round $2.59 to the nearest dollar.
Round up to **$3.**

Example B—Round 15.73 to the nearest tenth.
Round down to **15.7.**

Example C—Round 6.2122 to the nearest hundredth.
Round down to **6.21.**

1.8 Rounding Decimals

Kevin is going to work on his neighbor's car. He went to the auto supply store to buy the parts. As Kevin found each item, he wrote down its price. Kevin is in the checkout line and wants to quickly find if he has enough money with him to pay for the parts.

Kevin can quickly estimate the total amount of his bill by rounding the figures and adding.

Examples

To round decimals, determine the place value you will round to. Then examine the digit to the right. Use the Rule of Rounding:
Round down if the digit is less than 5.
Round up if the digit is 5 or greater.

A Round $21.49 to the nearest dollar.

The digit to the right of the decimal point is less than 5. 21.4 is closer to 21 than 22.

Round down to **$21.**

B Round 12.86 to the nearest tenth.

The digit to the right of the tenths place is 5 or greater. 12.86 is closer to 12.9 than 12.8.

Round up to **12.9.**

C Round 7.9354 to the nearest hundredth.

The digit to the right of the hundredths place is 5.

Round up to **7.94.**

▶ Think and Discuss

1. What digit is in the ten-thousandths place in 10.37185?

2. Round $15.59 to the nearest ten cents.

3. Refer to the introduction to this lesson. To estimate his total, Kevin rounded each amount to the nearest dollar and then added. What estimate did Kevin get?

4. When you round 3.999 to the nearest tenth, why do you write 4.0 and not 4?

5. If a price is rounded to $9, what is the highest amount it could be? What is the lowest amount?

SKILLS

Exercises

Round to the nearest whole number or dollar. (See Example A.)

6. 6.3 6 **7.** 9.5 10 **8.** $2.81 $3 **9.** $14.36 $14 **10.** 47.93 48

11. $218.52 $219 **12.** 373.007 373 **13.** $99.89 $100 **14.** 407.581 408 **15.** 8.099 8

Round to the nearest tenth or ten cents. (See Example B.)

16. 1.62 1.6 **17.** 3.47 3.5 **18.** $9.85 $9.90 **19.** $41.54 $41.50 **20.** 71.899 71.9

21. 40.02 40.0 **22.** 611.58 611.6 **23.** 18.215 18.2 **24.** $20.25 $20.30 **25.** 9.519 9.5

Round to the nearest hundredth. (See Example C.)

26. 0.987 0.99 **27.** 1.426 1.43 **28.** 8.733 8.73 **29.** 6.9108 6.91 **30.** 43.0071 43.01

31. 0.0915 0.09 **32.** 14.8157 14.82 **33.** 0.2525 0.25 **34.** 2.3623 2.36 **35.** 8.909 8.91

▶ Mixed Practice (For more practice, see page 402.)

Round 473.1486 to the nearest

36. tenth. 473.1 **37.** whole number. 473 **38.** thousandth. 473.149

Round $837.527 to the nearest

39. 10 dollars. $840 **40.** dollar. $838 **41.** 10 cents. $837.50 **42.** 100 dollars. $800

Round 12,932.7117 to the nearest

43. hundred. 12,900 **44.** thousandth. 12,932.712 **45.** whole number. 12,933

▶ Applications

46. On a recent bicycling trip, Hector rode 268.3 miles in two days. When he told his friends about his trip, he rounded the number to the nearest ten. What number did he report? 270

47. Fran finished first in a long jump contest. Rounded to the nearest centimeter, her jump was four hundred forty-seven centimeters. What is the shortest distance she could have jumped to receive her score? 446.5 centimeters

▶ Review (Lessons 1.5, 1.6)

Compare. Use >, <, or =.

48. 5.8 ___ 8.123 < **49.** 39.3 ___ 39.300 = **50.** 0.0309 ___ 0.00489 >

51. 481 ___ 2026 < **52.** 752,894 ___ 752,849 > **53.** 49.35 ___ 4.935 >

▶ Think and Discuss Answers

1. 8
2. $15.60
3. $102
4. to show that you rounded to the nearest tenth, not the nearest whole number
5. $9.49; $8.50

★ Error Alert

Mistakes may occur when students think that rounding down means that the place value of the digit they are rounding to should go down. For example, when rounding 32.824 to the nearest tenth, the 8 does not become 7, it remains 8.

Reinforcement

Extra Practice, page 402
EP/MR Worksheet 8, TRB, page 8

Project

Go to a grocery store, a fast-food restaurant, or a clothing store with a friend. Write down the actual prices of ten things. Then one of you should estimate the price of each item by rounding to the nearest dollar. The other person should round to the nearest dime. Calculate a total of each estimate. Then add up the actual prices. Which of you is closest to the actual total? Explain why. (Answers may vary, but the total of estimates rounded to the nearest dime will usually be closest.)

Objectives

- To add whole numbers with up to 5 digits
- To add decimals with up to 3 decimal digits
- To add 3 and 4 ragged decimals

Purpose

Adding is a skill you use almost every day—in shopping, in counting money, and in finding total measurements.

Introducing the Lesson

Ask students to name specific ways they use addition in everyday life. In each example, have them identify the units that are being added. Point out that the units must be the same for the addition to be meaningful. Thus, you cannot add monkeys and gorillas, unless you convert them to a common unit—animals.

If necessary, review place value for decimals and whole numbers (Lessons 1.1, 1.2).

Alternative Examples

Example A—Add.   48,653 + 50,628

        48,653
      + 50,628
        99,281

48,653 + 50,628 = **99,281**

Example B—Add.   0.263 + 0.938

        0.263
      + 0.938
        1.201

0.263 + 0.938 = **1.201**

Example C—Add.   6.3 + 5 + 2.635 + 8.37

        6.300
        5.000
        2.635
      + 8.370
       22.305

6.3 + 5 + 2.635 + 8.37 = **22.305**

1.9 Adding Whole Numbers and Decimals

Television sponsors spend great amounts of money for commercial time. On a recent sports special, two commercial spots each cost $28,329 and $40,397. How much did the two commercials cost in all?

You need to add the two amounts to figure out the total cost.

Examples

To add, align numbers by place value. Begin at the right and add each column. Regroup when a sum is 10 or greater.

A Add. $28,329 + $40,397

$$
\begin{array}{r}
\$2\,8,\overset{1}{3}\,\overset{1}{2}\,9 \\
+\quad 4\,0,3\,9\,7 \\
\hline
\$6\,8,7\,2\,6
\end{array}
$$

Align the ones place.
Add and regroup.
9 + 7 = 16 = 1 ten + 6 ones
1 + 2 + 9 = 12 tens = 1 hundred + 2 tens

$28,329 + $40,397 = **$68,726**

B Add.   0.348 + 0.897

$$
\begin{array}{r}
\overset{1}{0}.\overset{1}{3}\,\overset{1}{4}\,8 \\
+\; 0.8\,9\,7 \\
\hline
1.2\,4\,5
\end{array}
$$

Align the ones place.
Add and regroup.
Place a decimal point in the sum.

C Add.   4.2 + 8 + 3.185 + 7.69

$$
\begin{array}{r}
\overset{2}{4}.\overset{1}{2}\,\overset{1}{0}\,0 \\
8.0\,0\,0 \\
3.1\,8\,5 \\
+\; 7.6\,9\,0 \\
\hline
2\,3.0\,7\,5
\end{array}
$$

Place decimal points and zeros as needed.
Add and regroup.
Place a decimal point in the sum.

▶ Think and Discuss

1. 9 + 7 = 16. What digit is in the tens place in the sum 16?

2. Add.   4.362 + 17 + 2909.11 + 36.0303 + 5

3. Add $32,798 and $41,599. How many times must you regroup?

Objective

- To estimate whole number decimal sums with 3-digit, 4-digit, and 5-digit addends

Purpose

Estimating sums and differences can help you to keep a mental total of about how much money you are spending and how much you will have left.

Introducing the Lesson

Ask students what is means to *estimate*. (to determine an amount or number close to the actual amount or number) Have students give examples of times when they had to estimate a sum or a difference. (sample answers: a total bill in a restaurant; distance traveled)

Review rounding whole numbers and decimals (Lessons 1.7, 1.8).

Alternative Examples

Example A—Estimate the sum of $16.83, $0.75, and $2.20.

$16.83 ≈ $17
  0.75 ≈ 1
+ 2.20 ≈ 2
        $20

The sum is approximately **$20.**

Example B—Estimate.
58,230 − 14,876
  58,230 ≈ 60,000
− 14,876 ≈ 10,000
        50,000
or
  58,230 ≈ 58,000
− 14,876 ≈ 15,000
        43,000

Two possible estimates are **50,000** and **43,000.**

▶ Think and Discuss Answers

1. 397; 400   **2.** $81.00
3. Kirk has approximately $3 left; round the costs to the nearest whole dollar and then subtract from $25.
4. 4760; 4700
5. 900, 930, 929; 929

1.12 Estimating Sums and Differences

On their first date, Kirk and Tiffany went out for dinner. Everything was perfect until Tiffany ordered lobster for her main course. At $12.95, this was the most expensive item on the menu. Kirk knew he only had $25 to pay for the entire meal and the tip. Meanwhile, the waiter was waiting for Kirk to order.

Kirk quickly figured out what he could spend on his entree by estimating how much of his $25 he had left.

Examples

To estimate sums and differences, use rounding to establish numbers that you can compute mentally. The symbol ≈ means "is approximately equal to."

A Estimate the sum of $12.95, $0.80, and $1.10.

$12.95 ≈ $13   Round each
  0.80 ≈ 1   number. Then add.
+ 1.10 ≈ 1
      $15

The sum is approximately **$15.**

B Estimate.   67,312 − 43,897

  67,312 ≈ 70,000   Round to the
− 43,897 ≈ 40,000   nearest ten
        30,000   thousand.
or
  67,312 ≈ 67,000   Round to the
− 43,897 ≈ 44,000   nearest
        23,000   thousand.

Two possible estimates are **30,000** and **23,000.**

▶ Think and Discuss

1. Round 397.4 to the nearest whole number and the nearest ten.

2. Estimate the sum of $49.95, $7.29, and $24.49.

3. Refer to the introduction to this lesson. If Kirk orders a $7.45 dinner and two colas for $0.95 each, estimate how much he has left for tax and a tip. Explain how you estimated.

4. Estimate the sum of 3906 and 849 by rounding to the nearest ten and the nearest hundred.

5. Give three different estimates for the sum of 397.4 and 531.9. Which estimate is most exact?

Think and Discuss

1. Subtract 60.25 from 85.

2. Refer to the introduction to this lesson. How many fans must come to the Terriers' next game to break the record?

3. Show how you regroup 7 to solve the problem $7 - 3.25$.

4. Do you need to regroup to subtract 2043 from 3047? Explain.

SKILLS

Exercises

Subtract. (See Example A.)

5.	6.	7.	8.	9.
3008	12,004	16,038	28,140	46,004
− 1409	− 7,706	− 14,956	− 12,067	− 12,148
1599	4298	1082	16,073	33,856

Subtract. (See Example B.)

10. $7 - 4.6$
2.4

11. $402 - 11.8$
390.2

12. $1300 - 99.4$
1200.6

13. $20 - 11.3$
8.7

14. $238 - 163.74$
74.26

15. $109 - 40.38$
68.62

16. $40 - 13.76$
26.24

17. $632 - 209.74$
422.26

Subtract. (See Example C.)

18.	19.	20.	21.	22.
0.704	0.606	0.7	0.93	0.85
− 0.5993	− 0.4932	− 0.392	−0.5432	− 0.693
0.1047	0.1128	0.308	0.3868	0.157

▶ **Mixed Practice** (For more practice, see page 404.)

Subtract.

23.	24.	25.	26.	27.
34,000	48.007	66,090	0.7	3803
− 18,401	− 9.139	− 19,002	− 0.482	− 49
15,599	38.868	47,088	0.218	3754

28. $8 - 4.7$
3.3

29. $10 - 2.5$
7.5

30. $16 - 2.48$
13.52

31. $33 - 0.9$
32.1

32. $5 - 0.39$
4.61

▶ **Applications**

33. Mark Twain was born in 1835. He died in 1910. Approximately how old was he when he died? 75 years old

34. The stadium capacity for the football game was 14,007. Only 8,987 attended the game. How many seats were empty?
5020

▶ **Review** (Lessons 1.5, 1.6)

Order from least to greatest.

35. 2.0191 2.091 2.919
2.0191 < 2.091 < 2.919

36. 41.73 41 403 437 43.72
41 < 41.73 < 43.72 < 403 < 437

37. 78,536 87,536 76,536
76,536 < 78,536 < 87,536

38. 602 6002 62.02 60.2 620
60.2 < 62.02 < 602 < 620 < 6002

1.11 Subtracting Whole Numbers and Decimals with Zeros

Sam is a sports writer covering the Terriers' rugby match against the Blazers. An announcement comes over the public address system: "Today's attendance is 15,275, bringing the season total to 698,209." Sam wonders, "If the league's record for a season is 702,007, how many fans must come to the next game to break the record?" Sam has to subtract.

Examples

To subtract from numbers with zeros, remember the rules for regrouping.

A Subtract.   702,007 − 698,209

$$\overset{6\ \ 9\ \ 11\ \ 9\ \ 9\ \ 17}{7\ \ 0\ \ 2,\ 0\ \ 0\ \ 7} = 69 \text{ ten thousands} + 11 \text{ thousands} + 9 \text{ hundreds} + 9 \text{ tens} + 17 \text{ ones}$$

```
− 6 9 8,2 0 9
-------------
      3,7 9 8
```

B Subtract.   9 − 3.87

```
  8  9 10
  9 .0̸ 0̸     Align the ones place. Place decimal points and write zeros as
− 3 .8 7     needed. Subtract and regroup.
---------
  5 .1 3     Write a decimal point in the difference.
```

C Subtract.   0.805 − 0.6774

```
      7  9 14 10
0 .8̸ 0̸ 5̸ 0̸     Align the ones place. Write zeros as needed.
− 0 .6 7 7 4   Subtract and regroup.
-------------
  0 .1 2 7 6   Write a decimal point in the difference.
```

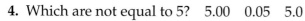

3. You can regroup 34 as 2 tens and 14 ones. How can you regroup 72?

4. Which are not equal to 5?   5.00   0.05   5.0

5. How can you check the result of a subtraction problem?

SKILLS

Exercises

Subtract. (See Example A.)

6. 6625	**7.** 3152	**8.** 9738	**9.** 5464	**10.** 2817
− 437	− 874	− 3869	− 863	− 1528
6188	2278	5869	4601	1289

11. 9249	**12.** 6443	**13.** 7411	**14.** 14,869	**15.** 85,728
− 637	− 4791	− 658	− 3,545	− 83,922
8612	1652	6753	11,324	1,806

Subtract. (See Example B.)

16. 0.37	**17.** 5.42	**18.** 6.35	**19.** 7.21	**20.** 0.726
− 0.29	− 3.61	− 4.21	− 5.83	− 0.363
0.08	1.81	2.14	1.38	0.363

21. 4.659	**22.** 8.943	**23.** 5.347	**24.** 23.13	**25.** 3.234
− 0.271	− 5.786	− 1.998	− 7.47	− 2.602
4.388	3.157	3.349	15.66	0.632

▶ Mixed Practice (For more practice, see page 403.)

Subtract.

26. 82,333	**27.** 9.34	**28.** 61.312	**29.** 18.763	**30.** 7482
− 4,949	− 7.67	− 0.049	− 7.98	− 847
77,384	1.67	61.263	10.783	6635

▶ Applications

31. Brian is buying his first car. He has narrowed down his choices to a blue car with an odometer reading of 65,721 miles and a red one with a reading of 98,035 miles. How much farther has the red car been driven? 32,314 miles

32. Zina ran the one-hundred-meter sprint in 13.15 seconds. The women's world record is 10.76 seconds. How much more time did Zina take? 2.39 seconds

▶ Review (Lesson 1.9)

Add.

33. 4506	**34.** 62.9	**35.** 499.85	**36.** 72,111	**37.** 6.7125
+ 893	+ 95.5	+ 23.99	+ 45,789	+ 0.8435
5399	158.4	523.84	117,900	7.5560

38. 4.607 + 82 + 0.11
86.717

39. 43,222 + 986 + 52
44,260

40. 0.115 + 0.87 + 0.6
1.585

▶ **Think and Discuss Answers**
1. 75.33
2. $170
3. 6 tens and 12 ones
4. 0.05
5. You can add the answer to the number you subtracted. If you did the subtraction correctly, the sum should equal the original number.

★ **Error Alert**
Incorrect answers may occur because students subtract the lesser from the greater digit, regardless of its position. Remind students that position of the number is important. Students may need to review regrouping.

Reinforcement
Extra Practice, page 403
EP/MR Worksheet 10, TRB, page 10

Teaching Aids
Blank check, deposit slip, and check register TA 1, TRB, page 154
Teaching suggestions precede the Teaching Aids worksheets.

Challenge
You have $30.00 and are shopping for CDs. You decide to buy a CD costing $15.99 including tax. Then you see another CD you want that costs $14.49 including tax. Can you purchase both CDs? (no) If yes, how much money do you have left? If not, how much money do you have left after buying the first CD? ($14.01)

Purpose

Subtracting whole numbers and decimals helps you find the difference between one quantity and another. This skill is useful when you balance your checkbook or when you compare prices as you shop.

Introducing the Lesson

Ask students to name specific ways they use subtraction in everyday life. In each example, have them identify the units that are being subtracted. Point out that the units must be the same for the subtraction to be meaningful. Thus, you cannot subtract 6 apples from 10 oranges. You must convert both to a common unit—pieces of fruit.

If necessary, review place value for decimals and whole numbers (Lessons 1.1, 1.2).

Alternative Examples

Example A—Subtract. $869 − $274
    $869
  − 274
    $595
$869 − $274 = **$595**

Example B—Subtract.   56.375 − 28.69
    56.375
  − 28.690
    27.685
56.375 − 28.69 = **27.685**

1.10 Subtracting Whole Numbers and Decimals

Simon saved $545 to buy a stereo system. In the Sunday paper he found the three ads shown here. "But wait," says Simon. "If I get the most expensive system, I won't have much money left for records and tapes."

To figure out how much money he would have left with each system, Simon has to subtract each price from $545.

Examples

To subtract, align numbers by place value. Begin at the right and subtract each column. Regroup whenever the top digit in a column is smaller than the bottom digit.

A **Subtract.** **$545 − $375**

$$\begin{array}{r} {\overset{4}{\cancel{5}}}\,{\overset{14}{\cancel{4}}}\,5 \\ -\ 3\ 7\ 5 \\ \hline \$1\ 7\ 0 \end{array}$$

Tens column: 4 is smaller than 7, so regroup.
540 = **4** hundreds + **14** tens

$545 − $375 = **$170**

B **Subtract.** **21.525 − 13.78**

$$\begin{array}{r} {\overset{1}{\cancel{2}}}\,{\overset{10}{\cancel{1}}}.{\overset{14}{\cancel{5}}}\,{\overset{12}{\cancel{2}}}\,5 \\ -\ 1\ 3\ .\ 7\ 8\ 0 \\ \hline 7\ .\ 7\ 4\ 5 \end{array}$$

Write a decimal point in the difference.

21.525 − 13.78 = **7.745**

▶ Think and Discuss

1. Subtract 165.9 from 241.23.
2. Refer to the introduction to this lesson. How much money would Simon have left if he bought the $375 stereo system?

4. Refer to the introduction to this lesson. What was the total cost of the two commercials?

5. Look at Example C. Explain why 8 and 8.000 are the same.

Exercises

Add. (See Example A.)

6. 5267 + 6924 12,191	**7.** 4328 + 3761 8089	**8.** 2854 + 3657 6511	**9.** 7649 + 8784 16,433	**10.** 24,372 + 81,989 106,361

Add. (See Example B.)

11. 0.77 + 0.19 0.96	**12.** 0.83 + 0.48 1.31	**13.** 0.845 + 0.194 1.039	**14.** 0.797 + 0.526 1.323	**15.** 1.78 + 5.56 7.34

Add. (See Example C.)

16. 4.3 + 0.5 + 2.22 7.02   **17.** 1.95 + 0.173 + 312 314.123

18. 0.9 + 0.99 + 0.999 + 9 11.889   **19.** 62 + 1.8 + 5.55 + 713 782.35

▶ Mixed Practice (For more practice, see page 403.)

Add.

20. 45,621 + 3,879 49,500	**21.** 0.78 + 0.53 1.31	**22.** 4387 + 5377 9764	**23.** 25.25 + 7.93 33.18	**24.** 54,849 + 3,478 58.327

▶ Applications

25. Megan bought a new dress, some earrings, and a necklace. The cost for these items was $54.59, $4.98, and $12, respectively. The sales tax was $4.65. How much did Megan pay in all? $76.22

26. A thirty-minute TV show had three commercial breaks. If the show aired in segments of 6.25 minutes, 9.75 minutes, 7 minutes, and 1.5 minutes, what was the actual length of the program? 24.5 minutes

▶ Review (Lessons 1.7, 1.8)

Round each number to the nearest hundred.

27. 8449 8400   **28.** 9511 9500   **29.** 16,087 16,100

30. 27,499 27,500   **31.** 35,631 35,600   **32.** 209,276 209,300

Round each number to the nearest tenth.

33. 166.88 166.9   **34.** 20.639 20.6   **35.** 474.853 474.9   **36.** 9.947 9.9   **37.** 3.9727 4.0   **38.** 27.88 27.9

Exercises

★ **Error Alert**

Errors may occur if students do not correctly round before they add or subtract.

Estimate the sum. (See Example A.)

6. 387
+ 522
≈ 900

7. 27.3
+ 5.6
≈ 33

8. 1653
+ 967
≈ 2700

9. 56,891
+ 13,555
≈ 70,000 or 71,000

10. 522.48
+ 749.83
≈ 1200, 1270, or 1272

11. $52.50
37.75
+ 12.20
≈ $100 or $103

12. 98
24
+ 122
≈ 200 or 240

13. 3,491
643
+ 49,113
≈ 53,000

14. $22.81
7.22
+ 41.99
≈ $70 or $72

15. 407.3
22.7
+ 373.4
≈ 800 or 803

Estimate the difference. (See Example B.)

16. 270
− 209
≈ 100 or 60

17. 489.7
− 43.2
≈ 450 or 447

18. $95.30
− 42.95
≈ $60 or $52

19. 4311
− 2909
≈ 1400 or 1000

20. 624
− 609
≈ 10

21. 23.599
− 7.741
≈ 10 or 16

22. $21.75
− 15.24
≈ $7

23. 72
− 49
≈ 20

24. 707
− 183
≈ 500 or 530

25. 4197
− 989
≈ 3200 or 3000

26. 473.21
− 58.74
≈ 410 or 400

27. $932.30
− 769.99
≈ $162, $160, or $100

▶ Mixed Practice (For more practice, see page 404.)

Estimate the sum or difference.

28. 49.7
− 19.9
≈ 30

29. 403
+ 771
≈ 1200 or 1170

30. $35.86
7.81
+ 29.99
≈ $74 or $80

31. 5211
− 4817
≈ 400

▶ Applications

32. Emma is in a bookstore. She has found four books that she would like to buy. They cost $4.95, $3.75, $12.95, and $7.25, respectively. Estimate how much she will have to spend. Approximately $29

33. Spenser is treating his 3 younger sisters to lunch at a seafood restaurant. Spenser has a $20 bill. Estimate how much change he will receive if they order items costing $2.95, $3.85, $3.60, $4.25, and four colas at $0.85 each? About $1

Reinforcement

Extra Practice, page 404
EP/MR Worksheet 12, TRB, page 12

Project

Work in small groups or individually. Identify two cities you would like to visit. Look them up in an atlas or on a map. Find the distance in miles between where you live and your destinations. Also find the distance in miles between the two places. Then answer the following problems. For each, identify whether you are estimating a sum or a difference.

1. Estimate your total mileage if you make two separate trips from where you live to each place. (Answers may vary, but students should estimate the sum of the two distances.)

2. Estimate how many more miles you must travel when you go to the farthest place. (Answers may vary, but students should estimate the difference between the two distances.)

3. Estimate the total mileage if you went from where you live, to the first place, directly to the second place, and then home. (Answers may vary, but students should estimate the sum of all distances.)

▶ Review (Lessons 1.9, 1.10, 1.11)

Add or subtract.

34. 78 + 499
577

35. 883 + 97
980

36. 1.9 + 71.1 + 5.5
78.5

37. 50.3 + 0.89
51.19

38. 800 − 123
677

39. 926 − 647
279

40. 475.24 − 89.5
385.74

41. 4.63 − 0.85
3.78

42. 70.03 − 27.985
42.045

Chapter 1 Review

REVIEW

Complete each statement. (Lessons 1.1, 1.2)

1. The 3 in the number 12,002.0031 is in the ▓ place.
Thousandths

2. The decimal point is read as the word ▓ .
and

3. The number 436,792.9183 has a(n) ▓ in the hundreds place.
7

4. A penny is one ▓ of a dollar.
Hundredth

5. 8,075,006.3 is written in words as ▓
Eight million, seventy-five thousand, six and three tenths

Write the whole number or decimal number. (Lessons 1.1, 1.2)

6. 2 million, 20 thousand, 93
2,020,093

7. 1 and 13 hundredths
1.13

8. 10 and 81 thousandths
10.081

9. five hundred eight thousandths
0.508

Order from least to greatest. (Lessons 1.5, 1.6)

10. 27,341   72,314   73,214   23,714   72,413
23,714 < 27,341 < 72,314 < 72,413 < 73,214

11. 6.03   2.9   6.294   6.87   2.694
2.694 < 2.9 < 6.03 < 6.294 < 6.87

Compare. Use >, <, or =. (Lessons 1.5, 1.6)

12. 7908 ▓ 8097 <

13. 862,112 ▓ 862,121 <

14. 5.2 ▓ 5.200 =

15. 4.603 ▓ 4603 <

Round each number to the nearest thousand. (Lesson 1.7)

16. 7455
7000

17. 529
1000

18. 3712
4000

19. 19,937
20,000

20. 83,096
83,000

Round each decimal to the nearest whole number. (Lesson 1.8)

21. 4.62
5

22. 0.9
1

23. 25.08
25

24. 49.516
50

25. 78.267
78

Add or subtract. (Lessons 1.9, 1.10, 1.11)

26.　　74,629
　　+　9,378
　　　84,007

27.　　106.43
　　－　27.59
　　　　78.84

28.　　72,846
　　－　23,752
　　　　49,094

Estimate. (Lesson 1.12)

29. Kim and Marcus ordered two pizzas at $9.89 each. They have $25. About how much change will they receive? $5

30. Tracy ordered items costing $1.89, $3.75, $0.65, and $1.49. She has nine $1 bills. Does she have enough money? Yes

SKILLS

Exercises

Estimate the sum. (See Example A.)

6.   387
       + 522
       ≈ 900

7.   27.3
       + 5.6
       ≈ 33

8.   1653
       + 967
       ≈ 2700

9.   56,891
       + 13,555
       ≈ 70,000 or 71,000

10.   522.48
        + 749.83
        ≈ 1200, 1270, or 1272

11. $52.50
        37.75
        + 12.20
        ≈ $100 or $103

12.   98
        24
        + 122
        ≈ 200 or 240

13.   3,491
        643
        + 49,113
        ≈ 53,000

14. $22.81
        7.22
        + 41.99
        ≈ $70 or $72

15.   407.3
        22.7
        + 373.4
        ≈ 800 or 803

Estimate the difference. (See Example B.)

16.   270
        − 209
        ≈ 100 or 60

17.   489.7
        − 43.2
        ≈ 450 or 447

18. $95.30
        − 42.95
        ≈ $60 or $52

19.   4311
        − 2909
        ≈ 1400 or 1000

20.   624
        − 609
        ≈ 10

21.   23.599
        − 7.741
        ≈ 10 or 16

22. $21.75
        − 15.24
        ≈ $7

23.   72
        − 49
        ≈ 20

24.   707
        − 183
        ≈ 500 or 530

25.   4197
        − 989
        ≈ 3200 or 3000

26.   473.21
        − 58.74
        ≈ 410 or 400

27. $932.30
        − 769.99
        ≈ $162, $160, or $100

▶ Mixed Practice (For more practice, see page 404.)

Estimate the sum or difference.

28.   49.7
        − 19.9
        ≈ 30

29.   403
        + 771
        ≈ 1200 or 1170

30. $35.86
        7.81
        + 29.99
        ≈ $74 or $80

31.   5211
        − 4817
        ≈ 400

▶ Applications

32. Emma is in a bookstore. She has found four books that she would like to buy. They cost $4.95, $3.75, $12.95, and $7.25, respectively. Estimate how much she will have to spend.
Approximately $29

33. Spenser is treating his 3 younger sisters to lunch at a seafood restaurant. Spenser has a $20 bill. Estimate how much change he will receive if they order items costing $2.95, $3.85, $3.60, $4.25, and four colas at $0.85 each? About $1

▶ Review (Lessons 1.9, 1.10, 1.11)

Add or subtract.

34. 78 + 499
577

35. 883 + 97
980

36. 1.9 + 71.1 + 5.5
78.5

37. 50.3 + 0.89
51.19

38. 800 − 123
677

39. 926 − 647
279

40. 475.24 − 89.5
385.74

41. 4.63 − 0.85
3.78

42. 70.03 − 27.985
42.045

Chapter 1 Review

REVIEW

Complete each statement. (Lessons 1.1, 1.2)

1. The 3 in the number 12,002.0031 is in the ___ place.
   Thousandths
2. The decimal point is read as the word ___ .
   and
3. The number 436,792.9183 has a(n) ___ in the hundreds place.
   7
4. A penny is one ___ of a dollar.
   Hundredth
5. 8,075,006.3 is written in words as ___
   Eight million, seventy-five thousand, six and three tenths

Write the whole number or decimal number. (Lessons 1.1, 1.2)

6. 2 million, 20 thousand, 93
   2,020,093
7. 1 and 13 hundredths
   1.13
8. 10 and 81 thousandths
   10.081
9. five hundred eight thousandths
   0.508

Order from least to greatest. (Lessons 1.5, 1.6)

10. 27,341   72,314   73,214   23,714   72,413
    23,714 < 27,341 < 72,314 < 72,413 < 73,214
11. 6.03   2.9   6.294   6.87   2.694
    2.694 < 2.9 < 6.03 < 6.294 < 6.87

Compare. Use >, <, or =. (Lessons 1.5, 1.6)

12. 7908 ___ 8097   <
13. 862,112 ___ 862,121   <
14. 5.2 ___ 5.200   =
15. 4.603 ___ 4603   <

Round each number to the nearest thousand. (Lesson 1.7)

16. 7455
    7000
17. 529
    1000
18. 3712
    4000
19. 19,937
    20,000
20. 83,096
    83,000

Round each decimal to the nearest whole number. (Lesson 1.8)

21. 4.62
    5
22. 0.9
    1
23. 25.08
    25
24. 49.516
    50
25. 78.267
    78

Add or subtract. (Lessons 1.9, 1.10, 1.11)

26.   74,629
    + 9,378
    —————
      84,007

27.   106.43
    − 27.59
    —————
      78.84

28.   72,846
    − 23,752
    —————
      49,094

Estimate. (Lesson 1.12)

29. Kim and Marcus ordered two pizzas at $9.89 each. They have $25. About how much change will they receive? $5

30. Tracy ordered items costing $1.89, $3.75, $0.65, and $1.49. She has nine $1 bills. Does she have enough money? Yes

Chapter 1 Test

Round each number to the nearest tenth.

1. 7.35
7.4

2. 6.52
6.5

3. 0.21
0.2

4. 87.92
87.9

5. 99.77
99.8

Add or subtract.

6. 8
   − 5.87
   ──────
    2.13

7.   4003
   −   965
   ──────
     3038

8.   0.706
   + 0.177
   ──────
    0.883

9.   69,387
   + 45,879
   ───────
    115,266

10.   2.68
    − 1.35
    ─────
     1.33

11. Paul spent $37.98. James spent $14.98 less than Paul. How much did James spend? Together did they spend more or less than $50? $23.00; more

12. Devon wants to buy items at the market costing $1.19, $2.48, and $0.45, and two items costing $0.85 each. She has $5. Does Devon have enough money to buy all of the items? No

Write the whole number or decimal number.

13. seven million, sixty-four thousand, nine hundred four 7,064,904

14. eight hundred and twenty-two thousandths 800.022

Write each number in words.

15. 390,005

16. 4.9

17. 1.608

18. 53.42

19. 6,400,690

Complete each statement.

20. The symbol > means ▓ . Greater than

21. The ▓ in a number is read as *and*. Decimal point

Order from least to greatest.

22. 9.7   9.08   9.085   9.009   9.721
9.009 < 9.08 < 9.085 < 9.7 < 9.721

23. 25,417   24,715   25,741   24,751   25,147
24,715 < 24,751 < 25,147 < 25,417 < 25,741

Estimate each sum or difference.

24. $395.98
    + 212.55
    ───────────
    ≈ $609 or $600

25. $136.72
    +   88.17
    ───────────
    ≈ $225 or $230

26. $943.18
    − 575.39
    ───────────
    ≈ $368 or $360

27.   864
    − 325
    ───────────
    ≈ 530 or 600

Compare. Use >, <, or =.

28. 4.2 ▓ 3.896 >

29. 6.8000 ▓ 6.8 =

30. 0.125 ▓ 0.215 <

31. 4780 ▓ 4870 <

Materials: pencils, papers, computer with Internet access

Procedure: Organize students into four groups. Students write a letter to a marine biologist or a related professional.

• All students brainstorm interview-type questions to place in the letter. The categories of questions should include those in the job description: what a marine biologist does, the attributes necessary in the performance of duties, where one could work, what education is necessary to qualify for this type of work, related careers, and how math is used on the job.

• The first group compiles the best questions.

• The second group researches on the Internet for possible businesses to which the class can send the letter.

• The third group composes the letter, including a return address.

• The fourth group reviews responses and reports on the results to the class.

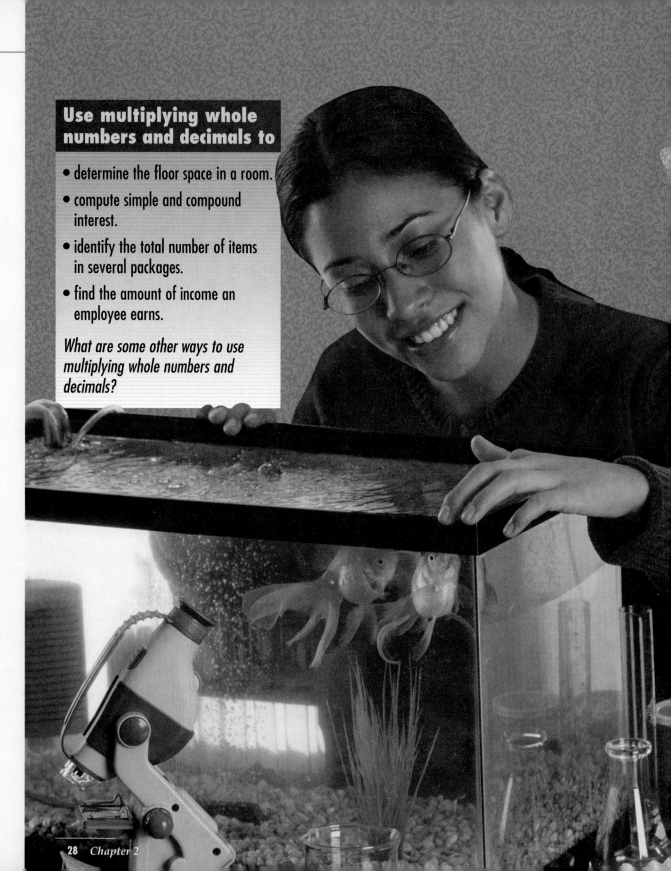

Use multiplying whole numbers and decimals to

• determine the floor space in a room.

• compute simple and compound interest.

• identify the total number of items in several packages.

• find the amount of income an employee earns.

What are some other ways to use multiplying whole numbers and decimals?

Multiplying Whole Numbers and Decimals

A marine biologist studies plants and animals that live in the sea.

- Marine biologists try to keep ocean plants and animals healthy.

- A marine biologist works in and around water, aquariums, fisheries, and in laboratories.

- A marine biologist collects and analyzes data about sea creatures and their environments and shares the information with others.

- To become a marine biologist, individuals complete a course of study in a four-year college program.

- Related careers include aquarium attendants, fish farmers, fishers, scuba divers, or jobs in the Coast Guard and Navy.

CAREER

MARINE BIOLOGIST

PORTFOLIO PROJECT: *Learn about a sea animal.*

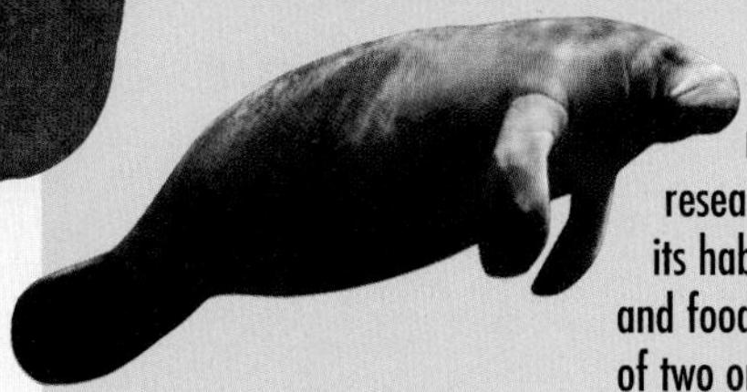

1. Choose a sea animal such as the Florida manatee.

2. Use reference materials to do research on the animal— its habitat, way of life, size, and food. Write a short report of two or three paragraphs about your animal.

3. In your report, include how much food one animal eats in a day. Use multiplication to determine how much food it eats in a year. *Show the math.*

About the Portfolio Project

Students should each choose a different sea creature and use various reference materials (at least three) for the research. Two or three paragraphs should include information on the four sub-topics. Students should show the math needed to determine how much the sea creature eats in a year using the formula: amount of food eaten in a day $\times$ 365 days in a year = food eaten in one year.

Assessment: The individual scoring rubric on page 161 of the Teacher's Resource Binder can be reproduced and used for assessment. Include the following information in the last two boxes. Students should have:
- written enough to cover all material asked for in steps 2 and 3.
- accurately multiplied to find the amount of food eaten in a year.

Purpose

This lesson helps you to understand how multiplication and addition are related. For example, to find the cost of 6 items priced at $0.25 each, you can multiply $0.25 by 6 rather than adding $0.25 six times.

Introducing the Lesson

Ask for examples of how students use multiplication in everyday life. (sample answers: finding the cost of several items of the same price; calculating what you should be paid if you are paid on an hourly basis)

Review the times table to show that multiplication is repeated addition. Use the example: $9 + 9 + 9 = 27, 3 \times 9 = 27$. Ask students to write other examples on the board.

▶ **Think and Discuss Answers**

1. Answers may include: buying same-priced items at a store; figuring out wages on a per-hour basis.
2. to figure out how much she must spend if she's buying several pairs of the socks
3. multiplication
4. addition
5. multiplication

2.1 Introduction to Multiplication

Suppose that muffins come 6 to a package and that you bought 4 packages. To find how many muffins you have, you add $6 + 6 + 6 + 6$. You can find the answer much more quickly, however, by solving the multiplication problem 4×6. For problems that can be solved by either addition or multiplication, multiplication is often the quicker method.

▶ **Think and Discuss**

1. Describe two situations when you have used multiplication.

2. Why might the girl in the picture need to use multiplication?

For each problem below, decide whether using addition or multiplication is more appropriate.

3. Mrs. Lopez arranged her classroom to make 8 rows with 5 desks in each row. How many student desks are in her room?

4. Jennifer bought presents for her family costing $21, $15, $11, and $30. How much did Jennifer spend?

5. Rafael's teacher assigned 6 homework questions every day for 5 days. How many questions did Rafael have to do in all?

▶ **Express Yourself**

Here are some terms used in multiplication.

times multiplied by

"3 times 5" means three multiplied by five.

product the result of multiplication

The product of 3 and 5 is 15.

multipliers or **factors**   the numbers being multiplied

To get 15, you can multiply the factors 3 and 5.

To get 15, you can multiply the multipliers 3 and 5.

doubled   multiplied by 2

Seven doubled is the same as 2×7.

Knowing the following two characteristics, or **properties,** of multiplication will help you to solve multiplication problems.

identity property   The product of 1 and any number is that number.

$1 \times 6 = 6$ $32 \times 1 = 32$

zero property   The product of 0 and any number is 0.

$0 \times 3 = 0$ $5,987,732 \times 0 = 0$

Complete each statement using the terms defined in this lesson.

6. In words, 15×2 is 15 ___■___ 2.

7. 20 multiplied by 7 can be written as 20 ___■___ 7.

8. The problem $7 \times 0 = 0$ illustrates the ___■___ .

9. When you multiply the ___■___ or ___■___ 7 and 5, the result is 35.

10. 24 is the ___■___ of 6 and 4.

11. The problem $500 \times 1 = 500$ illustrates the ___■___ .

▶ ## Practice What You Know

When you multiply, you must regroup if a product is 10 or greater. Regrouping in multiplication is much like regrouping in addition. When adding, you must regroup numbers if a sum is 10 or greater.

Regroup for addition.   **18 + 18 + 18**

```
   2
   18        Add the ones column.
   18        8 + 8 + 8 = 24 ones = 2 tens + 4 ones
 + 18        Add the tens column.
 ────
   54
```

12. Write three addition problems in which you have to regroup to find the answer.

2.2 Multiplying by 1-Digit Multipliers

During orientation, a group of freshmen overheard a senior remark, "Hey, only 172 school days until we graduate!" The remark prompted a couple of freshmen to figure out how many school days were left before their graduation.

The freshmen could multiply 172 by 4 to find their answer.

Examples

To multiply by a 1-digit number, begin at the ones places. Multiply each digit in the top number by the 1-digit number.

A Multiply. 27×6

$$\begin{array}{r} \overset{4}{2}\,7 \\ \times\quad 6 \\ \hline 2 \end{array}$$
$6 \times 7 = 42$
Regroup.
$42 = \mathbf{4}$ tens $+ \mathbf{2}$ ones

$$\begin{array}{r} \overset{4}{2}\,7 \\ \times\quad 6 \\ \hline 1\,6\,2 \end{array}$$
6×2 tens $= 12$ tens
12 tens $+ 4$ tens $= \mathbf{16}$ tens

$27 \times 6 = \mathbf{162}$

B Multiply. 172×4

$$\begin{array}{r} 1\,7\,2 \\ \times\quad 4 \\ \hline 8 \end{array}$$
$4 \times 2 = 8$

$$\begin{array}{r} \overset{2}{1}\,7\,2 \\ \times\quad 4 \\ \hline 8\,8 \end{array}$$
4×7 tens $= 28$ tens
Regroup.
$280 = \mathbf{2}$ hundreds $+ \mathbf{8}$ tens

$$\begin{array}{r} \overset{2}{1}\,7\,2 \\ \times\quad 4 \\ \hline 6\,8\,8 \end{array}$$
4×1 hundred $= 4$ hundreds
4 hundreds $+ 2$ hundreds $= \mathbf{6}$ hundreds

$172 \times 4 = \mathbf{688}$

▶ ## Think and Discuss

1. Find the product of 403 and 8. Explain each step.

2. Refer to the introduction to this lesson. How many school days do the freshmen have left before their graduation?

3. Rewrite 56 ones as tens and ones.

4. In Example A, it was necessary to regroup after the first multiplication step. In Example B, it was not necessary to regroup until the second step. Explain why.

Exercises

Multiply. (See Example A.)

5.	6.	7.	8.	9.	10.
73	31	55	32	47	86
× 3	× 5	× 6	× 9	× 4	× 7
219	155	330	288	188	602

11. 92×6 12. 67×9 13. 53×5 14. 45×2 15. 79×7 16. 98×3
 552   603   265   90   553   294

Multiply. (See Example B.)

17.	18.	19.	20.	21.
923	965	6513	2869	6024
× 6	× 2	× 7	× 8	× 3
5538	1930	45,591	22,952	18,072

22. 289×3 23. 263×4 24. 4821×2 25. 7152×7 26. 725×5
 867   1052   9642   50,064   3625

► Mixed Practice (For more practice, see page 405.)

Multiply.

27.	28.	29.	30.	31.
3844	603	49	908	6756
× 5	× 9	× 8	× 6	× 4
19,220	5427	392	5448	27,024

32. 84×3 33. 389×4 34. 7543×2 35. 825×7 36. 99×5
 252   1556   15,086   5775   495

► Applications

37. Kevin drives fifty-five miles an hour to get to a college football game. It takes him four hours. About how far away is the game? 220 miles

38. Three squads of 16 cheerleaders need new uniforms. Uniforms at All-Pro cost $33. Uniforms at Sports-Plus cost $36. How much money will the cheerleaders save in all if they buy from All-Pro? $144

► Review (Lesson 1.12)

Estimate each sum or difference.

39.	40.	41.	42.	43.
332	994	75	559	804
+ 614	+ 766	+ 88	− 51	− 443
≈ 900 or 940	≈ 1800 or 1760	≈ 170 or 200	≈ 500 or 510	≈ 400 or 360

Purpose

Multiplying by powers and multiples of 10 gives you a fast way to estimate. Were you overcharged? Are your answers reasonable?

Introducing the Lesson

Write the following on the board:

$1 \times 3 = 3$ $3 \times 2 = 6$
$10 \times 3 = 30$ $30 \times 2 = 60$
$100 \times 3 = 300$ $300 \times 2 = 600$

Point out that the number of zeros in each problem is the same in each product.

Alternative Examples

Example A—Multiply mentally.
14×10
Add a zero to the 14 for each zero at the end of the power of 10.
$14 \times 10 = $ **140**

Example B—Multiply mentally.
7×500
Multiply 7×5. Add a zero to the product for each zero at the end of the multiple.
$7 \times 500 = (7 \times 5) \times 100$
$\qquad\qquad 35 \times 100$
$7 \times 500 = $ **3500**

2.3 Multiplying by Powers and Multiples of 10

Sue had resolved to cut down on junk food. She was doing fine until one evening she suddenly craved something crunchy. All she could find was potato chips. "Well, there are only 12 calories in a chip," she thought. "That means 10 chips are 120 calories." Before she realized what she was doing, Sue had eaten 100 chips! "So much for that resolution," she said as she popped the 101st chip into her mouth.

Sue had multiplied mentally to find the number of calories in 10 potato chips.

Examples

To multiply by powers or multiples of 10 mentally, first count the number of zeros at the end of the power or multiple.
Numbers like 10, 100, 1000, and 10,000 are **powers** of 10.
Numbers like 10, 20, 50, 200, and 250 are **multiples** of 10.

A Multiply mentally. 12×10

Add a zero to the 12 for each zero at the end of the power of 10.

$12 \times 10 = 120$

one zero   one place

$12 \times 10 = $ **120**

B Multiply mentally. 9×400

Multiply 9 by 4. Add a zero to the product for each zero at the end of the multiple of 10.

$9 \times 400 = (9 \times 4) \times 100$
$\qquad\qquad\qquad 36 \times 100 = 3600$

$9 \times 400 = $ **3600**

▶ **Think and Discuss**

1. Multiply 126 by 1000. How many zeros did you add to 126?

2. Multiply 1260 by 10,000. How many zeros are in your answer?

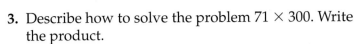

3. Describe how to solve the problem 71 × 300. Write the product.

4. Refer to the introduction to this lesson. If Sue had stopped at 30 potato chips, how many calories would she have consumed? How many calories are in 300 potato chips?

5. Describe how you would multiply 50 by 80 mentally. How many zeros are in the product?

SKILLS

Exercises

Multiply mentally. (See Example A.)

6. 9 × 10
90
7. 8920 × 100
892,000
8. 56 × 10,000
560,000
9. 72 × 100
7,200
10. 48 × 1000
48,000
11. 52 × 10,000
520,000
12. 8172 × 100
817,200
13. 8 × 10
80
14. 5063 × 1000
5,063,000
15. 47 × 100,000
4,700,000
16. 9 × 1000
9000
17. 430 × 100
43,000

Multiply mentally. (See Example B.)

18. 4 × 30
120
19. 800 × 60
48,000
20. 9 × 500
4500
21. 7 × 6000
42,000
22. 5 × 400
2000
23. 3 × 8000
24,000
24. 120 × 20
2400
25. 7 × 9000
63,000
26. 25 × 300
7500
27. 13 × 200
2600

▶ **Mixed Practice** (For more practice, see page 405.)

Multiply mentally.

28. 45 × 200
9000
29. 137 × 10
1370
30. 255 × 100
25,500
31. 4 × 400,000
1,600,000
32. 4 × 5000
20,000
33. 35 × 10,000
350,000
34. 7 × 700
4900
35. 75 × 10
750
36. 17 × 100
1700
37. 92 × 10,000
920,000
38. 50 × 300
15,000
39. 600 × 6000
3,600,000

▶ **Applications**

40. If sixty band members each invite six people to a concert, how many people will have been invited? 360 people

41. If each student in a class of 34 students sells 2 candles like the one below, how much money will be collected? $340

$5.00

▶ **Review** (Lessons 1.10, 1.11)

Subtract.

42.
$$\begin{array}{r} 6004 \\ -\ 2453 \\ \hline 3551 \end{array}$$

43.
$$\begin{array}{r} 8.9 \\ -\ 4.532 \\ \hline 4.368 \end{array}$$

44.
$$\begin{array}{r} 520.15 \\ -\ 318.67 \\ \hline 201.48 \end{array}$$

45.
$$\begin{array}{r} 338,714 \\ -\ 189,855 \\ \hline 148,859 \end{array}$$

45. 10 − 0.446
9.554
47. 82,695 − 66,787
15,908
48. 4129 − 754
3375

Objective

- To multiply by a 2-digit or 3-digit multiplier

Purpose

If you get paid on an hourly basis, you can multiply to help you check that you have been paid the correct amount.

Introducing the Lesson

Review multiplying by 1-digit multipliers (Lesson 2.2). Use the example: 62×8. Tell students that multiplying by 2-digit and 3-digit numbers uses the same procedure but involves more steps.

Alternative Examples

Example A Multiply.	Example B Multiply.
168×39	622×306

```
     168
   ×  39
    1512
    5040
    6552
```

```
      622
   ×  306
    3,732
  186,600
  190,332
```

Alternative Strategies

Show students how to regroup the multiplier, write two separate problems, and then add the products of the two problems. Use Example A.

$159 \times 48 = (159 \times 8) + (159 \times 40)$
$= 1272 + 6360$
$= \mathbf{7632}$

▶ Think and Discuss Answers

1. 10,887
2. 143,910; in this problem two 3-digit numbers are being multiplied, while in the first problem the multipliers have 3 and 2 digits respectively
3. 7632
4. 86×77 would be easier to find, since once 7×86 is found, 70×86 is easy to find.
5. The two problems both involve multiplying one digit at a time and regrouping; however, 1-digit multiplication does not require that products be added.

2.4 Multiplying by 2-Digit and 3-Digit Multipliers

Bernadette was so curious one day that she started to count the holes in the ceiling tiles. One tile had 159 holes. "It'll take me forever to count every hole in the ceiling," she thought.

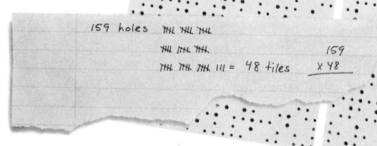

Since the ceiling was so large, Bernadette decided to simply multiply 159 by 48, the number of tiles in the ceiling.

Examples

To multiply by a 2-digit or 3-digit number, begin at the ones places. Multiply each digit in the top number by each digit in the bottom number. Add the products.

A Multiply. 159×48

```
      159
   ×   48
     1272    → 159 × 8
 +  6360     → 159 × 40
     7632
```
Regroup: $48 = 40 + 8$

B Multiply. 824×604

```
      824
   ×  604
    3,296      → 824 × 4
 + 494,400     → 824 × 600
  497,696
```
Regroup:
$604 = 600 + 4$

▶ Think and Discuss

1. Find the product of 573 and 19.

2. Find the product of 234 and 615. How is this problem different from the problem in Question 1?

3. Refer to the introduction to this lesson. How many holes does the ceiling have?

4. Which would be easier to find, 65×76 or 86×77? Explain.

5. How are the problems in Examples A and B like 1-digit multiplication? How are they different?

★ **Error Alert**
Errors may occur when students use the wrong column for recording the products of each multiplication step.

Exercises

Multiply. (See Example A.)

74 × 42 3108	**7.** 79 × 34 2686	**8.** 155 × 18 2790	**9.** 579 × 42 24,318	203 × 49 9947
11. 670 × 81 54,270	**12.** 943 × 71 66,953	**13.** 257 × 12 3084	**14.** 336 × 25 8400	**15.** 210 × 44 9240

16. 425 × 36 15,300   **17.** 376 × 34 12,784   **18.** 15 × 99 1485   **19.** 123 × 52 6396

Multiply. (See Example B.)

20. 569 × 143 81,367	**21.** 3104 × 379 1,176,416	**22.** 368 × 244 89,792	**23.** 3007 × 403 1,211,821	711 × 639 454,329
25. 750 × 179 134,250	**26.** 6348 × 205 1,301,340	**27.** 9002 × 791 7,120,582	**28.** 303 × 303 91,809	**29.** 4718 × 608 2,868,544

30. 204 × 99 20,196   **31.** 72 × 305 21,960   **32.** 601 × 207 124,407   **33.** 911 × 602 548,422

▶ Mixed Practice (For more practice, see page 406.)

Multiply.

34. 682 × 76 51,832	**35.** 5409 × 45 243,405	**36.** 82 × 49 4018	**37.** 707 × 95 67,165	**38.** 49 × 94 4606
39. 525 × 45 23,625	**40.** 4393 × 702 3,083,886	**41.** 7005 × 75 525,375	**42.** 823 × 44 36,212	**43.** 3909 × 64 250,176

44. 53 × 51 2703   **45.** 416 × 25 10,400   **46.** 905 × 387 350,235   **47.** 301 × 500 150,500

▶ Applications

48. Coach Murphy told each player to bring twelve tennis balls to the first practice. How many tennis balls will he have if there are twenty-four players on the team? 288

49. To raise money for their school, the 162 seniors sponsored a rock concert. They sold 748 of the tickets below. How much money did the seniors earn from ticket sales? $11,220

CENTER CITY HIGH SCHOOL
SHARKSKIN
Appearing in the main auditor
on Saturday at 8:00 PM
ROW A SEAT 20 $15.00

CENTER CITY HIGH SCHOOL
SHARKSKIN
Appearing in the main auditorium
on Saturday at 8:00 PM
ROW A SEAT 22 $15.00

▶ Review (Lesson 1.9)

Add.

50. 3.917 + 4.48 8.397	**51.** 87,420 + 29,658 117,078	**52.** 6956.3 + 6975.7 13,932	**53.** 4,396,087 + 5,857,317 10,253,404

Reinforcement
Extra Practice, page 406
EP/MR Worksheet 15, TRB, page 15

Teaching Aids
Multiplication table
TA 2, TRB, page 155
Teaching suggestions precede the Teaching Aids worksheets.

Challenge
Find the missing digits in each of the following problems.

A.
```
     (7)3 4
×     (1)2
    1 4(6)8
    7(3)4 0
   (8)8 0(8)
```

B.
```
        3(0)0 7
×       9(0)3
      (9)0(2)1
  2( 7)0 6(3 0)0
 (2),7(1)5,3 2(1)
```

C.
```
        8(9)8
×       5 1(2)
      (1) 7 9 6
     (8) 9(8)0
    4(4)9  0(0)0
   (4)5 9,(7)7(6)
```

Purpose
When you are faced with mathematical problems in everyday life, they do not present themselves as multiplication, division, addition, or subtraction computations. Learning to organize your thoughts or make a plan can help you decide which computations you need to use to solve such problems.

Introducing the Lesson
Review the 4-step problem-solving process (Lessons 1.3, 1.4). Elicit the 4 steps of problem solving and what they mean: **Read, Plan, Do,** and **Check.** Ask students to describe examples of non-mathematical plans they have made. (sample answers: planning a party; planning a series of moves in chess or checkers; planning a research paper) Encourage them to break down their examples into specific details, answering questions such as: What were they trying to do? What did they need to know? What did they do first? Second? Third?

2.5 4-Step Problem-Solving Process: Plan

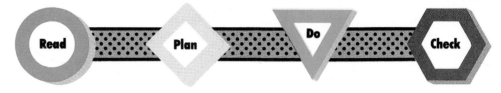

Step 1 in successful problem solving is **Read.** Step 2 is **Plan.** You can shape your plan by asking yourself certain questions. Read the example below and study the chart. You will see how questions and answers shape a plan for solving the example.

A class of 35 students and its teacher are going to a special show at the museum. Each ticket costs $2.50 and admits 2 people. The museum has provided the class with 6 free tickets. How much must the class spend to purchase enough additional tickets for everyone to see the show?

Questions	Answers	Plan
1. What exactly am I trying to find?	The cost of additional tickets.	The solution will be an amount of money.
2. What information do I need to solve the problem?	How many tickets the class needs to buy and the cost of each ticket.	
3. Of the information I need, what is given and what must I calculate?	The cost of each ticket is given. I must calculate the number of additional tickets needed.	Divide the number of people by 2 to find the total tickets needed. Subtract the number of free tickets to find the number of additional tickets needed.
4. Will organizing the information into a table or a diagram help solve the problem?	A diagram of the steps needed to solve the problem would be helpful.	• students + teacher = people • people ÷ 2 = total tickets • total tickets − 6 = tickets to purchase • tickets to purchase × $2.50 = cost of tickets

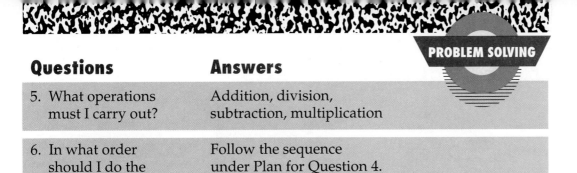

Questions	Answers
5. What operations must I carry out?	Addition, division, subtraction, multiplication
6. In what order should I do the operations?	Follow the sequence under Plan for Question 4.

Another point to consider when planning how to solve a problem is whether you have solved a similar problem before. Ask yourself if any of the steps that you used to solve that problem can be used to solve the new problem.

▶ **Think and Discuss**

1. Solve the example on page 38.

2. As you read the following problem, look for ways in which this problem is like the example on page 38.

   > Part of Mary's job is making book covers. It takes Mary 5 minutes to make each cover. Ned brought Mary 15 books that need covers. Mary put them with 9 other books that also need covers. If Mary already has 8 covers ready, how much time must she spend making covers for these books?

3. Complete these sentences to show how elements in the above problem can be compared to those in the example.
   - <u>Books</u> in this problem can be compared to <u>people</u> in the example.
   - <u>Covers</u> in this problem can be compared to ▨ in the example.
   - ▨ in this problem can be compared to <u>cost of tickets</u> in the example.
   - <u>Covers already made</u> can be compared to ▨ in the example.

4. Division is not needed in the problem in Exercise 2. Where was division used in the example on page 38?

5. Make a chart like the one in the example to plan how to solve the following problem.

   > To earn a jogging award, Tom must jog 90 miles. He jogs for $\frac{1}{2}$ hour a day, 5 days a week. If it takes Tom about 10 minutes to jog 1 mile, how many weeks will it take him to earn the award?

▶ **Think and Discuss Answers**

1. $30.00

2. Both problems are similar in structure, give limiting information (5 minutes/cover; $2.50/2 people), ask for answers related to this information, and require more than one operation to solve.

3. tickets; time needed to make a cover; free tickets

4. the fact that 1 ticket admits 2 people

5. The following answers and plans correspond to questions 1–6 in chart: 1. how many weeks it takes Tom to jog 90 miles; solution will be a number of weeks; 2. how long it takes Tom to jog 1 mile and how many minutes a week he jogs; 3. Information given includes Tom's jogging speed of 10 minutes/1 mile and jogging schedule. I can calculate the number of minutes it will take him to jog 90 miles and divide by the number of minutes a week he jogs; 4. A diagram of steps needed would be helpful.

- $90 \times 10 =$ minutes to jog 90 miles
- $5 \times 30 =$ minutes jogged each week
- time to jog 90 miles ÷ time jogged each week = weeks to jog 90 miles;

5. multiplication and division;
6. Follow sequence of steps given in number 4.

Reinforcement

EP/MR Worksheet 16, TRB, page 16

Challenge

Use the following facts to write a problem and a plan for solving it. Compare your problem and plan with those of other students. **Hint:** All of the facts may not be necessary. Facts: Beverly and Larry each make $30 a week working at a bookstore. Beverly is saving for a radio that costs $90. Larry pays $2 to ride a bus to and from work each day. (A possible solution may include: Problem: How many weeks will it take Beverly to save for the radio? Plan: Divide the cost of the radio by Beverly's weekly wages.)

Purpose

Estimating products is probably the most common way that you will multiply in daily life. Everyday situations seldom require finding exact figures with pencil and paper.

Introducing the Lesson

Review rounding numbers (Lesson 1.7). Use the following examples: Round to the nearest 10—165 (170), 2259 (2260), 10,152 (10,150); round to the nearest 100—975 (1000), 8345 (8300), 12,167 (12,200), 32,956 (33,000); round to the nearest 1000—8765 (9000), 10,502 (11,000), 82,003 (82,000).

Alternative Examples

Example A—Estimate.   27 × 3
27 rounds up to 30. There is no need to round 3.
30 × 3 = 90
27 × 3 ≈ **90**

Example B—Estimate.   236 × 67
236 rounds down to 200. 67 rounds up to 70.
200 × 70 = 14,000
236 × 67 ≈ **14,000**

2.6 Estimating Products

Ken borrowed his parents' car to take his girlfriend to a concert 45 miles away. The car got 19 miles to the gallon. Ken knew by looking at the gas gauge that he had about 4 gallons of gas. He didn't want to run out of gas on the way home.

Ken needed quickly to figure out how much gas he would need.

Examples

To estimate a product, round one or both multipliers. Then multiply. The symbol ≈ means "is approximately equal to."

A Estimate.   19 × 4

19 rounds up to 20.
There is no need to round 4.

20 × 4 = 80
19 × 4 ≈ **80**

B Estimate.   227 × 48

227 rounds down to 200.
48 rounds up to 50.

200 × 50 = 10,000
227 × 48 ≈ **10,000**

▶ Think and Discuss

1. Refer to the introduction to this lesson. About how many miles can Ken go on 4 gallons of gas? Estimate how many miles he can go with a full tank, or 16 gallons of gas. Explain how you estimated.

2. Nancy earns $6 an hour, and she works 18 hours a week. Estimate how much she earns each month.

3. If both multipliers are rounded down, will the estimated product be higher or lower than the actual product? Explain.

4. When is it useful to estimate?

Exercises

Estimate the product. (See Example A.)

5. 42 × 4 ≈160	**6.** 68 × 3 ≈210	**7.** 53 × 7 ≈350	**8.** 81 × 9 ≈720	**9.** 41 × 8 ≈320	**10.** 49 × 3 ≈150

Estimate the product. (See Example B.)

11. 15 × 11 ≈200 or 150	**12.** 172 × 23 ≈4000	**13.** 39 × 32 ≈1200	**14.** 478 × 68 ≈35,000	**15.** 25 × 13 ≈300 or 250	**16.** 93 × 11 ≈900
17. 98 × 32 ≈3000	**18.** 142 × 21 ≈2800	**19.** 283 × 46 ≈15,000	**20.** 17 × 92 ≈1700 or ≈1800 or ≈2000	**21.** 407 × 81 ≈32,000	**22.** 874 × 19 ≈18,000

▶ **Mixed Practice** (For more practice, see page 406.)

Estimate the product.

23. 77 × 17 ≈1600	**24.** 205 × 71 ≈14,000	**25.** 89 × 3 ≈270	**26.** 476 × 43 ≈20,000	**27.** 719 × 21 ≈14,000	**28.** 595 × 7 ≈4200
29. 43 × 2 ≈80	**30.** 68 × 87 ≈6300	**31.** 281 × 14 ≈2800	**32.** 29 × 6 ≈180	**33.** 18 × 6 ≈120	**34.** 348 × 92 ≈35,000

▶ **Applications**

35. Mr. Harris has just started a sales job that involves some driving. For accounting purposes, Mr. Harris must estimate his monthly mileage. He travels 185 miles 6 times a month. Estimate Mr. Harris's monthly mileage. Approximately 1200 miles

36. Rod, a speed reader, started reading a book one night and read eighty-five pages the first hour. He continued reading at the same pace for one hour each night. Did he finish the six-hundred-eighty-five-page book in seven days? Solve mentally using estimation. No

▶ **Review** (Lessons 1.5, 1.6)

Compare. Use >, <, or =.

37. 6.581 ▆ 6.481 >   **38.** 37,855 ▆ 37,585 >   **39.** 9.877 ▆ 98.77 <

40. 8.240 ▆ 8.2400 =   **41.** 1.74 ▆ 1.6985 >   **42.** 564,972 ▆ 571,792 <

Think and Discuss Answers

1. about 80 miles; about 300 or 400 miles; the first answer will involve multiplying 20 by 4, and the second will involve multiplying 20 by 15 or 20 by 20

2. about $480 ($6 × 20 × 4)

3. The estimated product will be lower than the actual product since the factors you multiply will be less than the actual factors.

4. Answers may include: estimating how many items one can buy at a market given a limited amount of cash; estimating how many gallons of gas to get with a certain amount of money.

★ **Error Alert**

Incorrect answers might indicate that students need to review place value or multiplying by powers and multiples of 10.

Reinforcement

Extra Practice, page 406
EP/MR Worksheet 17, TRB, page 17

Teaching Aids

Multiplication table
TA 2, TRB, page 155
Teaching suggestions precede the Teaching Aids worksheets.

Challenge

Estimate how many dollars are needed to buy lunch for your class, if student lunches cost $1.90 and adult lunches cost $2.20. (answer: number of students × $1.90 + number of adults × $2.20)

2.7 Multiplying Decimals by Powers and Multiples of 10

Carl figures that it costs him $0.18 a mile to operate his car. Working mentally, he says, "If I drive 10 miles, it costs me $1.80. Last week alone, I drove at least 200 miles. That's $36! I'm going to ride my bike whenever I can to save money."

Examples

To multiply a decimal by a multiple or power of 10 mentally, first count the number of zeros at the end of the power or multiple.

A **Multiply. 0.18×10**

Move the decimal point one place to the right.

$0.18 \times 10 = 0.1\underset{\text{one zero}}{8}$

$0.18 \times 10 = \textbf{1.80}$

B **Multiply. 4.5×100**

Move the decimal point two places. Add a zero.

$4.50 \times 100 = 4.50.\underset{\text{two zeros}}{}$

$4.5 \ \times 100 = \textbf{450}$

C **Multiply. 1.2×300**

Multiply 1.2 by 3. Move the decimal point two places. Add a zero.

$1.2 \times 300 =$
$(1.2 \times 3) \times 100 =$
$3.6 \times 100 = 3.60.$

$1.2 \times 300 = \textbf{360}$

▶ Think and Discuss

1. Suppose you were solving a problem that involved multiplying a decimal by 10,000. How many places to the right would you move the decimal point?

2. Multiply 2.2 by four million. How many zeros did you add? How many places did you move the decimal point? Now multiply 2.2 by four billion. Did you add more or fewer zeros? Why?

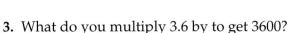

3. What do you multiply 3.6 by to get 3600?

4. How is multiplying by a multiple of ten similar to multiplying by a power of ten? How is it different?

SKILLS

Exercises

Multiply. (See Example A.)

5. 1.29 × 10
12.9

6. 4.751 × 100
475.1

7. 37.95 × 10
379.5

8. 0.002 × 1000
2

9. 0.3511 × 1000
351.1

10. 4293.61 × 10
42936.1

11. 9.3 × 10
93

12. 63.05 × 100
6305

Multiply. (See Example B.)

13. 0.9 × 100
90

14. 32.71 × 1000
32,710

15. 0.6 × 100
60

16. 439.7 × 1000
439,700

17. 0.97 × 10,000
9700

18. 113.3 × 1000
113,300

19. 3.01 × 100,000
301,000

20. 0.005 × 1000
5

Multiply. (See Example C.)

21. 0.95 × 400
380

22. $0.72 × 50
$36

23. 27.1 × 200
5420

24. $3.50 × 30
$105

25. 0.25 × 4000
1000

26. 0.009 × 70
0.63

27. $0.80 × 400
$320

28. 4.50 × 20
90

▶ **Mixed Practice** (For more practice, see page 407.)

Multiply.

29. $8.50 × 100
$850

30. 0.069 × 200
13.8

31. 321.1 × 1000
321,100

32. 0.9 × 10,000
9000

33. $0.75 × 800
$600

34. 0.07 × 7000
490

35. $0.69 × 30
$20.70

36. 9.123 × 10
91.23

37. 9.305 × 1000
9305

38. 4.1 × 20,000
82,000

39. $2.50 × 4000
$10,000

40. 4201.3 × 100
420,130

▶ **Applications**

41. Rachel bought ten yards of fabric to make curtains. The fabric cost $8.29 a yard. How much did Rachel pay? $82.90

42. A ticket to a Polar Bears hockey game costs $38.15. Estimate the team's ticket revenues for last year, when more than two million tickets were sold. $76,300,000

TIRE SALE
Drive 50,000 miles on a set of
RUGGED REX TIRES
and pay only $0.0072 a mile

43. How much does a set of four Rugged Rex Tires actually cost? $360

▶ **Review** (Lessons 1.1, 1.2)

Write each number in words.

44. 8077

45. 1.005

46. 43,983

47. 26.9

48. 0.044

49. 731

50. 6.85

51. 57,060

52. 4714.1

53. 0.209

54. 8207

55. 25.25

56. 9111

57. 467.09

58. 10.002

59. 4652

60. 987,414

61. 56.343

2.8 Multiplying Decimals and Whole Numbers

Winston teaches children's art classes at the Broomfield Arts Coalition. He has just bought supplies for several classes and must bill the Coalition for each class separately. For the children's watercolor class, he bought 39 paint boxes at $1.79 apiece. What was the total for this portion of his bill?

Examples

To multiply a whole number by a decimal, multiply as with whole numbers. The product has the same number of decimal places as the decimal factor.

A Multiply.   7 × 0.6

```
        7
  × 0.6  ← 1 decimal place
    4.2  ← 1 decimal place
```

B Multiply.   1.79 × 39

```
    1 . 7 9  ← 2 decimal
  ×     3 9      places
    1 6 1 1
    5 3 7 0
  6 9 . 8 1  ← 2 decimal
                 places
```

C Multiply.   4.815 × 235

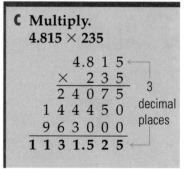

```
        4 . 8 1 5 ←
      ×     2 3 5
      2 4 0 7 5        3
    1 4 4 4 5 0      decimal
    9 6 3 0 0 0      places
  1 1 3 1 . 5 2 5 ←
```

▶ Think and Discuss

1. How many decimal places are in the product of 67 and 1.038?

2. Refer to the introduction to this lesson. How much money did Winston spend on watercolors?

3. Which problem is easier to solve, 15 × 5 or 15 × 0.05? Why?

4. How many decimal places are in the product when you multiply whole numbers by dollars-and-cents amounts? Why?

Exercises

Multiply. (See Example A.)

5. 8×2.6
20.8

6. 15×1.5
22.5

7. 6×9.8
58.8

8. 3×3.1
9.3

9. 2×9.7
19.4

10. 200×0.6
120.0

11. 4×0.3
1.2

12. 29×3.3
95.7

13. 42×0.7
29.4

14. 1.9×68
129.2

15. 75×1.5
112.5

16. 50×7.9
395.0

17. 90×0.2
18.0

18. 7×4.6
32.2

19. 11×7.2
79.2

Multiply. (See Example B.)

20. 3×0.49
1.47

21. 17×0.35
5.95

22. 42×1.99
83.58

23. 7×7.75
54.25

24. 5.61×23
129.03

25. 3.03×33
99.99

26. 99×0.33
32.67

27. 50×0.25
12.50

28. 25×4.05
101.25

29. 9.23×7
64.61

30. 42×0.06
2.52

31. 150×0.75
112.50

Multiply. (See Example C.)

32. 14×12.725
178.15

33. 5×0.909
4.545

34. 134×5.557
744.638

35. 0.789×62
48.918

36. 42×4.007
168.294

37. 400×0.999
399.600

38. 3.325×7
23.275

39. 8.125×25
203.125

40. 8×0.123
0.984

41. 25×1.125
28.125

42. 6.001×30
180.030

43. 2.689×4
10.756

▶ Mixed Practice (For more practice, see page 407.)

Multiply.

44. 702×1.7
1193.4

45. 1.93×4
7.72

46. 51×5.1
260.1

47. 0.405×9
3.645

48. 72×0.25
18.00

49. 63×0.333
20.979

50. 0.125×8
1.000

51. 49×0.08
3.92

52. 13.4×29
388.6

53. 0.909×555
504.495

54. $\$2.19 \times 32$
$70.08

55. 87×0.003
0.261

▶ Applications

56. Amy runs three and five-tenths miles five times a week. How far does she run in a week? 17.5 miles

57. A sheet of Baltic plywood is made up of 16 layers of birch. If each layer is 0.03 inches thick, how thick is one sheet?
0.48 inch

58. Alveta is making a poster for a school competition. She chose 17 colors of pastels. If each pastel crayon costs $0.87 and the total tax is $1.02, how much change will Alveta get back from $20? $4.19

▶ Review (Lesson 1.8)

Round each decimal to the nearest tenth and the nearest hundredth.

59. 6.581
6.6; 6.58

60. 37.855
37.9; 37.86

61. 9.877
9.9; 9.88

62. 4.99999
5.0; 5.00

63. 0.3695
0.4; 0.37

2.9 Making Magic Squares

The figure shown here is a magic square. In a magic square, numbers are arranged so that each row, column, and diagonal has the same sum.

1. How many rows are there in the magic square shown above? How many columns? How many diagonals?

2. Show that each row, column, and diagonal has the same sum.

The magic square above is called a 4 × 4 ("four by four") magic square, since there are 4 rows and 4 columns. Each whole number from 1 to 16 occupies one of the 16 spaces.

Now the task is to create a 3 × 3 magic square. There are 362,880 3 × 3 squares and only 8 are magic. Rather than guessing, you can look for patterns when making magic squares. Use the following questions to help you discover patterns.

3. How many rows are there in a 3 × 3 magic square?

4. Find the sum. $1 + 2 + 3 + 4 + 5 + 6 + 7 + 8 + 9$

5. Based on your answers to Questions 3 and 4, what is the sum of each row? Of each column? Of each diagonal?

PROBLEM SOLVING

The diagrams below are the key to creating a 3 × 3 magic square.

6. Look at the first diagram. How many sums is the number in a middle square a part of?

7. Look at the middle diagram. How many sums is the number in a corner square a part of?

8. Look at the last diagram. How many sums is the number in a side square a part of?

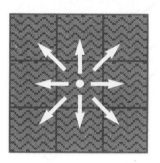
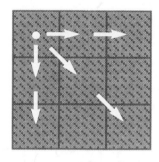
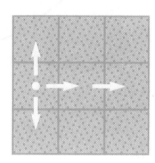

9. 1 + 6 + 8 = 15. List all the other ways 1 can be added to two different numbers from 2 to 9 to equal 15.

10. Use your answers to Questions 6–9 to decide whether 1 can fill a middle, corner, or side square. Explain your answer.

11. Which number fills the middle square? How did you find that number?

12. Which numbers fill the four corners?

13. Use your answers to Questions 6–12 to help you make a 3 × 3 magic square.

14. Compare all of the magic squares that your class created. How many different magic squares were made? Do you see a pattern in the answers? Describe the pattern.

▶ **Review** (Lessons 2.2, 2.4)

Multiply.

15.
$$\begin{array}{r} 63 \\ \times\ 4 \\ \hline 252 \end{array}$$

16.
$$\begin{array}{r} 8895 \\ \times\ 9 \\ \hline 80{,}055 \end{array}$$

17.
$$\begin{array}{r} 408 \\ \times\ 52 \\ \hline 21{,}216 \end{array}$$

18.
$$\begin{array}{r} 45 \\ \times\ 76 \\ \hline 3420 \end{array}$$

19.
$$\begin{array}{r} 179 \\ \times\ 81 \\ \hline 14{,}499 \end{array}$$

20.
$$\begin{array}{r} 59 \\ \times\ 23 \\ \hline 1357 \end{array}$$

Multiplying Whole Numbers and Decimals **47**

Answers (continued)

6. 4
7. 3
8. 2
9. 1 + 5 + 9
10. side square; the 1 is part of only 2 sums
11. 5; 5 is the only digit that is part of 4 different sums
12. 2, 4, 6, 8
13. eight solutions are possible; one solution is

$$\begin{array}{ccc} 6 & 7 & 2 \\ 1 & 5 & 9 \\ 8 & 3 & 4 \end{array}$$

14. Eight different magic squares are possible; the pattern has to do with symmetrical placement (around the middle number) of the side numbers and of the corner numbers.

★ **Error Alert**

Errors may occur if students do not add correctly as they work through the magic square.

Reinforcement

EP/MR Worksheet 20, TRB, page 20

Puzzle

Place addition and subtraction signs between the following digits to make an answer of 100. Do not change the order of the numbers.

9 8 7 6 5 4 3 2 1

Here is an example that is incorrect because the answer is 94.

98 − 76 + 54 − 3 + 21

(sample answer: 98 + 7 − 6 + 5 − 4 + 3 − 2 − 1 = 100)

T47

Objectives

- To multiply two decimals greater than 1
- To multiply two decimals less than 1
- To multiply one decimal less than 1 and one decimal greater than 1

Purpose

Multiplying decimals by decimals allows you to figure out costs of items that are priced by weight, such as produce.

Introducing the Lesson

Review multiplication procedures for whole numbers and decimals (Lesson 2.4, 2.7). Use the examples: 532 × 15 = (7980); 2.34 × 5 = (11.70).

Alternative Examples

Example A—Multiply.   1.78 × 6.5

```
    1.78
×    6.5
    890
  10680
  11.570
```

Example B—Multiply.   0.39 × 0.06

```
   0.39
×  0.06
 0.0234
```

Example C—Multiply.   0.916 × 2.08

```
   0.916
×   2.08
   7328
 183200
 1.90528
```

▶ Think and Discuss Answers

1. 0.2665

2. Yes; 3.5 × $1.09 = $3.815, which rounds to $3.82

3. Estimation helps you check the reasonableness of an answer.

4. The product will be less than 1; use examples to show that the product of any number and a number less than 1 is less than the first number.

T48

2.10 Multiplying Decimals by Decimals

GERTRUDE'S Fresh Fruit Market

Broccoli/
Cauliflower @ $1.09 lb.

Total weight   3.5 lb.

TOTAL $3.82

Thank you

Suppose you are buying snacks for a party. They cost $1.09 a pound, and the scale registers 3.5 pounds. The total cost displayed on the scale is $3.82. How do you know whether the total cost shown on the scale is correct?

Examples

To multiply two decimals, multiply as with whole numbers. Add the number of decimal places in the multipliers to get the number of decimal places in the product.

A Multiply.
1.09 × 3.5

```
   1.0 9  ←2 places
×    3.5  ←1 place
   5 4 5
 3 2 7 0
 3.8 1 5    3 places
```
1.09 × 3.5 = **3.815**

B Multiply.
0.49 × 0.05

```
   0.4 9  ← 2 places
× 0.0 5  ← 2 places
 0.0 2 4 5  ← 4 places
```
Write zeros for placeholders
0.49 × 0.05 = **0.0245**

C Multiply.
0.832 × 6.01

```
   0.8 3 2  ← 3 places
×   6.0 1  ← 2 places
     8 3 2
 4 9 9 2 0 0
 5.0 0 0 3 2  ← 5 places
```
0.832 × 6.01
= **5.00032**

▶ Think and Discuss

1. Find the product of 0.13 and 2.05.

2. Refer to the introduction to this lesson. Was the reading on the scale correct?

3. How can estimation help when you multiply decimals?

4. When you multiply two decimals that are less than 1, do you expect the product to be greater or less than 1? Discuss.

Exercises

★ **Error Alert**
Errors may show that students forgot to add the number of decimal places in *both* multipliers.

Multiply. (See Example A.)

5. 5.9
× 3.5
20.65

6. 1.401
× 8.2
11.4882

7. 9.04
× 7.18
64.9072

8. 1.246
× 3.9
4.8594

9. 9.11
× 3.2
29.152

10. 2.119 × 4.303
9.118057

11. 19.7 × 9.2
181.24

12. 401.5 × 50.75
20,376.125

13. 1.25 × 3.4
4.25

14. 6.003 × 5.12
30.73536

15. 37.49 × 3.5
131.215

16. 25.5 × 5.8
147.90

17. 25.5 × 55.75
1421.625

Multiply. (See Example B.)

18. 0.19 × 0.91
0.1729

19. 0.528 × 0.7
0.3696

20. 0.87 × 0.003
0.00261

21. 0.473 × 0.473
0.223729

22. 0.02 × 0.119
0.00238

23. 0.05 × 0.73
0.0365

24. 0.179 × 0.08
0.01432

25. 0.49 × 0.12
0.0588

Multiply. (See Example C.)

26. 0.308
× 5.25
1.617

27. 7.32
× 0.54
3.9528

28. 0.776
× 8.9
6.9064

29. 5.807
× 0.021
0.121947

30. 0.951
× 3.8
3.6138

31. 0.4 × 4.4
1.76

32. 1.25 × 0.25
0.3125

33. 33.33 × 0.33
10.9989

34. 92.15 × 0.5
46.075

▶ Mixed Practice (For more practice, see page 408.)

Multiply.

35. 9.06 × 3.35
30.351

36. 0.2 × 0.0011
0.00022

37. 5.71 × 0.246
1.40466

38. 1.0931 × 2.9
3.16999

39. 0.27
× 0.95
0.2565

40. 6.3
× 9.8
61.74

41. 2.615
× 0.83
2.17045

42. 0.707
× 0.15
0.10605

43. 4.023
× 1.351
5.435073

▶ Applications

44. Miriam is enlarging a photo for the school paper. The photo is three and five-tenths inches wide. She decides to have it enlarged to one and five-tenths times its original width. How wide will the photo be after it is enlarged? 5.25 inches

45. Carl owns Modesto Bakery. He overhears his assistant charge a customer $3.40 for a 1.89-pound loaf of rye bread. Carl knows that, at $1.29 a pound for rye bread, that amount is incorrect. How much should he refund to the customer? $0.96

▶ Review (Lesson 1.7)

Round each number to the nearest hundred and the nearest ten.

46. 18,609
18,600; 18,610

47. 9499
9500; 9500

48. 87,662
87,700; 87,660

49. 59,527
59,500; 59,530

50. 851,385
851,400; 851,390

51. 729,717
729,700; 729,720

52. 18,045
18,000; 18,050

53. 442
400; 440

54. 78
100; 80

55. 19,709
19,700; 19,710

Reinforcement
Extra Practice, page 408
EP/MR Worksheet 21, TRB, page 21

Teaching Aids
Multiplication table
TA 2, TRB, page 155
Teaching suggestions precede the Teaching Aids worksheets.

Challenge
For each problem below, find at least two ways to place decimal points in the factors so that the product is correct.

1. 25 × 21 = 5.25 (2.5 × 2.1; 0.25 × 21; 25 × 0.21)
2. 623 × 65 = 40.495 (0.623 × 65; 6.23 × 6.5; 62.3 × 0.65)
3. 2602 × 136 = 35.3872 (0.2602 × 136; 2.602 × 13.6; 26.02 × 1.36; 260.2 × 0.136)

2.11 Choosing Ways to Compute

The student council at Humboldt High is sponsoring dances in the school gymnasium.

The students plan to sponsor 4 or 5 dances and to charge $2.00 to $3.00 admission. They expect between 300 and 400 people to attend each dance.

The students wanted to estimate the amount of money they would raise. First they used the smaller numbers; then they used the larger numbers.

1. What was the smallest amount of money they expected to raise? Use the smaller numbers:
   4 dances × $2.00 admission × 300 people = ▨ .

2. What was the largest amount they expected to raise? Use the larger numbers:
   5 dances × $3.00 admission × 400 people = ▨ .

3. Could you use mental math to answer Questions 1 or 2? Explain how.

4. What is the difference between the largest and smallest amounts of money they expect to raise?

Sometimes, when numbers are easy to work with, you can solve a problem quickly in your head. At other times, the numbers are large or difficult to work with. Then you want to use paper-and-pencil or a calculator.

5. At the first dance, the students charged $2.50 admission and 345 people attended. How much money did they raise?
   $2.50 admission × 345 people = ▨ .

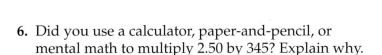

PROBLEM SOLVING

6. Did you use a calculator, paper-and-pencil, or mental math to multiply 2.50 by 345? Explain why.

7. For the second dance, the students charged $3.00 admission and 300 attended. How much money did they raise? $3.00 admission × 300 people = ___ Which method did you use to multiply 3.00 × 300? Explain why.

Work with 2 or 3 classmates. For Questions 8–10, write out your solution to the problem. Tell whether you used mental math, paper-and-pencil, or a calculator. Explain why you chose your method.

8. The school gave the student council $22.00 for publicity for each dance. After 4 dances, how much money had the council received for publicity?

9. The student council sponsored 4 dances, and charged $2.25 admission at each dance. There were 325 people at the first dance, 250 at the second dance, 310 at the third dance, and 302 at the fourth dance. How much money did they raise in all?

10. The students knew that more people would attend dances if the admission charge were low. They estimated that an admission charge of $2.25 would result in about 375 people attending, and an admission charge of $2.75 would result in about 300 people attending. If the estimates are correct, which admission charge would raise more money?

▶ **Review** (Lesson 1.4)

Read the following problems. Write what you must find and the facts you need to solve each problem.

11. Jacklyn took a taxi from the airport to her home. She lives 23 miles from the airport. If the taxi meter registered $2.10 for each mile, and if Jacklyn tipped the driver $3.00, what was the cost of the taxi ride?

12. Paul works 8 hours a week at a cafeteria in a department store. He makes $5.75 an hour. Will he make enough money in 2 weeks to buy a camera that costs $129.95?

Answers (continued)
  8. $88; mental math is appropriate, but answers may include paper-and-pencil or calculator
  9. $2670.75; paper-and-pencil or calculator
  10. $2.25; paper-and-pencil or calculator
  11. must find how many miles Jacklyn lives from the airport; need to know total fare, cost per mile, and tip
  12. must find how many weeks it will take Paul to earn $129.95; need to know how much Paul earns an hour and how many hours a week he works

★ **Error Alert**
Errors may occur if students use estimation when an exact answer is needed.

Problem Solving
PS Worksheet 1, TRB, pages 179–180

Puzzle
Use the problems and letter key below to make a palindrome. A palindrome is something that reads the same backward and forward.

First, estimate the product for each problem below. Then look at the letter key and find the range of numbers that includes your number. Write the corresponding letter in the blank after each problem. Read the palindrome.

a. 68 × 31 = (N)   i. 582 × 8 = (O)
b. 3 × 23 = (E)   j. 19 × 488 = (R)
c. 3 × 13 = (V)   k. 39 × 2 = (E)
d. 39 × 2 = (E)   l. 3 × 13 = (V)
e. 19 × 488 = (R)   m. 3 × 23 = (E)
f. 582 × 8 = (O)   n. 68 × 31 = (N)
g. 11 × 59 = (D)
h. 11 × 59 = (D)

Letter Key: Select the letter of the range of numbers that is closest to your estimate.

10–50; V	900–1000; S
60–90; E	1500–2500; N
100–200; A	4500–6000; O
300–400; L	6500–7500; I
500–700; D	8000–10,000; R

Can you write numbers that are palindromes? (yes; sample answers: 60,106; 1001; 13,131)

Vocabulary and Writing Practice
VW Worksheet 2, TRB, page 138

Calculator Activities
CA Worksheet 2, TRB, page 163

Enrichment
E Worksheet 2, TRB, pages 201–202

Real Life Applications
RL Worksheet 2, TRB, pages 235–236

Chapter 2 Review

REVIEW

Complete each statement. (Lesson 2.1)

1. The answer to a multiplication problem is called the ___ . Product

2. Numbers that are multiplied are called ___ . Multipliers or factors

Multiply mentally. (Lesson 2.3)

3. 50×700
35,000

4. $100,000 \times 76$
7,600,000

5. 519×1000
519,000

6. 90×30
2700

7. 38×100
3800

8. 600×800
480,000

9. 40×500
20,000

10. 2964×100
296,400

Multiply. (Lessons 2.2, 2.4)

11. 29×8
232

12. 6416×9
57,744

13. 55×25
1375

14. 871×43
37,453

15. 125×230
28,750

16. 657×801
526,257

17. 845×2
1690

18. 237×49
11,613

19. 11×14
154

20. 7007×8
56,056

21. A group of 22 people are going to a play. Tickets cost $12 each. How much must the playgoers spend on tickets in all? $264

22. A pear has about 63 calories. If you eat two pears a day for seven days, how many calories have you consumed? 882 calories

Estimate the product. (Lesson 2.6)

23. 166×1018
$\approx 200,000$

24. 456×781
$\approx 400,000$

25. 6340×374
$\approx 2,400,000$

26. 909×862
$\approx 810,000$

Multiply. (Lesson 2.7)

27. 1000×42.89
42,890

28. 0.04×20
0.8

29. 6.3×100
630

30. 50×8.2
410

Multiply. (Lesson 2.8)

31. 4.5×4
18

32. 783×1.9
1487.7

33. 15.25×62
945.5

34. 55×7.8
429

35. 8.1×18
145.8

36. 49.013×147
7204.911

37. 9.2×48
441.6

38. 607×2.1
1274.7

39. 50.5×49
2474.5

40. 28.69×54
1549.26

Multiply. (Lesson 2.10)

41. 1.2×8.4
10.08

42. 0.07×0.35
0.0245

43. 43.6×0.91
39.676

44. 5.3×0.9
4.77

45. 0.208×0.06
0.01248

Chapter 2 Test

Chapter Tests
Short Answer, Forms A and B, TRB, pages
271–272, 273–274
Multiple Choice, Forms A and B, TRB, pages
339–340, 341–342

Teaching Aids
Answer sheet
TA 8, TRB, page 161a
Teaching suggestions precede the Teaching
Aids worksheets.

Multiply.

1. $\begin{array}{r} 3055 \\ \times\ \ \ \ 5 \\ \hline 15{,}275 \end{array}$

2. $\begin{array}{r} 99 \\ \times\ 44 \\ \hline 4356 \end{array}$

3. $\begin{array}{r} 5.7 \\ \times\ 0.08 \\ \hline 0.456 \end{array}$

4. $\begin{array}{r} 404 \\ \times\ 2.3 \\ \hline 929.2 \end{array}$

5. $\begin{array}{r} 0.08 \\ \times\ 0.8 \\ \hline 0.064 \end{array}$

6. $\begin{array}{r} 600 \\ \times\ 90 \\ \hline 54{,}000 \end{array}$

7. $\begin{array}{r} 543 \\ \times\ 51 \\ \hline 27{,}693 \end{array}$

8. $\begin{array}{r} 205 \\ \times\ 55 \\ \hline 11{,}275 \end{array}$

9. $\begin{array}{r} 6263 \\ \times\ 290 \\ \hline 1{,}816{,}270 \end{array}$

10. 1000×43
    43,000

11. 21.89×10
    218.9

12. 0.004×0.01
    0.00004

13. 400×4.72
    1888

14. 80×70
    5600

15. 6.01×1.7
    10.217

16. $3.6 \times 10{,}000$
    36,000

17. 75.75×1.25
    94.6875

18. $8771 \times .43$
    3771.53

Estimate each product.

19. $\begin{array}{r} 626 \\ \times\ 551 \\ \hline 360{,}000 \end{array}$

20. $\begin{array}{r} 238 \\ \times\ 741 \\ \hline 140{,}000 \end{array}$

21. $\begin{array}{r} 97 \\ \times\ 139 \\ \hline 14{,}000 \end{array}$

Solve.

22. Jane works six hours on Saturdays. She earns $6.45 an hour. How much does she earn?
    $38.70

23. Gas costs $1.17 per gallon. If Nicholas buys 13.5 gallons, what is the total cost? $15.80

24. Samantha runs 3 miles a day during the week and 4 miles a day on Saturdays and Sundays. How far does she run in a week?
    23 miles

25. Karl makes $5.89 an hour at his summer job. If he works 27.5 hours a week for 13 weeks, how much will he earn? $2105.68

Complete each sentence.

26. When 7 is multiplied by 28, the result is called the ____ . product

27. Factors are numbers that are ____ . being multiplied

28. To multiply a number by 1000, move the decimal point three places to the ____ . right

Use dividing whole numbers and decimals to

• determine a unit rate or price.

• equally group items or find the number of items in a group.

• find averages.

• determine miles per gallon.

What are some other ways to use dividing whole numbers and decimals?

Dividing Whole Numbers and Decimals

An interior decorator plans and decorates homes and offices for beauty and use.

- Interior decorators work in homes, businesses, and design centers, and select furniture, carpets, drapes, and other things.

- Interior decorators should possess a sense of color and design, a flair for fashion, spatial sense, and be good with numbers.

- An interior decorator must be able to take accurate measurements, read scale drawings and blueprints, and determine costs.

- To become an interior decorator, an individual must attend a four-year college or design school, a fashion institute, or participate in an apprenticeship program.

- Related careers include painters, carpenters, woodworkers, and furniture sales representatives.

CAREER

INTERIOR DECORATOR

PORTFOLIO PROJECT: *Estimate the cost of furnishing a room.*

1. You have a $1,500 budget to furnish your room. You will need to purchase a bed, a chair, a dresser, and a book shelf. Shop or use a newspaper to find the best buys.

2. Determine the total cost of your purchases. *Show the math.*

3. Place the items on layaway. Determine the monthly cost if paid in 12 equal installments. *Show the math.*

About the Portfolio Project

Students may begin by gathering furniture advertisements from newspapers, Internet, or actual visits to a furniture store. Students determine the actual cost of each piece of furniture and a total cost, making sure they are within budget. All math must be well organized, and labeled at all points.

Assessment: The individual scoring rubric on page 161 of the Teacher's Resource Binder can be reproduced and used for assessment. Include the following information in the last two boxes. Students should have:

- found the cost of four pieces of furniture.
- accurately divided to find the total cost of 12 installments.

Objectives

• To identify the divisor, the dividend, and the quotient in a division problem
• To understand the relationship between division and multiplication

Purpose
This lesson helps you to understand how multiplication and division are related.

Introducing the Lesson
Ask for examples of how students use division in everyday life. (sample answers: splitting money among friends; figuring out how many miles per hour were driven; finding the cost of one item when you know the price of several)

If necessary, review basic multiplication facts, using examples from the times table.

3.1 Introduction to Division

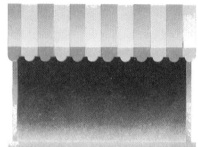

Robert can wash 9 windows in an hour. At this pace, how long would it take him to wash 81 windows? If he and 2 friends worked at the same pace, how long would it take them to complete the job? You can find the answers to these questions by dividing. But if you think about your multiplication facts, you will realize that you already know the answers.

Division is the inverse, or opposite, of multiplication. If you can multiply, then you can divide.

▶ **Think and Discuss**

Read the following problems.

150 freshmen are assigned to 5 homerooms. If all homerooms have the same number of students, how many are in each one?

Twenty presents are distributed evenly among four people. How many gifts did each person receive?

1. What is similar about the two problems?

2. Draw a diagram or picture that illustrates the second problem.

3. Write a division fact and a multiplication fact that describes the first problem.

4. How could you check your solution to the first problem?

5. Write a division fact and a multiplication fact that describes the second problem.

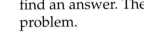
6. Write two multiplication facts. Then change each to a division fact.

7. Write two word problems that require multiplication to find an answer. Then change each to a division problem.

▶ Express Yourself

The parts of a division problem have names.
Look at the numbers in the following problems.

$$0.4\overline{)2.4}^{\,6}$$

The **dividend** is 2.4.
The **divisor** is 0.4.
The **quotient** is 6.

$10 \div 2 = 5$

The **dividend** is 10.
The **divisor** is 2.
The **quotient** is 5.

Identify the dividend, the divisor, and the quotient in each problem.

8. $5\overline{)45}^{\,9}$

9. $4.8\overline{)38.88}^{\,8.1}$

10. $49.2 \div 8.2 = 6$

11. $63 \div 7 = 9$

▶ Practice What You Know

A factor is missing in the multiplication statement below.

$6 \times \underline{\ \blacksquare\ } = 18$

You can rewrite this multiplication statement as a division problem.

$18 \div 6 = \underline{\ \blacksquare\ }$

Complete each statement.

12. $7 \times \underline{\ \blacksquare\ } = 21$, so $21 \div 7 = \underline{\ \blacksquare\ }$.

13. $8 \times \underline{\ \blacksquare\ } = 40$, so $40 \div 8 = \underline{\ \blacksquare\ }$.

14. $9 \times \underline{\ \blacksquare\ } = 36$, so $36 \div 9 = \underline{\ \blacksquare\ }$.

15. $5 \times \underline{\ \blacksquare\ } = 45$, so $45 \div 5 = \underline{\ \blacksquare\ }$.

Solve.

16. Suppose you were asked to arrange 30 desks so that each row had the same number of desks. List all the possible arrangements. Write the division and multiplication facts involved.

Dividing Whole Numbers and Decimals **57**

▶ **Think and Discuss Answers**

1. Both can be solved using division.
2. picture or diagram, showing 20 presents in 4 groups
3. $150 \div 5 = 30$; $30 \times 5 = 150$
4. by multiplying your answer by 5; the result should be 150
5. $20 \div 4 = 5$; $4 \times 5 = 20$
6. Answers may include $4 \times 9 = 36$, $9 \times 8 = 72$; $36 \div 9 = 4$, $72 \div 8 = 9$
7. Answers may vary.

Express Yourself Answers

8. 45; 5; 9
9. 38.88; 4.8; 8.1
10. 49.2; 8.2; 6
11. 63; 7; 9

Practice What You Know Answers

12. 3; 3
13. 5; 5
14. 4; 4
15. 9; 9
16. 1 row of 30 desks; 2 rows of 15 desks; 3 rows of 10 desks; 5 rows of 6 desks; 6 rows of 5 desks; 10 rows of 3 desks; 15 rows of 2 desks; 30 rows of 1 desk

$30 \div 1 = 30$	$30 \times 1 = 30$
$30 \div 2 = 15$	$15 \times 2 = 30$
$30 \div 3 = 10$	$10 \times 3 = 30$
$30 \div 5 = 6$	$6 \times 5 = 30$
$30 \div 6 = 5$	$5 \times 6 = 30$
$30 \div 10 = 3$	$3 \times 10 = 30$
$30 \div 15 = 2$	$2 \times 15 = 30$
$30 \div 30 = 1$	$1 \times 30 = 30$

★ **Error Alert**

Problems may occur because students do not understand the relationship between division and multiplication.

Challenge

Fill in the following blanks:

$3 \times (40) = 120$	$120 \div (30) = 4$
$5 \times (24) = 120$	$120 \div (20) = 6$
$8 \times (15) = 120$	$120 \div (12) = 10$
$12 \times (10) = 120$	$120 \div (8) = 15$
$20 \times (6) = 120$	$120 \div (5) = 24$
$30 \times (4) = 120$	$120 \div (3) = 40$
$60 \times (2) = 120$	$120 \div (1) = 120$

Objective

• To divide 2-digit, 3-digit, and 4-digit numbers by 1-digit divisors

Purpose

Dividing by a 1-digit divisor helps you to figure out costs, payments, and other quantities when you need to divide a total by less than 10.

Introducing the Lesson

Review multiplying by 1-digit multipliers (Lesson 2.2). Put $4 \times 70 = 280$ on the chalkboard. Ask: If $4 \times 70 = 280$, how many sets of 4 are in 280? Explain: There are 70 sets of 4 in 280, or you can divide 280 into 70 sets of 4. Remind students that division is the opposite of multiplication.

Alternative Examples

Example A—Divide. $435 \div 3$

```
      145
   3)435
      3
      ‾‾
      13
      12
      ‾‾
       15
       15
       ‾‾
        0
```
$435 \div 3 = \mathbf{145}$

Example B—Divide. $282 \div 5$

```
      56 R2
   5)282
      25
      ‾‾
       32
       30
       ‾‾
        2
```
$282 \div 5 = \mathbf{56\ R2}$

▶ Think and Discuss Answers

1. Think: How many 2s in 7? Think: How many 9s in 1? In 11?
2. $34
3. 3; 75; 25
4. 75 R8
5. Sample answers include: placing objects into different groups; splitting a length into equal parts.

T58

3.2 Dividing by 1-Digit Divisors

June saw a leather jacket in the store window. "I must have that jacket," she thought. "I wonder how much it costs." When she went in to ask, she was told that the jacket cost $136. It could be hers in four equal monthly payments.

To determine the amount of each payment, June divided $136 by 4.

Examples

To divide by a 1-digit divisor, remember: divide, multiply, subtract, bring down.

A Divide. $136 \div 4$

```
      3 4
   4)1 3 6      How many 4s in 1? 0 In 13? 3
     1 2 ↓      Multiply. Subtract. Bring down
     ‾‾‾        the 6.
       1 6
       1 6      How many 4s in 16? 4
       ‾‾‾      Multiply. Subtract.
         0      The remainder is 0.
```

$136 \div 4 = \mathbf{34}$

B Divide. $535 \div 7$

```
      7 6 R3
   7)5 3 5      How many 7s in 5? 0 In 53? 7
     4 9 ↓      Multiply. Subtract. Bring down
     ‾‾‾        the 5.
       4 5
       4 2      How many 7s in 45? 6
       ‾‾‾      Multiply. Subtract. The
         3      remainder is 3.
                Write the remainder in the
                quotient.
```

$535 \div 7 = 76$ remainder 3
This is written **76 R3.**

▶ Think and Discuss

1. What is the first step in the problem 2)730? In the problem 9)116?

2. Refer to the introduction to this lesson. How much was June's monthly payment?

3. Identify the divisor, the dividend, and the quotient in the problem 75 divided by 3.

4. Divide. $683 \div 9$

5. Describe three situations in which you might use division.

Exercises

Divide. (See Example A.)

6. 3)$\overline{81}$ 27 **7.** 6)$\overline{72}$ 12 **8.** 7)$\overline{350}$ 50 **9.** 7)$\overline{714}$ 102

10. 3)$\overline{690}$ 230 **11.** 4)$\overline{836}$ 209 **12.** 4)$\overline{8388}$ 2097 **13.** 9)$\overline{9513}$ 1057

14. 8040 ÷ 8 1005 **15.** 960 ÷ 2 480 **16.** 48 ÷ 4 12 **17.** 95 ÷ 5 19

Divide. (See Example B.)

18. 2)$\overline{33}$ 16 R1 _16.5_ **19.** 3)$\overline{92}$ 30 R2 _30.67_ **20.** 9)$\overline{60}$ 6 R6 _6.67_ **21.** 6)$\overline{64}$ 10 R4 _10.67_

22. 9)$\overline{39}$ 4 R3 _4.33_ **23.** 8)$\overline{59}$ 7 R3 _7.38_ **24.** 7)$\overline{79}$ 11 R2 _11.29_ **25.** 6)$\overline{98}$ 16 R2 _16.33_

26. 6699 ÷ 4 1674 R3 _1674.75_ **27.** 791 ÷ 4 197 R3 _197.75_ **28.** 435 ÷ 6 72 R3 _72.5_ **29.** 3401 ÷ 7 485 R6 _485.86_

▶ Mixed Practice (For more practice, see page 408.)

Divide.

30. 4)$\overline{404}$ 101 **31.** 3)$\overline{57}$ 19 **32.** 8)$\overline{6993}$ 874 R1 **33.** 2)$\overline{510}$ 255

34. 270 ÷ 9 30 **35.** 3)$\overline{711}$ 237 **36.** 6)$\overline{194}$ 32 R2 **37.** 391 ÷ 7 55 R6

38. 3)$\overline{960}$ 320 **39.** 4)$\overline{63}$ 15 R3 **40.** 8200 ÷ 8 1025 **41.** 2)$\overline{948}$ 474

42. 7)$\overline{781}$ 111 R4 **43.** 6)$\overline{3640}$ 606 R4 **44.** 9)$\overline{897}$ 99 R6 **45.** 6432 ÷ 2 3216

▶ Applications

46. Christiane had forty-eight cuttings from her plants that she was going to give to eight friends. If she gave the same number to each, how many cuttings did each receive? 6 cuttings

47. Kevin is a waiter. He must pay taxes every three months on his tips. This year, he expects to owe a total of $300 in taxes. How much will each of his payments be? $75

48. Look at the ad for a radio. What is the sale price? What is the monthly payment if the payments are equal? How much would you owe after one payment? After two? $90; $15; $75; $60

Radio Sale! One Day Only

6 Easy Payments

Was $95

Now $90

▶ Review (Lesson 1.9)

Add.

49. 8.9 + 335.68
344.58

50. 8924 + 36,951
45,875

51. 0.053 + 9.87
9.923

52. 375,209 + 617,959
933,168

53. 5.5 + 4.7 + 0.51
10.71

54. 0.07 + 0.008
0.078

3.3 Dividing by Powers and Multiples of 10

When Lucky Jim won $3,000,000, he announced, "I don't need the money. I'm splitting it evenly among all my relatives." Within an hour, 10 relatives called, claiming their shares. The next day, the total number of relatives had increased to 60. By the third day, Lucky Jim had 100 relatives.

To figure out how much money each relative would receive, divide Lucky Jim's winnings by the number of relatives.

Examples

To divide by powers or multiples of 10 mentally, begin by counting the number of zeros at the end of the power or multiple.

A   Divide.   3,000,000 ÷ 100

3,000,000 ÷ 100 = 30,000.00 = **30,000**   Move the decimal point two places to the left.

B   Divide.   625 ÷ 1000

625 ÷ 1000 = 0.625 = **0.625**   Move the decimal point three places to the left. Add a zero as a placeholder.

C   Divide.   350 ÷ 50

350 ÷ 50 = 35.0 ÷ 5.0
= 35 ÷ 5 = **7**   Move the decimal points one place to the left. Then divide.

▶ Think and Discuss

1. Divide. 15 ÷ 10,000

2. Refer to the introduction to this lesson. How much money would each of Lucky Jim's 100 relatives receive?

3. Describe how dividing by 100 is similar to multi-plying by 100. How is it different?

4. When might you divide by a power or other multiple of 10?

5. Describe what you do when you divide by 50. By 7000.

SKILLS

Exercises

Divide. (See Example A.)

6. 92,000 ÷ 10 9200
7. 10,600 ÷ 100 106
8. 8300 ÷ 10 830
9. 5000 ÷ 1000 5
10. 250,000 ÷ 100 2500
11. 390 ÷ 10 39

Divide. (See Example B.)

12. 47 ÷ 1000
    0.047
13. 7 ÷ 10
    0.7
14. 2725 ÷ 100
    27.25
15. 1185 ÷ 10
    118.5
16. 1457 ÷ 1000
    1.457
17. 110 ÷ 10,000
    0.011
18. 9527 ÷ 1000
    9.527
19. 495 ÷ 100
    4.95

Divide. (See Example C.)

20. 4900 ÷ 70
    70
21. 1500 ÷ 300
    5
22. 36,000 ÷ 600
    60
23. 760 ÷ 40
    19
24. 444 ÷ 200
    2.22
25. 960,000 ÷ 80
    12,000
26. 87,500 ÷ 50
    1750
27. 805 ÷ 50
    16.1

▶ **Mixed Practice** (For more practice, see page 409.)

Divide.

28. 4000 ÷ 10
    400
29. 3600 ÷ 60
    60
30. 45,000 ÷ 100
    450
31. 1525 ÷ 100
    15.25
32. 5000 ÷ 50
    100
33. 95 ÷ 1000
    0.095
34. 9113 ÷ 10
    911.3
35. 14,700 ÷ 70
    210
36. 105 ÷ 10,000
    0.0105

▶ **Applications**

37. Find the price of one tea bag from each of the boxes shown in the picture. Which box is the best value? $0.04; $0.043; $0.04; the largest or the smallest box

$4.00 $3.00 $2.00

100 Tea Bags   70 Tea Bags   50 Tea Bags

38. Mei spent four dollars on twenty party favors. How much did each one cost? $0.20

39. Craig works 10 hours a week. He earns $1100 in 20 weeks. What is his hourly pay? $5.50 per hour

▶ **Review** (Lessons 2.8, 2.10)

Multiply.

40.
    62.4
    × 0.08
    ───────
    4.992

41.
    3.38
    × 2.21
    ───────
    7.4698

42.
    107
    × 6.5
    ───────
    695.5

43.
    0.009
    × 0.006
    ──────────
    0.000054

44.
    $4.85
    ×   8
    ───────
    $38.80

▶ **Think and Discuss Answers**

1. 0.0015
2. $30,000
3. The decimal point is moved two places. In division, the decimal point is moved to the left; in multiplication, the decimal point is moved to the right.
4. Sample answers include: finding price per item, given price per 10-item carton; dividing check at restaurant among 10 diners; finding average weight of 20 football players.
5. Move the decimal point one place to the left and divide by 5. Move the decimal point three places to the left and divide by 7.

★ **Error Alert**

Incorrect answers may mean that students have moved the decimal point in the wrong direction.

Reinforcement

Extra Practice, page 409
EP/MR Worksheet 23, TRB, page 23

Challenge

Divide by powers and multiples of 10 to estimate an answer for each of the following and tell if the actual amount will be more or less than the estimate.

$14 ÷ 9 = ($1.40; more)
$140 ÷ 11 = ($14.00; less)
$1400 ÷ 99 = ($14.00; more)
$14,000 ÷ 101 = ($140.00; less)
$14,000,000 ÷ 999 = ($14,000.00, more)

Purpose

Estimating quotients allows you to approximate answers to problems in everyday life, such as price per unit or number of items per person.

Introducing the Lesson

Review estimating products (Lesson 2.6) and rounding whole numbers (Lesson 1.7). Ask: Why is rounding an important skill in estimation? (because it is easier to calculate when you have numbers with zeros) Discuss what happens to the result of a multiplication problem if both factors round up. (The estimated product will be larger than the actual product.) What happens if both factors round down? (The estimated product will be smaller.)

Alternative Examples

Example A—Estimate. $696 \div 73$
$696 \approx 700$
$73 \approx 70$
$700 \div 70 = 10$
$696 \div 73 \approx \mathbf{10}$

Example B—Estimate. $72{,}397 \div 890$
$72{,}397 \approx 72{,}000$
$890 \approx 900$
$72{,}000 \div 900 = 80$
$72{,}397 \div 890 \approx \mathbf{80}$

▶ **Think and Discuss Answers**

1. 20
2. 25; because the divisor is only halfway to 10; actual answer is 24 R4
3. because you often figure out the number of quarters in a given number of dollars
4. 5 boxes

3.4 Estimating Quotients

Kieron wants to organize his CDs. He needs to know if he already has enough boxes or if he needs to buy some more. He has 115 CDs and can fit 24 CDs into each CD box.

To quickly figure out about how many boxes he needs, Kieron estimates the quotient of $115 \div 24$.

Examples

To estimate a quotient, first round the divisor and the dividend. Then divide.

A   **Estimate. $115 \div 24$**

$115 \approx 120$ Round up to the nearest ten.
$24 \approx 20$ Round down to the nearest ten.
$120 \div 20 = 6$
$115 \div 24 \approx \mathbf{6}$

B   **Estimate. $64{,}305 \div 783$**

$64{,}305 \approx 64{,}000$ Round down to the nearest thousand.
$783 \approx 800$ Round up to the nearest hundred.
$64{,}000 \div 800 = 80$
$64{,}305 \div 783 \approx \mathbf{80}$

▶ **Think and Discuss**

1. Estimate. $14{,}080 \div 689$

2. Estimate the quotient of $124 \div 5$. Why is it not a good idea to round the divisor to the nearest 10? Find the actual answer.

3. Try Example A again, rounding the divisor to 25. Why is it easy to divide by 25?

4. Refer to the introduction to this lesson. How many boxes does Kieron really need?

Exercises

Estimate. (See Example A.)

5. $51 \div 9$ ≈5   **6.** $138 \div 19$ ≈7   **7.** $356 \div 88$ ≈4   **8.** $922 \div 38$ ≈23

9. $49 \div 11$ ≈5   **10.** $178 \div 18$ ≈9   **11.** $596 \div 41$ ≈15   **12.** $54 \div 7$ ≈8

13. $87 \div 6$ ≈15   **14.** $539 \div 92$ ≈6   **15.** $218 \div 14$ ≈20   **16.** $634 \div 68$ ≈9

Estimate. (See Example B.)

17. $1083 \div 23$ ≈50 or 55   **18.** $5579 \div 73$ ≈80   **19.** $3182 \div 49$ ≈60 or 64

20. $6255 \div 98$ ≈63   **21.** $4077 \div 79$ ≈50   **22.** $35,911 \div 632$ ≈60

23. $6432 \div 281$ ≈20   **24.** $8591 \div 97$ ≈86   **25.** $64,120 \div 807$ ≈80

▶ Mixed Practice (For more practice, see page 409.)

Estimate.

26. $403 \div 7$ ≈40   **27.** $97 \div 23$ ≈4 or 5   **28.** $5217 \div 110$ ≈50 or 52

29. $682 \div 7$ ≈100   **30.** $124 \div 5$ ≈25 or 24   **31.** $359 \div 59$ ≈6

32. $477 \div 124$ ≈4 or 5   **33.** $23,811 \div 62$ ≈400   **34.** $99 \div 18$ ≈5

35. $271 \div 32$ ≈9 or 10   **36.** $3816 \div 79$ ≈50   **37.** $9189 \div 576$ ≈15

38. $253 \div 48$ ≈5   **39.** $119,751 \div 19$ ≈6000   **40.** $16,327 \div 54$ ≈320

▶ Applications

41. One thousand seven hundred fifty-nine students attend Carver High School. If fifty-eight classes are scheduled each period, estimate the number of students in each class. ≈30 students

42. A minor league team had a season attendance of 78,422 people. If 42 home games were played, estimate the attendance per game. ≈2000 people

43. Peter is buying special paper for a science project. Estimate the cost of a single sheet of paper from each pad shown. Which pad is the better value? ≈$0.12; ≈$0.22; 1st pad is better value

50 Sheets
$6.29

20 Sheets
$4.39

▶ Review (Lessons 1.1, 1.2)

Write the whole number or decimal number.

44. eight and nine hundredths
8.09

45. six hundred thousand, twelve
600,012

46. seven million, forty
7,000,040

47. five thousand and five tenths
5000.5

Reinforcement
Extra Practice, page 409
EP/MR Worksheet 24, TRB, page 24

Project
Find out how many students there are in your school. Then divide into groups. Each group should count the number of classrooms in the school, the number of exit doors, and the number of teachers. Then, approximate how many classrooms, exit doors, and teachers there are for each student. Write out why you think these figures might be useful to calculate. (Students should round and then divide the total number of students in the school by the number of classrooms, exit doors, and teachers. Sample answers for written activity are: classrooms—class size and scheduling; exit doors—safety regulations; and teachers—courses to offer, number of classes, and class size.)

Purpose

Dividing by 2-digit divisors is a skill that you can use to estimate how many gallons of gas you'll use on a trip.

Introducing the Lesson

Review dividing by 1-digit divisors (Lesson 3.2). Point out that students should use the same pattern to divide by 2-digit divisors. Review the pattern: Divide, multiply, subtract, bring down.

Alternative Examples

Example A—961 ÷ 62

$$\begin{array}{r} 15\ R31 \\ 62\overline{)961} \\ \underline{62} \\ 341 \\ \underline{310} \\ 31 \end{array}$$

961 ÷ 62 = **15 R31**

Example B—7395 ÷ 83

$$\begin{array}{r} 89\ R8 \\ 83\overline{)7395} \\ \underline{664} \\ 755 \\ \underline{747} \\ 8 \end{array}$$

7395 ÷ 83 = **89 R8**

▶ **Think and Discuss Answers**

1. 52 R7

2. no, because 45 × 10 = 450, which is less than 587

3. yes, because 45 × 100 = 4500, which is greater than 587

4. If you are dividing objects into groups of equal size, there are none left over.

3.5 Dividing by 2-Digit Divisors

When Mrs. Hubbard had to divide a jar of jelly beans equally among her 31 students, she became quite concerned. You can imagine her relief when she discovered that dividing by 2-digit divisors was easier than she expected. After all, she already knew how to divide by 1-digit divisors.

Examples

To divide by a 2-digit divisor, remember: divide, multiply, subtract, bring down.

A Divide. 384 ÷ 52

$$\begin{array}{r} 0\ 7\ R20 \\ 52\overline{)3\ 8\ 4} \\ \underline{3\ 6\ 4} \\ 2\ 0 \end{array}$$

52 does not divide 38. Write a **0** in the quotient. How many times does 52 divide 384? To estimate, think: how many 5s in 38? **7** Write the remainder in the quotient.

384 ÷ 52 = **7 R20**

B Divide. 7862 ÷ 39

$$\begin{array}{r} 2\ 0\ 1\ R23 \\ 39\overline{)7\ 8\ 6\ 2} \\ \underline{7\ 8} \\ 0\ 6\ 2 \\ \underline{3\ 9} \\ 2\ 3 \end{array}$$

How many times does 39 divide 78? To estimate, think: how many 3s in 7? **2** Multiply, subtract, and bring down the 6. Since 39 does not divide 6, write a **0** in the quotient. Bring down the 2. How many times does 39 divide 62? To estimate, think: how many 3s in 6? **2** Multiply. You cannot subtract 78 from 62. Try **1.**

7862 ÷ 39 = **201 R23**

▶ **Think and Discuss**

1. Divide. 683 ÷ 13

2. Is 587 ÷ 45 < 10? Why?

3. Is 587 ÷ 45 < 100? Why?

4. What does it mean to have a remainder of zero?

Exercises

Divide. (See Example A.)

5. $45\overline{)892}$ 19 R37   **6.** $10\overline{)372}$ 37 R2   **7.** $52\overline{)777}$ 14 R49   **8.** $19\overline{)943}$ 49 R12

9. $65\overline{)731}$ 11 R16   **10.** $94\overline{)391}$ 4 R15   **11.** $39\overline{)303}$ 7 R30   **12.** $40\overline{)950}$ 23 R30

13. $715 \div 11$ 65   **14.** $216 \div 88$ 2 R40   **15.** $529 \div 23$ 23   **16.** $666 \div 73$ 9 R9

Divide. (See Example B.)

17. $43\overline{)4003}$ 93 R4   **18.** $90\overline{)5850}$ 65   **19.** $12\overline{)7100}$ 591 R8   **20.** $22\overline{)2012}$ 91 R10

21. $48\overline{)2687}$ 55 R47   **22.** $61\overline{)1342}$ 22   **23.** $84\overline{)2687}$ 31 R83   **24.** $57\overline{)6399}$ 112 R15

25. $1805 \div 25$ 72 R5   **26.** $3030 \div 55$ 55 R5   **27.** $1980 \div 30$ 66   **28.** $7171 \div 76$ 94 R27

▶ Mixed Practice (For more practice, see page 410.)

Divide.

29. $12\overline{)6660}$ 555   **30.** $3723 \div 62$ 60 R3   **31.** $25\overline{)555}$ 22 R5   **32.** $49\overline{)3000}$ 61 R11

33. $30\overline{)9999}$ 333 R9   **34.** $8442 \div 21$ 402   **35.** $909 \div 90$ 10 R9   **36.** $11\overline{)730}$ 66 R4

37. $41\overline{)1681}$ 41   **38.** $22\overline{)4444}$ 202   **39.** $4999 \div 50$ 99 R49   **40.** $73\overline{)737}$ 10 R7

41. $43\overline{)4343}$ 101   **42.** $1255 \div 25$ 50 R5   **43.** $44\overline{)1800}$ 40 R40   **44.** $77\overline{)777}$ 10 R7

▶ Applications

45. Roger is planning a trip from Dallas to Boston. His car gets 28 miles to the gallon on the highway. The total distance is 1805 miles. At $1.09 a gallon for gas, estimate how much Roger can expect to pay for gasoline one way. ≈$60

46. Shizuko is giving a party. She expects forty-five people to come. She has ordered fifteen large pizzas, which are cut into eight slices each. How many slices of pizza can each person have if all are to get the same number? How many slices will there be left over? 2 slices; 30 pieces

▶ Review (Lessons 1.10, 1.11)

Subtract.

47.
$$
\begin{array}{r} 8.03 \\ -\ 0.66 \\ \hline 7.37 \end{array}
$$

48.
$$
\begin{array}{r} 52.31 \\ -\ 46.55 \\ \hline 5.76 \end{array}
$$

49.
$$
\begin{array}{r} 6 \\ -\ 1.04 \\ \hline 4.96 \end{array}
$$

50.
$$
\begin{array}{r} 19.40 \\ -\ 11.872 \\ \hline 7.528 \end{array}
$$

51.
$$
\begin{array}{r} 7.8 \\ -\ 0.98 \\ \hline 6.82 \end{array}
$$

52.
$$
\begin{array}{r} 9.3 \\ -\ 0.457 \\ \hline 8.843 \end{array}
$$

53.
$$
\begin{array}{r} 4.7 \\ -\ 2.63 \\ \hline 2.07 \end{array}
$$

54.
$$
\begin{array}{r} 0.67 \\ -\ 0.28 \\ \hline 0.39 \end{array}
$$

55.
$$
\begin{array}{r} 0.581 \\ -\ 0.39 \\ \hline 0.191 \end{array}
$$

56.
$$
\begin{array}{r} 7.8 \\ -\ 0.9 \\ \hline 6.9 \end{array}
$$

Objective

- To divide whole numbers with 4 or more digits by 3-digit divisors, both with calculator and with paper and pencil

Purpose

Using pencil and paper, you can find quotients when the divisors have 3 digits. Most people find that it is more convenient to use a calculator when they have 3-digit divisors.

Introducing the Lesson

Review dividing by 2-digit divisors (Lesson 3.5). Use the examples: 678 ÷ 35 = (19 R13); 5698 ÷ 23 = (247 R17). Review the pattern for division: Divide, multiply, subtract, bring down.

Alternative Examples

Example A—Divide.   9973 ÷ 255

Calculator method:
Enter 9973 ÷ *255* = *39.109804.*
To find the remainder, multiply 39 × 255.
Enter 39 × *255* = *9945.*
Subtract the product from 9973.
Enter 9973 − *9945* = *28.*
9973 ÷ **255** = **39 R28**
Check to be sure your answer is reasonable by estimating.
9973 ÷ 255 ≈ 10,000 ÷ 250 = 40
So, 39 R28 is reasonable.

Paper and pencil method:
```
       39 R28
255) 9973
     765
     2323
     2295
       28
```

Example B—35,685 ÷ 636 = **56 R69**
Use the same method as in Example A.

3.6 Dividing by 3-Digit Divisors

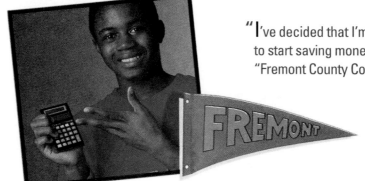

"I've decided that I'm going to college and I want to start saving money now," Lonnie told his parents. "Fremont County Community College costs $6800 for 2 years tuition. I need to figure out how soon I will have enough money to pay the tuition if I save $225 a month."

To find out how long it would take, Lonnie divided $6800 by $225.

Examples

To divide by a 3-digit divisor, it is helpful to use a calculator. Otherwise, use the method taught in Lesson 3.5.

A Divide.   2800 ÷ 125

Calculator Method

Enter 6800 ÷ 225 = 30.2.
To find the remainder,
multiply 30 by 225.
Enter 30 × 225 = 6750.
Subtract the product from 6800.
Enter 6800 − 6750 = 50.

6800 ÷ 225 = **30 R50**
Check to be sure your answer is reasonable by estimating.
6800 ÷ 225 ≈ 6800 ÷ 200 = 34, so 30 R50 is reasonable.

Paper-and-Pencil Method

```
          3 0 R50
225) 6 8 0 0
     6 7 5
         5 0
```

B Divide.   14,500 ÷ 325

Calculator Method

Enter 14500 ÷ 325 = 44.615385.
Enter 44 × 325 = 14300.
Enter 14500 − 14300 = 200.

14,500 ÷ 325 = **44 R200**
Check your answer.

Paper-and-Pencil Method

```
            4 4 R200
325) 1 4 5 0 0
     1 3 0 0
       1 5 0 0
       1 3 0 0
         2 0 0
```

Think and Discuss

SKILLS

1. Estimate the quotient of 7572 ÷ 247. Then use a calculator to find the exact quotient. Compare your estimate with those of your classmates.

2. Refer to the introduction to this lesson. How long would it take Lonnie to save $6800?

3. Solve this mystery. The divisor was 789. The quotient was 80 R91. What was the dividend?

4. Sara used a calculator to find 37,920 ÷ 632. Her answer was 600. What might she have done wrong?

Exercises

Divide. (See Example A.)

5. 1411 ÷ 234
6 R7

6. 4003 ÷ 511
7 R426

7. 7316 ÷ 491
14 R442

8. 3113 ÷ 369
8 R161

9. 2789 ÷ 405
6 R359

10. 5250 ÷ 735
7 R105

11. 6090 ÷ 801
7 R483

12. 1999 ÷ 101
19 R80

Divide. (See Example B.)

13. 419,377 ÷ 572
733 R101

14. 516,168 ÷ 856
603

15. 42,905 ÷ 285
150 R155

16. 37,737 ÷ 212
178 R1

17. 579,811 ÷ 666
870 R391

18. 79,008 ÷ 374
211 R94

19. 831,111 ÷ 909
914 R285

20. 207,702 ÷ 431
481 R391

Mixed Practice (For more practice, see page 410.)

Divide.

21. 2970 ÷ 495
6

22. 121,112 ÷ 345
351 R17

23. 400,707 ÷ 289
1386 R153

24. 4300 ÷ 826
5 R170

25. 83,113 ÷ 491
169 R134

26. 9190 ÷ 609
15 R55

27. 79,097 ÷ 336
235 R137

28. 5725 ÷ 225
25 R100

Applications

29. A rock group sold 137,528 tickets on their tour. If they held 41 concerts, estimate the number of tickets sold for each concert.
≈ 3000 tickets

30. Fifty-six thousand three hundred twenty-four dollars was donated to South High to buy computers. A computer costs two thousand four hundred thirty-nine dollars. How many computers can the students buy? How much money will they have left over?
23 computers; $227 left over

Review (Lesson 2.3)

Multiply mentally.

31. 600 × 90
54,000

32. 700 × 1000
700,000

33. 5000 × 50
250,000

34. 100 × 40
4000

▶ **Think and Discuss Answers**
1. 30; 30 R162
2. 31 months; the remainder represents the amount he must save the last (31st) month
3. 63,211
4. She might have pressed an extra zero to make 37,920 become 379,200.

★ **Error Alert**
Incorrect answers may occur because students are not placing numbers in the quotients directly above the correct numbers in the dividend.

Reinforcement
Extra Practice, page 410
EP/MR Worksheet 26, TRB, page 26

Challenge
Amy Brown earns $40,950 per year. She budgets her yearly salary as follows: food, $8060; house payments, $8100; utilities, $3500; gasoline, $1212; clothes, $1800; insurance, $1256; car, $3000; vacation, $2000; taxes, $12,022. Using 365 days in a year, how much would each item cost her per day? (answers: food, $22.08; house, $22.19; utilities, $9.59; gasoline, $3.32; clothes, $4.93; insurance, $3.44; car, $8.22; vacation, $5.48; taxes, $32.94)

Objective

- To perform the **Do** and **Check** steps in problem-solving

Purpose

After you have read a math problem and planned how to go about solving it, you are ready to do the computations and check your work. Learning a process for the Do and Check steps helps you carry out your plan and evaluate your answer.

Introducing the Lesson

Review the 4-step problem-solving process (Lessons 1.3, 2.5). Ask: What step in the problem-solving process involves deciding what you are going to do? (step 2: **Plan**) What step would you use to carry out your plan? (step 3: **Do**) What step would you use to make sure your answer is reasonable and the computations are correct? (step 4: **Check**)

Alternative Strategies

Ask students to apply the 4-step problem-solving process to the following situation: They are employees at a hardware store. One evening the boss leaves them the following message: "The large carton in the back room contains a new display rack for our home-improvement books. Please replace the old rack with the new rack." You open the carton and find that the rack is unassembled. (step 1: **Read**—read the message and assembly instructions. Make sure you understand what the boss wants and how to build the new rack; step 2: **Plan**—plan how you will go about assembling the new rack and replacing the old rack; step 3: **Do**—assemble rack, replace old rack with new; step 4: **Check**—check assembly for soundness and proper functioning) Ask students to describe what problems they might encounter if they omit one of the steps. Discuss how each step in assembling the rack is like solving math problems.

3.7 4-Step Problem-Solving Process: Do and Check

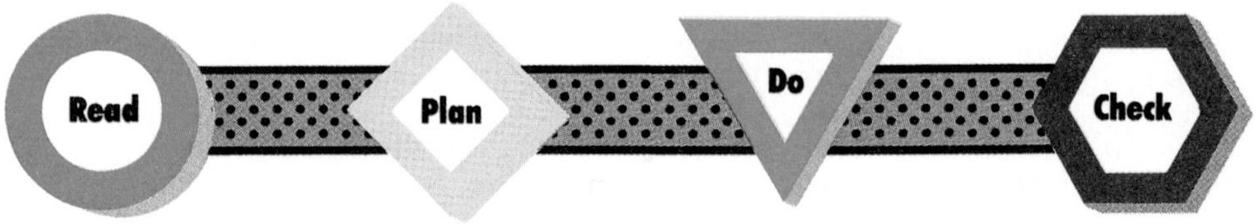

As you learned in Lessons 1.4 and 2.5, the first steps in successful problem solving are Read and Plan. You are now ready for the last two steps, Do and Check.

- **Step 3: Do**

In the Do step, you carry out the plan that you decided on in Step 2. Before you begin to compute, answer the following:

A Does your plan seem reasonable?
- **Yes** Write a mathematical sentence for solving the problem. Go to **B**.
- **No** Rethink you plan. Repeat **A**.

B Are the numbers in your mathematical sentence correct?
- **Yes** Compute.
- **No** Write the correct numbers. Then compute.

- **Step 4: Check**

In the Check step, determine if your answer is correct. If your answer is not correct, ask the following questions:

Questions	Hints
A Did you check your answer correctly?	
• Have you used the correct numbers?	• Check that you have copied the numbers correctly.
• Does your answer seem reasonable?	• Estimate the solution to the problem.
• Have you computed correctly?	
B Did you follow your plan?	
• Did you calculate the necessary information?	• Check your work against your plan.
• Did you follow the steps?	• Remember what you are computing: time, money, miles, etc.
• Is your answer in the correct form?	

▶ Think and Discuss

PROBLEM SOLVING

Use Read, Plan, Do, and Check to solve the problem below.

1. Cecil earns $80.00 per week. After payroll deductions, his take-home pay is $64.00. He saves half of his take-home pay and keeps the rest for expenses. His weekly expenses are $8.00 for bus fare and $12.00 for lunches. How much spending money does Cecil have left each week?

2. Three students solved the above problem. They were surprised when they realized that their answers were different. Their work is shown below. Study their plans. What errors did each student make?

Student A	Student B	Student C
Plan:	Plan:	Plan:
bus fare + lunch = expenses	take-home pay ÷ 2 = savings	take-home pay ÷ 2 = savings
take-home pay − expenses = savings and spending money	bus fare + lunches = expenses	bus fare + lunches = expenses
savings and spending money ÷ 2 = spending money	savings − expenses = spending money	savings − expenses = spending money
Computation:	Computation:	Computation:
8 + 12 = 20	80 ÷ 2 = 40	64 ÷ 2 = 32
64 − 20 = 44	8 + 12 = 20	8 + 12 = 16
44 ÷ 2 = 22	40 − 20 = 20	32 − 16 = 16
Solution: $22.00	Solution: $20.00	Solution: $16.00

Read the following problem. Write a Plan. Do the problem. Check your work.

3. Eli can carry 40 pounds. Mr. Smith hired him to carry some bricks and building equipment up from his cellar. One piece of equipment weighs 40 pounds and three other pieces each weigh 13 pounds. There are 100 2-pound bricks. Mr. Smith has offered Eli two rates: either a $40.00 flat rate or else $5.00 per trip, provided that Eli carries all he can each trip. At which rate would Eli make more money?

▶ Think and Discuss Answers

1. $12.00
2. Student A's plan is incorrect: savings and spending money divided by 2 is not equal to spending money. Student B incorrectly copied take-home pay as $80. Student C incorrectly computed that 8 plus 12 equals 16.
3. **Plan:** A possible plan is to see which rate makes Eli the most money:
   1. Find the number of trips for equipment.
   2. number of pounds for bricks ÷ 40 = number of trips for bricks
   3. number of trips for equipment + number of trips for bricks = total number of trips
   4. total number of trips × $5.00 = amount earned
   5. Compare the amount earned and the flat rate to see at which rate Eli will earn the most money.

   Do: Calculations for each step are shown.
   1. 3 × 13 = 39, so he can carry the three 13-pound pieces of equipment in 1 trip and the 40-lb. piece in 1 trip, equaling 2 trips
   2. 100 × 2 = 200 pounds for bricks; 200 ÷ 40 = 5 trips
   3. 2 trips + 5 trips = 7 trips
   4. 7 trips × $5.00 = $35.00
   5. $35 is less than $40; Eli will earn more at a flat rate of $40

   Check: Students should check to see that they followed their plans and computed correctly.

★ Error Alert

Incorrect answers may reveal that students have made mistakes in their plans or computations.

Reinforcement

EP/MR Worksheet 27, TRB, page 27

Project

Use the travel section of a newspaper to help you plan a trip and compute the costs for 2 adults and 2 children to fly from any major city to a vacation area. Prepare your trip using **Read, Plan, Do,** and **Check.** Total costs must include airfare, lodging for 5 days, food expenses, and spending money. (Answers will vary but should include work in each step of the problem-solving process.)

3.8 Choosing the Operation

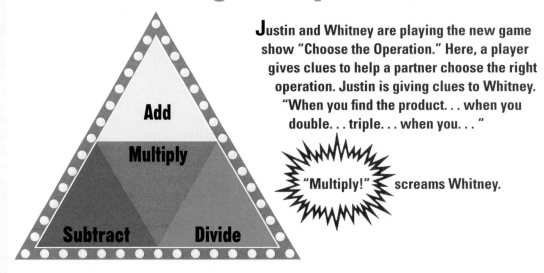

Justin and Whitney are playing the new game show "Choose the Operation." Here, a player gives clues to help a partner choose the right operation. Justin is giving clues to Whitney. "When you find the product. . . when you double. . . triple. . . when you. . . "

"Multiply!" screams Whitney.

1. Is Whitney correct? Yes

   Continue playing the game with Justin and Whitney. "When you want to find out how much money you'll have left after you spend some. . . or how many eggs will remain if you take 2 out of a dozen. . . sometimes called finding the difference."

2. What is the correct response? Subtraction
   Continue playing. "How to find the cost of one item if you know the cost of a dozen. . . or if you separate a crowd into small groups. . . sometimes called finding the quotient."

3. What is the correct response? Division

   The last operation is addition.

4. What clues would you give to describe addition?

   Justin and Whitney advanced to the next game: "Choose It and Use It." Whitney showed Justin 10 piles of baseball cards. Each pile contained a dozen cards. Whitney asked the questions. Help Justin by answering the questions.

5. How many piles of cards does Whitney have? 10 piles

6. How many cards are in each pile? 12 cards

7. What operation would you use to find how many cards are in all the piles? Multiplication

8. How many cards are there in all? 120 cards

★ **Error Alert**
Errors may occur when students do not read a problem carefully and draw incorrect conclusions about which operation to use.

Then Justin and Whitney played another game. This time Justin asked the questions. "I have 124 CDs and 18 cassettes. Which operation would you use to find how many CDs and cassettes I have in all?"

"Put them together. . . join. . . Add!" Whitney said. "So, Whitney, how many CDs and cassettes do I have in all?"

"Add CDs and cassettes. . . 124 plus 18 is 142," exclaimed Whitney.

9. Be the judge for the game. Did Whitney use the correct operation? Was Whitney's answer correct? Yes; yes

Work with 2 or more classmates to answer the following questions. Take turns asking the questions, answering the questions, and being the judge.

10. There are 8 granola bars in every box. Which operation would you use to find how many bars there are in 7 boxes? How many bars are there? Multiplication; 56 bars

11. There are 1700 students enrolled in school. Which operation would you use to find how many girls are enrolled if there are 800 boys? How many girls are enrolled? Subtraction; 900 girls

12. Each bus holds 50 passengers. Which operation would you use to find how many buses will be needed to transport 1500 students to school? How many buses will be needed? Division; 30 buses

13. Which operation would you use to find how many quarters there are in $6? How many quarters are in $6? Division or multiplication; 24 quarters

14. Which operation would you use to find how much money Tyrone spent if he bought a poster for $7, a shirt for $15, socks for $3, and a paperback for $4? How much did he spend in all? Addition; $29

15. Which operation would you use to find how much change you should receive if you give the cashier a $20 bill for a $13.50 purchase? How much change should you receive? Subtraction; $6.50

▶ **Review** (Lesson 2.11)

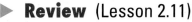

Solve. Did you use mental math, paper-and-pencil, or a calculator?

16. Find the cost of 6 greeting cards at $1.50 each. $9.00; mental math

17. What would you be paid for working 4.5 hours at a rate of $6.80 per hour? $30.60; paper-and-pencil or calculator

Problem Solving
PS Worksheet 2, TRB, pages 181–182

Challenge
Write the operations you would use to solve the following problem and then solve the problem.

Roger bought 3 pairs of jeans at $42.95 each, 5 shirts for $25.25 each, 1 jacket for $148.00, and 3 pairs of socks for $5.95 each. He paid for the clothes with five $100 bills. If there was no tax, how much change did he receive? (Multiply the price of each item times the number purchased. Add together these products to get the total cost. Multiply $100.00 by 5 to find out how much Roger paid. Subtract the total cost from the amount paid to find the change. Answer: $79.05)

3.9 Using the Order of Operations

The calendar shows the number of hours Jill worked her first week at her summer job. To compute the total number of hours for the week, she punched $3 + 7 \times 4 =$ into her calculator. To her amazement, Jill's calculator displayed 40. How many hours did Jill really work?

We need rules for working with expressions like $3 + 7 \times 4$. Otherwise, 2 people might read the same expression in 2 very different ways. The rules are called the *order of operations*.

Examples

To use the order of operations correctly, follow the steps below.

| 1. Do all operations within parentheses. |
| 2. Do all multiplications and divisions from left to right. |
| 3. Do all additions and subtractions from left to right. |

A Simplify. $3 + 7 \times 4$

$3 + 7 \times 4 =$ *Multiply.*
$3 + 28 =$ *Add.*
31
$3 + 7 \times 4 =$ **31**

B Simplify. $(2 + 7) \times 4 - 6$

$(2 + 7) \times 4 - 6 =$ Work within
                            parentheses.
$9 \times 4 - 6 =$ Multiply.
$36 - 6 =$ Subtract.
30
$(2 + 7) \times 4 - 6 =$ **30**

▶ Think and Discuss

1. Refer to the introduction to this lesson. How many hours did Jill really work?

2. Simplify $12 \div 2 \times 3$ by dividing first. Then simplify by multiplying first. Which answer is correct? Why?

3. Rewrite Example B without parentheses. Simplify and compare the two solutions.

4. One way to remember the rules for order of operations is as a set of symbols: $( ) \times \div + -$. Explain what the sequence of symbols represents.

Exercises

Simplify. (See Example A.)

5. $2 \times 4 + 8$ 16
6. $8 - 4 \div 2 - 2$ 4
7. $8 \div 4 - 2 \div 2$ 1
8. $12 + 6 \div 3$ 14
9. $12 \div 6 + 3$ 5
10. $1 + 2 \times 3 + 4$ 11

Simplify. (See Example B.)

11. $(8 - 4) \div 2$ 2
12. $7 + (3 \times 4) - 2$ 17
13. $(7 + 3) \times (4 - 2)$ 20
14. $(8 - 3) \div (2 + 3)$ 1
15. $(21 + 14) \div 7$ 5
16. $(35 \div 5) - (2 \times 3)$ 1

▶ Mixed Practice (For more practice, see page 411.)

Simplify.

17. $7 - 2 \times 3$ 1
18. $(7 - 2) \times 3$ 15
19. $(8 \div 2) + 3$ 7
20. $8 \div 2 + 3$ 7
21. $(1 + 2) \times 3 + 4$ 13
22. $(1 + 2) \times (3 + 4)$ 21
23. $1 \times 2 + 3 \times 4$ 14
24. $6 \div 6 \times 6 - 6 + 6$ 6
25. $(6 + 6) \times (6 \div 6)$ 12

▶ Applications

Solve. Add parentheses and operations signs to the numbers that follow each problem.

26. Andrea eats 3 apples each Sunday and 2 apples all the other days of the week. How many does she eat in 52 weeks?
$52 \times (3 + 2 \times 6)$

27. Felicia bought six postcards at 35¢ apiece and ten 20¢ stamps. How much did she spend in all?
$(6 \times 35) + (10 \times 20)$

▶ Review (Lessons 3.2, 3.3, 3.5)

Divide.

28. $695 \div 5$
139
29. $480 \div 40$
12
30. $8976 \div 25$
359 R1
31. $9257 \div 3$
3085 R2

▶ **Think and Discuss Answers**

1. 31
2. 18; 2; 18, because multiplications and divisions are performed from left to right and division comes first in this expression
3. $2 + 7 \times 4 - 6$; 24; they are different
4. The sequence of symbols represents working within parentheses first, multiplying and dividing next, and adding and subtracting last.

★ **Error Alert**

Errors may occur because students are not following the steps in the correct order. For example, students sometimes forget to do multiplication and division at the same time as they work from left to right in an expression.

Reinforcement

Extra Practice, page 411
EP/MR Worksheet 28, TRB, page 28

Challenge

Find the sum of 15 and 25 minus 4 times 15 divided by 6; then subtract the quantity 5 plus 9.

(answer: $15 + 25 - 4 \times 15 \div 6 - [5 + 9]$
$= 15 + 25 - 10 - 14$
$= 16$)

Objective

• To divide decimals by 1-digit and 2-digit whole number divisors

Purpose

Dividing decimals by whole numbers allows you to find the price per item when you know the price for more than one of the item.

Introducing the Lesson

Review dividing whole numbers by 1-digit and 2-digit divisors (Lessons 3.2 and 3.5). Use the examples: $375 \div 5 = (75)$; $770 \div 22 = (35)$.

Vicky & Rosa Go Fishing

"The Catch"

$19.56!

Vicky and Rosa received $19.56 for the fish they caught. They decided to split the profit equally.

To determine the amount of money each girl would receive, divide $19.56 by 2.

Alternative Examples

Example A—Divide. $29.56 \div 4$

```
  07.39
4)29.56
  28
  ‾‾
  1 5
  1 2
  ‾‾
    36
    36
    ‾‾
     0
```

$29.56 \div 4 = \mathbf{7.39}$

Example B—Divide. $6.025 \div 25$

```
   0.241
25)6.025
   5 0
   ‾‾‾
   1 02
   1 00
   ‾‾‾
     25
     25
     ‾‾
      0
```

$6.025 \div 25 = \mathbf{0.241}$

Examples

To divide a decimal by a whole number, place the decimal point in the quotient directly above the dividend's decimal point. Then divide as with whole numbers.

A Divide. $19.56 \div 2$

```
  0 9.7 8
2)1 9.5 6
  1 8
  ‾‾
    1 5
    1 4
    ‾‾
      1 6
      1 6
      ‾‾
        0
```
2 does not divide 1. Write a zero in the quotient. Divide as with whole numbers.

$19.56 \div 2 = \mathbf{9.78}$

B Divide. $1.08 \div 12$

```
   0.0 9
12)1.0 8
   1 0 8
   ‾‾‾‾
       0
```
12 does not divide 1 or 10. Write zeros in the quotient. Divide as with whole numbers.

$1.08 \div 12 = \mathbf{0.09}$

▶ Think and Discuss

1. Refer to the introduction to this lesson. How much money did Vicky earn?

2. Divide. $27.5 \div 11$

3. If a friend of Vicky and Rosa had helped them catch the fish and they had split the money three ways, how much money would each person have received?

4. Ramon claims that $638.35 \div 17 = \$37.55$. What are two ways to check Ramon's work? Which check is easier to perform?

◤ Exercises

Divide. (See Example A.)

5. $4\overline{)39.2}$ 9.8 | 6. $3\overline{)38.4}$ 12.8 | 7. $9\overline{)97.2}$ 10.8 | 8. $4\overline{)5.2}$ 1.3

9. $3.96 \div 6$ 0.66 | 10. $0.42 \div 7$ 0.06 | 11. $0.432 \div 9$ 0.048 | 12. $0.234 \div 3$ 0.078

Divide. (See Example B.)

13. $38\overline{)5.51}$ 0.145 | 14. $17\overline{)1.19}$ 0.07 | 15. $88\overline{)0.792}$ 0.009 | 16. $45\overline{)0.585}$ 0.013

17. $7.90 \div 10$ 0.79 | 18. $9.45 \div 63$ 0.15 | 19. $0.72 \div 12$ 0.06 | 20. $0.54 \div 18$ 0.03

▶ Mixed Practice (For more practice, see page 411.)

Divide.

21. $8.68 \div 7$ 1.24 | 22. $11\overline{)38.5}$ 3.5 | 23. $5\overline{)0.745}$ 0.149 | 24. $4.68 \div 12$ 0.39

25. $22\overline{)18.48}$ 0.84 | 26. $7\overline{)0.161}$ 0.023 | 27. $0.144 \div 4$ 0.036 | 28. $3.64 \div 52$ 0.07

▶ Applications

29. Ken, Jay, and Juan hiked forty-three and six-tenths miles in four days, covering the same distance each day. How many miles did they hike per day? 10.9 miles

30. Hannah and her two sisters bought their father a set of lures at the sale price shown. If each girl paid the same amount, how much did each girl spend? $11.65

31. Otis received a paycheck for $101.25 one week. If he worked 15 hours, how much did he earn per hour? $6.75

Was $39.95

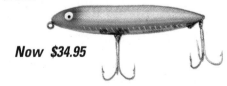

Now $34.95

▶ Review (Lesson 1.7)

Round to the nearest thousand.

32. 11,852 | 33. 65,395 | 34. 79,514 | 35. 492,186 | 36. 287,651
12,000 | 65,000 | 80,000 | 492,000 | 288,000

3.11 Rounding Quotients

Peter was selected by the 7 other members of the tennis team to buy a gift for their coach. He found a gift that cost $85.96. "So how much do we owe you?" asked Todd, one of the team members. After quickly dividing, Peter announced that each person owed $10.745. "You've got to be kidding!" responded Todd. "How are we supposed to pay half a cent?"

Perhaps Peter should have rounded $10.745. What would you have charged each person?

Examples

To round quotients, first divide. Then round.

A Divide. Round the quotient to the nearest tenth. 136.1 ÷ 56

```
          2.4 3
56) 1 3 6.1 0
    1 1 2
    ──────
      2 4 1
      2 2 4
    ──────
        1 7 0
        1 6 8
```
Since you are rounding to the nearest tenth, divide to the hundredths place. Then round 2.43 to 2.4.

136.1 ÷ 56 is about **2.4.**

B Divide. Round the quotient to the nearest cent. $85.96 ÷ 8

```
      1 0.7 4 5
8) 8 5.9 6 0
   8
   ──────
   0 5 9
     5 6
   ──────
       3 6
       3 2
   ──────
         4 0
         4 0
```
Divide to the thousandths place. Round to the hundredths place.

$85.96 ÷ 8 is about **$10.75.**

▶ Think and Discuss

1. Divide. Round the quotient to the nearest tenth. 86.4 ÷ 7

2. Divide. Round the quotient to the nearest cent. $58.95 ÷ 6

3. Is 156.98 closer to 156.9 or 157.0?

4. Round 289.95 to the nearest tenth.

5. Refer to the introduction to this lesson. If the 8 team members each contributed $10.75, how much money was collected?

6. Name a situation when rounding quotients might be useful.

Exercises

Divide. Round the quotient to the nearest tenth. (See Example A.)

7. 8)107.6
13.5

8. 19)5.63
0.3

9. 65)517
8.0

10. 9)47.35
5.3

11. 21)6.32
0.3

12. 7)10
1.4

13. 28)50.1
1.8

14. 19)4.87
0.3

15. 42)93.7
2.2

16. 61)102.8
1.7

17. 23.5 ÷ 41
0.6

18. 1.6 ÷ 3
0.5

19. 98 ÷ 52
1.9

20. 485 ÷ 7
69.3

21. 41)52
1.3

22. 38)98
2.6

Divide. Round the quotient to the nearest cent. (See Example B.)

23. 9)$126.43
$14.05

24. 24)$2575
$107.29

25. 5)$229.49
$45.90

26. 18)$500
$27.78

27. 2.6)$58
$22.31

28. 7)$47.52
$6.79

29. 55)$189
$3.44

30. 35)$637.95
$18.23

31. 43)$92.25
$2.15

32. 27)$100
$3.70

33. 68)$215.52
$3.17

34. 99)$870.50
$8.79

35. $1.98 ÷ 8
$0.25

36. $2.70 ÷ 16
$0.17

37. $383.50 ÷ 4
$95.88

38. $84.50 ÷ 8
$10.56

▶ **Mixed Practice** (For more practice, see page 412.)

Divide. Round the quotient to the nearest tenth or cent.

39. $22 ÷ 3
$7.33

40. 6)38
6.3

41. 4)$63.50
$15.88

42. $456.18 ÷ 5
$91.24

43. 11)381
34.6

44. 8)6.47
0.8

45. 3)$49.49
$16.50

46. 6.042 ÷ 7
0.9

47. 87)11.53
0.1

48. 29)608
21.0

49. 56)42.2
0.8

50. $6.45 ÷ 8
$0.81

51. 294)205.7
0.7

52. 36)$1200
$33.33

53. 50)5.381
0.1

54. $405.75 ÷ 10
$40.58

▶ **Applications**

55. Monique saw an automatic-focus camera in a catalog for $120. She plans to save the same amount of money each month for six months. How much should she save each month?
$20 per month

56. Suppose you wanted to buy the camera and a $40 lens kit. If you can save $20 each week, how many months will it take you to save the money for both items?
2 months

57. Aram wants to buy a stereo that costs $539.98. If he can pay for it in 8 equal payments, estimate how much he will owe after 2 payments.
≈$400

▶ **Review** (Lessons 2.2, 2.3, 2.4)

Multiply.

58.   8995
    × 9
    80,955

59.   22
    × 47
    1034

60.   907
    × 206
    186,842

61.   274
    × 10
    2740

62.   15,012
    × 5
    75,060

3.12 Dividing Decimals by Decimals

$14.40

$9.90

0.5 fl. oz.   2.25 fl. oz.

Richard wanted to buy his girlfriend some perfume. The salesperson suggested the bottles shown here.

How much does an ounce of perfume cost? You can find cost per ounce by dividing the total price by number of ounces.

Examples

To divide decimals, move the decimal point in the divisor to make a whole number. Then move the decimal point in the dividend the same number of places. Write zeros as needed. Write a decimal point in the quotient and divide.

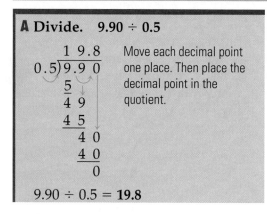

A Divide. $9.90 \div 0.5$

$$
\begin{array}{r}
1\,9.8 \\
0.5\overline{)9.9\,0} \\
5 \\
\hline
4\,9 \\
4\,5 \\
\hline
4\,0 \\
4\,0 \\
\hline
0 \\
\end{array}
$$

Move each decimal point one place. Then place the decimal point in the quotient.

$9.90 \div 0.5 = \mathbf{19.8}$

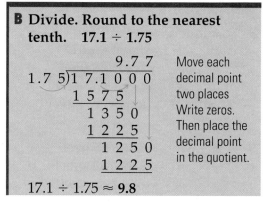

B Divide. Round to the nearest tenth. $17.1 \div 1.75$

$$
\begin{array}{r}
9.7\,7 \\
1.7\,5\overline{)1\,7.1\,0\,0\,0} \\
1\,5\,7\,5 \\
\hline
1\,3\,5\,0 \\
1\,2\,2\,5 \\
\hline
1\,2\,5\,0 \\
1\,2\,2\,5 \\
\hline
\end{array}
$$

Move each decimal point two places. Write zeros. Then place the decimal point in the quotient.

$17.1 \div 1.75 \approx \mathbf{9.8}$

▶ **Think and Discuss**

1. Divide. $0.588 \div 2.1$

2. Refer to the introduction to this lesson. What did each perfume cost per fluid ounce?

3. Write a division problem in which you need to move the decimal point 2 places.

4. In Example B, why was it necessary to write 3 zeros?

Exercises

Divide. (See Example A.)

5. $0.7\overline{)4.06}$
5.8

6. $0.9\overline{)15.3}$
17

7. $1.5\overline{)4.95}$
3.3

8. $3.4\overline{)8.84}$
2.6

9. $11.6 \div 0.4$
29

10. $31.2 \div 0.6$
52

11. $0.96 \div 0.2$
4.8

12. $2.58 \div 4.3$
0.6

Divide. Round to the nearest tenth. (See Example B.)

13. $1.43\overline{)0.322}$
0.2

14. $2.87\overline{)4.79}$
1.7

15. $1.32\overline{)11.99}$
9.1

16. $2.16\overline{)0.1732}$
0.1

17. $1.283 \div 8.5$
0.2

18. $8.7 \div 7.29$
1.2

19. $8.643 \div 5.08$
1.7

20. $10.376 \div 4.51$
2.3

▶ **Mixed Practice** (For more practice, see page 412.)

Divide. Round to the nearest tenth, if needed.

21. $1.134 \div 0.18$
6.3

22. $0.3\overline{)2.089}$
7.0

23. $5.12 \div 0.32$
16

24. $9.2\overline{)29.47}$
3.2

25. $4.83 \div 0.23$
21

26. $1.98\overline{)5.94}$
3

27. $7.2\overline{)25.92}$
3.6

28. $7.06\overline{)5.718}$
0.8

29. $12.7\overline{)80.01}$
6.3

30. $9.6\overline{)5.27}$
0.5

31. $70.1 \div 8.5$
8.2

32. $0.45\overline{)3.555}$
7.9

▶ **Applications**

33. Kevin wants to know if all of his CDs will fit into the CD rack he bought. Ten CDs are approximately ten and seven tenths centimeters wide. Estimate the number of CDs that fit in the CD rack.
20 CDs

├───── 39.2 cemtimeters ─────┤

34. A tin of popcorn that weighs 9.375 pounds costs $23.99. A 5.5-pound tin of caramel corn costs $14.49. Which tin is cheaper per pound?
1st tin

35. Mrs. Russell has a stack of homework papers on her desk 1.308 inches thick. If each sheet of paper is 0.003 inches thick, how many pages of homework does she have to grade?
436 pages

▶ **Review** (Lesson 3.3)

Divide.

36. $6921 \div 100$
69.21

37. $57.89 \div 10$
5.789

38. $800 \div 20$
40

39. $600 \div 30$
20

40. $192.4 \div 100$
1.924

41. $63,000 \div 70$
900

42. $3000 \div 60$
50

43. $3.7 \div 100$
0.037

Objective

- To divide whole numbers by 1-digit, 2-digit, and 3-digit decimal divisors

Purpose

Dividing whole numbers by decimals helps you to figure a car's gas mileage.

Introducing the Lesson

Review dividing decimals by decimals (Lesson 3.12). Use the examples: 86.1 ÷ 2.1 = (41); 254.8 ÷ 10.4 = (24.5).

Write the following numbers on the chalkboard. For each number, have students move the decimal point: one place to the right; two places to the right; and three places to the right.
162 (1620, 16,200, 162,000);
9.23 (92.3, 923, 9230);
4.251 (42.51, 425.1, 4251);
0.3856 (3.856, 38.56, 385.6);
6 (60, 600, 6000)

Alternative Examples

Example A—Divide.   924 ÷ 1.5

```
         61 6.
1.5.)924.0.
       90
       24
       15
       90
       90
        0
```

924 ÷ 15 = **616**

Example B—Divide. Round to the nearest tenth.   586 ÷ 4.07

```
          1 43.98
4.07.)586.00.00
      407
      1790
      1628
      1620
      1221
       3990
       3663
       3270
       3256
```

586 ÷ 4.07 ≈ **144.0**

3.13 Dividing Whole Numbers by Decimals

Imagine a car trip covering 304 miles and using 9.5 gallons of gas. To find the number of miles per gallon, you would divide 304 miles by 9.5 gallons.

Examples

To divide whole numbers by decimals, remember that the whole number has a decimal point to the right of the ones place. Then use the method taught in Lesson 3.12.

A Divide.   304 ÷ 9.5

```
         3 2.
9.5.)3 0 4.0
     2 8 5
       1 9 0
       1 9 0
           0
```
Move the decimal points one place. Write one zero.

304 ÷ 9.5 = **32**

B Divide. Round to the nearest tenth.   923 ÷ 3.06

```
              3 0 1.6 3
3.0 6.)9 2 3 0.0 0 0
       9 1 8
           5 0 0
           3 0 6
           1 9 4 0
           1 8 3 6
             1 0 4 0
               9 1 8
```
Move the decimal points two places. Place the decimal point in the quotient.

923 ÷ 3.06 ≈ **301.6**

▶ **Think and Discuss**

1. Refer to the introduction to this lesson. How many miles per gallon did the car get on the trip?

2. In Example A, how many places did you move the decimal point in the divisor? In the dividend? How many zeros did you write after the 4?

3. On another trip you travel 308 miles on 8.8 gallons of gas. Estimate the number of miles per gallon.

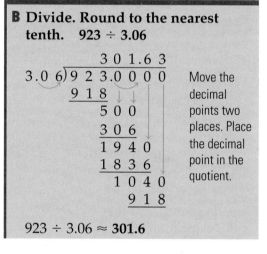

4. What do the division problems $0.008\overline{)10}$, $0.08\overline{)100}$, and $0.8\overline{)1000}$ have in common? Solve and see.

5. Why is it a good idea to estimate an answer when you begin a division problem? If you are using a calculator, is it still a good idea? Discuss.

▶ **Think and Discuss Answers**

1. 32 mi./gal.
2. 1; 1; 1
3. 30 mi./gal.
4. The answers will be the same because when the decimal points are moved, each problem becomes 10,000 ÷ 8.
5. to make sure you move the decimal points the correct number of places and to check for simple errors; yes

★ **Error Alert**

Errors may occur when students do not move both decimal points the same number of places. Remind them that a whole number has a decimal point to the right of the ones place.

Exercises

Divide. (See Example A.)

6. $0.4\overline{)6}$
   15
7. $0.6\overline{)9}$
   15
8. $2.5\overline{)16}$
   6.4
9. $5.6\overline{)14}$
   2.5

10. $4.5\overline{)18}$
    4
11. $0.7\overline{)280}$
    400
12. $3.5\overline{)182}$
    52
13. $0.5\overline{)475}$
    950

14. $3 \div 0.6$
    5
15. $75 \div 1.2$
    62.5
16. $221 \div 3.4$
    65
17. $16 \div 6.4$
    2.5

Divide. Round to the nearest tenth. (See Example B.)

18. $0.06\overline{)20}$
    333.3
19. $0.15\overline{)7}$
    46.7
20. $4.25\overline{)69}$
    16.2
21. $3.82\overline{)765}$
    200.3

22. $6.09\overline{)583}$
    95.7
23. $0.95\overline{)813}$
    855.8
24. $7.13\overline{)607}$
    85.1
25. $5.42\overline{)738}$
    136.2

26. $5065 \div 2.11$
    2400.5
27. $13 \div 0.75$
    17.3
28. $7470 \div 6.22$
    1201.0
29. $1690 \div 8.43$
    200.5

▶ **Mixed Practice** (For more practice, see page 413.)

Divide. Round to the nearest tenth, if needed.

30. $21 \div 0.5$
    42
31. $0.07\overline{)16}$
    228.6
32. $44 \div 2.5$
    17.6
33. $0.45\overline{)55}$
    122.2

34. $0.7\overline{)41}$
    58.6
35. $65 \div 2.58$
    25.2
36. $23.2\overline{)187}$
    8.1
37. $998 \div 0.16$
    6237.5

38. $872 \div 1.35$
    645.9
39. $7.6\overline{)702}$
    92.4
40. $3.6\overline{)5}$
    1.4
41. $6.3\overline{)957}$
    151.9

42. $0.92\overline{)1020}$
    1108.7
43. $527 \div 0.31$
    1700
44. $1018 \div 12.6$
    80.8
45. $7.6\overline{)689}$
    90.7

46. $0.48\overline{)3456}$
    7200
47. $0.2\overline{)21,828}$
    109,140
48. $9.27\overline{)33,380}$
    3600.9
49. $1188 \div 9.85$
    120.6

▶ **Applications**

50. A salesperson drove a rental car 725.2 miles and used 19.6 gallons of gasoline. What was his mileage per gallon?
    37 miles per gallon

51. Lockers are being installed along a wall that is 40 feet long. If each locker is 1.25 feet wide, how many lockers will fit?
    32 lockers

▶ **Review** (Lesson 3.9)

Simplify.

52. $9 + 6 \times 5 - 2$
    37
53. $(8 \times 8) + (49 \div 7)$
    71
54. $28 \div 7 \times 6$
    24

55. $25 \div 5 + 3 + 4 \times 5$
    28
56. $18 \div 3 \div 3$
    2
57. $8 - 36 \div 6 + 9$
    11

Chapter 3 Review

If the answer is true, write T. If the answer is false, write F and explain why the answer is incorrect. (Lesson 3.1)

1. The number inside the division bracket is called the divisor.
   F; dividend

2. The answer to a division problem is called the product. F; quotient

Divide. (Lessons 3.2, 3.3)

3. $6\overline{)96}$ 16   4. $703 \div 3$ 234 R1   5. $40\overline{)160}$ 4   6. $10\overline{)960}$ 96

7. $9000 \div 100$ 90   8. $872 \div 5$ 174 R2   9. $8\overline{)93}$ 11 R5   10. $50\overline{)3500}$ 70

Estimate. (Lesson 3.4)

11. $79 \div 17$ ≈4   12. $31\overline{)963}$ ≈32   13. $11\overline{)456}$ ≈46   14. $52\overline{)1004}$ ≈20

15. $502\overline{)2498}$ ≈5   16. $1222 \div 38$ ≈30   17. $73\overline{)492}$ ≈7   18. $6587 \div 99$ ≈66

Divide. (Lessons 3.5, 3.6)

19. $49\overline{)653}$ 13 R16   20. $491 \div 12$ 40 R11   21. $98\overline{)7625}$ 77 R79   22. $109\overline{)986}$ 9 R5

23. $533\overline{)872}$ 1 R339   24. $37\overline{)560}$ 15 R5   25. $387 \div 32$ 12 R3   26. $254\overline{)3670}$ 14 R114

Write which operation you would use to solve each problem. Then solve. (Lesson 3.8)

27. Pens come in packages of 18. How many packages can be made from 1158 pens?
    Division; 64 packages

28. Jolene spends an average of 45 minutes a night studying. About how many minutes does she spend each week studying?
    Multiplication; 315 minutes

29. An earthquake took place in China in 1556. In 1964 an earthquake took place in Alaska. How many years separated these events? Subtraction; 408 years

30. For assembly programs, all 962 students must sit in the 26 equal rows of chairs in the auditorium. How many chairs are there in each row? Division; 37 chairs

Simplify. (Lesson 3.9)

31. $10 + 7 \times 7 - 8$ 51   32. $39 - 90 \div 10$ 30   33. $7 \times 8 + 9 \times 9$ 137

Divide. Round the quotient to the nearest tenth or cent, if needed. (Lessons 3.10, 3.11, 3.12, 3.13)

34. $6\overline{)\$5.94}$
    $0.99

35. $24.80 \div 40$
    0.6

36. $0.3\overline{)78}$
    260

37. $0.50\overline{)0.625}$
    1.3

Chapter 3 Test

Chapter Tests
Short Answer, Forms A and B, TRB, pages
275–276, 277–278
Multiple Choice, Forms A and B, TRB, pages
343–344, 345–346

Teaching Aids
Answer sheet
TA 8, TRB, page 161a
Teaching suggestions precede the Teaching
Aids worksheets.

Divide.

1. $60\overline{)960}$
   16

2. $19\overline{)494}$
   26

3. $14.7 \div 0.07$
   210

4. $0.025\overline{)0.975}$
   39

5. $1000\overline{)5680}$
   5.68

6. $81\overline{)737.1}$
   9.1

7. $7500 \div 50$
   150

8. $113\overline{)904}$
   8

9. $400\overline{)84,000}$
   210

10. $10.71 \div 6.3$
    1.7

11. $1.43\overline{)7.15}$
    5

Complete each statement.

12. Order of operations tells you to ___ and ___ before you add
    or subtract.
    multiply   divide

13. The answer to a division problem is called the ___ .
    quotient

14. When you divide a number by 100, you move the decimal
    point ___ places to the ___ .
    two   left

Estimate.

15. $33\overline{)271}$ ≈9

16. $604 \div 99$ ≈6

17. $75\overline{)638}$ ≈8

18. $5\overline{)786}$ ≈160

19. $408 \div 52$ ≈8

20. $68\overline{)489}$ ≈7

21. $118 \div 17$ ≈6

22. $9\overline{)987}$ ≈110

Simplify.

23. $3 \times 9 + 8 \times 4$ 59

24. $16 - 72 \div 9 + 5$ 13

25. $45 + 6 \times 6 \div 2$ 63

26. $18 \div 2 - 5 \times 1$ 4

27. $14 + 49 \div 7 - 7$ 14

28. $100 \div 5 \times 4 + 7$ 87

Divide. Round the quotient to the nearest tenth or cent.

29. $7\overline{)\$51.49}$
    \$7.36

30. $30\overline{)90.6}$
    3.0

31. $\$984.73 \div 9$
    \$109.41

32. $4\overline{)73.93}$
    18.5

Write which operation you would use to solve each problem.
Then solve.

33. Kim rode 68 miles on his bike.
    Shishin rode eight times as far.
    How far did Shishin ride?
    Multiplication; 544 miles

34. In 1876 Alexander Graham Bell
    patented the telephone. The first
    American landed on the moon
    93 years later. In what year did
    that event occur? Addition; 1969

Career Focus Activity

Materials: journal, pen, prepared list of questions

Procedure: The career of being a veterinarian is an ideal opportunity for job shadowing. Students can actually follow a vet or other related professional through a day's activities.

• Contact a local veterinary clinic. Ask if one or two students may observe one vet or other related professional during the day.

• Each student should bring a journal and a pen to record events, impressions, and experiences of the day. They can share a prepared list of questions to be asked. Partners can take turns asking questions.

• The journal is to be signed by the vet or other related professional at the end of the visit.

• When students return, they should report on the experience for the class.

• A thank you note to the host business should be written and sent by all that attended within three days of the visit.

Use metric measurement

• in many track and field events.

• to determine the unit price on some products, such as soft drinks.

• to choose sockets when using a ratchet to work on a car.

• for quantities needed in a science lab.

What are some other ways to use metric measurement?

Metric Measurement

A veterinarian is an animal doctor.

- Veterinarians work in offices with treatment rooms, animal hospitals, and zoos. Some make visits to homes, farms, and stables.

- A veterinarian should love animals, enjoy taking care of them, and be patient.

- A veterinarian performs routine health checkups of animals, diagnoses illnesses, prescribes treatment and medicines, and performs surgeries.

- To become a veterinarian, an individual completes four years of veterinarian school after at least two years of college and must be licensed.

- Related careers include veterinarian assistants, kennel operators, animal breeders, animal handlers, zoo attendants, and pet shop owners.

CAREER

VETERINARIAN

PORTFOLIO PROJECT: *Prepare a weekly animal diet.*

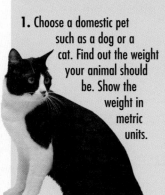

1. Choose a domestic pet such as a dog or a cat. Find out the weight your animal should be. Show the weight in metric units.

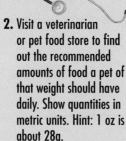

2. Visit a veterinarian or pet food store to find out the recommended amounts of food a pet of that weight should have daily. Show quantities in metric units. Hint: 1 oz is about 28g.

3. Prepare a weekly diet for the animal. Name the type of food and the quantities in metric units that the animal will be given each day. Add the daily quantities to show the weekly amounts of food needed for the pet. Don't forget the water the pet needs. *Show the math.*

About the Portfolio Project

Once the students choose a domestic pet, they can go to the grocery store. Most cans and bags of pet food offer recommended feedings to assist students in planning a weekly diet. Be sure to point out the conversion hint. Inform students that water is also vital to the diet. Information should be presented in report form. All math should be written and figured neatly and accurately at the end of the information.

Assessment: The individual scoring rubric on page 161 of the Teacher's Resource Binder can be reproduced and used for assessment. Include the following information in the last two boxes. Students should have:
- composed a weekly diet for a domestic pet.
- accurately converted from a customary to metric measure to determine daily and weekly amounts of food.

4.1 Introduction to the Metric System

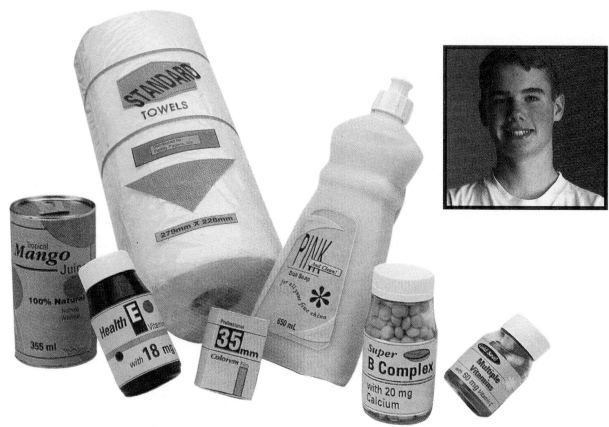

Todd works in a grocery store. One of his jobs is stocking shelves. When he first started working, Todd was surprised to find that many items in the store are labeled using metric units.

1. List the abbreviations shown above that represent metric units of measurement.
2. Determine whether each item shown above would be measured according to its length, mass, or liquid volume.

▶ Express Yourself

You are already familiar with many metric units of measurement. The basic units of the metric system are:

meters   used to measure length or distance

grams   used to measure mass

liters   used to measure liquid volume, or capacity

The prefixes below are used in the metric system.

kilo-	1000.	(times one thousand)
centi-	0.01	(times one hundredth)
milli-	0.001	(times one thousandth)

PROBLEM SOLVING

3. The basic unit of each of the following terms is underlined. Tell what each term means.

kilo*byte*　　　　milli*gram*　　　　milli*volt*　　　　centi*meter*

4. Look up the following terms in a dictionary: *decimal, decibel, decimate, decile.* What common meaning do these have?

▶ Practice What You Know

The metric system is organized by powers of ten. U.S. currency is another system that is organized by powers of ten.

100　　　　　　　10　　　　　　　1　　　　　0.10　0.01

If the dollar is the basic unit, what is a cent?

1¢ = $0.01 = one hundredth of a dollar

5. What would be a more reasonable way to say, "I earn 2500 cents a week?"

6. Suppose you want to exchange 2 one-dollar bills for dimes. You are changing a larger unit (dollars) to a smaller unit (dimes). How many dimes will you receive? Do you multiply or divide to get your answer?

7. Suppose you want to exchange 1800 pennies for dollar bills. You are changing a smaller unit (pennies) to a larger unit (dollars). How many dollars will you receive? Do you multiply or divide? By what number?

Remember that when you multiply by powers of ten, you move the decimal point to the right. When you divide by powers of ten, you move the decimal point to the left.

Multiply or divide.

8. 3×1000　　　　9. $120 \div 100$　　　　10. $650 \div 1000$　　　　11. 5.9×1000

12. $9.7 \div 100$　　　　13. $0.83 \div 1000$　　　　14. 40.2×1000　　　　15. $0.072 \div 100$

Metric Measurement **87**

Express Yourself Answers

3. kilobyte—1000 bytes; milligram—1/1000 of a gram; millivolt—1/1000 of a volt; centimeter—1/100 of a meter
4. dividing into 10 parts

Practice What You Know Answers

5. "I earn 25 dollars a week."
6. 20 dimes; multiply
7. 18 dollars; divide; 100
8. 3000
9. 1.2
10. 0.65
11. 5900
12. 0.097
13. 0.00083
14. 40,200
15. 0.00072

★ **Error Alert**

Errors may occur if students move the decimal the wrong way when they are multiplying and dividing.

Project

Look up the following words in a dictionary: *decagon, microvolt, deciliter, hectometer,* and *megabuck.* Use the definitions you find there to decide what the prefixes *micro, mega, hecto, deca,* and *deci* mean. Then make a new chart, like the one on page 87, including the 5 new prefixes. (*mega* = × 1,000,000; *hecto* = × 100; *deca* = × 10; *deci* = × 0.1; *micro* = × 0.000001)

T87

Objective

- To convert metric units of length to larger or smaller units

Purpose

Converting metric units allows you to compare the lengths of various items, using the same unit of measure.

Introducing the Lesson

Review the meaning of each metric prefix (Lesson 4.1). Also, review multiplying and dividing whole numbers and decimals by powers of 10 (Lessons 2.7, 2.8, 3.3). Use the examples: $57 \times 10 = (570)$; $57 \times 100 = (5700)$; $57 \times 1000 = (57,000)$; $8.3 \times 10 = (83)$; $8.3 \times 100 = (830)$; $8.3 \times 1000 = (8300)$; $638 \div 10 = (63.8)$; $638 \div 100 = (6.38)$; $638 \div 1000 = 0.638$; $3600 \div 10 = (360)$; $3600 \div 100 = (36)$; $3600 \div 1000 = (3.6)$.

Alternative Examples

Example A—Convert 47 mm to cm.
10 mm = 1 cm, so 47 mm = **4.7 cm**

Example B—Convert 5.8 km to m.
1 km = 1000 m, so 5.8 km = **5800 m**

Example C—Convert 26 km to cm.
26 km = 26,000 m
26,000 m = 2,600,000 cm
26 km = **2,600,000 cm**

Alternative Strategies

Kilo	Hecto	Deca	BASE	Deci	Cent	Milli

Locate the prefix you are trying to convert on the chart. Count the number of places right or left to the new prefix. Move the decimal the same number of places right or left, adding zeros as needed. Use the example: Change 7 km to cm.

Find *kilo* on the chart, and count 5 places right to *centi*. Move the decimal 5 places right.
7.00000 km = 700,000 cm

4.2 Converting Metric Units of Length

Jolene and Amy both claimed to have the longest fingernails in their class. To settle the dispute, they decided to measure the nail on their right index fingers. Jolene's nail was 3 centimeters long and Amy's nail was 26 millimeters long.

Who wins? To find out, you must convert metric units.

Examples

To convert metric units, first determine if you are converting to a larger or smaller unit.

$$\times 1000 \qquad \times 100 \qquad \times 10$$

kilometer (km) meter (m) centimeter (cm) millimeter (mm)

$$\div 1000 \qquad \div 100 \qquad \div 10$$

A Convert 26 mm to cm.

Divide since you are changing to a larger unit.
10 mm = 1 cm, so
26 mm = **2.6 cm.**

B Convert 4.7 km to m.

Multiply since you are changing to a smaller unit.
1 km = 1000 m, so
4.7 km = **4700 m.**

C Convert 8 km to cm.

First convert to meters. Then convert to centimeters.
8 km = 8000 m, and
8000 m = 800000 cm, so
8 km = **800,000 cm.**

▶ Think and Discuss

1. Convert 63 centimeters to kilometers.

2. Convert 6 kilometers to centimeters.

3. Describe how to multiply and divide by powers of 10.

4. How do you convert measurements from millimeters to kilometers?

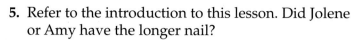
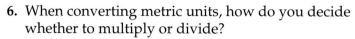

5. Refer to the introduction to this lesson. Did Jolene or Amy have the longer nail?

6. When converting metric units, how do you decide whether to multiply or divide?

Exercises

Convert each measure. (See Example A.)

7. 53 mm to cm
5.3 cm

8. 77 mm to cm
7.7 cm

9. 134 cm to m
1.34 m

10. 280 cm to m
2.80 m

11. 6384 m to km
6.384 km

12. 915 m to km
0.915 km

Convert each measure. (See Example B.)

13. 2.9 km to m
2900 m

14. 6.1 km to m
6100 m

15. 42 m to cm
4200 cm

16. 0.15 m to cm
15 cm

17. 8.4 cm to mm
84 mm

18. 27 cm to mm
270 mm

Convert each measure. (See Example C.)

19. 9 mm to m
0.009 m

20. 431 mm to m
0.431 m

21. 5364 cm to km
0.05364 km

22. 0.8 km to cm
80,000 cm

23. 0.0052 m to mm
5.2 mm

24. 12 km to mm
12,000,000 mm

▶ Mixed Practice (For more practice, see page 413.)

Convert each measure.

25. 3100 m to km
3.1 km

26. 3.6 cm to mm
36 mm

27. 5.8 m to cm
580 cm

28. 3470 mm to m
3.470 m

29. 1.9 m to mm
1900 mm

30. 115 mm to cm
11.5 cm

31. 3.2 km to m
3200 m

32. 0.73 km to cm
73,000 cm

33. 629 cm to km
0.00629 km

▶ Applications

34. List the trails shown in the diagram at the right in order from shortest to longest.
Mirror Lake, Blue Heron, Marsh

35. The Blue Heron Trail is how many meters longer than the Mirror Lake Trail? 2200 m

Blue Heron Trail
3.01 km

Mirror Lake Trail
810 m

Marsh Trail
4.8 km

▶ Review (Lessons 3.10, 3.11, 3.12)

Divide. Round the quotient to the nearest tenth.

36. 6.8 ÷ 3.2 2.1

37. 44.731 ÷ 9 5.0

38. 0.2695 ÷ 0.05 5.4

39. 684.5 ÷ 4 171.1

40. 3.91 ÷ 17 0.2

41. 3.575 ÷ 6.5 0.6

42. 87.55 ÷ 25 3.5

43. 0.897 ÷ 0.3 3.0

▶ **Think and Discuss Answers**

1. 0.00063 km
2. 600,000 cm
3. Move the decimal point to the right to multiply; move the decimal point to the left to divide.
4. Divide by 1,000,000 (move the decimal point 6 places to the left).
5. Jolene
6. When converting to a smaller unit, multiply; when converting to a larger unit, divide.

★ **Error Alert**

Errors may indicate that students are not dividing to change to a larger unit and are not multiplying to change to a smaller unit.

Reinforcement

Extra Practice, page 413
EP/MR Worksheet 33, TRB, page 33

Challenge

A map has a scale of 1:1,000,000 where 1 centimeter on the map equals 1,000,000 centimeters on the ground. Find out how many kilometers apart the following cities are, using the map distances shown:

St. Louis–Kansas City   4.11 cm
Boston–New York   348 mm
Atlanta–New Orleans   0.0792 m
(answers: 41.1 km; 348 km; 79.2 km)

Objectives

- To measure to the nearest millimeter or centimeter
- To choose reasonable units of length

Purpose

Metric units of length are used more and more, especially in international sporting events. This lesson helps you get a better sense of the length of these units.

Introducing the Lesson

Review the metric measures—*mm, cm, m, km* (Lesson 4.2). Have students predict a reasonable unit for measuring each of the following: a pencil (cm); the state of Vermont (km); a room (m or cm, depending on the reason for measuring)

Alternative Examples

Example A—Measure the length of one of the pages from your math textbook to the nearest centimeter. The page is closer to **23 cm** than 24 cm.

Example B—Complete the statement. Choose the more reasonable measure. A giraffe is 5 ___ tall. m km
5 km would be a distance between towns, so **meters** is the reasonable measure.

▶ Think and Discuss Answers

1. Answer will depend on the size of the student's notebook.

2. Examples are: *mm*—thickness of a magazine; *cm*—length of a pencil; *m*—length of a room; *km*—distance between two cities.

3. 80; 75; 85

4.3 Measuring Length with Metric Units

James was in charge of getting trophies engraved for a sports banquet. When Coach Walker looked at the trophies, he exclaimed, "Let me see the list you gave the engraver. Somebody made a big mistake!"

What was the mistake? Were the measurements reasonable?

Examples

To measure length, line up one end of a measuring stick with one end of an object. Depending on the precision you need, you can round to the nearest millimeter, centimeter, or meter.

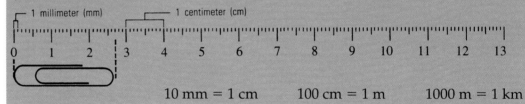

10 mm = 1 cm   100 cm = 1 m   1000 m = 1 km

A Measure the paper clip to the nearest centimeter.

The paper clip is closer to **3 centimeters** than 2 centimeters.

B Choose the more reasonable measure.

A man is 2 ___ tall. m km
The more reasonable measure is **meters**.

Two kilometers would be a distance between towns.

▶ Think and Discuss

1. Measure the length of your notebook to the nearest centimeter.

2. Name objects that can be measured in mm, cm, m, and km.

3. To the nearest cm, a bolt is 8 cm long. 8 cm = ___ mm. The bolt is at least ___ mm long but not as long as ___ mm.

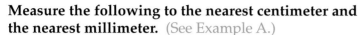

★ **Error Alert**
Mistakes in measuring may occur when students do not begin at the zero mark on the ruler.

Exercises

Measure the following to the nearest centimeter and the nearest millimeter. (See Example A.)

4. the length of the line segment ————————————
   6 cm; 58 mm

5. the length of your shoe
   Answers may range from 20 to 35 centimeters and 200 to 350 millimeters.

6. the distance from your wrist to your elbow
   Answers may range from 20 to 30 centimeters and 200 to 300 millimeters.

Complete each statement. Choose the more reasonable measure. (See Example B.)

7. The length of a public swimming pool is 25 ___ .   cm   (m)

8. The width of your palm is 8 ___ .   mm   (cm)

9. The length of a classroom is 10 ___ .   (m)   km

▶ **Mixed Practice** (For more practice, see page 414.)

Measure the following to the nearest centimeter and the nearest millimeter.

10. the height of the frame at the right   4 cm; 38 mm

11. the width of the frame at the right   4 cm; 39 mm

12. the length of a sheet of notebook paper
   Answers might include: 28 cm; 279 mm

Complete each statement. Choose the more reasonable measure.

13. A cat's nose is about 2 ___ wide.   mm   (cm)

14. A marathon is about 40 ___ .   m   (km)

▶ **Applications**

15. Measure the length, width, and height of your desk to the nearest centimeter and the nearest millimeter.
   Answers may include: l = 70 cm; 700 mm
   w = 50 cm; 500 mm h = 70 cm; 700 mm

16. Juan's goal is to swim a kilometer every day. If the length of the pool is 25 meters, how many lengths must he swim?
   40 lengths

▶ **Review** (Lessons 1.9, 1.11)

Add or subtract.

17. 6.88 + 3.29 10.17	**18.** 567,564 + 78,946 646,510	**19.** 0.876 + 2.45 3.326	**20.** 7 − 3.459 3.541
21. 8007 − 414 7593	**22.** 25 + 5.06 30.06	**23.** 3.004 − 1.927 1.077	**24.** 97.03 − 8.174 88.856

Reinforcement
Extra Practice, page 414
EP/MR Worksheet 34, TRB, page 34

Challenge
Think of an object you usually have with you to use as an approximate measure for 1 mm, 1 cm, and 1 m. (answers: thickness of a dime, width of little fingernail, distance from tip of nose to end of middle finger of an extended arm)

Objectives

- To estimate the time required for an object to fall given distances
- To investigate patterns

Purpose

In science, you may not be able to experiment with all possible situations. This lesson shows you how to make a table of results found in your experiments, so you can find a rule.

Introducing the Lesson

Review estimating sums, differences, and products (Lessons 1.12, 2.6) and making a plan to solve a problem (Lesson 2.5).

Discuss the purpose of experimentation in science. (to discover an unknown effect or law, to test or establish a hypothesis, or to illustrate a known law) Ask students to give examples of experiments they have heard of or conducted. (sample answers: Benjamin Franklin's experiments with the kite and electricity, breathing on a mirror to show the condensation of water from your breath, growing plants in both sunlight and darkness to show the effects of light on growth)

Note: Galileo's experiment works in a vacuum. Air resistance is a factor with objects that are not very dense. This explains why a feather does not fall like a brick.

Answers

1. You might conduct this experiment by dropping an object from various heights and timing the drops.

4.4 Measuring in Science

Suppose you hold a heavy stone and a light stone at eye level and drop them both. Which will hit the ground first? The scientist Galileo discovered that they will both hit the ground at the same time. But just how long would it take for the stones to reach the ground? More than 1 second? Less than 1 second? Estimate.

Mrs. Gravity's physical science class tried an experiment. They wanted to know how high above the ground a marble should be so that it would take exactly 1 second to reach the ground.

1. How might you conduct such an experiment?

The students were surprised by the results. They discovered that the answer is about 5 meters.

2. Look at a meter stick in your classroom. Are you 5 meters tall? Is your school building? How many meters above the ground is a basketball hoop? No; perhaps; about 3 m

3. Is anyone so tall that a marble dropped at eye level would take a full second to reach the ground? No

4. Estimate the height, in meters, of the tallest student in the class. How many centimeters is this? How many kilometers? 2 m; 200 cm; 0.002 km

5. If it takes 1 second for an object to fall 5 meters, estimate how long a drop of 10 meters would take. Answers will vary.

The students in Mrs. Gravity's science class wondered about the answer to Question 5. "A drop of 5 meters takes 1 second, so for 10 meters, it's 2 seconds. It's obvious!" stated Rhonda.

Mrs. Gravity didn't agree. "Let's test it out. Let's take a field trip tomorrow. There's a well in my backyard that's about 10 meters deep. Rhonda, bring your stopwatch."

PROBLEM SOLVING

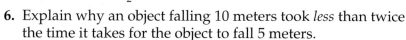

The next day, they dropped a stone down the well and listened for the splash. "Less than 2 seconds? Do it again!" Rhonda protested. They conducted the experiment several times, with both small rocks and large ones. Each time, it took about $1\frac{1}{2}$ seconds.

6. Explain why an object falling 10 meters took *less* than twice the time it takes for the object to fall 5 meters.

A science book stated that from the top of the Empire State Building, a stone would take about 8 seconds to reach the ground. The Empire State Building has a height of about 300 meters.

7. Give the height of the Empire State Building in centimeters and then in kilometers. 30,000 cm; 0.3 km

The class made a table like the one below. They used the table to look for a pattern.

Height in meters	5	10	300
Time of fall in seconds	1	1.5	8

8. Estimate the height of a cliff if a stone, dropped from the edge, took 4 seconds to reach the bottom. ≈80 m

9. A tree is about 30 meters tall. Estimate how long it would take an acorn to fall from the top to the ground. ≈2.5 seconds

10. Complete the table below. Work with 2 or 3 classmates. Discuss your estimation.

Height in meters	5	▦	▦	80	▦	▦	▦	300
Time of fall in seconds	1	2	3	4	5	6	7	8

20; 45; 125; 175; 240

Compare your group's answers with those of other groups.

11. A football is kicked about 25 yards straight up into the air. About how long is the ball in the air? ≈3 seconds

▶ **Review** (Lesson 2.6)

Estimate.

12. 19×58
1200

13. 72×103
7000

14. 194×83
16,000

15. 312×47
15,000

16. 986×68
70,000

17. $\begin{array}{r} 87 \\ \times 63 \\ \hline 5400 \end{array}$

18. $\begin{array}{r} 78 \\ \times 62 \\ \hline 4800 \end{array}$

19. $\begin{array}{r} 367 \\ \times 431 \\ \hline 160,000 \end{array}$

20. $\begin{array}{r} 627 \\ \times 832 \\ \hline 480,000 \end{array}$

21. $\begin{array}{r} 782 \\ \times 918 \\ \hline 720,000 \end{array}$

Reinforcement
EP/MR Worksheet 35, TRB, page 35

Challenge
Can you show that every number from 1 to 20 is either a square or the sum of two or three squares? For example: 1 is a square; 5 = 4 + 1 and is therefore the sum of two squares; 11 = 9 + 1 + 1 and is therefore the sum of three squares. **Hint: A square is the product of a number multiplied by itself.**
(answer: no; 7 is 1 + 1 + 1 + 1 + 4, the sum of four squares)

4.5 Metric Units of Mass

"**D**id you know," Pat asked Eileen, "that if I moved to Europe I'd weigh only 47 kilograms? Doesn't that sound great?" "No thanks," said Eileen, who wants to gain weight. "I'll stick with pounds." Pat thought for a moment. "Well then, how does 47,000 grams sound?" "Now you're talking," laughed Eileen.

Examples

To convert from one unit of mass to another, first determine if you are converting to a larger or smaller unit.

Equivalents	Abbreviations	
1 gram = 1000 milligrams	milligram **mg**	kilogram **kg**
1 kilogram = 1000 grams	gram **g**	metric ton **T**
1 metric ton = 1000 kilograms		

A Convert 47,000 grams to kilograms.

Divide since you are changing to a larger unit.

1000 g = 1 kg, so 47,000 g = 47.000 kg or **47 kg.**

B Complete the statement. Choose the more reasonable measure.

A frozen turkey has the mass of about 9 _____ . g kg

A large paper clip has the mass of about 1 gram.
A hammer has the mass of about 1 kilogram.

A turkey is fairly heavy.
The more reasonable measure is **kilograms.**

▶ **Think and Discuss**

1. Convert 6 kilograms to grams.

2. Convert 96,802 milligrams to grams.

3. How would you convert kilograms to milligrams?

4. Name two objects that might be measured using the following units: T, kg, g, mg.

Exercises

Convert each measure. (See Example A.)

5. 3700 mg to g 3.7 g

6. 4.2 kg to g 4200 g

7. 900 mg to g 0.9 g

8. 430 g to kg 0.430 kg

9. 750 kg to g 750,000 g

10. 0.7 kg to g 700 g

11. 8725 g to kg 8.725 kg

12. 36 mg to g 0.036 g

13. 45 kg to g 45,000 g

Complete each statement. Choose the more reasonable measure. (See Example B.)

14. The mass of a canary is about 220 ___ . ⓖ kg

15. The mass of a newborn baby is about 3.5 ___ . g ⓚg

▶ Mixed Practice (For more practice, see page 414.)

Convert each measure.

16. 8 kg to g
    8000 g

17. 500 g to kg
    0.500 kg

18. 37.5 kg to g
    37,500 g

19. 0.04 mg to g
    0.00004 g

20. 51 g to mg
    51,000 mg

21. 9257 mg to g
    9.257 g

Complete each statement. Choose the more reasonable measure.

22. The mass of a sewing needle is about 380 ___ . ⓜg g

23. The mass of a quarterback is about 80 ___ . g ⓚg

24. The mass of a pair of scissors is about 150 ___ . ⓖ kg

▶ Applications

25. The Great Pyramid is built of 2 million blocks of sandstone. The total mass of the pyramid is 4.6 million metric tons. Estimate the mass of each block. 2.3 T

26. Mr. Guzman brought eight kilograms of peanuts to be divided among his 32 students. How many grams of peanuts did each student get? 250 g

▶ Review (Lessons 2.8, 2.10)

Multiply

27. 8.1
    × 9.4
    ―――
    76.14

28. 0.75
    × 5.32
    ―――
    3.99

29. 0.004
    × 0.008
    ――――
    0.000032

30. 327
    × 4.7
    ―――
    1536.9

4.6 Metric Units of Capacity

The owner's manual for Jean's car states that she needs 4.75 liters of oil for each oil change. At the store she found containers of oil as shown here. How many containers should she buy?

Objectives

- To change metric units of capacity to larger or smaller units
- To choose reasonable units of capacity

Purpose

Many liquids, such as soft drinks and medicine, are commonly sold by metric units. This lesson helps you get a better sense of the meaning of these units.

Introducing the Lesson

If necessary, review: prefixes of metric measures (Lesson 4.1); multiplying and dividing by powers of 10 (Lessons 2.3, 2.8, 3.3); and the concept of reasonable measures (Lesson 4.3, 4.5).

Make sure students understand the difference between *mass* (how much something weighs) and *capacity* (how much something holds). Ask students for examples of items measured by capacity. (soft drinks, water, gasoline, liquid detergent)

Alternative Examples

Example A—Convert 6.81 L to mL.
1 L = 1000 mL, so 6.81 L = **6810 mL**

Example B—Complete the statement. Choose the more reasonable measure.
A bathtub holds about 80 ___ L mL.
A large bottle of a soft drink is 2 L.
A spoonful of cough syrup is 5 mL.
A tub holds a large amount of water, so the reasonable unit is **liters.**

Jean needs to convert metric units before she can determine the number of containers to buy.

Examples

To convert from one metric unit of capacity to another, first determine if you are converting to a larger or smaller unit.

Equivalent
1 liter = 1000 milliliters

Abbreviations
milliliter **mL**   liter **L**

A Convert 4.75 L to mL.

Multiply since you are changing to a smaller unit.
1 L = 1000 mL, so 4.75 L = **4750 mL.**

B Complete the statement. Choose the more reasonable measure.

A sink holds about 20 ___ .   L   mL

A large carton of milk could be measured in liters. A spoonful of vanilla or a small glass of juice could be measured in milliliters.

A sink holds a large amount of water, so the more reasonable unit is a **liter.**

▶ Think and Discuss

1. Convert 6.21 liters to milliliters.

2. Convert 0.3 milliliters to liters.

3. Refer to the introduction to this lesson. How many containers of oil does Jean need?

SKILLS

4. A kiloliter (kL) = 1000 L. What might be measured in kiloliters?

5. Which is larger, a 750-milliliter bottle or a 1-liter bottle?

Exercises

Convert each measure. (See Example A.)

6. 10.5 L to mL 10,500 mL   **7.** 43,000 mL to L 43 L   **8.** 0.75 L to mL 750 mL

9. 200 mL to L 0.2 L   **10.** 3 L to mL 3000 mL   **11.** 3750 mL to L 3.75 L

Complete each statement. Choose the more reasonable measure.
(See Example B.)

12. A thimble holds about 5 ___ of liquid.   L   (mL)

13. A gas tank has a capacity of about 60 ___ .   (L)   mL

14. A vase holds about 0.5 ___ of water.   (L)   mL

15. A can of soup contains about 500 ___ of liquid.   L   (mL)

▶ **Mixed Practice** (For more practice, see page 415.)

Convert each measure.

16. 50 mL to L 0.05 L   **17.** 45 L to mL 45,000 mL   **18.** 5500 mL to L 5.5 L

19. 9.3 L to mL 9300 mL   **20.** 483 mL to L 0.483 L   **21.** 0.8 L to mL 800 mL

Complete each statement. Choose the more reasonable measure.

22. An eyedropper can hold 10 ___ of fluid.   L   (mL)

23. A glass contains 250 ___ of milk.   L   (mL)

24. A large pitcher holds 2 ___ of water.   (L)   mL

25. A bottle of shampoo holds about 0.535 ___ .   (L)   mL

▶ **Applications**

26. A can of soup holds 350 milliliters. If Hank adds 3 cans of water to 3 cans of soup, how many liters of soup will he make? 2.1 L

27. Mike made 6 liters of punch for a party. If 82 ladles were served, how much punch was left? 96 mL

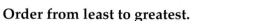

72 mL

▶ **Review** (Lessons 1.5, 1.6)

Order from least to greatest.

28. 53,462   5482   52,642   53,624   5842 5482 5842 52,642 53,462 53,624

29. 4.065   4.605   4.506   4.650   4.056 4.056 4.065 4.506 4.605 4.650

4.7 Using a Table to Find Information

Before you even open the envelope, you could start mentally planning your trip with the help of a map and a kilometer table.

Use the kilometer table to answer the following questions.

1. How far is it from Alice Springs to Perth? Look down the column from Alice Springs until you come to the row that goes across to Perth. 3772 km

2. Which city is 2853 kilometers from Sydney? Find 2853 in the row that goes across to Sydney, and see which city is at the head of that column. Cairns

3. Which two cities are 755 kilometers apart? Find 755 in the table, and read the cities for that column and row. Adelaide, Melbourne

For part of your trip, you plan to take trains. Below is a train schedule for four cities. Each train is named after one of the special animals of Australia.

Train	Arrives at Sydney	Arrives at Wollongong	Arrives at Canberra	Arrives at Melbourne
Kangaroo	8:30 a.m.	10:00 a.m.	11:50 a.m.	4:30 p.m.
Wallaby	12:00 noon	1:40 p.m.	3:45 p.m.	8:45 p.m.
Koala	4:00 p.m.	5:30 p.m.	7:15 p.m.	11:30 p.m.

Use the train schedule to answer the following questions.

4. What time does the Wallaby arrive at Canberra? 3:45 p.m.

5. About how long is the trip from Sydney to Wollongong? Is it the same for all three trains? 1 hour and 30 minutes or 1 hour and 40 minutes; it is not always the same

6. It is 11:00 a.m. in Canberra. How long will it be until the next train to Melbourne leaves? 50 minutes

7. The trip from Canberra to Melbourne is about 500 kilometers. Use the schedule to find how long the trip on the Koala takes. Then estimate how fast the train travels.
4 hours and 15 minutes; about 118 km/hr

For another part of your trip, you plan to rent a car. The table below shows how far you can go, in kilometers, on a single tank of gasoline, depending on the size of the car's gas tank and the car's kilometer-per-liter rating.

Size of Tank	Maximum Distance (per tank of gas)			
	5.9 km/L	7.8 km/L	9.9 km/L	13.7 km/L
32 L	188.8	249.6	316.8	438.4
40 L	236	312	396	548
50 L	295	390	495	685
65 L	383.5	507	643.5	890.5

Use the table above to answer the following questions.

8. What is the greatest distance you can travel on one tank of gasoline if your tank holds 40 liters and your car averages 7.8 kilometers per liter? 312 km

9. On one tank, how far could you go in a car with a 32-liter tank that averages 5.9 kilometers per liter? How much farther could you go in a car with a 65-liter tank that averages 13.7 kilometers per liter? 188.8 km; 890.5 − 188.8 = 701.7 km

▶ **Review** (Lesson 3.8)

10. Each section of a theater seats 175 people. There are 8 sections. What operation would you use to find how many seats are in the theater? How many seats are there?
Multiplication; 1400 seats

Objectives

- To make a table that organizes information
- To use the table to solve problems

Purpose

Sometimes, you may need to compare information to make a decision about where to go, what to do, or how much money to spend. Making a table can help you organize and compare information and then make a reasonable decision.

Introducing the Lesson

If necessary, review multiplying decimals by powers and multiples of 10 (Lesson 2.7). Use the examples: $0.03 × 10 = ($0.30); $0.23 × 100 = ($23.00)

Also, review using a table to find information (Lesson 4.7). Draw the following empty table on the chalkboard. Have students identify the rows and columns. Let the class fill in the rows and columns with information. (sample answers: rows = different types of vehicles; columns = color, size, purpose, number of passengers held)

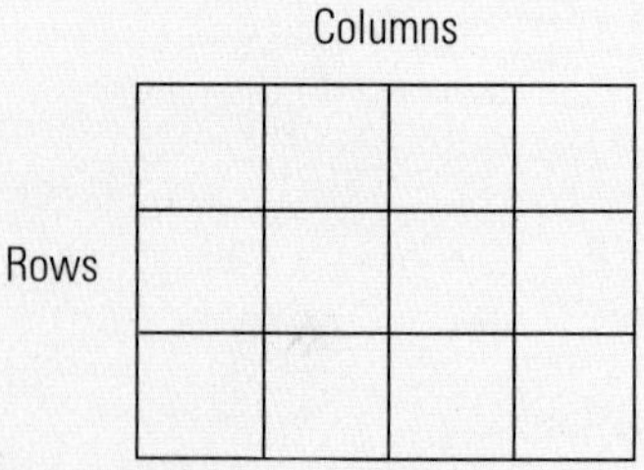

Answers

1. $490; $490; $300; $475
2. $490; $475
3. Deluxe Minijeep
4. The table should reflect information in the following order: ABC—$140, $600, $740; Land-rover—$490, 0, $490; Deluxe—$175; $450; $625
5. Landrover

4.8 Making a Table to Organize Information

Imagine that your free trip to Australia gives you the opportunity to visit the nearby island of Tasmania at your own expense. Since you only have one week to see the entire island, you decide to rent a jeep. The local Tasmanian newspaper contains the following ads.

9 Classifieds-Car Rentals TASMANIAN TIMES

ABC Jeep Rental	Landrover Jeep Rental	Deluxe Minijeep
$20 per day	$70 per day	$175 per week
$0.15 per km	No kilometer charge	First 1000 km free then $0.15 per km

You plan to rent the jeep for 7 days and to drive about 3000 kilometers. You can make a table to help figure out the costs.

Company	Rental Cost for 7 days	Km Charges	Total 7-day Cost
ABC	7 × $20 = $140	3000 × $0.15 = $450	$590
Landrover	7 × $70 = ■	no charge	■
Deluxe Minijeep	$175	1000 km free 2000 × $0.15 = ■	■

1. Copy the table above and fill in the missing costs.
2. What would the total cost be with Landrover Jeep Rental? What would the total cost be with Deluxe Minijeep?
3. Which jeep has the lowest cost for 7 days and 3000 kilometers?
4. Suppose you plan to drive 4000 kilometers in the 7 days. Make a table that shows the rental costs, kilometer charges, and costs for the week with each company.
5. Based on your table from Question 4, which company should have the lowest cost for 7 days and 4000 kilometers?

There are three vacation packages for your trip through Tasmania.

Plan A: The bed-and-breakfast plan charges $24 per person for a room and morning meal.

Plan B: The motel-only plan charges $20 per person for a room.

Plan C: The vacation-entertainment plan charges $36 per person for a room, an evening meal, and evening entertainment.

You have budgeted the following amounts to spend when an item is not covered by a package: $6 for breakfasts, $8 for lunches, $12 for dinners, and $8 for each evening's entertainment.

6. Copy the table below, and fill in the missing amounts.

Plan	Room	Breakfast	Lunch	Evening Meal	Entertainment	Total Cost
Plan A	24	(included)	8	12	8	▨
Plan B	▨	6	▨	▨	▨	▨
Plan C	36	▨	▨	(included)	(included)	▨

7. Which plan gives the lowest total cost per day?

8. If you use Plan A for 2 days, Plan B for 3 days, and Plan C for 2 days, what will be your total cost?

9. If you make a reservation early, Plan A charges $20, Plan B charges $16, and Plan C charges $35. Make another table with the costs of rooms, meals, and entertainment using the advance registration costs.

10. Using the table for Question 9, decide which plan gives you the lowest total cost per day.

▶ Review (Lesson 2.11)

Solve. Did you use mental math, paper-and-pencil, or a calculator?

11. Find the cost per camera if 12 cameras cost $2880. $240; calculator

12. Divide 5800 by 100.
58; mental math

13. Find the sum $17 + 83 + 60 + 40$.
200; any choice

Chapter 4 Review

Vocabulary and Writing Practice
VW Worksheet 4, TRB, page 140

Calculator Activities
CA Worksheet 4, TRB, page 165

Enrichment
E Worksheet 4, TRB, pages 205–206

Real Life Applications
RL Worksheet 4, TRB, pages 239–240

Complete each statement. (Lesson 4.1)

1. The metric system is based on powers of ___ . 10

2. The three basic units in the metric system are ___ , ___ , and ___ . Meter; Liter; Gram

Convert each measure. (Lesson 4.2)

3. 24 cm to mm 240 mm
4. 7 m to cm 700 cm
5. 4.8 km to m 4800 m

6. 9.3 m to mm 9300 mm
7. 36.3 cm to m 0.363 m
8. 82.5 m to km 0.0825 km

9. 0.54 m to cm 54 cm
10. 1.98 cm to mm 19.8 mm
11. 0.36 km to cm 36,000 cm

Measure the line segments below to the nearest centimeter and the nearest millimeter. (Lesson 4.3)

12. _____
7 cm; 66 mm

13. _____
2 cm; 19 mm

Complete each statement. Choose the more reasonable measure.
(Lessons 4.3, 4.5, 4.6)

14. The distance across a small town is about 1 ___ . m (km)

15. The mass of a button is about 1 ___ . (g) kg

16. The capacity of a large glass jar is about 1 ___ . mL (L)

Convert each measure. (Lessons 4.5, 4.6)

17. 39 mL to L 0.039 L
18. 71 kg to g 71,000 g
19. 9.76 g to kg 0.00976 kg

20. 0.8 kg to g 800 g
21. 4.21 mL to L 0.00421 L
22. 5 kg to mg 5,000,000 mg

23. 0.41 g to kg 0.00041 kg
24. 32,840 mg to g 32.84 g
25. 4751 mg to kg 0.004751 kg

Make a table of the following information. Then use the table to answer the questions below. (Lessons 4.7, 4.8)

The areas in square miles of five island nations are as follows:
Fiji 7056 Australia 2,968,125 New Zealand 103,744
Madagascar 226,674 Japan 143,761.

26. Which country has the greatest area? The smallest? Australia; Fiji

27. Which two countries are closest in area? New Zealand; Japan

28. Which country is about twice the size of New Zealand? Madagascar

Answers

Table for questions 26–28

Country	Area in square miles
Fiji	7056
New Zealand	103,744
Japan	143,761
Madagascar	226,674
Australia	2,968,125

(Information may be entered in any order, but should include the above categories.)

Chapter 4 Test

TEST

Complete each statement. Choose the more reasonable measure.

1. A large milk carton contains about 4 ____ . mL (L)

2. The mass of a book is about 1 ____ . g (kg)

3. The length of a glove is about 23 ____ . mm (cm)

4. A sheet of paper is about 0.1 ____ thick. (mm) m

Make a table of the following information. Then use the table to answer the questions below.

The kangaroo is about 1.8 meters tall and has a mass of about 45 kilograms.
A koala is about 70 centimeters long and has a mass between 7 and 14 kilograms.
A platypus has a mass of about 2.3 kilograms. It is between 40 and 55 centimeters long.

5. Which mammal has the greatest mass? Kangaroo

6. How tall is the kangaroo in centimeters? 180 cm

7. What is the mass of the platypus in grams? 2300 g

8. How long is the koala in meters? 0.7 m

9. Three large koalas would have about the same mass as what other mammal? Kangaroo

Measure these lines to the nearest centimeter and the nearest millimeter.

10. ————————— 11. ———————————————
4 cm; 38 mm   6 cm; 57 mm

12. ———————————————————————
11 cm; 114 mm

Convert each measure.

13. 98 L to mL
98,000 mL

14. 11.6 g to kg
0.0116 kg

15. 492 mm to cm
49.2 cm

16. 3.8 kg to g
3800 g

17. 5.7 mL to L
0.0057 L

18. 91 cm to mm
910 mm

19. 64 mg to g
0.064 g

20. 225 m to km
0.225 km

21. 177 km to m
177,000 m

22. 4.2 L to mL
4200 mL

23. 53.9 km to m
53,900 m

24. 37 mm to m
0.037 m

Chapter Tests
Short Answer, Forms A and B, TRB, pages 279–280, 281–282
Multiple Choice, Forms A and B, TRB, pages 347–348, 349–350

Teaching Aids
Answer sheet
TA 8, TRB, page 161a
Teaching suggestions precede the Teaching Aids worksheets.

Answers
Table for questions 5–9

Mammal	Length	Mass
Kangaroo	1.8 m	45 kg
Koala	70 cm	7–14 kg
Platypus	40–55 cm	2.3 kg

Cumulative Test Chapters 1–4

▶ **Choose the letter that shows the correct answer. Round each number to the nearest**

1. tenth.
7.35
  a. 7.3
  b. 7.4
  c. 7.5
  d. not given

2. hundredth.
99.7928
  a. 99.80
  b. 100
  c. 99.79
  d. not given

3. thousand.
39,622
  a. 40,000
  b. 39,000
  c. 39,600
  d. not given

4. dollar.
$25.49
  a. $25.50
  b. $26
  c. $24
  d. not given

▶ **Compute.**

5. 900×800
  a. 72,000
  b. 7200
  c. 720,000
  d. not given

6. $679.4 \div 100$
  a. 67.94
  b. 67,940
  c. 6.794
  d. not given

7. 8.5×1000
  a. 85,000
  b. 0.085
  c. 8500
  d. not given

8. $9 \div 1000$
  a. 0.009
  b. 0.09
  c. 0.9
  d. not given

9. 6.7×0.3
  a. 2.01
  b. 201
  c. 20.1
  d. not given

10. $4515 \div 60$
  a. 75
  b. 85
  c. 71 R15
  d. not given

11. $903 - 265$
  a. 748
  b. 638
  c. 648
  d. not given

12.
$\begin{array}{r} 69,387 \\ + \ 45,879 \\ \hline \end{array}$
  a. 115,266
  b. 114,266
  c. 115,366
  d. not given

13.
$\begin{array}{r} 8 \\ - \ 5.87 \\ \hline \end{array}$
  a. 3.87
  b. 2.23
  c. 2.13
  d. not given

14.
$\begin{array}{r} 29 \\ \times \ 94 \\ \hline \end{array}$
  a. 2728
  b. 2027
  c. 2726
  d. not given

15. $0.49 + 5 + 3.9 + 7.672$
  a. 7.765
  b. 77.65
  c. 17.62
  d. not given

▶ **Write the standard numeral or decimal.**

16. thirty-five thousand, seventeen
    a. 350,017   **b.** 3517   **c.** 35,017   **d.** not given

17. two thousand and nine tenths
    a. 0.209   **b.** 2,009.9   **c.** 2,000.9   **d.** not given

18. eight hundred forty-four and twenty-two thousandths
    a. 800.4422   **b.** 844.22   **c.** 844.202   **d.** not given.

▶ **Compare. Use <, >, or =.**

19. 4.2 _____ 3.896   **20.** 573,652 _____ 572,978   **21.** 6.60 _____ 6.6
    a. <   **a.** <   **a.** <
    b. >   **b.** >   **b.** >
    c. =   **c.** =   **c.** =
    d. not given   **d.** not given   **d.** not given

▶ **Simplify.**

22. $9 \times 2 + 56 \div 8$
    a. 9.25   **b.** 25   **c.** 126   **d.** not given

23. $19 + 21 \div 3 - 6$
    a. 21   **b.** 7.33   **c.** 20   **d.** not given

▶ **Complete each statement. Choose the most reasonable measure.**

24. A high school student is about 1.75 _____ tall.
    a. cm   **b.** m   **c.** km

25. A small dog has a mass of about 5 _____ .
    a. kg   **b.** mg   **c.** g

26. A gas tank of a car contains about 60 _____ .
    a. mL   **b.** mg   **c.** L

▶ **Convert each measure.**

27. 91 mm to cm
    a. 9100 cm   **b.** 0.91 cm   **c.** 910 cm   **d.** not given

28. **0.765 kg to g**
    a. 765 g   **b.** 7.65 g   **c.** 765,000 g   **d.** not given

Open-Ended Questions

36. Scoring Rubric

4 explanation shows a good understanding of how to round prices and solve the problem, there are no computation errors, the meals are within the budget and presentation is organized.

3 shows a basic understanding of how to solve the problem, but uses trial and error rather than rounding and using mental math; there are some computation errors, but the meal is within the budget; the presentation shows some organization.

2 adds numbers to find the actual combinations; makes computation errors; meal may not be within the budget, the presentation is disorganized.

1 shows little or no understanding of how to solve the problem.

37. Scoring Rubric

4 computes each weekly salary by multiplying, and then comparing the products (Alberto — $223.75; Jesse — $300); gives clear explanation of how to increase Alberto's hours and decrease Jesse's hours so that they are more equitable, with supporting computation.

3 computes and compares salaries; explanation shows some understanding of how to find the midpoint between the two, but lacks support.

2 shows an understanding of how to solve the first part of the problem, but not the second part; some computation errors.

1 shows little or no understanding of how to solve the problem.

▶ **Choose the letter that shows the operation you would use to solve each problem.**

29. Alfonso works 9 hours a week and earns $6.95 an hour. How much does he earn in one week?

   a. division

   b. addition

   (**c.**) multiplication

   d. not given

30. Kiri ordered a cheeseburger for $1.15, a salad for $2.45, and two milkshakes for $0.85 each. What is the total cost?

   (**a.**) addition

   b. multiplication

   c. subtraction

   d. not given

31. Jonita and her family drove 1278 miles in four days. They drove the same number of miles each day. How many miles did they drive each day?

   a. multiplication

   (**b.**) division

   c. subtraction

   d. not given

32. Juan saw an ad for a car that gets 30.5 miles per gallon on the road. His family car gets only 22.9 miles per gallon. How many more miles per gallon does the car in the ad get?

   (**a.**) subtraction

   b. division

   c. addition

   d. not given

▶ **Solve.**

Apples sell for $0.89 a pound. Oranges cost $1.77 for three pounds. Bananas are being sold for four pounds for $1.

33. What is the cost of 6 pounds of apples?

   a. $4.34

   (**b.**) $5.34

   c. $0.15

   d. not given

34. What is the cost of 2 pounds of bananas?

   a. $2

   b. $0.75

   c. $4

   (**d.**) not given

35. What is the cost of 6 pounds of oranges, 3 pounds of apples, and 6 pounds of bananas?

   (**a.**) $7.71   **b.** $3.65   **c.** $8.19   **d.** not given

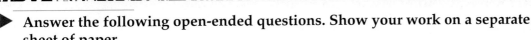

► **Answer the following open-ended questions. Show your work on a separate sheet of paper.**

36. Molly has $6.00 to spend for lunch. By rounding the cost of each item, find a balanced lunch combination of three items that she can buy. Find two balanced lunch combinations that can be purchased for $6.00. Explain how you found your answer. Show your work. Skills used—adding and subtracting whole numbers and decimals.

Seaside Snacks			
Hot dog	$1.49	Ice Cream	$1.29
Pizza	$1.25	with topping	$1.69
Taco	$2.29	Ices	$0.99
Chicken Salad	$2.89	Soda	$0.79
Tuna Salad	$3.89	Juice	$0.89
French Fries	$0.99	Chips	$0.99

37. Alberto and Jesse each have a summer job at the local video store. Alberto has experience and will operate the cash register for $8.95 per hour. He will work 25 hours per week. Jesse will stock the shelves and earn $7.50 per hour. He will work 40 hours per week. Who will earn more money, Alberto or Jesse? If you were the manager, how would you change their schedules so that each earned about the same amount? Explain how you found your answer. Show your work. Skills used—multiplying whole numbers and decimals

38. The Turner family is driving 3,410 miles from Miami to Seattle. Their car gets 24 miles per gallon of gas. Gas costs about $1.25 per gallon. If they allow $170.00 for gas for the trip, will they have enough money? Explain what steps you must take to solve this problem. Then, find the answer. Show your work. Skills used—dividing whole numbers and decimals

39. How many kilometers is it from Seattle to Washington DC?

How many kilometers is it from New York City to San Francisco?

Which is further from Salt Lake City, New York City or Seattle? How much further?
Skills used—using a table to find information

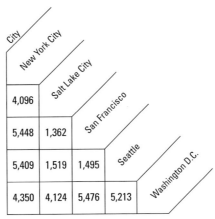

Driving Distances
(Distances shown in kilometers)

40. Every morning Davida jogs $\frac{5}{8}$ of a mile from her house to the high school and back. Crystal jogs from her house to the high school and back for a total distance of 1.35 miles. Who jogs the longer distance? Explain how you found your answer. Show your work. Skills used—converting fractions to decimals and comparing fractions

Open-Ended Questions (continued)
38. Scoring Rubric
4 clearly explains all the steps of the problem beginning with division, then multiplication, then comparison; computation is correct (gas costs $212.50, they are $42.50 short).
3 shows a basic understanding of how to solve the problem, but misplaces the decimal point, OR solves the problem, but does not provide an adequate explanation.
2 shows limited understanding of the steps involved in solving the problem; makes computation errors.
1 shows little or no understanding of how to solve the problem.

39. Scoring Rubric
4 reads the chart and solves the problem correctly.
3 finds the distances between cities, but makes computational errors.
2 finds some of the distances between cities, which results in incorrect answers.
1 shows little or no understanding of how to read the chart or solve the problem.

40. Scoring Rubric
4 computes and compares each runner's distance, converting between fractions and decimals; gives a clear explanation and computes correctly.
3 shows an understanding of how to solve the problem, but makes a calculation error.
2 calculates Davida's distance correctly, but makes some errors when converting between fractions and decimals.
1 shows no understanding of how to compute Davida's total distance or compare the two distances.

Materials: pencils, papers, computer with Internet access

Procedure: Organize students into four groups. Students write a letter to an environmentalist or a related professional.

• All students brainstorm interview-type questions to place in the letter. The categories of questions should include those in the job description: what an environmentalist does, the attributes necessary in the performance of duties, where one could work, what education is necessary to qualify for this type of work, related careers, and how math is used on the job.

• The first group compiles the best questions.

• The second group researches on the Internet for possible businesses to which the class can send the letter.

• The third group composes the letter, including a return address.

• The fourth group reviews responses and reports on the results to the class.

Use fractions and mixed numbers to describe

• time.

• shoe sizes.

• the quantities of ingredients in a recipe.

• the price of a stock.

What are some other ways to use fractions and mixed numbers?

Introducing Fractions and Mixed Numbers

An environmentalist works to protect wildlife and natural resources.

- Environmentalists work for city, state, and federal governments; businesses; and research organizations.

- An environmentalist should appreciate natural resources and work for their survival.

- An environmentalist uses and applies natural resources statistics.

- To become an environmentalist, an individual completes a course of study in a four-year college program. Yet everyone can help protect the environment in many ways, including recycling.

- Related careers include environmental chemists, forest rangers, game wardens, gardeners, park maintenance workers, and conservationists.

CAREER

ENVIRONMENTALIST

PORTFOLIO PROJECT: *Investigate a budget for waste management.*

1. Research to find the name of a major corporation in your area.

2. Write a formal business letter to the waste-management division of the company, asking what its budget is and how much money is spent on recycling.

ENTRANCE ←
♻ RECYCLE CENTER

3. Convert the results to a fraction, reduced to lowest terms. *Show the math.*

BUDGET PROPOSAL

About the Portfolio Project

Students should know enough about the general locale to suggest names of major corporations located within a 25-mile radius. Each student chooses a business and writes a formal business letter to the waste-management division of the company. Make sure each letter contains both a request for a budget with the suggested specifics and the school's return address for immediate reply. (A stamped, self-addressed envelope for a return reply will speed the process.) On a separate paper, students can identify the company, label the information they have received, and figure out the math.

Assessment: The individual scoring rubric on page 161 of the Teacher's Resource Binder can be reproduced and used for assessment. Include the following information in the last two boxes. Students should have:
- made the request, in formal business letter form, for a copy of a budget.
- accurately converted the monetary information to a fraction of the total budget in lowest terms.

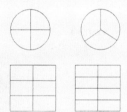
5.1 Understanding Fractions

What might have caused the confusion in the situation above?

When you use the fraction $\frac{1}{2}$, you know that something is divided into two equal parts. But $\frac{1}{2}$ of a 12-inch sandwich and $\frac{1}{2}$ of a 6-foot sandwich are quite different in size.

Numbers such as $\frac{1}{2}$, $\frac{1}{4}$, $\frac{3}{8}$, and $\frac{99}{100}$ are fractions.

▶ Express Yourself

fraction a number that names part of a whole or part of a group. A fraction consists of a numerator and a denominator.

numerator → 3 This fraction is read as "three-fourths"
denominator → 4 or "three-quarters."

A fraction can be used to describe how much of a picture is shaded. Use the numerator to tell how many parts are shaded. Use the denominator to tell the number of parts that make up the whole.

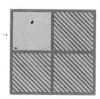

Write a fraction for the shaded part in each picture.

1.

2.

3.

4.

Knowing the following terms will help you when you work with fractions.

proper fraction　a fraction with a numerator less than the denominator; $\frac{2}{5}$, $\frac{14}{15}$, and $\frac{99}{100}$ are proper fractions.

improper fraction　a fraction with a numerator greater than or equal to the denominator; $\frac{11}{7}$, $\frac{50}{25}$, and $\frac{8}{8}$ are improper fractions.

mixed number　a number with a whole-number part and a fractional part; $4\frac{3}{5}$ and $12\frac{7}{12}$ are mixed numbers.

Identify each number below as either a proper fraction, an improper fraction, or a mixed number.

5. $\frac{1}{3}$　　6. $4\frac{2}{5}$　　7. $\frac{4}{7}$　　8. $\frac{11}{6}$　　9. $\frac{10}{10}$　　10. $1\frac{1}{4}$　　11. $\frac{6}{11}$

12. $\frac{2}{3}$ is read as "two-thirds." $\frac{3}{4}$ is read as "three-fourths." How is $\frac{4}{5}$ read? How is $\frac{4}{15}$ read?

13. Name five things, each of which is made up of equal parts. How might you use a fraction to describe the parts?

▶ **Practice What You Know**

When you work with fractions, you use multiplication facts to find the factors of numerators and denominators.

factors　numbers that are multiplied

$1 \times 6 = 6$　　$2 \times 3 = 6$
$6 \times 1 = 6$　　$3 \times 2 = 6$

The factors of 6 are 1, 2, 3, and 6.

14. Find the factors of 12.　　15. Find the factors of 28.

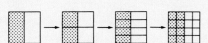
5.2 Finding Equivalent Fractions

Everyone thought Francine was an excellent chef, until the day she made chili for her family. Suddenly everyone turned bright red and started coughing. "This stuff is *hot*!" her brother managed to choke out. Francine immediately knew what was wrong. The recipe called for $\frac{3}{8}$ teaspoon of hot sauce and she had added $\frac{3}{4}$ teaspoon.

To figure out how much extra hot pepper sauce she had added, Francine could find an equivalent fraction for $\frac{3}{4}$.

Examples

To find an equivalent fraction, multiply or divide the numerator and denominator by the same number.

A Find 3 fractions equivalent to $\frac{3}{4}$.

$\frac{3 \times 2}{4 \times 2} = \frac{6}{8}$ $\frac{3 \times 3}{4 \times 3} = \frac{9}{12}$ $\frac{3 \times 4}{4 \times 4} = \frac{12}{16}$ $\frac{3}{4} = \frac{6}{8} = \frac{9}{12} = \frac{12}{16}$

$\frac{3}{4}, \frac{6}{8}, \frac{9}{12}$, and $\frac{12}{16}$ are equivalent fractions.

B Use division to find a fraction equivalent to $\frac{20}{25}$.

$\frac{20 \div 5}{25 \div 5} = \frac{4}{5}$ $\frac{20}{25} = \frac{4}{5}$

$\frac{4}{5}$ is equivalent to $\frac{20}{25}$.

▶ Think and Discuss

1. Use division to find a fraction equivalent to $\frac{9}{21}$.

2. Refer to the introduction to this lesson. How many $\frac{1}{8}$ teaspoonfuls did Francine actually add?

SKILLS

3. What number do you multiply the numerator and the denominator of $\frac{3}{8}$ by to get $\frac{12}{32}$?

4. How many fractions are equivalent to $\frac{3}{8}$?

Exercises

Find 3 fractions equivalent to each fraction. (See Example A.)

5. $\frac{1}{2}$ 6. $\frac{1}{4}$ 7. $\frac{5}{4}$ 8. $\frac{4}{9}$ 9. $\frac{6}{7}$ 10. $\frac{5}{8}$

11. $\frac{1}{6}$ 12. $\frac{5}{9}$ 13. $\frac{3}{5}$ 14. $\frac{2}{3}$ 15. $\frac{1}{8}$ 16. $\frac{6}{5}$

Use division to find a fraction equivalent to each fraction.
(See Example B.)

17. $\frac{3}{6}$ $\frac{1}{2}$

18. $\frac{4}{8}$ $\frac{1}{2}$ or $\frac{2}{4}$

19. $\frac{12}{16}$ $\frac{6}{8}$ or $\frac{3}{4}$

20. $\frac{10}{15}$ $\frac{2}{3}$

21. $\frac{6}{27}$ $\frac{2}{9}$

22. $\frac{32}{24}$ $\frac{16}{12}$ $\frac{8}{6}$ or $\frac{4}{3}$

23. $\frac{4}{10}$ $\frac{2}{5}$

24. $\frac{6}{18}$ $\frac{3}{9}$ $\frac{2}{6}$ or $\frac{1}{3}$

25. $\frac{25}{20}$ $\frac{5}{4}$

26. $\frac{28}{38}$ $\frac{14}{19}$

27. $\frac{60}{72}$ $\frac{30}{36}$ $\frac{15}{18}$ or $\frac{5}{6}$

28. $\frac{25}{45}$ $\frac{5}{9}$

▶ Mixed Practice (For more practice, see page 415.)

29. Find 3 fractions equivalent to $\frac{1}{3}$.

30. Find 3 fractions equivalent to $\frac{7}{8}$.

31. Find a fraction equivalent to $\frac{36}{24}$.

32. Find a fraction equivalent to $\frac{9}{21}$.

33. Find 3 fractions equivalent to $\frac{1}{10}$.

34. Find a fraction equivalent to $\frac{16}{20}$.

▶ Applications

35. Charles bought 18 cans from the case shown here. Write a fraction equivalent to $\frac{18}{24}$. $\frac{3}{4}$

36. There are 16 ounces in a pound. Using equivalent fractions, find how many ounces are in $\frac{1}{4}$ pound. 4 ounces

37. A yard is divided into 36 inches. Using equivalent fractions, find how many inches are in $\frac{2}{3}$ yard.
24 inches

▶ Review (Lesson 1.9)

Add.

38. $\begin{array}{r} 67 \\ + 29 \\ \hline 96 \end{array}$

39. $\begin{array}{r} 583 \\ + 32 \\ \hline 615 \end{array}$

40. $\begin{array}{r} 79 \\ + 8 \\ \hline 87 \end{array}$

41. $\begin{array}{r} 494 \\ + 344 \\ \hline 838 \end{array}$

42. $\begin{array}{r} 91 \\ + 36 \\ \hline 127 \end{array}$

5.3 Writing Fractions and Mixed Numbers

A man went into a pizza parlor. "I'm starved!" he called to the chef. "Give me a large pizza to go." As the chef pulled the pizza from the oven, he asked, "Do you want that cut into six pieces or eight pieces?" "Six is plenty," replied the man. "I couldn't possibly eat eight!"

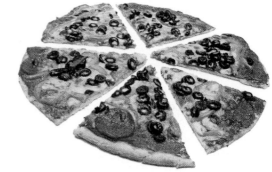

Did the man understand fractions? Which is more, $\frac{6}{6}$ or $\frac{8}{8}$ pizza?

Examples

To write fractions and mixed numbers, identify the parts and the whole.

A Write 2 as an improper fraction with a denominator of 8.

$2 = \frac{2}{1}$ Write 2 over a denominator of 1.

$2 = \frac{2 \times 8}{1 \times 8} = \frac{16}{8}$ Multiply the numerator and denominator by 8.

$2 = \frac{16}{8}$

B Write $2\frac{1}{6}$ as an improper fraction.

$2\frac{1}{6} = 2 + \frac{1}{6}$ Write the whole number as an improper fraction.

$2\frac{1}{6} = \frac{12}{6} + \frac{1}{6} = \frac{13}{6}$ Add the numerators.

Shortcut: $2\frac{1}{6}$ $6 \times 2 = 12$
               $12 + 1 = 13$ Write 13 over the original denominator.

$2\frac{1}{6} = \frac{13}{6}$

C Write $\frac{23}{7}$ as a mixed number.

$\frac{23}{7} = 23 \div 7$

$$\begin{array}{r} 3\frac{2}{7} \\ 7\overline{)23} \\ -21 \\ \hline 2 \end{array} \qquad \text{Divide the numerator by the denominator.}$$

$\frac{23}{7} = 3\frac{2}{7}$

▶ Think and Discuss

1. Write $\frac{14}{5}$ as a mixed number.

2. Write 5 as 3 different improper fractions.

3. Refer to the introduction to this lesson. Explain why the man in the pizza shop might have been confused.

◢ Exercises

Write each whole number as an improper fraction.
(See Example A.)

4. $4 = \frac{\blacksquare}{4}$ $\frac{16}{4}$ 5. $10 = \frac{\blacksquare}{5}$ $\frac{50}{5}$ 6. $16 = \frac{\blacksquare}{8}$ $\frac{128}{8}$ 7. $24 = \frac{\blacksquare}{2}$ $\frac{48}{2}$ 8. $100 = \frac{\blacksquare}{9}$ $\frac{900}{9}$

Write each mixed number as an improper fraction.
(See Example B.)

9. $4\frac{5}{6}$ $\frac{29}{6}$ 10. $10\frac{3}{4}$ $\frac{43}{4}$ 11. $2\frac{7}{8}$ $\frac{23}{8}$ 12. $5\frac{3}{8}$ $\frac{43}{8}$ 13. $3\frac{3}{9}$ $\frac{30}{9}$

Write each quotient as a whole or mixed number. (See Example C.)

14. $\frac{7}{3}$ $2\frac{1}{3}$ 15. $9\overline{)33}$ $3\frac{6}{9}$ 16. $\frac{45}{5}$ 9 17. $\frac{55}{4}$ $13\frac{3}{4}$ 18. $12\overline{)65}$ $5\frac{5}{12}$ 19. $\frac{72}{10}$ $7\frac{2}{10}$

▶ Mixed Practice (For more practice, see page 416.)

Write each improper fraction as a whole or mixed number.

20. $\frac{19}{6}$ $3\frac{1}{6}$ 21. $\frac{10}{2}$ 5 22. $\frac{31}{5}$ $6\frac{1}{5}$ 23. $\frac{35}{10}$ $3\frac{5}{10}$ 24. $\frac{7}{7}$ 1

Write each mixed or whole number as an improper fraction.

25. $4\frac{3}{7}$ $\frac{31}{7}$ 26. $1\frac{3}{4}$ $\frac{7}{4}$ 27. 3 $\frac{3}{1}, \frac{6}{2}, \frac{9}{3},$ etc.   28. $9\frac{2}{3}$ $\frac{29}{3}$ 29. $1\frac{15}{16}$ $\frac{31}{16}$

▶ Applications

30. Juice comes in packages of 6 cartons. If Quentin has 7 full packages and one that is $\frac{5}{6}$ full, how many cartons does he have? 47 cartons

31. The maximum capacity of an elevator is shown here. If ninety-two people are waiting, what is the least number of trips needed to get everyone to the top? 8 trips

EMPIRE STATE BUILDING ELEVATOR CAPACITY 12 PEOPLE

▶ Review (Lessons 4.2, 4.5, 4.6)

Convert each measure.

32. 43 g to kg 0.043 kg   33. 8.9 m to cm 890 cm   34. 319 mL to L 0.319 L

Objectives

- To compare fractions with the same denominator
- To compare fractions with different denominators
- To compare mixed numbers

Purpose

Comparing fractions and mixed numbers is useful in comparing prices or amounts. For example: Is $\frac{1}{2}$ off the price of an item a better deal than $\frac{2}{3}$ off? Is $2\frac{2}{3}$ yards of canvas more than $2\frac{3}{4}$ yards?

Introducing the Lesson

If necessary, review with the symbols $>$ (greater than) and $<$ (less than).

Have students find the locations of the following measurements on a ruler: $1\frac{1}{2}$ in., $\frac{12}{8}$ in., and $\frac{6}{4}$ in. Ask: What can you say about the location of each measurement on the ruler? (The locations are the same.) How do the values of the mixed number and the improper fractions in the above example compare? (They are the same.)

Alternative Examples

Example A—Compare. $\frac{4}{7}$ ▨ $\frac{6}{7}$
Compare the numerators: $4 < 6$.
$\frac{4}{7} < \frac{6}{7}$

Example B—Compare. $\frac{5}{7}$ ▨ $\frac{4}{6}$
Use the same method as in Example B.
$\frac{5}{7} > \frac{4}{6}$

Example C—Compare. $1\frac{2}{7}$ ▨ $1\frac{1}{4}$
Use the same method as in Example C.
$1\frac{2}{7} > 1\frac{1}{4}$

▶ Think and Discuss Answers

1. $\frac{5}{6} > \frac{1}{6}$ 2. $\frac{5}{7} > \frac{7}{10}$
3. the recipe that called for $\frac{1}{3}$ cup of honey
4. Sample answers: tailor (measuring materials in fractions of yards); surveyor (measuring distances); and bookkeeper (computing payroll in time-and-a-half situations).

5.4 Comparing Fractions and Mixed Numbers

Korinne was about to make banana bread when she discovered that she was almost out of honey. She found one recipe that called for $\frac{1}{3}$ cup of honey, and another that called for $\frac{3}{8}$ cup of honey. Which recipe required less honey?

Examples

To compare fractions, rewrite the fractions with a common denominator and compare their numerators. Use $<$, $>$, or $=$.

A Compare. $\frac{5}{9}$ ▨ $\frac{7}{9}$

Compare the numerators.

$\frac{5}{9}$ ▨ $\frac{7}{9}$ $5 < 7$

$\frac{5}{9} < \frac{7}{9}$

B Compare. $\frac{3}{8}$ ▨ $\frac{1}{3}$

Rewrite the fractions with a common denominator. Compare numerators.

$\frac{3}{8}$ —— $\frac{1}{3}$ $\frac{3 \times 3}{8 \times 3} = \frac{9}{24}$

$\frac{1 \times 8}{3 \times 8} = \frac{8}{24}$

$\frac{9}{24}$ —— $\frac{8}{24}$

$\frac{3}{8} > \frac{1}{3}$ $9 > 8$

C Compare. $2\frac{5}{8}$ ▨ $2\frac{4}{7}$

First compare the whole number parts. Since $2 = 2$, compare the fractions.

$\frac{5}{8}$ —— $\frac{4}{7}$ $\frac{5 \times 7}{8 \times 7} = \frac{35}{56}$

$\frac{4 \times 8}{7 \times 8} = \frac{32}{56}$

$\frac{35}{56}$ —— $\frac{32}{56}$

$\frac{5}{8} > \frac{4}{7}$ $35 > 32$

▶ Think and Discuss

1. Compare $\frac{5}{6}$ and $\frac{1}{6}$.

2. Compare $\frac{5}{7}$ and $\frac{7}{10}$.

3. Refer to the introduction to this lesson. Which of Korinne's recipes required less honey?

4. Name three jobs that require knowledge of fractions. Describe how fractions are used in these jobs.

SKILLS

Exercises

Compare. Use <, >, or =. (See Example A.)

5. $\frac{3}{8}$ ___ $\frac{6}{8}$ <

6. $\frac{6}{7}$ ___ $\frac{5}{7}$ >

7. $\frac{9}{10}$ ___ $\frac{10}{10}$ <

8. $\frac{9}{16}$ ___ $\frac{5}{16}$ >

9. $\frac{2}{12}$ ___ $\frac{5}{12}$ <

10. $\frac{75}{78}$ ___ $\frac{76}{78}$ <

Compare. Use <, >, or =. (See Example B.)

11. $\frac{3}{5}$ ___ $\frac{6}{10}$ =

12. $\frac{7}{12}$ ___ $\frac{7}{14}$ >

13. $\frac{8}{9}$ ___ $\frac{9}{16}$ >

14. $\frac{7}{3}$ ___ $\frac{9}{5}$ >

15. $\frac{3}{4}$ ___ $\frac{3}{5}$ >

16. $\frac{5}{15}$ ___ $\frac{1}{3}$ =

17. $\frac{2}{7}$ ___ $\frac{6}{21}$ =

18. $\frac{2}{9}$ ___ $\frac{3}{10}$ <

Compare. Use <, >, or =. (See Example C.)

19. $4\frac{1}{2}$ ___ $4\frac{2}{4}$ =

20. $3\frac{3}{7}$ ___ $4\frac{3}{7}$ <

21. $2\frac{7}{9}$ ___ $2\frac{7}{8}$ <

22. $\frac{7}{3}$ ___ $2\frac{1}{3}$ =

23. $1\frac{3}{10}$ ___ $1\frac{4}{9}$ <

24. $3\frac{1}{2}$ ___ $\frac{9}{2}$ <

25. $2\frac{1}{4}$ ___ $\frac{5}{3}$ >

26. $8\frac{2}{5}$ ___ $5\frac{2}{5}$ >

▶ Mixed Practice (For more practice, see page 416.)

Compare. Use <, >, or =.

27. $\frac{3}{5}$ ___ $\frac{4}{5}$ <

28. $4\frac{1}{4}$ ___ $\frac{12}{4}$ >

29. $3\frac{2}{3}$ ___ $2\frac{2}{3}$ >

30. $2\frac{2}{7}$ ___ $1\frac{9}{7}$ =

31. $7\frac{1}{3}$ ___ $7\frac{3}{8}$ <

32. $\frac{9}{10}$ ___ $\frac{7}{10}$ >

33. $2\frac{1}{2}$ ___ $\frac{5}{2}$ =

34. $8\frac{2}{5}$ ___ $5\frac{2}{5}$ >

35. $\frac{4}{4}$ ___ $\frac{7}{7}$ =

36. $3\frac{1}{3}$ ___ $3\frac{1}{2}$ <

37. $6\frac{5}{6}$ ___ $\frac{42}{6}$ <

38. 6 ___ $\frac{36}{6}$ =

▶ Applications

39. Tony has completed two-thirds of his homework, Sue has completed three-fourths of her homework, and Greg has completed five-sixths of his homework. If they all have the same amount of homework, who has completed the most? Greg

40. Coralee has found these 3 pieces of fabric in the remnant bin. She wants to buy the longest piece. Which piece should she buy?
The middle piece

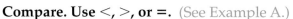

$2\frac{1}{2}$ yds. $2\frac{2}{3}$ yds. $2\frac{3}{8}$ yds.

▶ Review (Lessons 4.3, 4.5, 4.6)

Complete each sentence.

41. A chopstick has a length of about 24 ___ . (cm) km

42. A large thermos has a capacity of about 1 ___ . (L) mL

43. A baby has a mass of about 10 ___ . g (kg)

5.5 Factoring to Find the Greatest Common Factor

Breaking a number into its factors is the first step in writing fractions in lowest terms.

Examples

To find the greatest common factor (GCF) of 2 or more numbers, list the factors of each. The GCF is the greatest factor that is on both lists.

A List the factors of 20.

$1 \times \underline{20} = 20$ List the factors in order.

$2 \times \underline{10} = 20$

$3 \times \underline{\quad} = 20$ 3 is not a factor of 20.

$4 \times \underline{5} = 20$

$5 \times \underline{4} = 20$ When factors begin to repeat, you have found all factors.

The factors of 20 are **1, 2, 4, 5, 10, and 20.**

B Find the GCF of 12 and 16.

$12 = 1 \times 12$
$12 = 2 \times 6$
$12 = 3 \times 4$ The factors of 12 are 1, 2, 3, **4**, 6, and 12.

$16 = 1 \times 16$
$16 = 2 \times 8$
$16 = 4 \times 4$ The factors of 16 are 1, 2, **4**, 8, and 16.

The GCF of 12 and 16 is **4.**

▶ Think and Discuss

1. List the factors of 42.

2. Find the GCF of 24 and 36.

3. Describe the steps you would take to find the GCF of 3 whole numbers.

4. The factors of 2 are 1 and 2. Find the other whole numbers less than 20 that have exactly 2 factors.

Exercises

List the factors. (See Example A.)

5. 6   **6.** 10   **7.** 14   **8.** 15   **9.** 18   **10.** 36   **11.** 24

Find the GCF of each pair of numbers. (See Example B.)

12. 16   24 8   **13.** 12   8 4   **14.** 24   6 6   **15.** 27   21 3

16. 17   13 1   **17.** 20   100 20   **18.** 12   18 6   **19.** 36   27 9

▶ Mixed Practice (For more practice, see page 417.)

List the factors.

20. 5   **21.** 8   **22.** 45   **23.** 13   **24.** 48   **25.** 33   **26.** 64

Find the GCF of each pair of numbers.

27. 42   14 14   **28.** 7   38 1   **29.** 3   35 1   **30.** 10   15 5

31. 12   40 4   **32.** 9   33 3   **33.** 6   30 6   **34.** 18   60 6

▶ Applications

35. Square tiles are packed in cartons like the one shown here. To fit the cartons exactly, the length of each side must be a factor of both 16 and 24. What four sizes of tile fit the cartons exactly? 1 in., 2 in., 4 in., 8 in.

36. Mark's eldest sister, Pam, is eighteen years old. The GCF of Mark's and Pam's ages is nine. How old is Mark? 9 years old

▶ Review (Lessons 1.1, 1.2)

Write the standard numeral.

37. 66 thousand, 8 hundred 3
66,803

39. two million, ninety
2,000,090

38. 4 and 35 hundredths
4.35

40. 23 and 8 thousandths
23.008

▶ Think and Discuss Answers

1. 1, 2, 3, 6, 7, 14, 21, 42
2. 12
3. List the factors of the three numbers, then find the greatest factor common to all three lists.
4. 3, 5, 7, 11, 13, 17, 19

Answers

5. 1, 2, 3, 6   **6.** 1, 2, 5, 10

7. 1, 2, 7, 14   **8.** 1, 3, 5, 15

9. 1, 2, 3, 6, 9, 18

10. 1, 2, 3, 4, 6, 9, 12, 18, 36

11. 1, 2, 3, 4, 6, 8, 12, 24

20. 1, 5   **21.** 1, 2, 4, 8

22. 1, 3, 5, 9, 15, 45   **23.** 1, 13

24. 1, 2, 3, 4, 6, 8, 12, 16, 24, 48

25. 1, 3, 11, 33

26. 1, 2, 4, 8, 16, 32, 64

★ Error Alert

Mistakes may reveal that students need to review the basic multiplication facts.

Reinforcement

Extra Practice, page 417
EP/MR Worksheet 42, TRB, page 42

Puzzle

Form two teams and choose a scorekeeper. The scorekeeper draws a large square on the chalkboard and divides it into 36 equal squares, numbered left to right from 1 to 36. Team A begins by choosing a number from the square and receives points equal to the value of the number chosen. The scorekeeper crosses the number off the square. Team B then factors the chosen number and receives points equal to the value of each factor. The scorekeeper then crosses off the factors. Then Team B chooses a number and Team A factors it. The team factoring the number gets points only for factors that are not yet crossed off. For example, if Team A chooses the number 18, and 6 and 1 have already been crossed off, Team B can score only a maximum of 14 points (2 + 3 + 9). The game ends when all the numbers have been crossed off. The team with the highest score wins.

5.6 Writing Fractions in Lowest Terms

*"**L**et's see," said Tanya. "It's 4:30 now. I'll meet you in thirty-sixtieths of an hour."*

Tanya's friend may not know exactly when to meet her. Fortunately, most people express fractions of hours in lowest terms.

Examples

To write a fraction in lowest terms, find the GCF of the numerator and denominator. Divide both by their GCF.

A Write $\frac{8}{12}$ in lowest terms.

The factors of 8 are 1, 2, **4**, and 8.
The factors of 12 are 1, 2, 3, **4**, 6, and 12.
The GCF is 4.
$\frac{8}{12} = \frac{8 \div 4}{12 \div 4}$ Divide by the GCF.
$\frac{8}{12} = \frac{2}{3}$

B List the factors of 9 and 25. Write $\frac{9}{25}$ in lowest terms.

The factors of 9 are 1, 3, 9.
The factors of 25 are 1, 5, 25.
The GCF is 1.

$\frac{9}{25}$ is in lowest terms.

▶ Think and Discuss

1. In Example A, what was the GCF of 8 and 12?

2. Refer to the introduction to this lesson. What is a clearer way to express thirty-sixtieths of an hour?

3. A case of motor oil contains 24 cans. What part of a case is 6 cans of oil? Write your answer in lowest terms.

4. Which of the following fractions are in lowest terms?
$\frac{3}{6}$ $\frac{12}{8}$ $\frac{14}{24}$ $\frac{19}{38}$ $\frac{5}{2}$ $\frac{1}{8}$ $\frac{18}{33}$

5. Write the following improper fractions and mixed numbers in lowest terms.
$\frac{25}{9}$ $1\frac{3}{6}$ $\frac{14}{12}$ $6\frac{6}{8}$

6. Why is 25¢ called a quarter?

Exercises

Write in lowest terms. (See Example A.)

7. $\frac{4}{6}$ $\frac{2}{3}$ 8. $\frac{9}{18}$ $\frac{1}{2}$ 9. $\frac{6}{10}$ $\frac{3}{5}$ 10. $\frac{100}{300}$ $\frac{1}{3}$ 11. $\frac{8}{12}$ $\frac{2}{3}$ 12. $\frac{6}{9}$ $\frac{2}{3}$

13. $\frac{8}{14}$ $\frac{4}{7}$ 14. $\frac{6}{15}$ $\frac{2}{5}$ 15. $\frac{6}{20}$ $\frac{3}{10}$ 16. $\frac{18}{24}$ $\frac{3}{4}$ 17. $\frac{30}{90}$ $\frac{1}{3}$ 18. $\frac{5}{12}$ $\frac{5}{12}$

19. $\frac{15}{45}$ $\frac{1}{3}$ 20. $\frac{80}{160}$ $\frac{1}{2}$ 21. $\frac{18}{80}$ $\frac{9}{40}$ 22. $\frac{40}{42}$ $\frac{20}{21}$ 23. $\frac{15}{18}$ $\frac{5}{6}$ 24. $\frac{32}{48}$ $\frac{2}{3}$

25. $\frac{28}{21}$ $\frac{4}{3}$ 26. $\frac{72}{81}$ $\frac{8}{9}$ 27. $\frac{50}{125}$ $\frac{2}{5}$ 28. $\frac{30}{36}$ $\frac{5}{6}$ 29. $\frac{24}{15}$ $\frac{8}{5}$ 30. $\frac{72}{100}$ $\frac{18}{25}$

List the factors and write in lowest terms. (See Example B.)

31. $\frac{2}{5}$ 32. $\frac{1}{4}$ 33. $\frac{13}{14}$ 34. $\frac{8}{3}$ 35. $\frac{15}{16}$ 36. $\frac{24}{25}$

▶ Mixed Practice (For more practice, see page 417.)

Write in lowest terms.

37. $\frac{9}{12}$ $\frac{3}{4}$ 38. $\frac{14}{20}$ $\frac{7}{10}$ 39. $\frac{28}{35}$ $\frac{4}{5}$ 40. $\frac{18}{12}$ $\frac{3}{2}$ 41. $\frac{3}{8}$ $\frac{3}{8}$ 42. $\frac{25}{40}$ $\frac{5}{8}$

43. $\frac{5}{9}$ $\frac{5}{9}$ 44. $\frac{18}{10}$ $\frac{9}{5}$ 45. $\frac{55}{65}$ $\frac{11}{13}$ 46. $\frac{48}{72}$ $\frac{2}{3}$ 47. $\frac{12}{16}$ $\frac{3}{4}$ 48. $\frac{75}{100}$ $\frac{3}{4}$

49. $\frac{21}{24}$ $\frac{7}{8}$ 50. $\frac{18}{48}$ $\frac{3}{8}$ 51. $\frac{60}{48}$ $\frac{5}{4}$ 52. $1\frac{7}{21}$ $1\frac{1}{3}$ 53. $4\frac{4}{8}$ $4\frac{1}{2}$ 54. $\frac{35}{15}$ $\frac{7}{3}$

▶ Applications

55. Every Friday afternoon Marylu spends about 20 minutes cleaning her desk. What part of an hour is 20 minutes? Write your answer in lowest terms. $\frac{1}{3}$ hour

56. Fifteen bus lines run from the bus depot. Five lines go north, three lines go west, and the rest go south. What fraction of lines goes in each direction? Write your answers in lowest terms. $\frac{1}{3}$ go north; $\frac{1}{5}$ go west; $\frac{7}{15}$ go south

57. Manny bought two dozen eggs. On his way home, he tripped and fell. Eight eggs broke. What fractional part of the total was unbroken? Write your answer in lowest terms. $\frac{2}{3}$

▶ Review (Lesson 1.12)

Estimate each sum or difference.

58. $2564 + 8375$ $\approx 11,000$
59. $9281 - 6429$ ≈ 3000
60. $7723 + 8615$ $\approx 16,300$ or $17,000$
61. $10,942 - 3,751$ ≈ 7000
62. $15,180 + 25,372$ $\approx 40,000$

Answers

31. 2: 1, 2; 5: 1, 5; $\frac{2}{5}$
32. 1: 1; 4: 1, 2, 4; $\frac{1}{4}$
33. 13: 1, 13; 14: 1, 2, 7, 14; $\frac{13}{14}$
34. 8: 1, 2, 4, 8; 3: 1, 3; $\frac{8}{3}$
35. 15: 1, 3, 5, 15; 16: 1, 2, 4, 8, 16; $\frac{15}{16}$
36. 24: 1, 2, 3, 4, 6, 8, 12, 24; 25: 1, 5, 25; $\frac{24}{25}$

★ **Error Alert**
Mistakes may occur if students do not divide the numerator and the denominator by the same number when they convert fractions to lowest terms.

Reinforcement
Extra Practice, page 417
EP/MR Worksheet 43, TRB, page 43

Puzzle
Reduce the following fractions to lowest terms. Then use the code to find the answer to the riddle: How do bacteria multiply?

$\frac{16}{32}$ (B)
$\frac{155}{170}$ (Y)
$\frac{60}{108}$ (D)
$\frac{63}{84}$ (I)
$\frac{590}{708}$ (V)
$\frac{243}{324}$ (I)
$\frac{200}{360}$ (D)
$\frac{183}{244}$ (I)
$\frac{180}{270}$ (N)
$\frac{144}{176}$ (G)

Code: $\frac{2}{25}$ = S, $\frac{1}{12}$ = P, $\frac{2}{5}$ = M, $\frac{5}{9}$ = D, $\frac{1}{2}$ = B, $\frac{2}{3}$ = N, $\frac{3}{4}$ = I, $\frac{9}{11}$ = G, $\frac{5}{6}$ = V, $\frac{7}{8}$ = U, $\frac{31}{34}$ = Y, $\frac{12}{13}$ = E

- Two write fractions as terminating and repeating decimals
- To write decimals as fractions or mixed numbers
- To use a calculator to convert fractions to decimals

Purpose
Knowing how to write fractions as decimals and decimals as fractions enables you to compare a fraction and a decimal. This is useful when comparing two measurements, such as 0.70 pound and $\frac{3}{4}$ pound.

Introducing the Lesson
Review dividing decimals by whole numbers (Lesson 3.10). Use the examples:

$$5)\overline{3.0}\ (0.6) \qquad 5)\overline{9.0}\ (1.8) \qquad 2)\overline{1.0}\ (0.5)$$

Draw two equal-sized squares and write the decimal 0.5 on the chalkboard. Ask students to explain how they would shade in 0.5 of the square. Then write the fraction $\frac{1}{2}$ on the chalkboard. Ask: How would you shade in $\frac{1}{2}$ of the other square? Compare 0.5 and $\frac{1}{2}$. Convert 0.5 to $\frac{5}{10}$ and reduce it to lowest terms. ($\frac{5}{10} = \frac{1}{2}$)

 0.5 $\frac{1}{2}$

Alternative Examples

Example A—Write $\frac{2}{5}$ as a decimal. Use the same method as in Example A.
$\frac{2}{5} = \mathbf{0.4}$

Example B—Write $\frac{2}{3}$ as a decimal. Use the same method as in Example B.
$\frac{2}{3} = \mathbf{0.\overline{6}}$

Example C—Write 2.45 as a fraction. Use the same method as in Example C.
$2.45 = \mathbf{2\frac{9}{20}}$

Example D—Write $4\frac{3}{4}$ as a decimal. Use the same method as in Example D.
$4\frac{3}{4} = \mathbf{4.75}$

5.7 Writing Fractions and Decimals

Kelly and Benjamin were shopping for party snacks. At the dairy case Kelly asked how much cheese they needed for nachos. "Well," said Benjamin, "the recipe calls for $\frac{3}{4}$ pound of cheese, but these packages show decimal weights. How much should I buy?"

To find the answer, Benjamin can convert $\frac{3}{4}$ to a decimal.

Examples

To write a fraction as a decimal, divide the numerator by the denominator.

To write a decimal as a fraction, use a denominator that is a power of 10. Write the fraction in lowest terms.

A Write $\frac{3}{4}$ as a decimal.

$$\begin{array}{r} 0.7\ 5 \\ 4)\overline{3.0\ 0} \\ 2\ 8 \\ \hline 2\ 0 \\ 2\ 0 \\ \hline 0 \end{array}$$ Write zeros in the dividend.

$\frac{3}{4} = \mathbf{0.75}$

B Write $\frac{1}{3}$ as a decimal.

$$\begin{array}{r} 0.3\ 3 \\ 3)\overline{1.0\ 0} \\ 9 \\ \hline 1\ 0 \\ 9 \\ \hline 1 \end{array}$$ If you continue, you will always get 3.

$\frac{1}{3} = \mathbf{0.\overline{3}}$ A bar over the 3 means the 3 repeats.

C Write 3.25 as a mixed number.

3.25 is 3 and 25 hundredths.

$3.25 = 3 + \frac{25}{100} = 3\frac{25}{100} = 3\frac{1}{4}$

$3.25 = \mathbf{3\frac{1}{4}}$

D Write $2\frac{1}{2}$ as a decimal.

$2\frac{1}{2} = 2 + \frac{1}{2}$

$2\frac{1}{2} = 2 + 0.5$

$2\frac{1}{2} = \mathbf{2.5}$

$$\begin{array}{r} 0.5 \\ 2)\overline{1.0} \\ 1.0 \\ \hline 0 \end{array}$$

Think and Discuss

1. Write $\frac{1}{8}$ as a decimal.

2. Write 0.08 as a fraction in lowest terms.

3. On a calculator, $\frac{7}{11}$ is 0.6363636. Write this decimal as shown in Example B.

4. Refer to the introduction to this lesson. How much cheese should Benjamin buy?

SKILLS

Think and Discuss Answers
1. 0.125
2. $\frac{2}{25}$
3. $0.\overline{63}$
4. 0.75 pound

★ Error Alert
Mistakes may occur if students misplace the decimal point when dividing.

Exercises

Write as a decimal. (See Example A.)

5. $\frac{1}{2}$ 0.5   6. $\frac{1}{4}$ 0.25   7. $\frac{2}{5}$ 0.4   8. $\frac{5}{8}$ 0.625   9. $\frac{3}{5}$ 0.6   10. $\frac{7}{10}$ 0.7   11. $\frac{9}{16}$ 0.5625

Write as a decimal. (See Example B.)

12. $\frac{2}{3}$ $0.\overline{6}$ 13. $\frac{1}{6}$ $0.1\overline{6}$ 14. $\frac{2}{9}$ $0.\overline{2}$ 15. $\frac{5}{11}$ $0.\overline{45}$ 16. $\frac{5}{6}$ $0.8\overline{3}$ 17. $\frac{9}{11}$ $0.\overline{81}$ 18. $\frac{1}{15}$ $0.0\overline{6}$

Write as a fraction or mixed number in lowest terms.
(See Example C.)

19. 4.75 $4\frac{3}{4}$ 20. 0.9 $\frac{9}{10}$ 21. 0.201 $\frac{201}{1000}$ 22. 0.036 $\frac{9}{250}$ 23. 0.001 $\frac{1}{1000}$ 24. 3.08 $3\frac{2}{25}$

Write as a decimal. (See Example D.)

25. $3\frac{1}{5}$ 26. $9\frac{8}{125}$ 27. $4\frac{7}{12}$ 28. $5\frac{3}{4}$ 29. $11\frac{1}{10}$ 30. $6\frac{1}{7}$ 31. $2\frac{1}{3}$
    3.2   9.064 $4.58\overline{3}$ 5.75   11.1   6.142857 $2.\overline{3}$

▶ Mixed Practice (For more practice, see page 418.)

Convert each fraction to a decimal and each decimal to a fraction.

32. $\frac{4}{5}$ 0.8   33. 0.019 $\frac{19}{1000}$ 34. $4\frac{8}{9}$ $4.\overline{8}$ 35. 0.7 $\frac{7}{10}$ 36. $\frac{11}{16}$ 0.6875   37. 1.64 $1\frac{16}{25}$

38. 8.15 $8\frac{3}{20}$ 39. $5\frac{14}{25}$ 5.56   40. $\frac{7}{30}$ $0.2\overline{3}$ 41. $\frac{4}{15}$ $0.2\overline{6}$ 42. 0.048 $\frac{6}{125}$ 43. $\frac{29}{60}$ $0.48\overline{3}$

▶ Applications

44. Every morning Mrs. Sneedly walks her pet chihuahua, Smily. Their route is seven-eighths mile long. Write the distance as a decimal. 0.875 mile

45. June needs $\frac{1}{4}$ pound of walnuts for a dip recipe. If she buys a package marked 0.45 pound, what fractional part of a pound will she have left over? $\frac{1}{5}$ pound

Reinforcement
Extra Practice, page 418
EP/MR Worksheet 44, TRB, page 44

Challenge
Match each decimal in Column A with the equivalent fraction in Column B.

Column A	Column B
1. $0.\overline{1}$	a. $\frac{3}{16}$
2. $0.\overline{428571}$	b. $\frac{9}{40}$
3. 0.1875	c. $\frac{8}{5}$
4. $0.\overline{63}$	d. $\frac{1}{9}$
5. 1.6	e. $\frac{5}{12}$
6. 0.225	f. $\frac{3}{7}$
7. $2.1\overline{6}$	g. $\frac{13}{6}$
8. 0.015	h. $\frac{12}{25}$
9. $0.41\overline{6}$	i. $\frac{3}{200}$
10. $0.\overline{48}$	j. $\frac{7}{11}$

(1. d,   2. f,   3. a,   4. j,   5. c,   6. b,   7. g,
8. i,   9. e,   10. h)

▶ Review (Lessons 3.10, 3.11, 3.12)

Divide. Round each quotient to the nearest hundredth.

46. $2\overline{)365.99}$ 47. $12\overline{)67.48}$ 48. $0.8\overline{)49.33}$ 49. $0.06\overline{)0.977}$
    183.00   5.62   61.66   16.28

Objective

- To express fractions as decimals, repeating or terminating

Purpose

Learning about repeating decimals shows you some of the patterns that exist in mathematics. You will often encounter repeating decimals when you convert fractions to decimals.

Introducing the Lesson

Review converting fractions to decimals (Lesson 5.7). Use the examples: Write $\frac{1}{8}$, $\frac{1}{16}$, and $\frac{2}{3}$ as decimals. (0.125, 0.0625, 0.$\overline{6}$) Write the following musical scale on the board: *Do, Re, Mi, Fa, Sol,* ____, ____, ____. Ask students to supply the missing notes. (*La, Ti, Do*) Ask: What comes after the second *Do*? (*Re, Mi, Fa,* etc.) Explain that a musical scale repeats the same notes over and over again. Then write *Monday, Tuesday, Wednesday, Thursday,* ____, ____, ____. Ask students to fill in the missing days of the week. (*Friday, Saturday, Sunday*) Ask: What is the sequence for 10 more days? How do you know? (The days of the week keep repeating as an unending pattern.) Explain to students that unending patterns also occur in mathematics.

Note to the Teacher: You may wish to have calculators available for this lesson.

Caution: When you divide the numerator by the denominator in some fractions, such as $\frac{1}{7}$ and $\frac{2}{7}$, it may not be immediately obvious what the pattern is, from what the calculator displays. Thus, this lesson illustrates both the power and the limitations of using a calculator.

Answers

1. 0.$\overline{18}$, 0.$\overline{142857}$, 0.$4\overline{71}$
2. 0.$\overline{142857}$, 0.$\overline{285714}$, 0.$\overline{428571}$, 0.$\overline{571428}$, 0.$\overline{714285}$, 0.$\overline{857142}$
3. The arrows from each fraction point to the first digit of the decimal for that fraction. The arrows from the first digit point to the second digit, the arrows from the second point to the third, etc.

5.8 Finding Patterns with Fractions and Repeating Decimals

You might be surprised to learn that a simple fraction like $\frac{1}{3}$ is equivalent to a decimal that never ends.

Using a calculator, you can uncover surprises and patterns in decimals.

Here are some examples of repeating decimals.

$\frac{2}{11} = 0.18181818\ldots$
pattern: 18 repeats

$\frac{1}{7} = 0.142857142857\ldots$
pattern: 142857 repeats

$\frac{467}{990} = 0.4717171\ldots$
pattern: 71 repeats

To indicate the pattern of repeating decimals, place a bar over the digits that repeat.

$\frac{4}{11} = 0.363636\ldots$
$= 0.\overline{36}$

$\frac{3}{7} = 0.428571428571\ldots$
$= 0.\overline{428571}$

$\frac{511}{990} = 0.51616\ldots$
$= 0.5\overline{16}$

Use a calculator to help you answer the following questions.

1. What is the pattern for $\frac{2}{11}$, $\frac{1}{7}$, and $\frac{467}{990}$? Use a bar over the repeating digits.

▶ The Harmonious Sevenths

2. Find the decimals for $\frac{1}{7}$, $\frac{2}{7}$, $\frac{3}{7}$, $\frac{4}{7}$, $\frac{5}{7}$, and $\frac{6}{7}$. Use a bar over the repeating digits.

3. Diana, exploring the sevenths, was so impressed by the pattern in their decimals that she drew the diagram shown at the right. Explain how the diagram works.

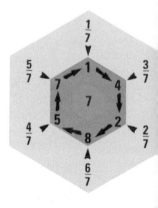

▶ Nines and Ones

4. Find the decimals for $\frac{1}{9}$, $\frac{1}{99}$, and $\frac{1}{999}$. Describe the pattern you see in these repeating decimals.

5. Based on the pattern you found, predict the decimal for $\frac{1}{9999}$. Can you check your prediction with a calculator?

6. Repeat this activity for $\frac{1}{11}$, $\frac{1}{111}$, and $\frac{1}{1111}$. Is the pattern similar to the one you found in Question 4? Predict the decimal for $\frac{1}{11,111}$.

▶ The Terminators

Terminating decimals are decimals that do not repeat forever. Examples of terminating decimals are:

$$\frac{1}{2} = 0.5 \qquad \frac{1}{4} = 0.25 \qquad \frac{1}{5} = 0.2 \qquad \frac{1}{8} = 0.125$$

Work with 2 or 3 classmates to solve the following problems.

7. Find the decimals for the fractions $\frac{1}{2}$, $\frac{1}{3}$, $\frac{1}{4}$, and so on down to $\frac{1}{25}$. Use a bar over repeating digits.

8. Find four decimals from Question 7 that you know for certain are terminating decimals. Explain how you know.

9. Is $\frac{1}{17}$ a terminating or repeating decimal? Does your calculator help you answer this question? Discuss.

▶ Review

Write which operation you would use to solve each problem. Then solve.

10. How many inches are in 17 feet? Multiplication; 204 inches

11. Look at the class roster on the right. How many students are studying French? Addition; 51 students

12. There are nine hundred calories in six cups of milk. How many calories are there in one cup of milk? Divide; 150 calories

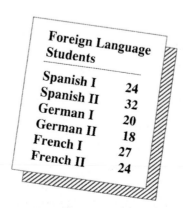

Foreign Language Students

Spanish I	24
Spanish II	32
German I	20
German II	18
French I	27
French II	24

Chapter 5 Review

Complete each sentence. (Lesson 5.1)

1. The top part of a fraction is called the ▓ . Numerator

2. The part of a fraction that shows how many parts make up the whole is called the ▓ . Denominator

Write a fraction or a mixed number for the shaded part in each picture. (Lesson 5.1)

3.

$\frac{1}{3}$

4.
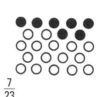
$\frac{7}{23}$

5.

$\frac{1}{2}$ or $\frac{2}{4}$

Find 3 fractions equivalent to each fraction. (Lesson 5.2)

6. $\frac{5}{8}$ 7. $\frac{7}{10}$ 8. $\frac{3}{16}$ 9. $\frac{4}{9}$

Use division to find a fraction equivalent to each fraction. (Lesson 5.2)

10. $\frac{5}{15}$ $\frac{1}{3}$ 11. $\frac{6}{33}$ $\frac{2}{11}$ 12. $\frac{27}{30}$ $\frac{9}{10}$ 13. $\frac{25}{50}$ $\frac{1}{2}$ or $\frac{5}{10}$ 14. $\frac{4}{14}$ $\frac{2}{7}$ 15. $\frac{18}{32}$ $\frac{9}{16}$

Write as an improper fraction. (Lesson 5.3)

16. $4\frac{1}{2}$ $\frac{9}{2}$ 17. 6 $\frac{6}{1}, \frac{12}{2}, \frac{18}{3}$, etc. 18. $3\frac{1}{3}$ $\frac{10}{3}$ 19. $7\frac{9}{10}$ $\frac{79}{10}$

Compare. Use <, >, or =. (Lesson 5.4)

20. $\frac{3}{8}$ ▓ $\frac{3}{16}$ > 21. $2\frac{1}{2}$ ▓ $\frac{5}{2}$ = 22. $4\frac{3}{4}$ ▓ $5\frac{1}{8}$ < 23. $\frac{11}{12}$ ▓ $\frac{13}{15}$ >

Find the GCF of each pair of numbers. (Lesson 5.5)

24. 6 5 1 25. 9 18 9 26. 10 15 5 27. 4 16 4 28. 14 21 7 29. 12 32 4

Write each fraction in lowest terms. (Lesson 5.6)

30. $\frac{12}{10}$ $\frac{6}{5}$ or $1\frac{1}{5}$ 31. $\frac{14}{27}$ $\frac{14}{27}$ 32. $\frac{80}{100}$ $\frac{4}{5}$ 33. $\frac{48}{24}$ $\frac{2}{1}$ 34. $\frac{30}{45}$ $\frac{2}{3}$ 35. $\frac{10}{16}$ $\frac{5}{8}$ 36. $1\frac{18}{32}$ $1\frac{9}{16}$

Convert each fraction to a decimal and each decimal to a fraction. (Lesson 5.7)

37. $\frac{1}{4}$ 0.25 38. $\frac{1}{3}$ $0.\overline{3}$ 39. 9.3 $9\frac{3}{10}$ 40. $\frac{4}{5}$ 0.8 41. 0.125 $\frac{1}{8}$ 42. $6\frac{5}{8}$ 6.625

Chapter 5 Test

TEST

Write a fraction for the shaded parts in each set of pictures.
Then compare the fractions. Use <, >, or =.

1.

$\frac{1}{2} < \frac{3}{4}$

2.

$\frac{2}{3} > \frac{3}{5}$

3.

$\frac{4}{5} < \frac{7}{8}$

4.

$\frac{2}{10} = \frac{1}{5}$

Convert each fraction to a decimal and each decimal to a fraction.

5. $\frac{1}{2}$ 0.5

6. 7.6 $7\frac{3}{5}$

7. $\frac{3}{4}$ 0.75

8. 0.875 $\frac{7}{8}$

9. $3\frac{9}{10}$ 3.9

Write in lowest terms.

10. $\frac{10}{16}$ $\frac{5}{8}$

11. $\frac{40}{50}$ $\frac{4}{5}$

12. $\frac{9}{18}$ $\frac{1}{2}$

13. $\frac{12}{16}$ $\frac{3}{4}$

14. $\frac{5}{15}$ $\frac{1}{3}$

Write each whole or mixed number as an improper fraction.

15. 7 $\frac{7}{1}, \frac{14}{2}$, etc.

16. $4\frac{1}{8}$ $\frac{33}{8}$

17. $2\frac{3}{4}$ $\frac{11}{4}$

18. $9\frac{1}{2}$ $\frac{19}{2}$

Find the GCF of each pair of numbers.

19. 8 12 4

20. 20 25 5

21. 10 13 1

22. 18 27 9

Identify the fraction that is NOT equivalent in each list.

23. $\frac{3}{4}$ a. $\frac{9}{12}$ b. $\frac{21}{28}$ ⓒ $\frac{12}{15}$ d. $\frac{18}{24}$

24. $\frac{4}{5}$ a. $\frac{8}{10}$ ⓑ $\frac{26}{35}$ c. $\frac{40}{50}$ d. $\frac{32}{40}$

Write T if the statement is true. Write F if the statement is false,
and explain why.

25. In an improper fraction, the numerator is greater than or
equal to the denominator. T

26. To convert a fraction to a decimal, you divide the
denominator by the numerator. F; you divide the numerator by the denominator.

Chapter Tests

Short Answer, Forms A and B, TRB, pages
283–284, 285–286
Multiple Choice, Forms A and B, TRB, pages
351–352, 353–354

Teaching Aids

Answer sheet
TA 8, TRB, page 161a
Teaching suggestions precede the Teaching
Aids worksheets.

Career Focus Activity

Materials: journal, pen, prepared list of questions

Procedure: The career of being an electronics repairperson is an ideal opportunity for job shadowing. Students can actually follow an electronics repairperson or other related professional through a day's activities.

- Contact a local electronics repair business.
- Ask if one or two students may observe one electronics repairperson or other related professional during the day.
- Each student should bring a journal and a pen to record events, impressions, and experiences of the day. They can share a prepared list of questions to be asked. Partners can take turns asking questions.
- The journal is to be signed by the electronics repairperson or other related professional at the end of the visit.
- When students return, they should report on the experience for the class.
- A thank-you note to the host business should be written and sent by all that attended within three days of the visit.

Use multiplying and dividing fractions and mixed numbers to

- find out how many miles per hour a car has been driven.
- reduce the number of servings in a recipe.
- compute scale drawing distances.
- determine the price of a product sold by fractions of a pound.

What are some other ways to use multiplying and dividing fractions and mixed numbers?

Multiplying and Dividing Fractions and Mixed Numbers

An electronics technician installs, operates, maintains, and repairs electronic equipment.

- Electronics technicians work for small repair shops, large corporations, and retail stores that sell and service electronic equipment.

- An electronics technician understands technology and enjoys using reasoning skills to troubleshoot and solve problems.

- An electronics technician uses mathematics to determine the cost of parts and labor.

- To become an electronics technician, an individual can complete a course of study in a vocational school, a two-year college, or in the military.

- Related careers include electronics engineers, electronics sales representatives, computer technicians, and cable service representatives.

CAREER

ELECTRONICS TECHNICIAN

PORTFOLIO PROJECT: *Determine labor costs.*

1. Suppose you are a computer-service technician. On one service call, you spent $1\frac{1}{2}$ hours repairing a printer, $\frac{1}{2}$ hour installing a new battery and computer chips in a used computer, and $3\frac{1}{2}$ hours installing five new computers.

2. You earn $50 an hour for repairing and working on old equipment and $40 an hour for installing new equipment.

3. Prepare an itemized bill for the customer. Multiply hours *times* cost per hour for each kind of work. Add the items to show the total cost of your service call. *Show the math.*

Students will create and design an itemized bill with a company logo, address, phone number, and lines on which to write. All math should be shown on the bills.

Assessment: The individual scoring rubric on page 161 of the Teacher's Resource Binder can be reproduced and used for assessment. Include the following information in the last two boxes. Students should have:
- designed a bill to include the suggested items.
- accurately figured out all the math presented in Steps 1 and 2.

Objectives

- To multiply fractions
- To multiply fractions and whole numbers

Purpose

This lesson helps you to multiply fractions. For example, to find how far you jogged if you went $\frac{1}{2}$ of the way around a $\frac{3}{4}$-mile track, you need to multiply $\frac{3}{4}$ by $\frac{1}{2}$.

Introducing the Lesson

Review writing fractions in lowest terms (Lesson 5.6). Use the examples: $\frac{6}{12} = (\frac{1}{2})$, $\frac{2}{16} = (\frac{1}{8})$, $\frac{9}{15} = (\frac{3}{5})$.

Draw a large square on the board and divide it in half. Further divide one half in half. Shade in one of these small squares. Write "$\frac{1}{2}$ of $\frac{1}{2}$" on the board. Ask: Is $\frac{1}{2}$ of $\frac{1}{2}$ greater than, less than, or equal to $\frac{1}{2}$? (less than) What fraction of the square is shaded? ($\frac{1}{4}$) Looking at this diagram, can you tell what fraction is $\frac{1}{2}$ of $\frac{1}{2}$? ($\frac{1}{4}$) Point out to students that the word "of" when used in questions such as "What is $\frac{1}{2}$ of $\frac{1}{2}$?" means "times."

Alternative Examples

Example A—Multiply. $\frac{3}{7} \times \frac{2}{7}$
$\frac{3}{7} \times \frac{2}{7} = \frac{6}{49}$

Example B—Multiply. $\frac{2}{3} \times \frac{5}{6}$
$\frac{2}{3} \times \frac{5}{6} = \frac{10}{18} = \frac{5}{9}$

Example C—Multiply. $3 \times \frac{5}{9}$
$\frac{3}{1} \times \frac{5}{9} = \frac{15}{9}$, or $1\frac{2}{3}$

▶ Think and Discuss Answers

1. $\frac{1}{8}$ cup
2. 8, 16
3. $\frac{35}{8}$ or $4\frac{3}{8}$

6.1 Multiplying Fractions

Smoked Salmon and Spinach Salad   Serves 4
3/4 cup smoked salmon
1 pound spinach
1 small onion, minced
1 tablespoon lemon juice
1/4 cup minced celery
1/2 cup salad dressing
salt and pepper

Sharon's Aunt Zenia was coming to visit, and Sharon needed a special dish to serve for lunch. "How about this Smoked Salmon and Spinach Salad recipe?" her roommate suggested. "Great," said Sharon.

Sharon can determine how much of each ingredient to buy for lunch with Aunt Zenia by multiplying the given amounts by $\frac{1}{2}$.

Examples

To multiply fractions, multiply the numerators. Then multiply the denominators. Write the answer in lowest terms.

A Multiply. $\frac{3}{4} \times \frac{1}{2}$

$\frac{3}{4} \times \frac{1}{2} = \frac{3}{8}$

B Multiply. $\frac{4}{9} \times \frac{3}{8}$

$\frac{4}{9} \times \frac{3}{8} = \frac{12}{72} = \frac{1}{6}$

C Multiply. $5 \times \frac{3}{4}$

$\frac{5}{1} \times \frac{3}{4} = \frac{15}{4}$, or $3\frac{3}{4}$

▶ Think and Discuss

1. Refer to the introduction to this lesson. How much minced celery does Sharon need?

2. Fill in the missing numbers. $\frac{5}{6} \times \frac{3}{\blacksquare} = \frac{15}{48} = \frac{5}{\blacksquare}$

3. Multiply 7 by $\frac{5}{8}$.

4. Find $\frac{1}{4}$ of 16.

5. Describe the steps you use when you multiply a fraction by a whole number.

Exercises

Multiply. Write the answers in lowest terms. (See Example A.)

6. $\frac{2}{3} \times \frac{4}{5}$ $\frac{8}{15}$ **7.** $\frac{1}{5} \times \frac{1}{3}$ $\frac{1}{15}$ **8.** $\frac{5}{8} \times \frac{1}{6}$ $\frac{5}{48}$ **9.** $\frac{3}{4} \times \frac{3}{5}$ $\frac{9}{20}$ **10.** $\frac{1}{9} \times \frac{1}{3}$ $\frac{1}{27}$

11. $\frac{4}{9} \times \frac{2}{5}$ $\frac{8}{45}$ **12.** $\frac{5}{8} \times \frac{3}{4}$ $\frac{15}{32}$ **13.** $\frac{3}{5} \times \frac{2}{5}$ $\frac{6}{25}$ **14.** $\frac{4}{5} \times \frac{3}{7}$ $\frac{12}{35}$ **15.** $\frac{2}{5} \times \frac{1}{9}$ $\frac{2}{45}$

Multiply. Write the answers in lowest terms. (See Example B.)

16. $\frac{3}{7} \times \frac{2}{9}$ $\frac{2}{21}$ **17.** $\frac{5}{8} \times \frac{2}{3}$ $\frac{5}{12}$ **18.** $\frac{2}{5} \times \frac{3}{4}$ $\frac{3}{10}$ **19.** $\frac{5}{6} \times \frac{3}{4}$ $\frac{5}{8}$ **20.** $\frac{7}{12} \times \frac{2}{3}$ $\frac{7}{18}$

21. $\frac{3}{8} \times \frac{4}{9}$ $\frac{1}{6}$ **22.** $\frac{7}{10} \times \frac{5}{6}$ $\frac{7}{12}$ **23.** $\frac{8}{9} \times \frac{5}{6}$ $\frac{20}{27}$ **24.** $\frac{5}{7} \times \frac{4}{15}$ $\frac{4}{21}$ **25.** $\frac{5}{16} \times \frac{4}{5}$ $\frac{1}{4}$

26. $\frac{1}{4} \times \frac{4}{7}$ $\frac{1}{7}$ **27.** $\frac{2}{5} \times \frac{1}{2}$ $\frac{1}{5}$ **28.** $\frac{5}{7} \times \frac{3}{5}$ $\frac{3}{7}$ **29.** $\frac{9}{15} \times \frac{2}{3}$ $\frac{2}{5}$ **30.** $\frac{1}{4} \times \frac{8}{11}$ $\frac{2}{11}$

Multiply. Write the answers in lowest terms. (See Example C.)

31. $4 \times \frac{3}{4}$ 3 **32.** $7 \times \frac{9}{10}$ $6\frac{3}{10}$ **33.** $3 \times \frac{2}{7}$ $\frac{6}{7}$ **34.** $8 \times \frac{2}{3}$ $5\frac{1}{3}$ **35.** $5 \times \frac{7}{9}$ $3\frac{8}{9}$

36. $10 \times \frac{1}{3}$ $3\frac{1}{3}$ **37.** $2 \times \frac{11}{16}$ $1\frac{3}{8}$ **38.** $9 \times \frac{1}{2}$ $4\frac{1}{2}$ **39.** $4 \times \frac{2}{11}$ $\frac{8}{11}$ **40.** $8 \times \frac{2}{5}$ $3\frac{1}{5}$

41. $3 \times \frac{3}{7}$ $1\frac{2}{7}$ **42.** $11 \times \frac{1}{2}$ $5\frac{1}{2}$ **43.** $4 \times \frac{2}{3}$ $2\frac{2}{3}$ **44.** $15 \times \frac{3}{5}$ 9 **45.** $2 \times \frac{7}{10}$ $1\frac{2}{5}$

▶ Mixed Practice (For more practice, see page 418.)

Multiply. Write the answers in lowest terms.

46. $\frac{1}{6} \times \frac{7}{10}$ $\frac{7}{60}$ **47.** $7 \times \frac{8}{9}$ $6\frac{2}{9}$ **48.** $\frac{3}{5} \times \frac{1}{8}$ $\frac{3}{40}$ **49.** $\frac{7}{8} \times \frac{6}{7}$ $\frac{3}{4}$ **50.** $5 \times \frac{2}{3}$ $3\frac{1}{3}$

51. $3 \times \frac{1}{8}$ $\frac{3}{8}$ **52.** $\frac{6}{10} \times \frac{4}{9}$ $\frac{4}{15}$ **53.** $\frac{3}{8} \times \frac{1}{8}$ $\frac{3}{64}$ **54.** $9 \times \frac{3}{5}$ $5\frac{2}{5}$ **55.** $\frac{2}{3} \times \frac{1}{12}$ $\frac{1}{18}$

56. $\frac{7}{8} \times \frac{3}{4}$ $\frac{21}{32}$ **57.** $\frac{9}{10} \times \frac{5}{6}$ $\frac{3}{4}$ **58.** $\frac{9}{16} \times \frac{2}{3}$ $\frac{3}{8}$ **59.** $4 \times \frac{5}{8}$ $2\frac{1}{2}$ **60.** $\frac{8}{9} \times \frac{8}{9}$ $\frac{64}{81}$

▶ Applications

61. A printer's assistant earns $\frac{2}{5}$ of the total profit of every job he works on. How much does he earn on a profit of $45? $18

62. A pudding recipe calling for one-half cup of sugar serves four. How much sugar would you use to make three servings? $\frac{3}{8}$ cup

▶ Review (Lesson 5.5)

Find the GCF of each pair of numbers.

63. 12   18 6 **64.** 21   28 7 **65.** 20   11 1 **66.** 9   15 3 **67.** 25   5 5

68. 8   32 8 **69.** 26   10 2 **70.** 40   16 8 **71.** 34   17 17 **72.** 13   5 1

73. 12   16 4 **74.** 50   25 25 **75.** 21   3 3 **76.** 15   10 5 **77.** 16   18 2

Objectives

- To use a shortcut method to multiply fractions
- To use a shortcut method to multiply fractions and whole numbers

Purpose

This lesson teaches a shortcut method to multiply fractions. This method simplifies your calculations. For example: Which is easier to multiply—$\frac{1}{5} \times \frac{2}{3}$ or $\frac{18}{90} \times \frac{36}{54}$? Notice that both problems are the same, but the fractions in the first problem are expressed in lowest terms.

Introducing the Lesson

Write the following problem on the board: $\frac{4}{5} \times \frac{15}{16}$. Ask: Are the fractions in lowest terms? (yes) Ask students to find the product and reduce it to lowest terms. ($\frac{3}{4}$) Then write the problem $\frac{15}{5} \times \frac{4}{16}$ on the board. Ask: How are the two problems similar? (The numerators and denominators are the same but have been switched.) Are the fractions in lowest terms? (no) Have students reduce both fractions to lowest terms and multiply. ($\frac{15}{5} = 3$; $\frac{4}{16} = \frac{1}{4}$; $3 \times \frac{1}{4} = \frac{3}{4}$)

Alternative Examples

Example A—Multiply. $\frac{4}{8} \times \frac{3}{5}$
Use the same method as in Example A.
$\frac{4}{8} \times \frac{3}{5} = \frac{3}{10}$

Example B—Multiply. $\frac{300}{17} \times \frac{19}{900}$
Use the same method as in Example B.
$\frac{300}{17} \times \frac{19}{900} = \frac{19}{51}$

▶ Think and Discuss Answers

1. $\frac{1}{5}$; by dividing the 4s by 4
2. $\frac{1}{6}$; answers may include changing $\frac{6}{9}$ to $\frac{2}{3}$ and $\frac{3}{12}$ to $\frac{1}{4}$, and dividing the numerator, 2, and the denominator, 4, by 2

6.2 Multiplying Fractions: A Shortcut

$$\frac{250}{9} \times \frac{67}{750} =$$

Sharif rushed into mathematics class late one day. The other students were working furiously to find a solution to the problem shown above. "I'm sorry I'm late," Sharif said. "Oh, by the way, the answer to the problem is $\frac{67}{27}$." How do you think Sharif solved the problem so quickly?

Examples

To multiply fractions using a shortcut method, first divide numerators and denominators by a common factor.

A Multiply. $\frac{4}{10} \times \frac{3}{7}$

Write fractions in lowest terms. Multiply.

$$\frac{4 \div 2}{2}$$

$$\frac{4}{10} \times \frac{3}{7} = \frac{4}{10} \times \frac{3}{7} = \frac{6}{35}$$

$$\frac{5}{10 \div 2}$$

$$\frac{4}{10} \times \frac{3}{7} = \frac{6}{35}$$

B Multiply. $\frac{250}{9} \times \frac{67}{750}$

Divide by the GCF of a numerator and a denominator.

$$\frac{250 \div 250}{1}$$

$$\frac{250}{9} \times \frac{67}{750} = \frac{250}{9} \times \frac{67}{750} = \frac{67}{27}, \text{ or } 2\frac{13}{27}$$

$$\frac{3}{750 \div 250}$$

$$\frac{250}{9} \times \frac{67}{750} = 2\frac{13}{27}$$

▶ Think and Discuss

1. Multiply $\frac{1}{4}$ by $\frac{4}{5}$. How did you simplify the problem?

2. Multiply $\frac{6}{9}$ by $\frac{3}{12}$. How did you simplify the problem?

3. Explain how to simplify in the problem $\frac{6}{8} \times \frac{24}{27}$.

4. Explain why it helps to simplify fractions before multiplying.

Third guess: 42 minutes.
Awake: 42 minutes
Asleep: 42 + 25 = 67 minutes
Total: 42 + 67 = 109 minutes
109 = 109
That works! Bernice was awake for 42 minutes of the movie before she fell asleep.

- **Check** Put your calculation into words. Bernice was awake for 42 minutes and asleep for 67 minutes, which adds up to 109 minutes. And 67 is 25 more than 42.

Refer to the problem about Bernice to answer the following questions.

1. Describe in your own words why your first guess should be a number less than half of 109.

2. When should your second guess be lower than your first guess? When should your second guess be higher than your first guess?

3. Explain why you know the guess of 40 is closer to the correct answer than the guess of 50.

Use Guess and Check to solve each problem.

4. Miss Quintana's Spanish class is next door to Mr. Alouette's French class. The two classes have a total of 72 students. There are 16 more students in Spanish than in French. Is a guess of 20 students in French class too high or too low? How many students are in each class? Too low; 28 French students; 44 Spanish students

5. José and Cecile went out for dinner. Together they spent $28. José spent $5 more than Cecile. Is a guess of $18 for José too high or too low? How much money did each spend?
Too high; José spent $16.50 and Cecile spent $11.50.

▶ **Review** (Lesson 5.7)

Change each fraction to a decimal.

6. $\frac{5}{18}$ 0.2$\overline{7}$

7. $\frac{11}{18}$ 0.6$\overline{1}$

8. $\frac{13}{44}$ 0.29$\overline{54}$

9. $\frac{3}{22}$ 0.1$\overline{36}$

Objectives

- To multiply mixed numbers
- To multiply mixed numbers and fractions
- To multiply mixed numbers and whole numbers

Purpose

You multiply mixed numbers and whole numbers when calculating amounts of materials such as flooring, recipe ingredients, and fabrics. For example, if $10\frac{2}{3}$ yards of fabric are required to cover 1 couch, but you have to cover 5 couches, you would multiply $10\frac{2}{3} \times 5$ to find the total amount of fabric needed.

Introducing the Lesson

Review writing mixed numbers as fractions (Lesson 5.3). Use the examples: Write the following mixed numbers as improper fractions—$2\frac{1}{8}$ ($\frac{17}{8}$), $1\frac{3}{5}$ ($\frac{8}{5}$), $7\frac{5}{9}$ ($\frac{68}{9}$). Write $\frac{3}{4} \times \frac{2}{7}$ on the board and ask students to multiply. ($\frac{3}{14}$) Then write $\frac{4}{3} \times \frac{7}{2}$ on the board and ask students to multiply, leaving the answer as an improper fraction. ($\frac{14}{3}$) Ask students to convert the fractions in the last problem to mixed numbers. ($1\frac{1}{3} \times 3\frac{1}{2} = 4\frac{2}{3}$)

Alternative Examples

Example A—Multiply. $2\frac{1}{5} \times 3\frac{1}{2}$

$2\frac{1}{5} = \frac{11}{5}$ $3\frac{1}{2} = \frac{7}{2}$

$\frac{11}{5} \times \frac{7}{2} = \frac{77}{10}$, or $\mathbf{7\frac{7}{10}}$

Example B—Multiply. $\frac{5}{6} \times 4\frac{3}{5}$

$\frac{5}{6} \times 4\frac{3}{5} = \frac{\overset{1}{\cancel{5}}}{6} \times \frac{23}{\underset{1}{\cancel{5}}} = \frac{23}{6}$, or $\mathbf{3\frac{5}{6}}$

Example C—Multiply. $3\frac{4}{7} \times 2$

$3\frac{4}{7} \times \frac{2}{1} = \frac{25}{7} \times \frac{2}{1} = \frac{50}{7}$, or $\mathbf{7\frac{1}{7}}$

6.4 Multiplying Mixed Numbers

"**S**orry, I've got to run," Etta said. "I don't want to be late. I make $9 an hour today!" "Wait a second," exclaimed Annie. "You told me you made $6 an hour." "I do on most days, but today is Sunday and I get time and a half."

"Time and a half" means $1\frac{1}{2}$ times the usual pay. To find out whether Etta is correct, multiply $1\frac{1}{2}$ by 6.

Examples

To multiply mixed numbers, first write each mixed number as an improper fraction.

A Multiply. $2\frac{3}{4} \times 2\frac{1}{2}$

$2\frac{3}{4} = \frac{11}{4}$ $2\frac{1}{2} = \frac{5}{2}$

$\frac{11}{4} \times \frac{5}{2} = \frac{55}{8}$, or $6\frac{7}{8}$

$2\frac{3}{4} \times 2\frac{1}{2} = 6\frac{7}{8}$

B Multiply. $\frac{3}{4} \times 2\frac{2}{5}$

$\frac{3}{4} \times 2\frac{2}{5} = \frac{3}{4} \times \frac{12}{5}$

$\frac{3}{4} \times \frac{\overset{3}{\cancel{12}}}{5} = \frac{9}{5}$, or $1\frac{4}{5}$

$\frac{3}{4} \times 2\frac{2}{5} = 1\frac{4}{5}$

C Multiply. $1\frac{1}{2} \times 6$

$1\frac{1}{2} \times 6 = \frac{3}{2} \times \frac{6}{1}$

$\frac{3}{2} \times \frac{\overset{3}{\cancel{6}}}{1} = \frac{6}{1} = 9$

$1\frac{1}{2} \times 6 = 9$

▶ Think and Discuss

1. Write $2\frac{2}{5}$ as an improper fraction.

2. Multiply $1\frac{2}{3}$ by $3\frac{3}{4}$.

3. What shortcut is used in Example B?

4. Refer to the introduction to this lesson. Was Etta's calculation correct? Show the problem and solution.

5. Select two mixed numbers between 3 and 4. Explain why their product will be greater than 9 and less than 16.

Exercises

Multiply. Write the answers in lowest terms. (See Example A.)

6. $1\frac{1}{3} \times 2\frac{1}{2}$ $3\frac{1}{3}$ **7.** $2\frac{2}{3} \times 5\frac{1}{4}$ 14 **8.** $6\frac{1}{2} \times 1\frac{2}{3}$ $10\frac{5}{6}$ **9.** $3\frac{5}{7} \times 9\frac{1}{3}$ $34\frac{2}{3}$

10. $1\frac{1}{10} \times 4\frac{1}{3}$ $4\frac{23}{30}$ **11.** $4\frac{3}{4} \times 5\frac{1}{5}$ $24\frac{7}{10}$ **12.** $8\frac{1}{5} \times 4\frac{2}{7}$ $35\frac{1}{7}$ **13.** $4\frac{8}{9} \times 2\frac{4}{5}$ $13\frac{31}{45}$

Multiply. Write the answers in lowest terms. (See Example B.)

14. $\frac{1}{3} \times 2\frac{1}{2}$ $\frac{5}{6}$ **15.** $\frac{6}{15} \times 1\frac{1}{3}$ $\frac{8}{15}$ **16.** $\frac{2}{5} \times 8\frac{1}{7}$ $3\frac{9}{35}$ **17.** $\frac{1}{2} \times 4\frac{5}{8}$ $2\frac{5}{16}$ **18.** $\frac{3}{7} \times 1\frac{2}{5}$ $\frac{3}{5}$

19. $6\frac{1}{3} \times \frac{1}{2}$ $3\frac{1}{6}$ **20.** $5\frac{3}{4} \times \frac{2}{9}$ $1\frac{5}{18}$ **21.** $\frac{4}{7} \times 5\frac{1}{5}$ $2\frac{34}{35}$ **22.** $10\frac{2}{3} \times \frac{1}{6}$ $1\frac{7}{9}$ **23.** $4\frac{4}{9} \times \frac{2}{11}$ $\frac{80}{99}$

Multiply. Write the answers in lowest terms. (See Example C.)

24. $4 \times 2\frac{1}{3}$ $9\frac{1}{3}$ **25.** $15\frac{4}{5} \times 5$ 79 **26.** $3\frac{14}{15} \times 4$ $15\frac{11}{15}$ **27.** $9\frac{1}{2} \times 5$ $47\frac{1}{2}$

28. $18\frac{1}{10} \times 20$ 362 **29.** $10 \times 5\frac{7}{10}$ 57 **30.** $7 \times 4\frac{5}{6}$ $33\frac{5}{6}$ **31.** $1\frac{1}{4} \times 3$ $3\frac{3}{4}$

▶ Mixed Practice (For more practice, see page 419.)

Multiply. Write the answers in lowest terms.

32. $2\frac{1}{3} \times 6$ 14 **33.** $\frac{2}{3} \times 5\frac{1}{2}$ $3\frac{2}{3}$ **34.** $1\frac{1}{5} \times 2\frac{2}{3}$ $3\frac{1}{5}$ **35.** $11 \times 6\frac{2}{3}$ $73\frac{1}{3}$

36. $7\frac{1}{24} \times 7$ $49\frac{7}{24}$ **37.** $\frac{2}{5} \times 2\frac{3}{4}$ $1\frac{1}{10}$ **38.** $1\frac{4}{5} \times 6\frac{7}{8}$ $12\frac{3}{8}$ **39.** $2 \times 4\frac{3}{4}$ $9\frac{1}{2}$

▶ Applications

40. Bill normally works seven-hour days. This week he worked four full days and one half-day. How many hours did he work? $31\frac{1}{2}$ hours

41. How much oats and water do you need to make $2\frac{1}{2}$ cups of hot oatmeal? $1\frac{2}{3}$ cups oats; 5 cups water

Oatmeal Cooking Instructions
Add 2/3 cup rolled oats and 3/4 tsp salt to 2 cups boiling water.
Boil 5-8 minutes.
Makes two 1/2 cup servings

▶ Review (Lessons 2.2, 2.4, 2.8, 2.10)

Multiply.

42.	**43.**	**44.**	**45.**	**46.**
36	0.09	8925	1.24	307
$\times\ 4.5$	$\times\ 0.004$	$\times\ 6$	$\times\ 0.53$	$\times\ 207$
162.0	0.00036	$53,550$	0.6572	$63,549$

47.	**48.**	**49.**	**50.**	**51.**
2.7	9.5	66.6	0.001	78
$\times\ 6.3$	$\times\ 0.5$	$\times\ 403$	$\times\ 0.001$	$\times\ 81$
17.01	4.75	$26,839.8$	0.000001	6318

▶ Think and Discuss Answers

1. $\frac{12}{5}$
2. $\frac{25}{4}$ or $6\frac{1}{4}$
3. dividing a numerator and a denominator by 4
4. yes; $\$6 \times 1\frac{1}{2} = \$9$
5. Answers may include $3\frac{1}{2} \times 3\frac{1}{4} = 11\frac{3}{8}$. The product of any two mixed numbers between 3 and 4 must be between 3×3 and 4×4.

★ Error Alert

Errors may indicate that students are trying to multiply without first expressing mixed numbers as improper fractions.

Reinforcement

Extra Practice, page 419
EP/MR Worksheet 47, TRB, page 47

Challenge

Use a calculator to help you convert the following numbers to decimals, multiply, and then convert the product back to a mixed number.

Hint: Convert $2\frac{1}{2}$ to a decimal by writing $\frac{1}{2}$ as a decimal and then adding the whole number 2. The decimal name for $\frac{1}{2}$ is found by dividing the numerator of the fraction by the denominator—$1 \div 2 = 0.5$. Reduce fractions to lowest terms.

1. $2\frac{3}{4} \times 1\frac{1}{8} \times 1\frac{3}{5} =$
($2.75 \times 1.125 \times 1.6 = 4.95 = 4\frac{19}{20}$)
2. $1\frac{1}{2} \times \frac{4}{5} \times 2\frac{1}{10} =$
($1.5 \times 0.8 \times 2.1 = 2.52 = 2\frac{13}{25}$)
3. $3\frac{1}{5} \times 1\frac{1}{4} \times 1\frac{2}{5} =$
($3.2 \times 1.25 \times 1.4 = 5.6 = 5\frac{3}{5}$)
4. $1\frac{9}{10} \times 2\frac{1}{50} \times 3\frac{3}{4} =$
($1.9 \times 2.02 \times 3.75 = 14.3925 = 14\frac{157}{400}$)
5. $4\frac{9}{20} \times 2\frac{3}{10} \times 3\frac{1}{5} =$
($4.45 \times 2.3 \times 3.2 = 37.752 = 32\frac{94}{125}$)

Objective

- To estimate the products of fractions and mixed numbers

Purpose

This lesson helps you to estimate products of fractions and mixed numbers. Estimating products is useful when you do not need an exact answer.

Introducing the Lesson

Review rounding whole numbers (Lesson 1.7) and estimating products (Lesson 2.6).

Draw number lines on the board like the ones shown below. The number lines are divided into halves, fourths, tenths, and thirty-seconds, respectively, with 0 at a point on the far left of the number line and 1 at a point on the far right of the number line. Write the fractions $\frac{1}{32}$, $\frac{31}{32}$, $\frac{1}{10}$, $\frac{7}{10}$, $\frac{3}{4}$, $\frac{14}{32}$, and $\frac{16}{32}$ on the board. Have students decide if the fractions are closer to 0, $\frac{1}{2}$, or 1. (0, 1, 0, $\frac{1}{2}$, $\frac{1}{2}$ or 1, $\frac{1}{2}$, $\frac{1}{2}$)

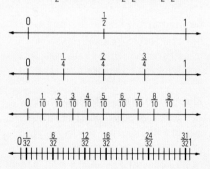

Answers

1. yes, because it is only $\frac{1}{8}$ less than 1; 0.875

2. yes, because it is only $\frac{1}{50}$ greater than $\frac{1}{2}$; 0.52

3. close to 1: $\frac{11}{10}$, $\frac{21}{20}$, $\frac{15}{16}$; close to $\frac{1}{2}$: $\frac{5}{9}$, $\frac{9}{20}$, $\frac{100}{205}$; close to neither: $\frac{7}{29}$, $\frac{1}{20}$

4. The numerator and the denominator will be close in value; the numerator will be close to $\frac{1}{2}$ of the denominator.

6.5 Estimating Products of Fractions and Mixed Numbers

"When you use math, you don't always need an exact answer," Mrs. Oxtoby told her class. "Let's look at the problem $\frac{7}{8} \times \frac{13}{25}$. Can you estimate that product mentally?"

Melanie raised her hand. "7 times 13 is about 100. 8 times 25 is 200. So the product is about $\frac{1}{2}$."

$$\frac{7}{8} \times \frac{13}{25} \approx \frac{100}{200} = \frac{1}{2}$$

Thomas said, "I got $\frac{1}{2}$ too, but I worked with each fraction first. Since $\frac{7}{8}$ is about 1 and $\frac{13}{25}$ is about $\frac{1}{2}$, the product is about $\frac{1}{2}$.

$$\frac{7}{8} \times \frac{13}{25} \approx 1 \times \frac{1}{2} = \frac{1}{2}$$

1. Is $\frac{7}{8}$ really about 1? Write $\frac{7}{8}$ as a decimal.

2. Is $\frac{13}{25}$ really about $\frac{1}{2}$? Write $\frac{13}{25}$ as a decimal.

3. Which of the fractions in the following list are close to 1? Which are close to $\frac{1}{2}$? Which are close to neither 1 nor $\frac{1}{2}$?

$$\frac{11}{10} \quad \frac{7}{29} \quad \frac{5}{9} \quad \frac{21}{20} \quad \frac{15}{16} \quad \frac{1}{20} \quad \frac{9}{20} \quad \frac{100}{205}$$

4. How can you tell if a fraction is close to 1? To $\frac{1}{2}$? Discuss.

"Estimation becomes even more important when the numbers get bigger. How would you estimate $6\frac{1}{5} \times 3\frac{5}{7}$ mentally?" Mrs. Oxtoby asked.

Rafael raised his hand. "I'd just use whole numbers. $6\frac{1}{5}$ is close to 6. $3\frac{5}{7}$ is close to 4. The product is about 24."

$$6\frac{1}{5} \times 3\frac{5}{7} \approx 6 \times 4 = 24$$

5. One student said her estimate for $8\frac{3}{8} \times 9\frac{11}{16}$ is somewhere between 72 and 90. How do you think she arrived at her estimate? What would your estimate be?

6. Using estimation, determine if the following statement is true: $3\frac{1}{8} \times 8\frac{1}{7} > 24$. Explain your reasoning.

Exercises

Estimate each product mentally.

7. $\frac{3}{8} \times \frac{5}{12}$ **8.** $4\frac{9}{10} \times 2\frac{1}{4}$ **9.** $\frac{7}{8} \times 4\frac{7}{16}$ **10.** $\frac{8}{11} \times \frac{3}{7}$ **11.** $\frac{5}{8} \times 10\frac{2}{9}$

12. $1\frac{1}{8} \times 1\frac{7}{8}$ **13.** $\frac{10}{19} \times 5\frac{3}{4}$ **14.** $\frac{9}{20} \times \frac{19}{20}$ **15.** $8\frac{12}{21} \times 2\frac{1}{8}$ **16.** $\frac{21}{50} \times \frac{17}{30}$

17. $5\frac{4}{5} \times \frac{19}{21}$ **18.** $25\frac{1}{3} \times 2\frac{1}{4}$ **19.** $\frac{7}{9} \times \frac{16}{33}$ **20.** $13\frac{2}{15} \times 2\frac{8}{9}$ **21.** $\frac{11}{20} \times 8\frac{1}{2}$

▶ Applications

22. Mrs. Ras works $37\frac{1}{2}$ hours a week and earns $11 per hour. Estimate his gross pay.

23. Rodney is going backpacking. His route is $23\frac{5}{8}$ miles long. He plans to walk $\frac{1}{5}$ of the total distance each day. About how many miles will he walk each day?

$23\frac{5}{8}$

▶ Review (Lessons 3.2, 3.5)

Divide.

24. $4\overline{)17}$ **25.** $11\overline{)123}$ **26.** $8\overline{)69}$ **27.** $7\overline{)49}$ **28.** $9\overline{)852}$

29. $15\overline{)316}$ **30.** $22\overline{)78}$ **31.** $25\overline{)555}$ **32.** $16\overline{)271}$ **33.** $32\overline{)467}$

Multiplying and Dividing Fractions and Mixed Numbers **139**

Answers   (continued)

5. She knew that the answer would be somewhere between $8 \times 9 = 72$ and $9 \times 10 = 90$. Answers may include numbers between 72 and 90.

6. $3 \times 8 = 24$ and $3\frac{1}{8} > 3$, $8\frac{1}{7} > 8$, so $3\frac{1}{8} \times 8\frac{1}{7} > 3 \times 8$

Answers ▶

Answers to Questions 7–23 may include:

7. $\approx \frac{1}{4}$ **8.** ≈ 10

9. ≈ 4 or $4\frac{1}{2}$ **10.** $\approx \frac{1}{2}$

11. ≈ 5 **12.** ≈ 2

13. $\approx 2\frac{3}{4}$ or ≈ 3 **14.** $\approx \frac{1}{2}$

15. ≈ 17 or ≈ 18 **16.** $\approx \frac{1}{4}$

17. ≈ 6 **18.** ≈ 50 or ≈ 51

19. $\approx \frac{1}{2}$ **20.** ≈ 39

21. $\approx 4\frac{1}{4}$

22. about $375 per week

23. about 5 miles

24. $4\frac{1}{4}$ or 4.25

25. 11 R2, $11\frac{2}{11}$, or $11.\overline{18}$

26. 8 R5, $8\frac{5}{8}$, or 8.625

27. 7

28. 94 R6, $94\frac{2}{3}$, or $94.\overline{6}$

29. 21 R1, $21\frac{1}{15}$, or $21.0\overline{6}$

30. 3 R12, $3\frac{6}{11}$, or $3.\overline{54}$

31. 22 R5, $22\frac{1}{5}$, or 22.2

32. 16 R15, $16\frac{15}{16}$, or 16.9375

33. 14 R19, $14\frac{19}{32}$, or 14.59375

Reinforcement

EP/MR Worksheet 48, TRB, page 48

Challenge

Mentally estimate the products of the following problems to the nearest whole number. Round each fraction to the nearest whole number or whole number-and-a-half before multiplying.

1. $3\frac{9}{10} \times 2\frac{1}{8} \times 1\frac{1}{11} \approx$ (8)

2. $1.8 \times 3.1 \times 4.99 \approx$ (30)

3. $3\frac{8}{9} \times 4\frac{3}{5} \times 1\frac{9}{13} \approx$ (36 or 40)

4. $0.89 \times 10\frac{3}{31} \times 5\frac{4}{5} \approx$ (60)

5. $0.5 \times \frac{4}{9} \times 3\frac{5}{6} \approx$ (1)

T139

Objectives

- To divide fractions by fractions
- To divide fractions by whole numbers

Purpose

This lesson helps you to solve problems in which you have to divide parts of a whole by fractions or by whole numbers. Examples might include dividing distances, ingredients, and materials.

Introducing the Lesson

Review multiplication of fractions (Lessons 6.1, 6.2).

Draw a rectangle on the chalkboard and divide it into fourths. Shade in one-fourth of the rectangle. Divide the entire rectangle into eighths. Ask: How many eighths are in one-fourth? (2) Write the problem $\frac{1}{4} \div \frac{1}{8} = 2$ on the chalkboard. Use the diagram on the chalkboard to point out to students that dividing $\frac{1}{4}$ by $\frac{1}{8}$ resulted in a quotient that is greater than one. Introduce the term *reciprocal*. Explain that reciprocals are two numbers whose product is 1. Rewrite $\frac{1}{4} \div \frac{1}{8}$ as $\frac{1}{4} \times \frac{8}{1}$ and ask students to multiply (2). Explain that dividing $\frac{1}{4}$ by $\frac{1}{8}$ is the same as multiplying by the reciprocal of $\frac{1}{8}$, which is 8.

Alternative Examples

Example A—Find the reciprocal of $\frac{2}{3}$.

$\frac{2}{3} \times \frac{3}{2}$

Since $\frac{2}{3} \times \frac{3}{2} = 1$, the reciprocal of $\frac{2}{3}$ is $\mathbf{\frac{3}{2}}$.

Example B—Divide. $\frac{5}{8} \div \frac{1}{4}$

$\frac{5}{8} \div \frac{1}{4} = \frac{5}{8} \times \frac{4}{1} = \frac{20}{8}$, or $2\frac{1}{2}$

$\frac{5}{8} \div \frac{1}{4} = \mathbf{2\frac{1}{2}}$

Example C—Divide. $\frac{4}{7} \div 6$

$\frac{4}{7} \div 6 = \frac{4}{7} \times \frac{1}{6}$

$\frac{4}{7} \div 6 = \frac{4}{42}$, or $\frac{2}{21}$

$\frac{4}{7} \div 6 = \mathbf{\frac{2}{21}}$

6.6 Dividing Fractions

When a community play was proposed, Greg suggested that half of the play's profits be divided equally among the three organizations involved. What part of the total profit should each get?

Divide to determine each group's part of the total profit.

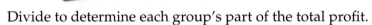

Examples

To divide a fraction, multiply by the reciprocal of the divisor. **Reciprocals** are two numbers whose product is 1.

For example, $\frac{3}{8} \times \frac{8}{3} = \frac{24}{24} = 1$.   The reciprocal of $\frac{3}{8}$ is $\frac{8}{3}$.

A Find the reciprocal of $\frac{5}{6}$.

$\frac{5}{6} \times \frac{6}{5}$ Invert the numerator and the denominator.

Since $\frac{5}{6} \times \frac{6}{5} = 1$, the reciprocal of $\frac{5}{6}$ is $\frac{6}{5}$.

B Divide. $\frac{2}{3} \div \frac{1}{2}$

$\frac{2}{3} \div \frac{1}{2} = \frac{2}{3} \times \frac{2}{1}$

$\frac{2}{3} \div \frac{1}{2} = \frac{4}{3}$, or $1\frac{1}{3}$

$\frac{2}{3} \div \frac{1}{2} = 1\frac{1}{3}$

C Divide. $\frac{1}{2} \div 3$

$\frac{1}{2} \div 3 = \frac{1}{2} \times \frac{1}{3}$

$\frac{1}{2} \div 3 = \frac{1}{6}$

▶ Think and Discuss

1. Write 3 as a fraction. Find the reciprocal of 3.

2. Divide $\frac{3}{8}$ by $\frac{5}{6}$.

3. Refer to the introduction of this lesson. What part of the profits did each group get?

4. What is the reciprocal of 1?

5. What is the product of 6 and its reciprocal?

6. What is the product of any number multiplied by its reciprocal?

Exercises

Find the reciprocal. (See Example A.)

7. $\frac{2}{3}$ $\frac{3}{2}$ 8. $\frac{5}{7}$ $\frac{7}{5}$ 9. $4\frac{1}{4}$ 10. $\frac{1}{2}$ 2   11. $\frac{5}{16}$ $\frac{16}{5}$ 12. $10\frac{1}{10}$ 13. $\frac{1}{5}$ 5   14. $\frac{7}{300}$ $\frac{300}{7}$

Divide. Write the answers in lowest terms. (See Example B.)

15. $\frac{8}{9} \div \frac{4}{9}$ 2   16. $\frac{3}{4} \div \frac{5}{8}$ $1\frac{1}{5}$ 17. $\frac{4}{5} \div \frac{8}{15}$ $1\frac{1}{2}$ 18. $\frac{8}{9} \div \frac{5}{6}$ $1\frac{1}{15}$ 19. $\frac{7}{11} \div \frac{11}{12}$ $\frac{84}{121}$

20. $\frac{2}{3} \div \frac{5}{8}$ $1\frac{1}{15}$ 21. $\frac{8}{11} \div \frac{1}{2}$ $1\frac{5}{11}$ 22. $\frac{9}{16} \div \frac{3}{8}$ $1\frac{1}{2}$ 23. $\frac{5}{6} \div \frac{1}{4}$ $3\frac{1}{3}$ 24. $\frac{4}{7} \div \frac{4}{9}$ $1\frac{2}{7}$

Divide. Write the answers in lowest terms. (See Example C.)

25. $\frac{3}{4} \div 3$ $\frac{1}{4}$ 26. $\frac{5}{6} \div 7$ $\frac{5}{42}$ 27. $\frac{9}{10} \div 9$ $\frac{1}{10}$ 28. $\frac{2}{3} \div 6$ $\frac{1}{9}$ 29. $\frac{1}{6} \div 2$ $\frac{1}{12}$

30. $\frac{11}{12} \div 7$ $\frac{11}{84}$ 31. $\frac{6}{7} \div 3$ $\frac{2}{7}$ 32. $\frac{8}{15} \div 4$ $\frac{2}{15}$ 33. $\frac{12}{25} \div 5$ $\frac{12}{125}$ 34. $\frac{4}{5} \div 10$ $\frac{2}{25}$

▶ Mixed Practice   (For more practice, see page 420.)

Divide. Write the answers in lowest terms.

35. $\frac{4}{9} \div 2$ $\frac{2}{9}$ 36. $\frac{5}{6} \div \frac{3}{4}$ $1\frac{1}{9}$ 37. $\frac{15}{16} \div 10$ $\frac{3}{32}$ 38. $\frac{7}{12} \div \frac{7}{8}$ $\frac{2}{3}$ 39. $\frac{15}{16} \div \frac{2}{3}$ $1\frac{13}{32}$

40. $\frac{3}{8} \div \frac{1}{4}$ $1\frac{1}{2}$ 41. $\frac{7}{8} \div 14$ $\frac{1}{16}$ 42. $\frac{4}{5} \div \frac{1}{2}$ $1\frac{3}{5}$ 43. $\frac{4}{5} \div 2$ $\frac{2}{5}$ 44. $\frac{4}{11} \div 7$ $\frac{4}{77}$

▶ Applications

45. Cris is building a record holder that is three-quarters of a yard long. He wants to divide it into three equal sections. How wide will each section be? $\frac{1}{4}$ yard

46. About $\frac{1}{18}$ of the world's population lives in the United States. About $\frac{1}{216}$ of the world's population lives in New York State. About what part of the U.S. population lives in New York State? $\frac{1}{12}$

▶ Review (Lessons 1.12, 2.6)

Estimate each sum or product.

47. $\begin{array}{r} 428 \\ \times\ 75 \\ \hline \approx 40{,}000 \end{array}$ 48. $\begin{array}{r} 669 \\ +\ 741 \\ \hline \approx 1400 \end{array}$ 49. $\begin{array}{r} 189 \\ \times\ 537 \\ \hline \approx 100{,}000 \end{array}$ 50. $\begin{array}{r} 919 \\ +\ 850 \\ \hline \approx 1800 \end{array}$ 51. $\begin{array}{r} 647 \\ \times\ 636 \\ \hline \approx 360{,}000 \end{array}$

▶ **Think and Discuss Answers**
1. $\frac{3}{1}, \frac{1}{3}$ 2. $\frac{9}{20}$ 3. $\frac{1}{6}$
4. $\frac{1}{1}$ or 1   5. 1   6. 1

★ **Error Alert**
Mistakes may occur if students multiply by the reciprocal of the dividend rather than the reciprocal of the divisor. For example, in the problem $\frac{1}{4} \div \frac{1}{8}$, an incorrect answer would result if students multiplied $\frac{4}{1} \times \frac{1}{8} = \frac{1}{2}$, instead of $\frac{1}{4} \times \frac{8}{1} = 2$.

Reinforcement
Extra Practice, page 420
EP/MR Worksheet 49, TRB, page 49

Puzzle
Divide the following and use the code below to find a hidden message:

$\frac{2}{3} \div 4$ (Y)
$6 \div \frac{1}{3}$ (O)
$\frac{4}{5} \div \frac{7}{10}$ (U)
$\frac{5}{8} \div \frac{5}{8}$ (D)
$\frac{1}{5} \div 2$ (I)
$\frac{3}{8} \div \frac{3}{8}$ (D)
$\frac{8}{90} \div \frac{8}{9}$ (I)
$\frac{1}{9} \div \frac{3}{2}$ (T)
$\frac{2}{3} \div \frac{1}{9}$ (!)

Code: $\frac{1}{18} = $ E; $\frac{2}{27} = $ T; $\frac{1}{10} = $ I; $\frac{1}{6} = $ Y; $\frac{3}{4} = $ A; $\frac{7}{8} = $ C; 1 = D; $1\frac{1}{7} = $ U; $\frac{3}{2} = $ B; $\frac{7}{4} = $ L; 6 = !; 10 = P; $13\frac{1}{2} = $ S; 18 = O

Objectives

- To divide mixed numbers by mixed numbers
- To divide fractions by mixed numbers and vice versa

Purpose

This lesson helps you to divide mixed numbers. For example, you can use division to find how many shelves you could make from a board that was $12\frac{1}{2}$ feet long if each shelf was $2\frac{1}{4}$ feet long.

Introducing the Lesson

Review multiplying mixed numbers (Lesson 6.4) and writing mixed numbers as fractions (Lesson 5.3).

Write $3\frac{1}{5} \times 1\frac{1}{3}$ on the chalkboard. Ask: What must you do before you multiply? (Change the mixed numbers to improper fractions.) Rewrite and solve the problem using improper fractions. ($\frac{16}{5} \times \frac{4}{3} = \frac{64}{15} = 4\frac{4}{15}$) Now change the multiplication symbol to a division symbol. Ask: What must you do before you divide? (take the reciprocal of the divisor) Solve. ($\frac{16}{5} \div \frac{4}{3} = \frac{16}{5} \times \frac{3}{4} = \frac{12}{5} = 2\frac{2}{5}$)

Alternative Examples

Example A—Divide. $2\frac{3}{8} \div 4\frac{1}{9}$

$2\frac{3}{8} \div 4\frac{1}{9} = \frac{19}{8} \div \frac{37}{9}$

$2\frac{3}{8} \div 4\frac{1}{9} = \frac{19}{8} \times \frac{9}{37}$

$2\frac{3}{8} \div 4\frac{1}{9} = \frac{171}{296}$

Example B—Divide. $\frac{1}{3} \div 1\frac{1}{4}$

$\frac{1}{3} \div 1\frac{1}{4} = \frac{1}{3} \div \frac{5}{4}$

$\frac{1}{3} \div 1\frac{1}{4} = \frac{1}{3} \times \frac{4}{5}$

$\frac{1}{3} \div 1\frac{1}{4} = \frac{4}{15}$

Example C—Divide. $3\frac{1}{6} \div \frac{1}{6}$

$3\frac{1}{6} \div \frac{1}{6} = \frac{19}{6} \div \frac{1}{6}$

$3\frac{1}{6} \div \frac{1}{6} = \frac{19}{6} \times \frac{6}{1} = \frac{19}{1}$

$3\frac{1}{6} \div \frac{1}{6} = 19$

6.7 Dividing Mixed Numbers

ROAD RUNNER CLUB MARATHON

Magda is training for a race. One day she ran $4\frac{1}{2}$ miles in $\frac{1}{2}$ hour. To find how many miles per hour she ran, Magda can divide $4\frac{1}{2}$ by $\frac{1}{2}$.

Examples

To divide mixed numbers, first write each mixed number as an improper fraction. Then proceed as with fractions.

A Divide. $3\frac{3}{4} \div 4\frac{2}{5}$

$3\frac{3}{4} \div 4\frac{2}{5} = \frac{15}{4} \div \frac{22}{5}$

$3\frac{3}{4} \div 4\frac{2}{5} = \frac{15}{4} \times \frac{5}{22}$

$3\frac{3}{4} \div 4\frac{2}{5} = \frac{75}{88}$

B Divide. $\frac{4}{5} \div 1\frac{1}{2}$

$\frac{4}{5} \div 1\frac{1}{2} = \frac{4}{5} \div \frac{3}{2}$

$\frac{4}{5} \div 1\frac{1}{2} = \frac{4}{5} \times \frac{2}{3}$

$\frac{4}{5} \div 1\frac{1}{2} = \frac{8}{15}$

C Divide. $4\frac{1}{2} \div \frac{1}{2}$

$4\frac{1}{2} \div \frac{1}{2} = \frac{9}{2} \div \frac{1}{2}$

$4\frac{1}{2} \div \frac{1}{2} = \frac{9}{2} \times \frac{\overset{1}{2}}{1} = \frac{9}{1}$

$4\frac{1}{2} \div \frac{1}{2} = 9$

▶ Think and Discuss

1. Divide $\frac{1}{4}$ by $1\frac{1}{2}$.

2. Refer to the introduction to this lesson. How many miles per hour did Magda run?

3. Suppose you were asked to tutor a younger student in mixed-number division. Explain how to solve this problem: $4\frac{1}{5} \div \frac{1}{4}$.

4. If you estimate $3\frac{1}{8} \div 4\frac{3}{7}$, will the quotient be less than 1 or greater than 1? Explain.

5. When is 1 the quotient of two mixed numbers? Explain.

Exercises

Divide. Write the answers in lowest terms. (See Example A.)

6. $1\frac{1}{5} \div 3\frac{1}{2}$ **7.** $3\frac{1}{7} \div 1\frac{1}{4}$ **8.** $1\frac{3}{5} \div 3\frac{2}{3}$ **9.** $2\frac{2}{3} \div 4\frac{1}{2}$ **10.** $1\frac{9}{10} \div 1\frac{2}{5}$

11. $3\frac{1}{3} \div 2\frac{1}{2}$ **12.** $5\frac{1}{3} \div 1\frac{3}{5}$ **13.** $5\frac{2}{5} \div 2\frac{2}{9}$ **14.** $8\frac{1}{3} \div 3\frac{1}{3}$ **15.** $1\frac{1}{5} \div 3\frac{3}{5}$

Divide. Write the answers in lowest terms. (See Example B.)

16. $\frac{6}{9} \div 2\frac{1}{2}\ \frac{4}{15}$ **17.** $\frac{1}{3} \div 4\frac{2}{7}\ \frac{7}{90}$ **18.** $\frac{2}{5} \div 10\frac{1}{12}\ \frac{24}{605}$ **19.** $\frac{1}{4} \div 1\frac{1}{4}\ \frac{1}{5}$ **20.** $\frac{7}{9} \div 2\frac{1}{3}\ \frac{1}{3}$

21. $\frac{4}{8} \div 5\frac{1}{5}\ \frac{5}{52}$ **22.** $\frac{1}{2} \div 1\frac{1}{9}\ \frac{9}{20}$ **23.** $\frac{12}{18} \div 3\frac{3}{5}\ \frac{5}{27}$ **24.** $\frac{2}{3} \div 4\frac{3}{8}\ \frac{16}{105}$ **25.** $\frac{4}{5} \div 9\frac{1}{10}\ \frac{8}{91}$

Divide. Write the answers in lowest terms. (See Example C.)

26. $4\frac{3}{5} \div \frac{2}{3}$ **27.** $5\frac{3}{4} \div \frac{1}{2}$ **28.** $2\frac{1}{2} \div \frac{4}{5}$ **29.** $3\frac{5}{8} \div \frac{2}{3}$ **30.** $6\frac{9}{10} \div \frac{4}{9}$

31. $1\frac{3}{4} \div \frac{10}{11}$ **32.** $7\frac{1}{7} \div \frac{5}{7}$ **33.** $2\frac{7}{8} \div \frac{1}{3}$ **34.** $1\frac{7}{16} \div \frac{1}{4}$ **35.** $8\frac{4}{5} \div \frac{5}{6}$

▶ Mixed Practice   (For more practice, see page 420.)

Divide. Write the answers in lowest terms.

36. $\frac{1}{5} \div 1\frac{2}{3}$ **37.** $2\frac{5}{8} \div \frac{7}{8}$ **38.** $\frac{5}{8} \div 2\frac{1}{12}$ **39.** $4\frac{1}{2} \div 2\frac{2}{3}$ **40.** $10\frac{1}{10} \div \frac{2}{7}$

41. $7\frac{1}{2} \div 1\frac{1}{2}$ **42.** $11\frac{1}{4} \div \frac{1}{8}$ **43.** $\frac{2}{5} \div 4\frac{4}{5}$ **44.** $3\frac{3}{7} \div 2\frac{1}{6}$ **45.** $\frac{4}{9} \div 9\frac{4}{9}$

46. $8\frac{1}{4} \div \frac{1}{2}$ **47.** $1\frac{2}{3} \div 1\frac{1}{4}$ **48.** $\frac{3}{4} \div 1\frac{2}{3}$ **49.** $5\frac{2}{5} \div 1\frac{2}{5}$ **50.** $\frac{6}{11} \div 6\frac{4}{5}$

▶ Applications

51. A carpenter is constructing a $21\frac{1}{3}$-foot wall from panels that are $1\frac{1}{3}$ feet wide. How many full panels are needed? 16 panels

52. Sara is typing a photo caption for the school paper. If each typed character is $\frac{1}{12}$ inch wide, how many characters will fit on a line that measures $7\frac{1}{2}$ inches long? 90 characters

▶ Review (Lessons 2.3, 2.7)

Multiply mentally.

53. 60×800
48,000
54. 300×900
270,000
55. 8.57×10
85.7
56. 100×0.9
90
57. 50×80
4000
58. 7000×80
560,000
59. 5.4×1000
5400
60. 10×0.065
0.65
61. 1000×0.6
600
62. 70×40
2800
63. 55.4×10
554
64. 400×600
240,000

Objective

- To work with fractions in a real-life application

Purpose

Fractions are commonly used in businesses where people build or construct things. This lesson shows you how a doll maker might apply knowledge of fractions to making dolls.

Introducing the Lesson

Review multiplying decimals and whole numbers (Lesson 2.8) and rounding quotients (Lesson 3.11). Use the examples: Multiply— $5 \times 2.85 = (14.25)$. Round to the nearest cent—$13.75 \div 8 = (\$1.72)$.

Show students how to multiply decimals by fractions. Use the example: $\frac{2}{3} \times \$0.79 = \frac{2 \times 0.79}{3} = \frac{1.58}{3} \approx \$0.53$.

Assist students in making a chart like the one below listing occupations that involve using fractions and how they are used.

Occupation	How Fractions Are Used
flooring installer	measures flooring in fractions of yards
cook	measures recipe amounts using fractions
interior designer	measures fabrics, materials, rooms, windows, and floors using fractions

▶ Think and Discuss Answers

1. Unit cost is the price per unit; with fabric, for example, it is the price per yard of fabric.

2. $\frac{5}{8}$ yard; $3.69/yard; $2.31

3. Multiply each amount of materials needed by the appropriate unit cost and then add all the results; 8 calculations are needed (7 multiplication calculations, 1 addition calculation).

4. $8.37, or $8.81 if you assume she has to buy a whole bag of stuffing

5. $18.75

6. $27.12, or $27.56 if you assume she has to buy a whole bag of stuffing

6.8 Fractions: A Business Application

Rae makes life-size dolls of celebrities, politicians, and famous people from history. Recently, Rae got an order from Desert Community College. Their school mascot is Laurence the Lion, and they want 250 Laurence dolls to sell in the student center bookstore.

Rae's first task is to plan what supplies she will need for each lion. The table below shows her figures:

Materials for 1 Lion	Amount	Unit Cost
gold velour (body)	$\frac{5}{8}$ yard	$3.69/yd.
white fleece (chest)	$\frac{1}{3}$ yard	$4.25/yd.
brown fleece (mane)	$\frac{3}{8}$ yard	$4.25/yd
blue satin (school letter and cap)	$\frac{1}{4}$ yard	$8.99/yd.
black cord (trim)	$\frac{2}{3}$ yard	$0.45/yd.
buttons (eyes)	2	$2\frac{1}{2}$¢
stuffing	$\frac{1}{2}$ bag	$0.89/bag

▶ Think and Discuss

1. What does "unit cost" in the table above mean?

2. How much gold velour does Rae need for each lion? What is the unit cost of the velour? How much must Rae spend on the velour?

3. Describe how Rae can find what one lion will cost to make. How many calculations does she need to make?

4. Find the cost of materials for one lion.

5. Rae charges $12.50 per hour for labor (the time she spends sewing). When she made a sample doll for the community college, it took her 3 hours. Once she begins production, though, she estimates that she can cut that time in half. How much will each lion cost in labor alone?

6. What does one lion cost in supplies and labor together?

Rae must buy large quantities of expensive fabric, so she wants to waste as little fabric as possible.

7. Make a table like the one Rae made. Add two new columns: "Total Amount" and "Total Cost." Use Rae's table to figure the amounts of materials that are needed to make 250 lions. Write the answers under "Total Amount." Calculate the cost of each of the materials for 250 lions. Write the answers under "Total Cost."

8. Find the total cost of materials for 250 lions.

9. Find the total time it will take Rae to produce the entire order. How much will she charge for her labor?

Rae always adds on a profit of $\frac{1}{5}$ the total cost of materials when estimating her total charge.

10. What will Rae's profit be?

11. How will Rae calculate her total charge for 250 Laurence the Lion dolls? Find the total charge.

12. Rae's next project will be to make 7 large tropical fish for a pet store. Use the following table to figure out what each fish will cost to make and what the total of 7 will cost.

Materials for 1 Fish	Amount	Unit Cost
multicolored satin	$1\frac{1}{2}$ yards	$8.99/yd.
gold cord for trim	$3\frac{1}{4}$ yards	$0.45/yd.
gold buttons for eyes	2	$8\frac{1}{2}$¢
gold thread for detailing	$\frac{1}{4}$ spool	$0.99/spool
stuffing	$1\frac{1}{2}$ bags	$0.89/bag

13. If it takes $\frac{3}{4}$ hour to make 1 fish and Rae charges $12.50 an hour, what will be her total labor charge for 7 fish?

14. If Rae adds on a profit of $\frac{1}{5}$ the total cost of materials, what will her profit be for 7 fish?

▶ **Review** (Lessons 2.8, 2.10)

Multiply.

15. 42×0.46
19.32

16. 2.9×4.5
13.05

17. 9.125×45
410.625

18. 603×9.55
5758.65

19. 0.75×0.99
0.7425

20. 475×0.5
237.5

21. 91×0.1
9.1

22. 7654×2.2
16,838.8

Multiplying and Dividing Fractions and Mixed Numbers **145**

▶ **Think and Discuss Answers**
(continued)

7. Material	Total Amount	Total Cost
gold velour	$156\frac{1}{4}$ yd.	$576.56
white fleece	$83\frac{1}{3}$ yd.	354.17
brown fleece	$93\frac{3}{4}$ yd.	398.44
blue satin	$62\frac{1}{2}$ yd.	561.88
black cord	$166\frac{2}{3}$ yd.	75.00
buttons	500	12.50
stuffing	125 bags	111.25

8. $2089.80

9. 375 hours (not including prototype); $4687.50

10. $417.96

11. by adding labor, materials, and profit; $7195.26

12. One fish will cost $13.49 + $1.46 + $0.17 + $0.25 + $1.34 = $16.71. If you assume she has to buy whole bags of stuffing and whole spools of thread, one fish will cost $13.49 + $1.46 + $0.17 + $0.99 + $1.78 = $17.89. Possible answers for the cost of 7 fish are: $16.71 × 7 = $116.97, or $94.40 + $10.24 + $1.19 + $1.98 + $9.79 = $117.60.

13. $65.63

14. Answers will depend on students' answers to Question 12. Answers include: $116.97 × $\frac{1}{5}$ = $23.398, or $117.60 × $\frac{1}{5}$ = $23.52.

★ **Error Alert**
Mistakes may occur if students do not realize that some materials are not available as fractions of the whole. For example, when you use only $\frac{1}{2}$ bag of stuffing, you still must buy a whole bag.

Reinforcement
EP/MR Worksheet 51, TRB, page 51

Project
Take turns measuring the height of each student in the classroom using a measuring tape or a yardstick. Measure in inches using fractions as small as $\frac{1}{4}$ inch. Compute how far students would reach if all were laid end to end. Convert the total to feet and then to yards. Find what fraction of a mile the total is. (Answers depend on the heights and the number of students.)

Answers
14. $1\frac{1}{4}$
15. 58
16. $2\frac{3}{16}$
17. $16\frac{1}{2}$
18. $14\frac{1}{12}$
19. about 1
20. about $4\frac{1}{2}$
21. about 35
22. about 21
23. about 12

Chapter 6 Review

Multiply. Write the answers in lowest terms. (Lessons 6.1, 6.2)

1. $\frac{1}{2} \times \frac{3}{4}$ $\frac{3}{8}$
2. $\frac{5}{6} \times \frac{1}{8}$ $\frac{5}{48}$
3. $\frac{2}{3} \times \frac{4}{5}$ $\frac{8}{15}$
4. $\frac{1}{12} \times \frac{1}{3}$ $\frac{1}{36}$
5. $\frac{3}{8} \times \frac{4}{9}$ $\frac{1}{6}$

6. $\frac{2}{3} \times \frac{3}{10}$ $\frac{1}{5}$
7. $9 \times \frac{7}{8}$ $7\frac{7}{8}$
8. $\frac{5}{12} \times 6$ $2\frac{1}{2}$
9. $\frac{3}{5} \times \frac{5}{12}$ $\frac{1}{4}$
10. $\frac{5}{8} \times \frac{5}{6}$ $\frac{25}{48}$
11. $\frac{14}{15} \times \frac{5}{7}$ $\frac{2}{3}$

Use Guess and Check to solve. (Lesson 6.3)

12. Melissa went out to lunch twice last week. She spent $7.65 in all. The first lunch cost $0.45 less than the second lunch cost. How much money did she spend on each lunch? $4.05; $3.60

13. Video tapes cost $3.99. Audio tapes cost $2.49. Today Hernán spent $39.87 on tapes. The number of audio tapes he bought was 3 more than the number of video tapes he bought. How many of each kind did he buy? 5 video; 8 audio

Multiply. Write the answers in lowest terms. (Lesson 6.4)

14. $\frac{3}{4} \times 1\frac{2}{3}$
15. $5\frac{4}{5} \times 10$
16. $1\frac{7}{8} \times 1\frac{1}{6}$
17. $7\frac{1}{2} \times 2\frac{1}{5}$
18. $4\frac{1}{3} \times 3\frac{1}{4}$

Estimate each product. (Lesson 6.5)

19. $\frac{11}{12} \times \frac{5}{6}$
20. $4\frac{1}{2} \times \frac{9}{10}$
21. $7\frac{1}{4} \times 5\frac{1}{3}$
22. $6\frac{5}{8} \times 3\frac{2}{5}$
23. $2\frac{7}{8} \times 4\frac{1}{9}$

Find the reciprocal. (Lesson 6.6)

24. $\frac{4}{5}$ $\frac{5}{4}$
25. $\frac{13}{16}$ $\frac{16}{13}$
26. $\frac{7}{15}$ $\frac{15}{7}$
27. $\frac{9}{22}$ $\frac{22}{9}$
28. $\frac{13}{17}$ $\frac{17}{13}$
29. $\frac{16}{27}$ $\frac{27}{16}$
30. $\frac{23}{32}$ $\frac{32}{23}$

Divide. Write the answers in lowest terms. (Lessons 6.6, 6.7)

31. $\frac{7}{8} \div \frac{7}{12}$ $1\frac{1}{2}$
32. $\frac{3}{4} \div 8$ $\frac{3}{32}$
33. $3\frac{1}{5} \div \frac{2}{5}$ 8
34. $\frac{7}{10} \div 5\frac{1}{2}$ $\frac{7}{55}$
35. $\frac{9}{10} \div \frac{1}{3}$ $2\frac{7}{10}$

36. $6 \div 5\frac{3}{4}$ $1\frac{1}{23}$
37. $5\frac{5}{6} \div 2\frac{1}{2}$ $2\frac{1}{3}$
38. $9\frac{1}{3} \div 4\frac{2}{3}$ 2
39. $\frac{7}{8} \div 8\frac{1}{6}$ $\frac{3}{28}$
40. $\frac{4}{5} \div 1\frac{1}{4}$ $\frac{16}{25}$

Multiply or divide. Write each answer in lowest terms.
(Lessons 6.4, 6.7)

41. Kevin's room is $8\frac{3}{4}$ feet wide. How many posters $1\frac{3}{4}$ feet wide can he fit along the wall? 5 posters

42. Mary is doubling a recipe that calls for $2\frac{2}{3}$ cups of flour. How much flour should she use? $5\frac{1}{3}$ cups

Chapter 6 Test

TEST

Chapter Tests
Short Answer, Forms A and B, TRB, pages
287–288, 289–290
Multiple Choice, Forms A and B, TRB, pages
355–356, 357–358

Teaching Aids
Answer sheet
TA 8, TRB, page 161a
Teaching suggestions precede the Teaching
Aids worksheets.

Estimate each product.

1. $3\frac{7}{10} \times 2\frac{1}{6}$ 8   2. $\frac{11}{12} \times \frac{7}{8}$ 1   3. $5\frac{1}{3} \times 5\frac{3}{4}$ 30   4. $1\frac{5}{6} \times 2\frac{3}{8}$ 5 or 4

Find the reciprocal.

5. $\frac{10}{36}$ $\frac{36}{10}$ 6. $\frac{33}{56}$ $\frac{56}{33}$ 7. $\frac{9}{17}$ $\frac{17}{9}$

Multiply. Write the answers in lowest terms.

8. $\frac{3}{8} \times \frac{1}{3}$ $\frac{1}{8}$ 9. $5\frac{1}{2} \times 4$ 22   10. $\frac{7}{12} \times 6$ $3\frac{1}{2}$ 11. $4\frac{4}{9} \times 1\frac{4}{5}$ 8   12. $\frac{1}{3} \times \frac{6}{7}$ $\frac{2}{7}$

13. $9 \times 1\frac{5}{6}$ $16\frac{1}{2}$ 14. $3\frac{1}{3} \times 6\frac{1}{4}$ $20\frac{5}{6}$ 15. $\frac{7}{10} \times \frac{4}{5}$ $\frac{14}{25}$ 16. $2\frac{5}{8} \times 1\frac{2}{3}$ $4\frac{3}{8}$ 17. $\frac{4}{5} \times \frac{4}{7}$ $\frac{16}{35}$

18. Marcy is making 3 skirts. Each skirt requires $1\frac{3}{8}$ yards of fabric. How much fabric does she need altogether? $4\frac{1}{8}$ yards

19. To can 1 quart of apples you need $2\frac{1}{2}$ pounds of fresh apples. How many pounds of apples are needed to can 8 quarts? 20 pounds

Use Guess and Check to solve.

20. Yahna has 15 coins in her hand worth $3.00. Some are dimes and the rest are quarters. How many quarters and dimes does she have?
10 quarters, 5 dimes

21. Tickets to the championship game are $2 for students and $5 for adults. Ten times as many students as adults bought tickets. Ticket sales were $250. How many of each kind of ticket were sold?
100 student tickets; 10 adult tickets

Divide. Write the answers in lowest terms.

22. $\frac{15}{16} \div \frac{5}{8}$ $1\frac{1}{2}$ 23. $\frac{3}{7} \div \frac{7}{10}$ $\frac{30}{49}$ 24. $6\frac{1}{6} \div \frac{2}{3}$ $9\frac{1}{4}$ 25. $1\frac{3}{4} \div 2\frac{4}{5}$ $\frac{5}{8}$ 26. $\frac{2}{3} \div 1\frac{1}{2}$ $\frac{4}{9}$

27. $\frac{13}{16} \div 6\frac{1}{2}$ $\frac{1}{8}$ 28. $\frac{8}{9} \div \frac{7}{12}$ $1\frac{11}{21}$ 29. $3\frac{1}{5} \div 5\frac{1}{3}$ $\frac{3}{5}$ 30. $\frac{4}{5} \div \frac{5}{6}$ $\frac{24}{25}$ 31. $\frac{7}{8} \div 9$ $\frac{7}{72}$

Use adding and subtracting fractions and mixed numbers to find

- how your height changes.
- how much time has gone by.
- the amount of increase or decrease in the price of a stock.
- the number of hours worked over several days.

What are some other ways to use adding and subtracting fractions and mixed numbers?

Adding and Subtracting Fractions and Mixed Numbers

A carpenter builds and repairs structures made of wood.

- Carpenters work for businesses like home builders and contractors or are self-employed.

- A carpenter should enjoy working with his or her hands, know how to use tools, and be able to work within a deadline.

- A carpenter reads blueprints, takes measurements, cuts materials to given lengths, and calculates quickly.

- To become a carpenter, an individual works with other carpenters as an apprentice. An individual can also learn carpentry at a trade school.

- Related careers include furniture makers, cabinetmakers, and engineers.

CAREER

CARPENTER

PORTFOLIO PROJECT: *Make a construction blueprint.*

1. Choose an object from your classroom or home that is made from wood.

2. Make a blueprint of that object. A blueprint shows how to construct the object from individual pieces of wood. Use a scale of $\frac{1}{2}$ inch equals 1 foot on your drawing. Label each segment or part of your blueprint with a measurement.

3. A blueprint shows the distance around each surface of the object. Find the distance around each surface of the object by adding both lengths and both widths of the surface. *Show the math.*

About the Portfolio Project

Students may choose any item made of wood. You might request blueprint paper from a local architectural firm or blueprint copy shop. Provide a sheet of blueprint paper to each student; before committing the blueprint to final copy, suggest that students work on graph paper. Graph paper can be found on page 160 of the Teacher's Resource Binder. Each section of the drawing should include measurements.

Assessment: The individual scoring rubric on page 161 of the Teacher's Resource Binder can be reproduced and used for assessment. Include the following information in the last two boxes. Students should have:
- completed a blueprint of a wooden object on supplied paper.
- accurately figured the distance around each surface.

Objective

- To add and subtract fractions with like denominators

Purpose

You often have to add and subtract fractions with like denominators. For example, you may want to add $\frac{1}{4}$ cup of water to $\frac{3}{4}$ cup of water, or subtract $\frac{1}{8}$ yard of cloth from $\frac{3}{8}$ yard of cloth.

Introducing the Lesson

Draw a square on the chalkboard and divide it evenly into eighths. Show that $\frac{2}{8} + \frac{3}{8} = \frac{5}{8}$ by shading in $\frac{2}{8}$ and then $\frac{3}{8}$. Ask: How much of the square is shaded? ($\frac{5}{8}$) Show students that $\frac{5}{8} - \frac{3}{8} = \frac{2}{8}$ by erasing the shading from 3 of the small squares. Ask: How much of the square is shaded? ($\frac{2}{8}$)

Alternative Examples

Example A—Add. $\frac{23}{26} + \frac{5}{26}$
$\frac{23}{26} + \frac{5}{26} = \frac{28}{26} = 1\frac{2}{26} = \mathbf{1\frac{1}{13}}$

Example B—Subtract. $\frac{5}{12} - \frac{3}{12}$
$\frac{5}{12} - \frac{3}{12} = \frac{2}{12} = \mathbf{\frac{1}{6}}$

▶ Think and Discuss Answers

1. $1\frac{1}{3}$
2. $\frac{5}{6}$
3. $\frac{1}{4}$ inch
4. The denominators should not be added, only the numerators: $\frac{2}{3} + \frac{1}{3} = \frac{3}{3} = 1$.

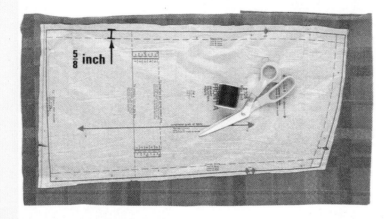

$\frac{5}{8}$ inch

Lila is altering the skirt pattern shown here. She needs to make the waist $\frac{3}{8}$ inch larger on each side of the skirt. She can do this by decreasing the $\frac{5}{8}$-inch seam allowance that is indicated on the pattern. What will each seam allowance measure?

To answer this question, you can subtract $\frac{3}{8}$ from $\frac{5}{8}$.

Examples

To add or subtract fractions with like denominators, add or subtract the numerators. The denominator remains the same.

A Add. $\frac{5}{12} + \frac{11}{12}$

$\frac{5}{12} + \frac{11}{12} = \frac{16}{12} = 1\frac{4}{12} = \mathbf{1\frac{1}{3}}$ Write the answer in lowest terms.

B Subtract. $\frac{5}{8} - \frac{3}{8}$

$\frac{5}{8} - \frac{3}{8} = \frac{2}{8} = \mathbf{\frac{1}{4}}$ Write the answer in lowest terms.

▶ Think and Discuss

1. Add. $\frac{7}{9} + \frac{5}{9}$

2. Subtract. $\frac{11}{12} - \frac{1}{12}$

3. Refer to the introduction to this lesson. How wide should Lila make the seam allowance on the pattern?

4. What is wrong with the statement "$\frac{2}{3} + \frac{1}{3} = \frac{3}{6}$"? What is the correct answer?

Exercises

★ **Error Alert**

Mistakes may reveal that students are adding the denominators or are not reducing the final answer to lowest terms.

Add. Write the answers in lowest terms. (See Example A.)

5. $\dfrac{6}{13}$ $+\dfrac{4}{13}$ $\dfrac{10}{13}$

6. $\dfrac{3}{11}$ $+\dfrac{4}{11}$ $\dfrac{7}{11}$

7. $\dfrac{2}{7}$ $+\dfrac{5}{7}$ 1

8. $\dfrac{7}{12}$ $+\dfrac{11}{12}$ $1\dfrac{1}{2}$

9. $\dfrac{9}{30}$ $+\dfrac{23}{30}$ $1\dfrac{1}{15}$

10. $\dfrac{5}{18}$ $+\dfrac{17}{18}$ $1\dfrac{2}{9}$

11. $\dfrac{5}{6}+\dfrac{5}{6}$ $1\dfrac{2}{3}$

12. $\dfrac{9}{14}+\dfrac{5}{14}$ 1

13. $\dfrac{11}{16}+\dfrac{9}{16}+\dfrac{7}{16}$ $1\dfrac{11}{16}$

14. $\dfrac{17}{20}+\dfrac{13}{20}+\dfrac{9}{20}$ $1\dfrac{19}{20}$

Subtract. Write the answers in lowest terms. (See Example B.)

15. $\dfrac{3}{5}$ $-\dfrac{1}{5}$ $\dfrac{2}{5}$

16. $\dfrac{9}{20}$ $-\dfrac{2}{20}$ $\dfrac{7}{20}$

17. $\dfrac{7}{9}$ $-\dfrac{1}{9}$ $\dfrac{2}{3}$

18. $\dfrac{9}{10}$ $-\dfrac{3}{10}$ $\dfrac{3}{5}$

19. $\dfrac{9}{16}$ $-\dfrac{5}{16}$ $\dfrac{1}{4}$

20. $\dfrac{17}{24}$ $-\dfrac{9}{24}$ $\dfrac{1}{3}$

21. $\dfrac{5}{9}-\dfrac{2}{9}$ $\dfrac{1}{3}$

22. $\dfrac{11}{18}-\dfrac{7}{18}$ $\dfrac{2}{9}$

23. $\dfrac{19}{25}-\dfrac{4}{25}$ $\dfrac{3}{5}$

24. $\dfrac{34}{35}-\dfrac{7}{35}$ $\dfrac{27}{35}$

25. $\dfrac{47}{50}-\dfrac{11}{50}$ $\dfrac{18}{25}$

▶ Mixed Practice (For more practice, see page 421.)

Add or subtract. Write the answers in lowest terms.

26. $\dfrac{15}{17}$ $-\dfrac{9}{17}$ $\dfrac{6}{17}$

27. $\dfrac{13}{20}$ $+\dfrac{17}{20}$ $1\dfrac{1}{2}$

28. $\dfrac{35}{36}$ $-\dfrac{32}{36}$ $\dfrac{1}{12}$

29. $\dfrac{21}{25}$ $-\dfrac{16}{25}$ $\dfrac{1}{5}$

30. $\dfrac{19}{50}$ $+\dfrac{11}{50}$ $\dfrac{3}{5}$

31. $\dfrac{43}{48}$ $+\dfrac{41}{48}$ $1\dfrac{3}{4}$

32. $\dfrac{15}{18}+\dfrac{5}{18}$ 1

33. $\dfrac{33}{36}-\dfrac{13}{36}$ $\dfrac{5}{9}$

34. $\dfrac{23}{27}-\dfrac{14}{27}$ $\dfrac{1}{3}$

35. $\dfrac{89}{100}-\dfrac{57}{100}$ $\dfrac{8}{25}$

36. $\dfrac{19}{35}+\dfrac{23}{35}$ $1\dfrac{1}{5}$

37. $\dfrac{3}{4}+\dfrac{1}{4}+\dfrac{3}{4}$ $1\dfrac{3}{4}$

38. $\dfrac{89}{90}-\dfrac{19}{90}$ $\dfrac{7}{9}$

39. $\dfrac{7}{9}+\dfrac{5}{9}+\dfrac{1}{9}$ $1\dfrac{4}{9}$

▶ Applications

40. Look at the charms from Cori's bracelet. How much longer is the first charm than the second? $\dfrac{1}{4}$ in.

$\dfrac{9}{16}$ inch $\dfrac{5}{16}$ inch

41. Roosevelt spends six hours in school, two hours at basketball practice, and eight hours sleeping. What fraction of his day is left for other activities? $\dfrac{1}{3}$

Reinforcement

Extra Practice, page 421
EP/MR Worksheet 52, TRB, page 52

▶ Review (Lesson 1.8)

Round to the nearest hundredth.

42. 8.164 — 8.16

43. 3.095 — 3.10

44. 6.847 — 6.85

45. 0.9325 — 0.93

46. 2.6891 — 2.69

47. 1.842 — 1.84

Round to the nearest tenth.

48. 16.79 — 16.8

49. 7.515 — 7.5

50. 9.053 — 9.1

51. 4.36 — 4.4

52. 0.829 — 0.8

53. 4.654 — 4.7

Challenge

Write each digit in your phone number over a denominator of 7. Add the fractions. Now, write each digit in your area code over a denominator of 7. Add the fractions. Subtract the smallest answer from the largest. Reduce to lowest terms. (possible answer for a phone number of 555/555-1212: $\dfrac{5}{7}+\dfrac{5}{7}+\dfrac{5}{7}+\dfrac{1}{7}+\dfrac{2}{7}+\dfrac{1}{7}+\dfrac{2}{7}=\dfrac{21}{7}$; $\dfrac{5}{7}+\dfrac{5}{7}+\dfrac{5}{7}=\dfrac{15}{7}$; $\dfrac{21}{7}-\dfrac{15}{7}=\dfrac{6}{7}$)

Objectives

- To list multiples of a given number
- To find the lowest common denominator (LCD) of two fractions
- To find the LCD of three fractions

Purpose

This lesson is about finding the lowest common denominator (LCD) of two or more fractions. For example, if you want to add $\frac{1}{2}$ cup and $\frac{1}{3}$ cup, you can do so by first finding the lowest common denominator of $\frac{1}{3}$ and $\frac{1}{2}$.

Introducing the Lesson

Review finding equivalent fractions (Lesson 5.2). Use the examples: Find equivalent fractions for $\frac{1}{5}, \frac{1}{4}, \frac{1}{2},$ and $\frac{1}{10}$ using a common denominator of 20.
$(\frac{1}{5} = \frac{4}{20}, \frac{1}{4} = \frac{5}{20}, \frac{1}{2} = \frac{10}{20}, \frac{1}{10} = \frac{2}{20})$

Alternative Examples

Example A—List the first five multiples of 16.
$16 \times 1 = \mathbf{16}, 16 \times 2 = \mathbf{32}, 16 \times 3 = \mathbf{48},$
$16 \times 4 = \mathbf{64}, 16 \times 5 = \mathbf{80}$

The first five multiples of 16 are **16, 32, 48, 64,** and **80**

Example B—Find the LCD of $\frac{1}{15}$ and $\frac{2}{9}$.

Multiples of 15:   15   30   **45**
Multiples of 9:   9   18   27   36   **45**

The LCD of $\frac{1}{15}$ and $\frac{2}{9}$ is **45**.

Example C—Find the LCD of $\frac{1}{3}, \frac{1}{6},$ and $\frac{1}{8}$.
Multiples of 3:   3   6   9   12   15   18   21   **24**
Multiples of 6: 6   12   18   **24**   30
Multiples of 8: 8   16   **24**   32   40

The LCD of $\frac{1}{3}, \frac{1}{6},$ and $\frac{1}{8}$ is **24**.

7.2 Finding the Lowest Common Denominator

A school track is shown here. Ken runs each lap in 6 minutes. Roger runs each lap in 8 minutes. Suppose that both boys begin at the starting line at the same time. After how many minutes will they both be at the starting line at the same time?

The answer is a multiple of 6 and 8.

Examples

> To find the lowest common denominator (LCD), list multiples of each denominator. The LCD is the smallest number that appears on all lists.

A List the first five multiples of 6.

$6 \times 1 = \mathbf{6}$ $6 \times 2 = \mathbf{12}$ $6 \times 3 = \mathbf{18}$ $6 \times 4 = \mathbf{24}$ $6 \times 5 = \mathbf{30}$
The first five multiples of 6 are **6, 12, 18, 24,** and **30.**

B Find the LCD of $\frac{2}{6}$ and $\frac{5}{8}$.

Multiples of 6:   6   12   18   **24**
Multiples of 8:   8   16   **24**   32   40
The LCD of $\frac{2}{6}$ and $\frac{5}{8}$ is **24.**

C Find the LCD of $\frac{1}{2}, \frac{1}{4},$ and $\frac{1}{5}$.

Multiples of 2:   2   4   6   8   10   12   14   16   18   **20**
Multiples of 4:   4   8   12   16   **20**   24   28
Multiples of 5:   5   10   15   **20**   25   30
The LCD of $\frac{1}{2}, \frac{1}{4},$ and $\frac{1}{5}$ is **20.**

▶ Think and Discuss

1. Find the LCD of $\frac{2}{3}, \frac{5}{6},$ and $\frac{7}{8}$.

2. Find the LCD of $\frac{2}{5}$ and $\frac{3}{10}$.

3. What are the first five multiples of 7? Of 9?

SKILLS

4. Refer to the introduction to this lesson. After how many minutes will both boys be at the starting line at the same time?

5. When would the LCD of two fractions be one of the denominators?

Exercises

List the first five multiples. (See Example A.)

6. 10   **7.** 15   **8.** 12   **9.** 22   **10.** 13   **11.** 18

Find the LCD. (See Example B.)

12. $\frac{1}{2}$ $\frac{3}{4}$ 4   **13.** $\frac{1}{3}$ $\frac{5}{9}$ 9   **14.** $\frac{7}{8}$ $\frac{5}{6}$ 24   **15.** $\frac{9}{10}$ $\frac{3}{4}$ 20   **16.** $\frac{5}{7}$ $\frac{2}{3}$ 21

Find the LCD. (See Example C.)

17. $\frac{1}{3}$ $\frac{1}{2}$ $\frac{1}{4}$ 12   **18.** $\frac{1}{2}$ $\frac{1}{5}$ $\frac{1}{8}$ 40   **19.** $\frac{1}{4}$ $\frac{3}{5}$ $\frac{5}{6}$ 60   **20.** $\frac{3}{7}$ $\frac{1}{4}$ $\frac{1}{6}$ 84   **21.** $\frac{2}{7}$ $\frac{4}{5}$ $\frac{21}{35}$ 35

▶ Mixed Practice (For more practice, see page 421.)

List the first five multiples.

22. 20   **23.** 11   **24.** 25   **25.** 30   **26.** 17   **27.** 32

Find the LCD.

28. $\frac{2}{3}$ $\frac{7}{10}$ 30   **29.** $\frac{1}{6}$ $\frac{2}{9}$ 18   **30.** $\frac{1}{3}$ $\frac{3}{4}$ $\frac{5}{6}$ 12   **31.** $\frac{2}{9}$ $\frac{13}{27}$ 27   **32.** $\frac{4}{5}$ $\frac{7}{8}$ 40

33. $\frac{1}{10}$ $\frac{2}{3}$ $\frac{2}{15}$ 30   **34.** $\frac{1}{12}$ $\frac{3}{8}$ 24   **35.** $\frac{1}{2}$ $\frac{2}{5}$ $\frac{3}{7}$ 70   **36.** $\frac{1}{6}$ $\frac{1}{7}$ $\frac{1}{2}$ 42   **37.** $\frac{7}{11}$ $\frac{5}{7}$ 77

▶ Applications

38. John bought stock at $\frac{3}{4}$ (of a dollar). It went up $\frac{1}{2}$ the first day. If John wants to figure out the stock's new value, he first needs to find the LCD of the two fractions. What is it?

39. In football, you get six points for a touchdown, seven points for a touchdown plus an extra point, three points for a field goal, and two points for a safety. List the eight different ways you can score fourteen points.

▶ Review (Lesson 1.9)

Add.

40.   6.7
   + 9.88
    16.58

41.   6006
   + 1984
    7990

42.   11
   + 7.45
    18.45

43.   86,471
   + 89,799
    176,270

44.   4.638
   + 0.975
    5.613

▶ **Think and Discuss Answers**
   1. 24
   2. 10
   3. 7   14   28   35;   9   18   27   36
   45
   4. 24 minutes
   5. when one denominator is a multiple of the other

Answers ▶

   6. 10   20   30   40   50
   7. 15   30   45   60   75
   8. 12   24   36   48   60
   9. 22   44   66   88   110
   10. 13   26   39   52   65
   11. 18   36   54   72   90

   22. 20   40   60   80   100
   23. 11   22   33   44   55
   24. 25   50   75   100   125
   25. 30   60   90   120   150
   26. 17   34   51   68   85
   27. 32   64   96   128   160

   38. 4
   39. 1 touchdown, 2 field goals, and 1 safety; 2 touchdowns and 2 extra points; 4 field goals and 1 safety; 7 safeties; 1 touchdown and 4 safeties; 1 touchdown, 1 extra point, 1 field goal, and 2 safeties; 2 touchdowns and 1 safety; 2 field goals and 4 safeties

★ **Error Alert**

Incorrect answers may reveal that students are not using a denominator common to all fractions in the problem. For example, the LCD of $\frac{1}{2}$, $\frac{1}{3}$, and $\frac{1}{4}$ is 12, not 8, although 8 is a common denominator for $\frac{1}{2}$ and $\frac{1}{4}$.

Reinforcement

Extra Practice, page 421
EP/MR Worksheet 53, TRB, page 53

Challenge

Rewrite the following times as fractions of hours; then find the LCD: 20 min., 15 min., 5 min., 10 min., 12 min., and 4 min. ($\frac{1}{3}$ hr., $\frac{1}{4}$ hr., $\frac{1}{12}$ hr., $\frac{1}{6}$ hr., $\frac{1}{5}$ hr., $\frac{1}{15}$ hr.; LCD = 60)

T153

Objective

• To add two fractions with unlike denominators

Purpose

Adding and subtracting fractions with unlike denominators allows you to find sums and differences of amounts measured in fractions with different denominators, such as $\frac{1}{3}$ cup + $\frac{3}{4}$ cup.

Introducing the Lesson

Display the following items in separate groups: 4 pens, 3 pencils, and 2 markers. Ask: How many of each do we have? (4 pens, 3 pencils, 2 markers) Now combine the items into one group and ask: What is the total of all objects? (9) Can you say that we have 9 pens, 9 pencils, or 9 markers? (no) How can you say that there are 9? (Give the items a common name, for example, *writing instruments*.) Explain to students that in much the same way, fractions must be given the same denominator before adding.

Review finding the LCD (Lesson 7.2). Use the example: Find the LCD of $\frac{5}{6}$ and $\frac{7}{8}$. (multiples of 6: 6 12 18 24 30 36; multiples of 8: 8 16 24 32 40; answer: 24)

Alternative Examples

Example A—Add. $\frac{5}{12} + \frac{1}{7}$

$\frac{5}{12} = \frac{5}{12} \times \frac{7}{7} = \frac{35}{84}$

$+ \frac{1}{7} = \frac{1}{7} \times \frac{12}{12} = \frac{12}{84}$

$\frac{47}{84}$

$\frac{5}{12} + \frac{1}{7} = \frac{47}{84}$

Example B—Add. $\frac{3}{4} + \frac{3}{8}$

$\frac{3}{4} = \frac{3}{4} \times \frac{2}{2} = \frac{6}{8}$

$+ \frac{3}{8} = \frac{3}{8} = \frac{3}{8}$

$\frac{9}{8}$ or $1\frac{1}{8}$

$\frac{3}{4} + \frac{3}{8} = 1\frac{1}{8}$

7.3 Adding Fractions with Unlike Denominators

Rainfall

	Daily	Total to Date
Monday 10/3	1/4 inch	1/4 inch
Tuesday 10/4	1/4 inch	1/2 inch
Wednesday 10/5	0 inch	1/2 inch
Thursday 10/6	7/8 inch	_____

Seth records rainfall for a science project in a table like the one shown here. What should he write in the second column for Thursday, October 4th?

To find the *Total to Date*, Seth needs to add $\frac{1}{2}$ inch and $\frac{7}{8}$ inch.

Examples

To add fractions with unlike denominators, rewrite them using their LCD. Then add the numerators.

A   Add. $\frac{1}{5} + \frac{2}{3}$

$\frac{1}{5} = \frac{1}{5} \times \frac{3}{3} = \frac{3}{15}$ Rewrite using the LCD.

$+ \frac{2}{3} = \frac{2}{3} \times \frac{5}{5} = \frac{10}{15}$

$\frac{13}{15}$

$\frac{1}{5} + \frac{2}{3} = \frac{13}{15}$

B Add. $\frac{1}{2} + \frac{7}{8}$

$\frac{1}{2} = \frac{1}{2} \times \frac{4}{4} = \frac{4}{8}$ Rewrite using the LCD.

$+ \frac{7}{8} = \frac{7}{8} = \frac{7}{8}$

$\frac{11}{8}$, or $1\frac{3}{8}$ Rewrite as a mixed number.

$\frac{1}{2} + \frac{7}{8} = 1\frac{3}{8}$

▶ Think and Discuss

1. Add. $\frac{9}{10} + \frac{3}{4}$

2. Add. $\frac{7}{12} + \frac{2}{3}$

3. Refer to the introduction to this lesson. What is the *Total to Date* for October 6th?

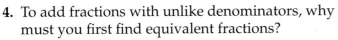

SKILLS

4. To add fractions with unlike denominators, why must you first find equivalent fractions?

5. How is adding fractions with unlike denominators different from adding fractions with like denominators?

6. Why did $\frac{7}{8}$ remain the same in Example B?

Exercises

Add. Write the answers in lowest terms. (See Example A.)

7. $\frac{1}{5}$ $\frac{+\frac{1}{2}}{}$ $\frac{7}{10}$

8. $\frac{7}{12}$ $\frac{+\frac{1}{6}}{}$ $\frac{3}{4}$

9. $\frac{3}{8}$ $\frac{+\frac{5}{16}}{}$ $\frac{11}{16}$

10. $\frac{7}{30}$ $\frac{+\frac{3}{5}}{}$ $\frac{5}{6}$

11. $\frac{1}{2}$ $\frac{+\frac{2}{7}}{}$ $\frac{11}{14}$

12. $\frac{2}{5}$ $\frac{+\frac{1}{4}}{}$ $\frac{13}{20}$

13. $\frac{4}{9} + \frac{1}{3}$ $\frac{7}{9}$

14. $\frac{7}{10} + \frac{1}{5} + \frac{1}{2}$ $1\frac{2}{5}$

15. $\frac{5}{12} + \frac{3}{8}$ $\frac{19}{24}$

16. $\frac{5}{11} + \frac{1}{4}$ $\frac{31}{44}$

Add. Write the answers in lowest terms. (See Example B.)

17. $\frac{1}{2}$ $\frac{+\frac{3}{4}}{}$ $1\frac{1}{4}$

18. $\frac{5}{6}$ $\frac{+\frac{2}{3}}{}$ $1\frac{1}{2}$

19. $\frac{2}{5}$ $\frac{+\frac{3}{4}}{}$ $1\frac{3}{20}$

20. $\frac{9}{10}$ $\frac{+\frac{3}{8}}{}$ $1\frac{11}{40}$

21. $\frac{7}{9}$ $\frac{+\frac{5}{12}}{}$ $1\frac{7}{36}$

22. $\frac{7}{11}$ $\frac{+\frac{4}{7}}{}$ $1\frac{16}{77}$

23. $\frac{4}{5} + \frac{5}{6}$ $1\frac{19}{30}$

24. $\frac{5}{8} + \frac{13}{24} + \frac{1}{3}$ $1\frac{1}{2}$

25. $\frac{9}{32} + \frac{3}{4}$ $1\frac{1}{32}$

26. $\frac{8}{9} + \frac{3}{5}$ $1\frac{22}{45}$

▶ **Mixed Practice** (For more practice, see page 422.)

Add. Write the answers in lowest terms.

27. $\frac{1}{4}$ $\frac{+\frac{3}{8}}{}$ $\frac{5}{8}$

28. $\frac{6}{7}$ $\frac{+\frac{3}{14}}{}$ $1\frac{1}{14}$

29. $\frac{9}{10}$ $\frac{+\frac{3}{4}}{}$ $1\frac{13}{20}$

30. $\frac{4}{9}$ $\frac{+\frac{1}{2}}{}$ $\frac{17}{18}$

31. $\frac{7}{16}$ $\frac{+\frac{2}{3}}{}$ $1\frac{5}{48}$

32. $\frac{9}{10}$ $\frac{+\frac{1}{12}}{}$ $\frac{59}{60}$

 33. $\frac{3}{4} + \frac{2}{11}$ $\frac{41}{44}$

34. $\frac{7}{15} + \frac{1}{2}$ $\frac{29}{30}$

35. $\frac{7}{8} + \frac{1}{2} + \frac{1}{4}$ $1\frac{5}{8}$

36. $\frac{3}{10} + \frac{1}{5} + \frac{1}{6}$ $\frac{2}{3}$

▶ **Applications**

37. Two partial sticks of butter are marked $\frac{2}{3}$ cup and $\frac{3}{8}$ cup. Susan needs 1 cup of butter for baking. Does she have enough? Yes

38. Calvin took a study break. He watched a half-hour show and then talked for twenty minutes. What part of an hour was his break? $\frac{5}{6}$ hr.

▶ **Review** (Lessons 4.2, 4.5, 4.6)

Convert each measure.

39. 72.6 cm to mm
726 mm

40. 8 mL to L
0.008 L

41. 28.1 kg to g
28,100 g

▶ **Think and Discuss Answers**

1. $1\frac{13}{20}$
2. $1\frac{1}{4}$
3. $1\frac{3}{8}$ inch
4. so you can add them as fractions with like denominators
5. with unlike denominators you find the LCD
6. because 8 was the LCD

★ **Error Alert**

Mistakes may reveal that students are adding the denominators and not finding the LCD.

Reinforcement

Extra Practice, page 422
EP/MR Worksheet 54, TRB, page 54

Challenge

Pat, John, Rodney, Traci, Lindsey, and Charlene each have a fraction of a pizza. Pat has $\frac{1}{6}$ of a pizza, John has $\frac{1}{8}$, Rodney has $\frac{1}{7}$, Traci has $\frac{1}{5}$, Lindsey has $\frac{1}{9}$, and Charlene has $\frac{1}{4}$. Add the fractions to find if they had one pizza, less than one, or more than one. (less than one) How much did they have? ($\frac{2509}{2520}$ of a pizza)

7.4 Adding Mixed Numbers

Willy's best score for the high jump is $71\frac{1}{2}$ inches. He must improve his best jump by $2\frac{3}{4}$ inches to match the school record. What is the school record?

Examples

To add mixed numbers, add the fractions and the whole numbers separately.

A Add. $7\frac{3}{5} + 4\frac{4}{5}$

$7\frac{3}{5} = \quad 7 + \frac{3}{5}$

$+ 4\frac{4}{5} = \quad 4 + \frac{4}{5}$

$\qquad\qquad 11 + \frac{7}{5} = 11 + 1\frac{2}{5}$

$\qquad\qquad\qquad\qquad = 12\frac{2}{5}$

$7\frac{3}{5} + 4\frac{4}{5} = \mathbf{12\frac{2}{5}}$

B Add. $71\frac{1}{2} + 2\frac{3}{4}$

$71\frac{1}{2} = 71 + \frac{1}{2} = 71 + \frac{2}{4}$

$+ \quad 2\frac{3}{4} = \quad 2 + \frac{3}{4} = \quad 2 + \frac{3}{4}$

$\qquad\qquad\qquad\qquad\qquad 73 + \frac{5}{4}$

$\qquad\qquad\qquad\qquad\quad = 73 + 1\frac{1}{4}$

$\qquad\qquad\qquad\qquad\quad = 74\frac{1}{4}$

$71\frac{1}{2} + 2\frac{3}{4} = \mathbf{74\frac{1}{4}}$

▶ Think and Discuss

1. Add. $8\frac{5}{8} + 3\frac{3}{8}$

2. Write $10\frac{11}{7}$ so that it does not contain an improper fraction.

3. Refer to the introduction to this lesson. What is the record?

4. When is the sum of two mixed numbers a whole number?

Exercises

Add. Write the answers in lowest terms. (See Example A.)

5. $2\frac{2}{5}$
$+ 3\frac{1}{5}$ $5\frac{3}{5}$

6. $4\frac{1}{4}$
$+ \frac{1}{4}$ $4\frac{1}{2}$

7. $3\frac{5}{8}$
$+ 6\frac{1}{8}$ $9\frac{3}{4}$

8. $5\frac{1}{6}$
$+ 7\frac{2}{6}$ $12\frac{1}{2}$

9. $2\frac{4}{7}$
$+ 3\frac{5}{7}$ $6\frac{2}{7}$

10. $4\frac{1}{2} + 8\frac{1}{2}$ 13   **11.** $3\frac{3}{8} + 4\frac{1}{8}$ $7\frac{1}{2}$ **12.** $5\frac{1}{5} + \frac{4}{5}$ 6   **13.** $6\frac{7}{8} + 9\frac{5}{8}$ $16\frac{1}{2}$

Add. Write the answers in lowest terms. (See Example B.)

14. $3\frac{1}{2}$
$+ 2\frac{1}{4}$ $5\frac{3}{4}$

15. $9\frac{1}{2}$
$+ 3\frac{1}{5}$ $12\frac{7}{10}$

16. $3\frac{1}{6}$
$+ 5\frac{1}{4}$ $8\frac{5}{12}$

17. $7\frac{2}{5}$
$+ 9\frac{1}{4}$ $16\frac{13}{20}$

18. $5\frac{1}{2}$
$+ \frac{1}{3}$ $5\frac{5}{6}$

19. $4\frac{5}{6}$
$+ 6\frac{5}{8}$ $11\frac{11}{24}$

20. $7\frac{1}{2} + 4\frac{5}{8}$ $12\frac{1}{8}$ **21.** $6\frac{2}{3} + 4\frac{5}{12}$ $11\frac{1}{12}$ **22.** $8\frac{3}{5} + 2\frac{5}{6}$ $11\frac{13}{30}$ **23.** $3\frac{5}{7} + \frac{1}{2}$ $4\frac{3}{14}$

▶ Mixed Practice (For more practice, see page 422.)

Add. Write the answers in lowest terms.

24. $7\frac{7}{8} + 8\frac{5}{6}$ $16\frac{17}{24}$ **25.** $8\frac{1}{4} + 6\frac{1}{6}$ $14\frac{5}{12}$ **26.** $6\frac{3}{7} + \frac{4}{9}$ $6\frac{55}{63}$ **27.** $6\frac{7}{15} + 3\frac{13}{15}$ $10\frac{1}{3}$

28. $3\frac{4}{7}$
$+ 6\frac{2}{7}$ $9\frac{6}{7}$

29. $9\frac{2}{3}$
$+ 3\frac{1}{6}$ $12\frac{5}{6}$

30. $5\frac{3}{4}$
$+ 2\frac{1}{8}$ $7\frac{7}{8}$

31. $4\frac{3}{10}$
$+ \frac{1}{2}$ $4\frac{4}{5}$

32. $5\frac{3}{8}$
$+ 9\frac{4}{5}$ $15\frac{7}{40}$

33. $7\frac{7}{9}$
$+ 2\frac{5}{9}$ $10\frac{1}{3}$

34. $2\frac{4}{5}$
$+ \frac{7}{8}$ $3\frac{27}{40}$

35. $8\frac{3}{4}$
$+ 6\frac{1}{4}$ 15

36. $5\frac{5}{9}$
$+ 7\frac{1}{2}$ $13\frac{1}{18}$

37. $2\frac{7}{10}$
$4\frac{1}{10}$
$+ 5\frac{3}{10}$ $12\frac{1}{10}$

38. $3\frac{3}{8}$
$9\frac{1}{4}$
$+ 1\frac{2}{3}$ $14\frac{7}{24}$

39. $7\frac{3}{4}$
$5\frac{3}{7}$
$+ 4\frac{1}{2}$ $17\frac{19}{28}$

▶ Applications

40. A baby grew $1\frac{1}{4}$ inches. If it was $22\frac{5}{8}$ inches long before, how long is the baby now? $23\frac{7}{8}$ inches

41. An antenna was added to the Eiffel Tower, shown here. What is the new height of the Eiffel Tower? $1053\frac{1}{3}$ ft.

$67\frac{5}{12}$ feet

$985\frac{11}{12}$ feet

▶ Review (Lesson 5.7)

Convert each fraction to a decimal.

42. $\frac{1}{5}$ 0.2   **43.** $\frac{7}{10}$ 0.7   **44.** $\frac{3}{4}$ 0.75   **45.** $\frac{7}{8}$ 0.875   **46.** $\frac{2}{3}$ $0.6\overline{6}$ **47.** $\frac{5}{6}$ $0.8\overline{3}$

Purpose

Subtracting fractions with unlike denominators helps you calculate how to cut one fractional piece from another. For example, you can find how much ribbon you have left after cutting a piece $\frac{1}{8}$ of a yard from a piece that was $\frac{3}{4}$ of a yard long.

Introducing the Lesson

Review subtracting fractions with like denominators (Lesson 7.1). Use the example: Subtract—$\frac{5}{15} - \frac{3}{15} = (\frac{2}{15})$. Then reduce each fraction and show students that $\frac{5}{15} - \frac{3}{15}$ is the same as $\frac{1}{3} - \frac{1}{5}$. Write the following on the board: $\frac{5}{15} = \frac{1}{3}$ and $\frac{3}{15} = \frac{1}{5}$. Ask: How would you subtract $\frac{1}{5}$ from $\frac{1}{3}$ to get $\frac{2}{15}$? (by subtracting $\frac{3}{15}$ from $\frac{5}{15}$)

Alternative Examples

Example A—Subtract. $\frac{7}{9} - \frac{1}{3}$

$\frac{7}{9} = \frac{7}{9} = \frac{7}{9}$
$-\frac{1}{3} = \frac{1}{3} \times \frac{3}{3} = \frac{3}{9}$
$\qquad\qquad\qquad \frac{4}{9}$

$\frac{7}{9} - \frac{1}{3} = \frac{4}{9}$

Example B—Subtract. $\frac{1}{2} - \frac{1}{5}$

$\frac{1}{2} = \frac{1}{2} \times \frac{5}{5} = \frac{5}{10}$
$-\frac{1}{5} = \frac{1}{5} \times \frac{2}{2} = \frac{2}{10}$
$\qquad\qquad\qquad \frac{3}{10}$

$\frac{1}{2} - \frac{1}{5} = \frac{3}{10}$

▶ Think and Discuss Answers

1. $\frac{1}{9}$

2. $\frac{3}{16}$ inch

3. 12

4. The second denominator was subtracted from the first.

7.5 Subtracting Fractions with Unlike Denominators

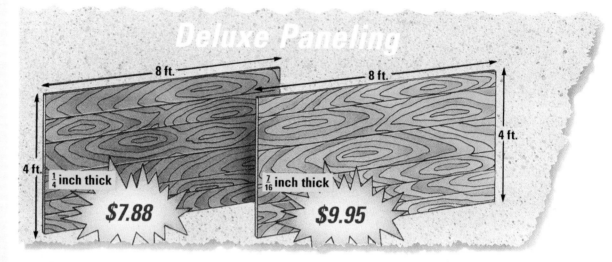

Deluxe Paneling

8 ft. — 4 ft. — $\frac{1}{4}$ inch thick — **$7.88**

8 ft. — 4 ft. — $\frac{7}{16}$ inch thick — **$9.95**

Look at the measurements for the two types of paneling shown above. How much thicker is the more expensive paneling?

Examples

To subtract fractions with unlike denominators, first rewrite them using their LCD. Then subtract the numerators.

A Subtract. $\frac{7}{16} - \frac{1}{4}$

$\frac{7}{16} = \frac{7}{16} = \frac{7}{16}$
$-\frac{1}{4} = \frac{1}{4} \times \frac{4}{4} = \frac{4}{16}$
$\qquad\qquad\qquad \frac{3}{16}$

Rewrite using the LCD.

$\frac{7}{16} - \frac{1}{4} = \frac{3}{16}$

B Subtract. $\frac{3}{4} - \frac{2}{3}$

$\frac{3}{4} = \frac{3}{4} \times \frac{3}{3} = \frac{9}{12}$
$-\frac{2}{3} = \frac{2}{3} \times \frac{4}{4} = \frac{8}{12}$
$\qquad\qquad\qquad \frac{1}{12}$

Rewrite using the LCD.

$\frac{3}{4} - \frac{2}{3} = \frac{1}{12}$

▶ Think and Discuss

1. Subtract. $\frac{17}{18} - \frac{5}{6}$

2. Refer to the introduction to this lesson. How much thicker is the more expensive paneling?

3. What is the LCD of $\frac{3}{4}$ and $\frac{1}{6}$?

4. Explain the following mistake: $\frac{2}{5} - \frac{1}{3} = \frac{1}{2}$.

Exercises

Subtract. Write the answers in lowest terms. (See Example A.)

5. $\frac{3}{8}$
$-\frac{1}{4}$ $\frac{1}{8}$

6. $\frac{2}{5}$
$-\frac{1}{10}$ $\frac{3}{10}$

7. $\frac{1}{2}$
$-\frac{1}{4}$ $\frac{1}{4}$

8. $\frac{2}{3}$
$-\frac{7}{12}$ $\frac{1}{12}$

9. $\frac{7}{9}$
$-\frac{2}{3}$ $\frac{1}{9}$

10. $\frac{7}{10}$
$-\frac{1}{5}$ $\frac{1}{2}$

11. $\frac{8}{15} - \frac{1}{3}$ $\frac{1}{5}$

12. $\frac{5}{6} - \frac{1}{2}$ $\frac{1}{3}$

13. $\frac{1}{2} - \frac{3}{8}$ $\frac{1}{8}$

14. $\frac{3}{4} - \frac{5}{12}$ $\frac{1}{3}$

15. $\frac{11}{18} - \frac{1}{2}$ $\frac{1}{9}$

Subtract. Write the answers in lowest terms. (See Example B.)

16. $\frac{1}{2}$
$-\frac{1}{3}$ $\frac{1}{6}$

17. $\frac{1}{2}$
$-\frac{1}{5}$ $\frac{3}{10}$

18. $\frac{2}{3}$
$-\frac{1}{4}$ $\frac{5}{12}$

19. $\frac{1}{4}$
$-\frac{1}{5}$ $\frac{1}{20}$

20. $\frac{1}{5}$
$-\frac{1}{6}$ $\frac{1}{30}$

21. $\frac{2}{3}$
$-\frac{2}{5}$ $\frac{4}{15}$

22. $\frac{3}{5} - \frac{1}{2}$ $\frac{1}{10}$

23. $\frac{5}{6} - \frac{3}{4}$ $\frac{1}{12}$

24. $\frac{5}{8} - \frac{2}{5}$ $\frac{9}{40}$

25. $\frac{5}{9} - \frac{1}{4}$ $\frac{11}{36}$

26. $\frac{6}{7} - \frac{2}{3}$ $\frac{4}{21}$

▶ Mixed Practice (For more practice, see page 423.)

Subtract. Write the answers in lowest terms.

27. $\frac{1}{2}$
$-\frac{3}{8}$ $\frac{1}{8}$

28. $\frac{1}{2}$
$-\frac{2}{9}$ $\frac{5}{18}$

29. $\frac{5}{8}$
$-\frac{1}{4}$ $\frac{3}{8}$

30. $\frac{1}{5}$
$-\frac{1}{10}$ $\frac{1}{10}$

31. $\frac{3}{4}$
$-\frac{2}{7}$ $\frac{13}{28}$

32. $\frac{2}{3}$
$-\frac{3}{7}$ $\frac{5}{21}$

33. $\frac{17}{21}$
$-\frac{1}{3}$ $\frac{10}{21}$

34. $\frac{9}{10}$
$-\frac{5}{6}$ $\frac{1}{15}$

35. $\frac{8}{9}$
$-\frac{3}{4}$ $\frac{5}{36}$

36. $\frac{4}{5}$
$-\frac{7}{25}$ $\frac{13}{25}$

37. $\frac{6}{7}$
$-\frac{3}{5}$ $\frac{9}{35}$

38. $\frac{10}{11}$
$-\frac{3}{5}$ $\frac{17}{55}$

39. $\frac{7}{10} - \frac{1}{5}$ $\frac{1}{2}$

40. $\frac{5}{7} - \frac{1}{2}$ $\frac{3}{14}$

41. $\frac{11}{20} - \frac{1}{4}$ $\frac{3}{10}$

42. $\frac{4}{9} - \frac{1}{6}$ $\frac{5}{18}$

43. $\frac{7}{8} - \frac{4}{5}$ $\frac{3}{40}$

▶ Applications

44. Rachel spent $\frac{3}{4}$ hour on her homework. Monty spent $\frac{1}{6}$ hour less than Rachel. What part of an hour did Monty spend on his homework? $\frac{7}{12}$ hr.

45. The bags of chips shown here both cost the same. Which bag weighs more? How much more? Bag on right; $\frac{3}{16}$ oz.

▶ Review (Lessons 2.3, 3.3)

Multiply or divide mentally.

46. 70×10 700
47. $600 \div 100$ 6
48. 54×100 5400
49. $4900 \div 70$ 70
50. $8100 \div 900$ 9
51. 33×1000 33,000
52. $48,000 \div 100$ 480
53. $67 \times 10,000$ 670,000

Challenge
A recipe for rice and ham chowder requires the following amounts of each ingredient. However, you do not have all of the ingredients you need. From the amounts indicated below, how much more of the ingredients will you need to complete the recipe?

Item	Required	Have	Need
Water	2 cup	2 cup	(0)
Rice	$\frac{3}{4}$ cup	$\frac{1}{3}$ cup	($\frac{5}{12}$ cup)
Flour	$\frac{1}{2}$ cup	$\frac{1}{6}$ cup	($\frac{1}{3}$ cup)
Onion	$\frac{1}{2}$ cup	$\frac{1}{3}$ cup	($\frac{1}{6}$ cup)
Butter	$\frac{1}{2}$ cup	$\frac{1}{4}$ cup	($\frac{1}{4}$ cup)
Potatoes	3 large	3 large	(0)
Carrots	$\frac{1}{2}$ cup	$\frac{5}{16}$ cup	($\frac{3}{16}$ cup)
Thyme	$\frac{1}{2}$ tsp.	$\frac{1}{8}$ tsp.	($\frac{3}{8}$ tsp.)
Nutmeg	$\frac{1}{2}$ tsp.	$\frac{1}{3}$ tsp.	($\frac{1}{6}$ tsp.)
Salt	$\frac{1}{8}$ tsp.	$\frac{1}{24}$ tsp.	($\frac{1}{12}$ tsp.)
Corn	$2\frac{1}{2}$ cup	$2\frac{1}{2}$ cup	(0)
Ham	3 cup	2 cup	(1 cup)

Purpose

Learning a different strategy for adding and subtracting fractions enables you to solve problems without finding the least common denominator.

Introducing the Lesson

Review adding and subtracting fractions with unlike denominators using the LCD approach (Lessons 7.3, 7.5). Use the examples:

Add—$\frac{3}{5} + \frac{7}{8}$

$$\frac{3}{5} = \frac{3}{5} \times \frac{8}{8} = \frac{24}{40}$$
$$+ \frac{7}{8} = \frac{7}{8} \times \frac{5}{5} = \frac{35}{40}$$
$$\frac{59}{40} = 1\frac{19}{40} \quad \frac{3}{5} + \frac{7}{8} = 1\frac{19}{40}$$

Subtract—$\frac{6}{7} - \frac{2}{5}$

$$\frac{6}{7} = \frac{6}{7} \times \frac{5}{5} = \frac{30}{35}$$
$$- \frac{2}{5} = \frac{2}{5} \times \frac{7}{7} = \frac{14}{35}$$
$$\frac{16}{35} \quad \frac{6}{7} - \frac{2}{5} = \frac{16}{35}$$

Then ask: What two numbers were multiplied to find the common denominator in each example? (5, 8; 7, 5) What parts of the fractions are these numbers? (denominators) Explain that when adding or subtracting fractions, a quick way to find a common denominator is to multiply the denominators.

Alternative Example

Add: $\frac{1}{4} + \frac{3}{5} + \frac{1}{6}$

Step 1: Multiply the denominators.
$4 \times 5 \times 6 = 120$

Step 2: Find equivalent fractions.
$\frac{1}{4} = \frac{30}{120}, \frac{3}{5} = \frac{72}{120}, \frac{1}{6} = \frac{20}{120}$

Step 3: Add.
$\frac{1}{4} + \frac{3}{5} + \frac{1}{6} = \frac{30}{120} + \frac{72}{120} + \frac{20}{120} = \frac{122}{120}$

Step 4: Reduce to lowest terms.
$\frac{122}{120} = \frac{61}{60} = 1\frac{1}{60}$

7.6 Working with Fractions: An Alternative Strategy

Mr. Lloyd began math class with the problem shown here. The students solved the problem by finding the LCD and then adding.

$$\frac{1}{2} + \frac{2}{3} + \frac{3}{4} =$$

1. What is the answer to Mr. Lloyd's problem?

Pleased with the students' response, Mr. Lloyd was ready to move on to another topic. "But wait!" Carla exclaimed. "I found another way to do these problems, and it's easier. Let me show you."

Carla went to the board. "You don't always have to find the LCD," she explained. Carla then taught the class her approach to adding and subtracting fractions.

STEP 1: Instead of finding the least common denominator, simply multiply all of the denominators. The product is a common denominator.
$2 \times 3 \times 4 = 24$

STEP 2: Rewrite each fraction using the new common denominator.
$\frac{1}{2} = \frac{12}{24} \quad \frac{2}{3} = \frac{16}{24} \quad \frac{3}{4} = \frac{18}{24}$

STEP 3: Add

STEP 4: Write the answer in lowest terms.

2. Complete Steps 3 and 4 of Carla's problem. Does her approach give the correct answer?

3. How is Carla's approach different from using the LCD? How is it easier? Discuss.

The class began to question Carla about her approach. "Does it work for subtraction, too?" one student asked. "Of course," she replied. "Is it easier?" "Not always, but try both approaches on some problems," she answered. "Then you can decide when each approach is better."

PROBLEM SOLVING

Exercises

Solve each problem using the LCD approach and Carla's approach.

4. $\frac{1}{2} + \frac{1}{4} + \frac{1}{8}$ $\frac{7}{8}$

5. $\frac{3}{8} - \frac{1}{5}$ $\frac{7}{40}$

6. $\frac{2}{9} + \frac{1}{6}$ $\frac{7}{18}$

7. $\frac{1}{7} + \frac{3}{5} + \frac{1}{2}$ $1\frac{17}{70}$

8. $\frac{2}{3} + \frac{8}{9} + \frac{26}{27}$ $2\frac{14}{27}$

9. $\frac{7}{12} - \frac{1}{7}$ $\frac{37}{84}$

10. $\frac{7}{12} - \frac{1}{8}$ $\frac{11}{24}$

11. $\frac{1}{3} + \frac{2}{3}$ 1

12. $\frac{1}{4} - \frac{1}{8}$ $\frac{1}{8}$

13. $\frac{2}{7} + \frac{3}{5}$ $\frac{31}{35}$

14. $\frac{1}{2} + \frac{4}{11} + \frac{1}{3}$ $1\frac{13}{66}$

15. $\frac{3}{4} + \frac{5}{7}$ $1\frac{13}{28}$

16. $\frac{3}{4} + \frac{3}{4}$ $1\frac{1}{2}$

17. $\frac{1}{2} - \frac{4}{9}$ $\frac{1}{18}$

18. $\frac{1}{4} + \frac{3}{8} + \frac{5}{16}$ $\frac{15}{16}$

19. $\frac{3}{13} + \frac{3}{4}$ $\frac{51}{52}$

20. $\frac{1}{5} + \frac{1}{25}$ $\frac{6}{25}$

21. $\frac{3}{7} - \frac{2}{14}$ $\frac{2}{7}$

22. $\frac{1}{2} + \frac{2}{3} + \frac{4}{5}$ $1\frac{29}{30}$

23. $\frac{5}{8} - \frac{1}{8}$ $\frac{1}{2}$

24. $\frac{5}{9} - \frac{4}{11}$ $\frac{19}{99}$

25. $\frac{2}{3} + \frac{1}{5} + \frac{4}{7}$ $1\frac{46}{105}$

26. $\frac{3}{4} + \frac{7}{8} + \frac{15}{16}$ $2\frac{9}{16}$

27. $\frac{1}{3} + \frac{5}{6} - \frac{3}{7}$ $\frac{31}{42}$

28. Sometimes Carla's approach gives the LCD. Examine the completed exercises. Write a rule that states when Carla's approach gives the LCD.

▶ Applications

29. A share of stock rose $\frac{1}{8}$ on Monday, $\frac{3}{4}$ on Tuesday, and $\frac{1}{2}$ on Wednesday. By how much did it rise over the three days? $1\frac{3}{8}$

30. On January 6, Gina cut $\frac{1}{4}$ inch off her hair. By March 6, her hair had grown $\frac{3}{8}$ inch. Did the length of her hair increase or decrease over the two months? Increase

▶ Review (Lessons 6.1, 6.2)

Multiply. Write the answers in lowest terms.

31. $\frac{1}{8} \times 7$ $\frac{7}{8}$

32. $\frac{5}{12} \times \frac{2}{3}$ $\frac{5}{18}$

33. $6 \times \frac{8}{9}$ $5\frac{1}{3}$

34. $\frac{1}{3} \times \frac{9}{10}$ $\frac{3}{10}$

35. $10 \times \frac{3}{16}$ $1\frac{7}{8}$

36. $9 \times \frac{3}{4}$ $6\frac{3}{4}$

37. $\frac{1}{2} \times \frac{15}{16}$ $\frac{15}{32}$

38. $\frac{4}{5} \times \frac{11}{12}$ $\frac{11}{15}$

39. $\frac{8}{15} \times 5$ $2\frac{2}{3}$

40. $\frac{1}{4} \times \frac{7}{10}$ $\frac{7}{40}$

Answers

1. $\frac{1}{2} = \frac{6}{12}$
$\frac{2}{3} = \frac{8}{12}$
$+ \frac{3}{4} = \frac{9}{12}$
$\frac{23}{12} = 1\frac{11}{12}$

2. $\frac{12}{24} + \frac{16}{24} + \frac{18}{24} = \frac{46}{24}$ or $1\frac{11}{12}$; yes

3. Carla's approach often requires that the final answer be reduced; it is easier because she just multiplies all the denominators instead of finding the LCD.

Answers

28. Carla's approach gives the LCD if the denominators don't have any common factors other than 1.

★ **Error Alert**

Mistakes may reveal that students are incorrectly multiplying the denominators or are having trouble finding equivalent fractions because the common denominator is a cumbersome number. For example, finding the common denominator of $\frac{2}{3} + \frac{1}{5} + \frac{4}{7}$ by multiplying $3 \times 5 \times 7$, results in a product of 105.

Reinforcement
EP/MR Worksheet 57, TRB, page 57

Challenge

Two phone company workers used a pavement cutter to saw through the street to bury a phone line. They kept track of their time for each phase of the project on the chart below. Use the chart to calculate the total depth to which they cut and the time it took to reach that depth.

Depth	Cutting Time
$\frac{3}{4}$ inch	$6\frac{1}{4}$ minutes
$\frac{5}{16}$ inch	$3\frac{1}{4}$ minutes
$\frac{1}{2}$ inch	4 minutes
$\frac{5}{8}$ inch	5 minutes
$\frac{3}{8}$ inch	$3\frac{1}{2}$ minutes
$\frac{13}{16}$ inch	$9\frac{1}{2}$ minutes

($3\frac{3}{8}$ inches; $31\frac{1}{2}$ minutes)

T161

Objectives

- To rename whole numbers as mixed numbers
- To subtract a mixed number from a whole number

Purpose

Subtracting mixed numbers from whole numbers enables you to find differences such as how much weight a runner lost if she weighed 125 pounds before a race and $122\frac{3}{4}$ pounds after a race.

Introducing the Lesson

Review writing fractions and mixed numbers (Lesson 5.3). Use the example: Write 2 as an improper fraction with a denominator of 5.
$2 = \frac{2}{1} \quad \frac{2 \times 5}{1 \times 5} = \frac{10}{5} \quad (2 = \frac{10}{5})$.
Write the mixed numbers $5\frac{4}{4}$, $5\frac{10}{10}$, and $5\frac{8}{8}$ on the board. Ask: What is the value of each mixed number? (6) How would you write 13 as a mixed number using 12 and the denominators of 5, 7, and 59? ($12\frac{5}{5}$, $12\frac{7}{7}$, $12\frac{59}{59}$)

Alternative Examples

Example A—Rename. $15 = 14\frac{\blacksquare}{3}$
$15 = 14 + 1 = 14 + \frac{3}{3} = 14\frac{3}{3}$
$15 = \mathbf{14\frac{3}{3}}$

Example B—Subtract. $26 - 23\frac{49}{51}$
$\begin{array}{r} 26 = 25\frac{51}{51} \\ - 23\frac{49}{51} = 23\frac{49}{51} \\ \hline 2\frac{2}{51} \end{array}$
$26 - 23\frac{49}{51} = \mathbf{2\frac{2}{51}}$

▶ Think and Discuss Answers

1. $16\frac{10}{10}$
2. $4\frac{3}{8}$
3. $1\frac{1}{5}$ seconds
4. Use the denominator in the mixed number.

7.7 Subtracting Mixed Numbers from Whole Numbers

Compare the times shown above. By how much did Timely Writer beat the record?

Examples

To subtract a mixed number from a whole number, first rename the whole number. Then subtract the fractions and whole numbers separately.

A Rename. $12 = 11\frac{\blacksquare}{3}$

$12 = 11 + 1 = 11 + \frac{3}{3} = 11\frac{3}{3}$
$12 = 11\frac{3}{3}$

B Subtract. $58 - 56\frac{4}{5}$

$\begin{array}{r} 58 = 57\frac{5}{5} \\ - 56\frac{4}{5} = 56\frac{4}{5} \\ \hline 1\frac{1}{5} \end{array}$ Rename 58 as a mixed number with a denominator of 5.

▶ Think and Discuss

1. Rename 17 as a mixed number with a denominator of 10.

2. Subtract. $9 - 4\frac{5}{8}$

3. Refer to the introduction to this lesson. By how much did Timely Writer beat the record?

4. If you are subtracting a mixed number from a whole number, how do you determine what denominator to use?

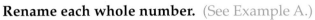

Exercises

Answers

40. seven and five tenths
41. eight thousand, thirteen and six hundredths
42. four hundred sixty-nine thousand, five hundred seventy
43. three hundred ninety-five thousandths
44. two hundred thousand and forty-three hundredths
45. thousands
46. hundredths
47. hundred thousands
48. thousandths
49. millions

Rename each whole number. (See Example A.)

5. $3 = 2\frac{\blacksquare}{4}$ 4   **6.** $9 = 8\frac{\blacksquare}{6}$ 6   **7.** $10 = 9\frac{\blacksquare}{8}$ 8   **8.** $7 = 6\frac{\blacksquare}{12}$ 12   **9.** $6 = 5\frac{\blacksquare}{7}$ 7

Subtract. Write the answers in lowest terms. (See Example B.)

10.	**11.**	**12.**	**13.**	**14.**	**15.**
5	8	9	12	15	27
$-1\frac{2}{3}$	$-6\frac{1}{5}$	$-4\frac{5}{7}$	$-3\frac{7}{10}$	$-10\frac{5}{6}$	$-14\frac{5}{8}$
$3\frac{1}{3}$	$1\frac{4}{5}$	$4\frac{2}{7}$	$8\frac{3}{10}$	$4\frac{1}{6}$	$12\frac{3}{8}$

16. $18 - 11\frac{3}{4}$ $6\frac{1}{4}$ **17.** $20 - 16\frac{5}{11}$ $3\frac{6}{11}$ **18.** $33 - 26\frac{4}{9}$ $6\frac{5}{9}$ **19.** $45 - 19\frac{17}{20}$ $25\frac{3}{20}$

▶ Mixed Practice (For more practice, see page 423.)

Subtract. Write the answers in lowest terms.

20.	**21.**	**22.**	**23.**	**24.**
7	11	15	21	37
$-2\frac{1}{4}$	$-7\frac{3}{8}$	$-2\frac{9}{15}$	$-14\frac{3}{10}$	$-20\frac{13}{16}$
$4\frac{3}{4}$	$3\frac{5}{8}$	$12\frac{2}{5}$	$6\frac{7}{10}$	$16\frac{3}{16}$

25.	**26.**	**27.**	**28.**	**29.**
53	42	62	75	87
$-27\frac{6}{25}$	$-39\frac{5}{13}$	$-47\frac{13}{30}$	$-32\frac{11}{50}$	$-68\frac{9}{48}$
$25\frac{19}{25}$	$2\frac{8}{13}$	$14\frac{17}{30}$	$42\frac{39}{50}$	$18\frac{13}{16}$

30. $8 - 3\frac{6}{7}$ $4\frac{1}{7}$ **31.** $10 - 5\frac{4}{5}$ $4\frac{1}{5}$ **32.** $17 - 13\frac{12}{13}$ $3\frac{1}{13}$ **33.** $35 - 21\frac{4}{21}$ $13\frac{17}{21}$

34. $42 - 28\frac{7}{12}$ $13\frac{5}{12}$ **35.** $50 - 19\frac{9}{14}$ $30\frac{5}{14}$ **36.** $61 - 13\frac{5}{8}$ $47\frac{13}{18}$ **37.** $72 - 47\frac{37}{100}$ $24\frac{63}{100}$

▶ Applications

38. The limbo record is $6\frac{1}{8}$ inches from the floor. Georgette's best try is 12 inches from the floor. How far away from the record is she? $5\frac{7}{8}$ in.

39. Earl is not supposed to eat more than four ounces of cheese a week. On Monday, he ate three snack packs like the one shown. How much more cheese can he eat this week? $1\frac{3}{4}$ oz.

SNACK PACK

3/4 oz.

▶ Review (Lessons 1.1, 1.2)

Write each number in words.

40. 7.5   **41.** 8013.06   **42.** 469,570   **43.** 0.395   **44.** 200,000.43

Find the place value of the underlined 5 in each number.

45. <u>5</u>324   **46.** 12.0<u>5</u>9   **47.** <u>5</u>97,307   **48.** 0.385<u>5</u>   **49.** <u>5</u>,205,769

Objectives

- To use simpler numbers to solve problems

Purpose

Substituting simpler numbers into problems is one of the ways to find how to solve difficult problems. For example, you can substitute whole numbers in problems instead of fractions or mixed numbers.

Introducing the Lesson

Review adding fractions with unlike denominators and adding mixed numbers (Lessons 7.3, 7.4).

Introduce the lesson by asking students the following: Suppose you are interested in building models of boats. Someone gives you an expensive and complicated model ship to build. You've never put a model ship together before and aren't sure how to go about it. What might you do before constructing the model to help you successfully complete it? (Guide the discussion so that students suggest building a simpler model first, or practicing fitting various pieces together to see how they work in the model.) Tell students that in mathematics it is sometimes helpful to substitute simpler numbers in problems to help you choose the correct operation and find how to solve them.

7.8 Simplifying the Problem

Alicia learned that every minute she roller skates, she burns $4\frac{2}{5}$ calories. She timed herself one day and skated $19\frac{1}{2}$ minutes before resting.

Would you add, subtract, multiply, or divide to find how many calories are burned?

Most people find it easier to work with whole numbers than fractions. Sometimes whole numbers are easier to work with and make it easier to see which operations to use. For example, suppose Alicia burned 4 calories a minute for 20 minutes. Solving this simpler problem can help you solve the original problem. The operation used for both the simpler problem and the original problem should be the same.

1. What operation would you use to solve the simpler problem?
   Multiplication
2. What is the answer to the simpler problem?
   80 calories
3. Use the same operation used in the simpler problem to solve the original problem. $85\frac{4}{5}$ calories
4. Is the answer to the original problem equal to the answer to the simpler problem? Why or why not?
   No; different numbers were used
5. If Alicia skated for $35\frac{1}{2}$ minutes, what whole numbers would you substitute in this problem to make a simpler one?
   Answers may vary
6. How many calories would she burn in $35\frac{1}{2}$ minutes? $156\frac{1}{5}$ calories

One day Ramzi spent $6\frac{1}{2}$ hours working, $\frac{5}{6}$ hour for a lunch break, and $1\frac{1}{4}$ hours riding the bus. How much of his day was spent from the time he left for work to the time he arrived home?

PROBLEM SOLVING

7. What whole numbers would you substitute into this problem to make a simpler problem? Answers may vary.

8. What operation would you use to solve the simpler problem? Addition

9. Solve the simpler problem. Answers may vary.

10. Solve the original problem. $8\frac{7}{12}$ hours

Each problem below involves fractions. A simpler problem using only whole numbers may help you see how to solve it. Write the operation used for each problem below, and then solve.

11. Edna's office is being remodeled to include a closet across the entire width of the room. If each closet door is $1\frac{1}{2}$ feet wide, how many doors are needed? Division; 7 doors

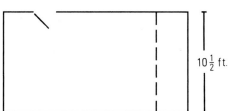

$10\frac{1}{2}$ ft.

12. Connie watched the neighbor's children for three hours and fifteen minutes at two-and-a-half dollars an hour. How much did Connie earn? Multiplication; $8.13

13. When Mickey's family moved in to a new house, the bathroom entrance was widened $6\frac{5}{8}$ inches to allow for his wheelchair. The door was $24\frac{7}{8}$ inches wide. How wide is it now? Addition; $31\frac{1}{2}$ in.

14. Ian claims that he can lift $2\frac{1}{2}$ times his weight. If he weighs 142 pounds, how much can he lift? Multiplication; 355 lb

15. The odometer in Louise's car was at $12,657\frac{9}{10}$ miles when she started her trip. When she arrived home, it was at $13,243\frac{1}{10}$ miles. How far did she travel? Subtraction; $585\frac{1}{5}$ mi.

16. Sue wanted to cover her bulletin board with music CD covers like the ones shown. Her bulletin board is $21\frac{1}{2}$ inches wide. If no space is left between the covers, how many will fit across the bulletin board? Division; 4 covers

$5\frac{1}{8}$ in.

▶ **Review** (Lesson 3.9)

Simplify.

17. $12 - 5 \div 5 \times 2$ 10

18. $16 + (15 - 3)$ 28

19. $9 \times 7 - (6 + 2)$ 55

Objectives

- To rename mixed numbers
- To subtract two mixed numbers

Purpose

Subtracting mixed numbers helps you determine differences involving amounts such as time, measurements, and amounts of materials.

Introducing the Lesson

Review finding equivalent fractions, writing mixed numbers as improper fractions and vice versa, and finding the LCD (Lessons 5.2, 5.3, 7.2). Use the examples:

Find 3 fractions equivalent to $\frac{5}{9}$.
$(\frac{5 \times 2}{9 \times 2} = \frac{10}{18}, \quad \frac{5 \times 3}{9 \times 3} = \frac{15}{27}, \quad \frac{5 \times 4}{9 \times 4} = \frac{20}{36})$.

Write $10\frac{6}{7}$ as an improper fraction.
$(10\frac{6}{7} = 10 + \frac{6}{7}, \frac{70}{7} + \frac{6}{7} = \frac{76}{7})$

Write $\frac{46}{8}$ as a mixed number.

$(\frac{46}{8} = 46 \div 8 =$

$\begin{array}{r} 5R6 \\ 8)\overline{46} \\ \underline{40} \\ 6 \end{array} = 5\frac{6}{8} \text{ or } 5\frac{3}{4})$

Find the LCD of $\frac{5}{9}$ and $\frac{7}{6}$. (multiples of 9: 9, 18, 27, 36; multiples of 6: 6, 12, 18, 24, 30; the LCD of $\frac{5}{9}$ and $\frac{7}{6}$ is 18.)

Alternative Examples

Example A—Rename. $4\frac{1}{16} = 3\frac{\blacksquare}{16}$
Use the same method as in Example A.
$4\frac{1}{16} = \mathbf{3\frac{17}{16}}$

Example B—Subtract. $215\frac{5}{9} - 101\frac{1}{3}$
Use the same method as in Example B.
$215\frac{5}{9} - 101\frac{1}{3} = \mathbf{114\frac{2}{9}}$

Example C—Subtract. $9\frac{1}{5} - 6\frac{3}{4}$
Use the same method as in Example C.
$9\frac{1}{5} - 6\frac{3}{4} = \mathbf{2\frac{9}{20}}$

7.9 Subtracting Mixed Numbers

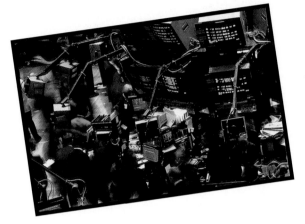

Stock prices rise and fall often. Sometimes, stock prices drop low enough to be called a **crash** or a **meltdown.** How much did the price of ABC Computers stock drop in the year shown below?

Prices per Share

	High	Low
ABC Computers	$175\frac{7}{8}$	$102\frac{1}{4}$
Meta Motors	$94\frac{1}{8}$	50
Local Lighting	$66\frac{3}{8}$	$38\frac{3}{4}$

Examples

To subtract mixed numbers, rewrite the fractions using their LCD. If necessary, rename the larger mixed number.

A Rename. $8\frac{3}{5} = 7\frac{\blacksquare}{5}$

$8\frac{3}{5} = 8 + \frac{3}{5}$

$8\frac{3}{5} = 7 + 1 + \frac{3}{5}$

$8\frac{3}{5} = 7 + \frac{5}{5} + \frac{3}{5} = 7\frac{8}{5}$

B Subtract. $175\frac{7}{8} - 102\frac{1}{4}$

$\begin{array}{l} 175\frac{7}{8} = 175 + \quad \frac{7}{8} \quad = 175 + \frac{7}{8} \\ -102\frac{1}{4} = 102 + \frac{1}{4} \times \frac{2}{2} = 102 + \frac{2}{8} \\ \hline \qquad\qquad\qquad\qquad\qquad 73 + \frac{5}{8} \end{array}$

$175\frac{7}{8} - 102\frac{1}{4} = \mathbf{73\frac{5}{8}}$

C Subtract. $6\frac{1}{5} - 2\frac{3}{4}$

$\begin{array}{l} 6\frac{1}{5} = 6 + \frac{1}{5} = 6 + \frac{1}{5} \times \frac{4}{4} = 6 + \frac{4}{20} = 5 + \frac{24}{20} \\ -2\frac{3}{4} = 2 + \frac{3}{4} = 2 + \frac{3}{4} \times \frac{5}{5} = 2 + \frac{15}{20} = 2 + \frac{15}{20} \\ \hline \qquad\qquad\qquad\qquad\qquad\qquad\qquad 3 + \frac{9}{20} \end{array}$

Rewrite using the LCD.

Rename $6\frac{4}{20}$ as $5\frac{24}{20}$.

$6\frac{1}{5} - 2\frac{3}{4} = \mathbf{3\frac{9}{20}}$

▶ Think and Discuss

1. Rename $94\frac{1}{8}$.

2. Subtract. $66\frac{3}{8} - 38\frac{3}{4}$

3. Refer to the introduction to this lesson. By how much did the price of ABC Computers stock drop in the year shown?

4. When is it necessary to rename a mixed number?

Exercises

Rename each mixed number. (See Example A.)

5. $7\frac{1}{3} = 6\frac{\blacksquare}{3}$ 4   **6.** $3\frac{2}{5} = 2\frac{\blacksquare}{5}$ 7   **7.** $6\frac{8}{9} = 5\frac{\blacksquare}{9}$ 17   **8.** $10\frac{7}{12} = 9\frac{\blacksquare}{12}$ 19

Subtract. Write the answers in lowest terms. (See Example B.)

9. $\begin{array}{r} 6\frac{7}{8} \\ -2\frac{2}{3} \\ \hline \end{array}$ $4\frac{5}{24}$ **10.** $\begin{array}{r} 5\frac{4}{7} \\ -1\frac{1}{2} \\ \hline \end{array}$ $4\frac{1}{14}$ **11.** $\begin{array}{r} 9\frac{3}{5} \\ -6\frac{1}{4} \\ \hline \end{array}$ $3\frac{7}{20}$ **12.** $\begin{array}{r} 5\frac{7}{8} \\ -2\frac{2}{5} \\ \hline \end{array}$ $3\frac{19}{40}$ **13.** $\begin{array}{r} 3\frac{3}{4} \\ -1\frac{1}{9} \\ \hline \end{array}$ $2\frac{23}{36}$ **14.** $\begin{array}{r} 6\frac{5}{6} \\ -3\frac{7}{10} \\ \hline \end{array}$ $3\frac{2}{15}$

Subtract. Write the answers in lowest terms. (See Example C.)

15. $\begin{array}{r} 9\frac{1}{3} \\ -6\frac{2}{3} \\ \hline \end{array}$ $2\frac{2}{3}$ **16.** $\begin{array}{r} 5\frac{2}{5} \\ -2\frac{7}{10} \\ \hline \end{array}$ $2\frac{7}{10}$ **17.** $\begin{array}{r} 8\frac{3}{8} \\ -3\frac{3}{4} \\ \hline \end{array}$ $4\frac{5}{8}$ **18.** $\begin{array}{r} 7\frac{1}{4} \\ -5\frac{5}{6} \\ \hline \end{array}$ $1\frac{5}{12}$ **19.** $\begin{array}{r} 4\frac{4}{5} \\ -1\frac{7}{8} \\ \hline \end{array}$ $2\frac{37}{40}$ **20.** $\begin{array}{r} 6\frac{1}{6} \\ -3\frac{9}{10} \\ \hline \end{array}$ $2\frac{4}{15}$

▶ Mixed Practice (For more practice, see page 424.)

Subtract. Write the answers in lowest terms.

21. $\begin{array}{r} 5\frac{1}{2} \\ -1\frac{3}{4} \\ \hline \end{array}$ $3\frac{3}{4}$ **22.** $\begin{array}{r} 6\frac{3}{8} \\ -2\frac{7}{8} \\ \hline \end{array}$ $3\frac{1}{2}$ **23.** $\begin{array}{r} 9\frac{1}{4} \\ -3\frac{2}{3} \\ \hline \end{array}$ $5\frac{7}{12}$ **24.** $\begin{array}{r} 6\frac{7}{8} \\ -4\frac{1}{3} \\ \hline \end{array}$ $2\frac{13}{24}$ **25.** $\begin{array}{r} 5\frac{1}{4} \\ -3\frac{4}{5} \\ \hline \end{array}$ $1\frac{9}{20}$ **26.** $\begin{array}{r} 3\frac{1}{8} \\ -2\frac{1}{3} \\ \hline \end{array}$ $\frac{19}{24}$

27. $8\frac{3}{5} - 7\frac{4}{5}$ $\frac{4}{5}$ **28.** $5\frac{3}{4} - 2\frac{1}{7}$ $3\frac{17}{28}$ **29.** $3\frac{2}{3} - \frac{5}{7}$ $2\frac{20}{21}$ **30.** $7\frac{1}{8} - 5\frac{2}{5}$ $1\frac{29}{40}$

▶ Applications

31. The men's world speed-skating record for 500 meters is $45\frac{2}{25}$ seconds. The women's record is $48\frac{89}{100}$ seconds. How much faster is the men's record than the women's? $3\frac{81}{100}$ sec.

32. Jenny threw the discus 101 feet $4\frac{1}{8}$ inches. Jami threw it 101 feet $1\frac{3}{4}$ inches. Who threw the discus farther? How much farther?
Jenny; $2\frac{3}{8}$ in.

▶ Review (Lessons 6.6, 6.7)

Divide.

33. $\frac{9}{10} \div \frac{5}{6}$ $1\frac{2}{25}$ **34.** $\frac{11}{12} \div 6$ $\frac{11}{72}$ **35.** $3\frac{1}{2} \div \frac{3}{4}$ $4\frac{2}{3}$ **36.** $1\frac{1}{5} \div 2\frac{1}{4}$ $\frac{8}{15}$

Objective

- To estimate a sum or difference by rounding each fraction or mixed number to the nearest whole number or to the nearest $\frac{1}{2}$, and then adding or subtracting

Purpose

Estimating with fractions and mixed numbers allows you to make approximations, such as the total time used for a project when the individual times are $2\frac{1}{4}$ hours, $\frac{1}{3}$ hour, and $1\frac{1}{2}$ hours.

Introducing the Lesson

Review estimating sums and differences (Lesson 1.12). Use the example:

Estimate the sum of $5.26, $10.98, and $0.86. (approximately $17)

Ask students which whole numbers are the following numbers closest to :

$\frac{7}{8}$, $2\frac{11}{12}$, $1\frac{3}{4}$, $5\frac{5}{6}$, $3\frac{1}{6}$, $4\frac{1}{3}$, $25\frac{15}{16}$, $17\frac{1}{16}$ (1, 3, 2, 6, 3, 4, 26, 17)

Alternative Examples

Example A—Estimate to the nearest whole number. $6\frac{3}{22} - 1\frac{7}{9}$
Use the same method as in Example A.
$6\frac{3}{22} - 1\frac{7}{19}$ is **about 4.**

Example B—Estimate to the nearest $\frac{1}{2}$.
$4\frac{4}{7} + 3\frac{1}{6}$
Use the same method as in Example B.
$4\frac{4}{7} + 3\frac{1}{6}$ is **about $7\frac{1}{2}$.**

▶ Think and Discuss Answers

1. closer to 1; 7 is closer to 8 than to half of 8, or 4.
2. 6
3. $4\frac{1}{2}$
4. Sample answers include: one trip around all 3 paths plus 1 more time on the $\frac{9}{10}$ mi. path; 3 times on the $1\frac{3}{5}$ mi. path plus 1 time on the $\frac{9}{10}$ mi. path; 2 times on the $\frac{9}{10}$ mi. path plus 2 times on the $1\frac{3}{5}$ mi. path.

7.10 Estimating Sums and Differences of Fractions and Mixed Numbers

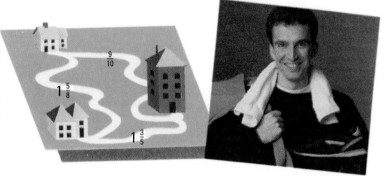

Martin set a goal to run about 5 miles a day during summer vacation. Which combinations of paths shown here can Martin run in order to accomplish his daily goal?

Martin can estimate sums to figure out which paths are at least 5 miles long.

Examples

To estimate sums and differences of fractions and mixed numbers, determine the nearest $\frac{1}{2}$ or the nearest whole number for each fraction or mixed number. Then add or subtract.

A Estimate to the nearest whole number. $7\frac{8}{19} - 4\frac{21}{25}$

$7\frac{8}{19}$ → closer to 7 than 8 → 7

$4\frac{21}{25}$ → closer to 5 than 4 → $\dfrac{-5}{2}$

$7\frac{8}{19} - 4\frac{21}{25}$ is **about 2.**

B Estimate to the nearest $\frac{1}{2}$.
$1\frac{3}{5} + 1\frac{9}{10}$

$1\frac{3}{5}$ → closer to $1\frac{1}{2}$ than 2 → $1\frac{1}{2}$

$1\frac{9}{10}$ → closer to 2 than $1\frac{1}{2}$ → $\dfrac{+2}{3\frac{1}{2}}$

$1\frac{3}{5} + 1\frac{9}{10}$ is **about $3\frac{1}{2}$.**

▶ Think and Discuss

1. Is $\frac{7}{8}$ closer to $\frac{1}{2}$ or 1? How can you tell?

2. Estimate to the nearest whole number. $1\frac{19}{20} + 4\frac{3}{7}$

3. Estimate to the nearest $\frac{1}{2}$. $5\frac{1}{9} - \frac{8}{13}$

4. Refer to the introduction to this lesson. What are three combinations of paths Martin can run to accomplish his goal?

3. Refer to the introduction to this lesson. By how much did the price of ABC Computers stock drop in the year shown?

4. When is it necessary to rename a mixed number?

SKILLS

Exercises

Rename each mixed number. (See Example A.)

5. $7\frac{1}{3} = 6\frac{\blacksquare}{3}$ 4

6. $3\frac{2}{5} = 2\frac{\blacksquare}{5}$ 7

7. $6\frac{8}{9} = 5\frac{\blacksquare}{9}$ 17

8. $10\frac{7}{12} = 9\frac{\blacksquare}{12}$ 19

Subtract. Write the answers in lowest terms. (See Example B.)

9. $6\frac{7}{8}$
$-2\frac{2}{3}$ $4\frac{5}{24}$

10. $5\frac{4}{7}$
$-1\frac{1}{2}$ $4\frac{1}{14}$

11. $9\frac{3}{5}$
$-6\frac{1}{4}$ $3\frac{7}{20}$

12. $5\frac{7}{8}$
$-2\frac{2}{5}$ $3\frac{19}{40}$

13. $3\frac{3}{4}$
$-1\frac{1}{9}$ $2\frac{23}{36}$

14. $6\frac{5}{6}$
$-3\frac{7}{10}$ $3\frac{2}{15}$

Subtract. Write the answers in lowest terms. (See Example C.)

15. $9\frac{1}{3}$
$-6\frac{2}{3}$ $2\frac{2}{3}$

16. $5\frac{2}{5}$
$-2\frac{7}{10}$ $2\frac{7}{10}$

17. $8\frac{3}{8}$
$-3\frac{3}{4}$ $4\frac{5}{8}$

18. $7\frac{1}{4}$
$-5\frac{5}{6}$ $1\frac{5}{12}$

19. $4\frac{4}{5}$
$-1\frac{7}{8}$ $2\frac{37}{40}$

20. $6\frac{1}{6}$
$-3\frac{9}{10}$ $2\frac{4}{15}$

▶ **Mixed Practice** (For more practice, see page 424.)

Subtract. Write the answers in lowest terms.

21. $5\frac{1}{2}$
$-1\frac{3}{4}$ $3\frac{3}{4}$

22. $6\frac{3}{8}$
$-2\frac{7}{8}$ $3\frac{1}{2}$

23. $9\frac{1}{4}$
$-3\frac{2}{3}$ $5\frac{7}{12}$

24. $6\frac{7}{8}$
$-4\frac{1}{3}$ $2\frac{13}{24}$

25. $5\frac{1}{4}$
$-3\frac{4}{5}$ $1\frac{9}{20}$

26. $3\frac{1}{8}$
$-2\frac{1}{3}$ $\frac{19}{24}$

27. $8\frac{3}{5} - 7\frac{4}{5}$ $\frac{4}{5}$

28. $5\frac{3}{4} - 2\frac{1}{7}$ $3\frac{17}{28}$

29. $3\frac{2}{3} - \frac{5}{7}$ $2\frac{20}{21}$

30. $7\frac{1}{8} - 5\frac{2}{5}$ $1\frac{29}{40}$

▶ **Applications**

31. The men's world speed-skating record for 500 meters is $45\frac{2}{25}$ seconds. The women's record is $48\frac{89}{100}$ seconds. How much faster is the men's record than the women's? $3\frac{81}{100}$ sec.

32. Jenny threw the discus 101 feet $4\frac{1}{8}$ inches. Jami threw it 101 feet $1\frac{3}{4}$ inches. Who threw the discus farther? How much farther?
Jenny; $2\frac{3}{8}$ in.

▶ **Review** (Lessons 6.6, 6.7)

Divide.

33. $\frac{9}{10} \div \frac{5}{6}$ $1\frac{2}{25}$

34. $\frac{11}{12} \div 6$ $\frac{11}{72}$

35. $3\frac{1}{2} \div \frac{3}{4}$ $4\frac{2}{3}$

36. $1\frac{1}{5} \div 2\frac{1}{4}$ $\frac{8}{15}$

Objective

- To estimate a sum or difference by rounding each fraction or mixed number to the nearest whole number or to the nearest $\frac{1}{2}$, and then adding or subtracting

Purpose

Estimating with fractions and mixed numbers allows you to make approximations, such as the total time used for a project when the individual times are $2\frac{1}{4}$ hours, $\frac{1}{3}$ hour, and $1\frac{1}{2}$ hours.

Introducing the Lesson

Review estimating sums and differences (Lesson 1.12). Use the example:

Estimate the sum of $5.26, $10.98, and $0.86. (approximately $17)

Ask students which whole numbers are the following numbers closest to :

$\frac{7}{8}$, $2\frac{11}{12}$, $1\frac{3}{4}$, $5\frac{5}{6}$, $3\frac{1}{6}$, $4\frac{1}{3}$, $25\frac{15}{16}$, $17\frac{1}{16}$ (1, 3, 2, 6, 3, 4, 26, 17)

Alternative Examples

Example A—Estimate to the nearest whole number. $6\frac{3}{22} - 1\frac{7}{9}$
Use the same method as in Example A.
$6\frac{3}{22} - 1\frac{7}{19}$ is **about 4.**

Example B—Estimate to the nearest $\frac{1}{2}$.
$4\frac{4}{7} + 3\frac{1}{6}$
Use the same method as in Example B.
$4\frac{4}{7} + 3\frac{1}{6}$ is **about $7\frac{1}{2}$.**

▶ **Think and Discuss Answers**

1. closer to 1; 7 is closer to 8 than to half of 8, or 4.
2. 6
3. $4\frac{1}{2}$
4. Sample answers include: one trip around all 3 paths plus 1 more time on the $\frac{9}{10}$ mi. path; 3 times on the $1\frac{3}{5}$ mi. path plus 1 time on the $\frac{9}{10}$ mi. path; 2 times on the $\frac{9}{10}$ mi. path plus 2 times on the $1\frac{3}{5}$ mi. path.

7.10 Estimating Sums and Differences of Fractions and Mixed Numbers

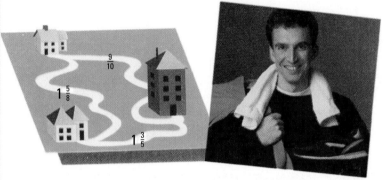

Martin set a goal to run about 5 miles a day during summer vacation. Which combinations of paths shown here can Martin run in order to accomplish his daily goal?

Martin can estimate sums to figure out which paths are at least 5 miles long.

Examples

To estimate sums and differences of fractions and mixed numbers, determine the nearest $\frac{1}{2}$ or the nearest whole number for each fraction or mixed number. Then add or subtract.

A Estimate to the nearest whole number. $7\frac{8}{19} - 4\frac{21}{25}$

$7\frac{8}{19}$ → closer to 7 than 8 → 7

$4\frac{21}{25}$ → closer to 5 than 4 → $\dfrac{-5}{2}$

$7\frac{8}{19} - 4\frac{21}{25}$ is **about 2.**

B Estimate to the nearest $\frac{1}{2}$.
$1\frac{3}{5} + 1\frac{9}{10}$

$1\frac{3}{5}$ → closer to $1\frac{1}{2}$ than 2 → $1\frac{1}{2}$

$1\frac{9}{10}$ → closer to 2 than $1\frac{1}{2}$ → $\dfrac{+2}{3\frac{1}{2}}$

$1\frac{3}{5} + 1\frac{9}{10}$ is **about $3\frac{1}{2}$.**

▶ **Think and Discuss**

1. Is $\frac{7}{8}$ closer to $\frac{1}{2}$ or 1? How can you tell?

2. Estimate to the nearest whole number. $1\frac{19}{20} + 4\frac{3}{7}$

3. Estimate to the nearest $\frac{1}{2}$. $5\frac{1}{9} - \frac{8}{13}$

4. Refer to the introduction to this lesson. What are three combinations of paths Martin can run to accomplish his goal?

Exercises

SKILLS

Estimate to the nearest whole number. (See Example A.)

5. $\frac{9}{16}$
$+\frac{7}{10}$ 2

6. $1\frac{7}{10}$
$+2\frac{4}{9}$ 4

7. $6\frac{12}{13}$
$+5\frac{3}{16}$ 12

8. $4\frac{5}{8}$
$-2\frac{3}{13}$ 3

9. $6\frac{8}{9}$
$-3\frac{7}{15}$ 4

10. $9\frac{1}{12}$
$-5\frac{4}{17}$ 4

11. $\frac{9}{10} + \frac{8}{9}$ 2

12. $4\frac{3}{7} + 3\frac{5}{9}$ 8

13. $2\frac{1}{3} - \frac{5}{8}$ 1

14. $4\frac{4}{17} - 2\frac{1}{9}$ 2

Estimate to the nearest $\frac{1}{2}$. (See Example B.)

15. $7\frac{9}{11}$
$+1\frac{7}{16}$ $9\frac{1}{2}$

16. $2\frac{4}{9}$
$+7\frac{8}{11}$ 10

17. $9\frac{5}{37}$
$+8\frac{21}{23}$ 18

18. $2\frac{3}{16}$
$-1\frac{5}{12}$ $\frac{1}{2}$

19. $4\frac{7}{9}$
$-2\frac{13}{15}$ 2

20. $9\frac{3}{10}$
$-6\frac{1}{24}$ $3\frac{1}{2}$

21. $1\frac{1}{5} + 2\frac{1}{10}$ 3

22. $3\frac{4}{9} + 5\frac{10}{21}$ 9

23. $3\frac{1}{6} - 1\frac{1}{7}$ 2

24. $5\frac{4}{9} - 2\frac{1}{8}$ $3\frac{1}{2}$

▶ Mixed Practice (For more practice, see page 424.)

Estimate to the nearest whole number and to the nearest $\frac{1}{2}$.

25. $2\frac{9}{11}$
$-1\frac{10}{21}$ 2; $1\frac{1}{2}$

26. $3\frac{20}{21}$
$+4\frac{5}{19}$ 8; 8

27. $6\frac{5}{48}$
$-3\frac{13}{25}$ 2; $2\frac{1}{2}$

28. $9\frac{5}{16}$
$+8\frac{1}{7}$ 17; $17\frac{1}{2}$

29. $4\frac{5}{11}$
$+\frac{9}{16}$ 5; 5

30. $7\frac{9}{20}$
$+4\frac{3}{20}$ 11; $11\frac{1}{2}$

31. $1\frac{1}{7} + 2\frac{5}{9}$ 4; $3\frac{1}{2}$

32. $3\frac{3}{5} - 1\frac{3}{9}$ 3; 2

33. $1\frac{1}{8} + \frac{7}{9}$ 2; 2

34. $4\frac{5}{8} - 1\frac{3}{7}$ 4; 3

▶ Applications

35. It rained $\frac{7}{8}$ inch Monday, $1\frac{1}{4}$ inches Tuesday, and $\frac{3}{8}$ inch Wednesday. Estimate the total rainfall for the 3 days to the nearest $\frac{1}{2}$ inch. 3 in.

36. Look at the picture. Estimate the distance each player's hand is from the rim.

$1\frac{1}{2}$ feet

▶ Review (Lessons 4.2, 4.5)

Complete each statement.

37. A marathon is about 45 ___ long. m km km

38. The mass of a feather is about 2 ___. g kg g

39. The child grew about 6 ___ in a year. cm m cm

Adding and Subtracting Fractions and Mixed Numbers **169**

Vocabulary and Writing Practice
VW Worksheet 7, TRB, page 143

Calculator Activities
CA Worksheet 7, TRB, page 168

Enrichment
E Worksheet 7, TRB, pages 211–212

Real Life Applications
RL Worksheet 7, TRB, pages 245–246

Answers
5. 10 20 30 40 50
6. 4 8 12 16 20
7. 9 18 27 36 45
8. 12 24 36 48 60
9. 15 30 45 60 75
10. 30 60 90 120 150

Chapter 7 Review

Add or subtract. Write the answers in lowest terms. (Lesson 7.1)

1. $\frac{5}{6} + \frac{5}{6}$ $1\frac{2}{3}$ **2.** $\frac{7}{8} + \frac{3}{8} + \frac{5}{8}$ $1\frac{7}{8}$ **3.** $\frac{11}{12} - \frac{5}{12}$ $\frac{1}{2}$ **4.** $\frac{9}{10} - \frac{1}{10}$ $\frac{4}{5}$

List the first five multiples. (Lesson 7.2)

5. 10   **6.** 4   **7.** 9   **8.** 12   **9.** 15   **10.** 30

Find the LCD. (Lesson 7.2)

11. $\frac{1}{2}$ $\frac{3}{8}$ 8   **12.** $\frac{5}{6}$ $\frac{3}{5}$ 30   **13.** $\frac{3}{4}$ $\frac{4}{5}$ $\frac{7}{10}$ 20   **14.** $\frac{6}{7}$ $\frac{7}{9}$ 63   **15.** $\frac{1}{3}$ $\frac{5}{8}$ $\frac{1}{6}$ 24

Add. Write the answers in lowest terms. (Lessons 7.3, 7.4)

16. $\frac{1}{4}$
$+ \frac{1}{3}$ $\frac{7}{12}$

17. $\frac{5}{8}$
$+ \frac{1}{3}$ $\frac{23}{24}$

18. $\frac{5}{6}$
$+ \frac{3}{4}$ $1\frac{7}{12}$

19. $9\frac{11}{12}$
$+ 6\frac{7}{8}$ $16\frac{19}{24}$

20. $2\frac{1}{2}$
$+ 3\frac{7}{8}$ $6\frac{3}{8}$

21. $4\frac{3}{5}$
$+ 5\frac{2}{3}$ $10\frac{4}{15}$

22. Carl lost $\frac{3}{4}$ pound one week and $1\frac{1}{2}$ pounds the next week. How many pounds did he lose in 2 weeks? $2\frac{1}{4}$ lb.

23. Pam swam $\frac{11}{12}$ mile, Maria swam $\frac{5}{6}$ mile, and Joan swam $\frac{3}{4}$ mile. How many miles did they swim altogether? $2\frac{1}{2}$ mi.

Rename each whole number. (Lesson 7.7)

24. $9 = 8\frac{\blacksquare}{12}$ 12   **25.** $5 = 4\frac{\blacksquare}{6}$ 6   **26.** $7 = 6\frac{\blacksquare}{10}$ 10   **27.** $2 = 1\frac{\blacksquare}{7}$ 7   **28.** $8 = 7\frac{\blacksquare}{25}$ 25

Subtract. Write the answers in lowest terms. (Lessons 7.5, 7.7, 7.9)

29. $\frac{7}{10}$
$- \frac{1}{5}$ $\frac{1}{2}$

30. $\frac{11}{12}$
$- \frac{1}{8}$ $\frac{19}{24}$

31. 10
$- 4\frac{1}{4}$ $5\frac{3}{4}$

32. 8
$- 2\frac{3}{10}$ $5\frac{7}{10}$

33. 4
$- 1\frac{3}{5}$ $2\frac{2}{5}$

34. 7
$- 5\frac{5}{9}$ $1\frac{4}{9}$

35. $5\frac{1}{5}$
$- 1\frac{1}{2}$ $3\frac{7}{10}$

36. $6\frac{7}{8}$
$- 3\frac{3}{4}$ $3\frac{1}{8}$

37. $9\frac{1}{4}$
$- 2\frac{3}{5}$ $6\frac{13}{20}$

38. $7\frac{1}{12}$
$- 4\frac{2}{3}$ $2\frac{5}{12}$

39. $2\frac{2}{3}$
$- 1\frac{4}{5}$ $\frac{13}{15}$

40. $8\frac{2}{7}$
$- 6\frac{3}{4}$ $1\frac{15}{28}$

Estimate to the nearest whole number. (Lesson 7.10)

41. $5\frac{1}{4} + 8\frac{1}{10}$ 13   **42.** $9\frac{3}{4} - 3\frac{1}{6}$ 7   **43.** $2\frac{7}{12} + 4\frac{3}{5}$ 8   **44.** $12\frac{5}{8} - 9\frac{7}{8}$ 3

Chapter 7 Test

Subtract. Write the answers in lowest terms.

1. $\frac{4}{5}$
   $-\frac{1}{3}$ $\frac{7}{15}$

2. 6
   $-3\frac{2}{3}$ $2\frac{1}{3}$

3. $9\frac{1}{8}$
   $-5\frac{3}{4}$ $3\frac{3}{8}$

4. $\frac{11}{12}$
   $-\frac{5}{12}$ $\frac{1}{2}$

5. $3\frac{1}{6}$
   $-\frac{7}{8}$ $2\frac{7}{24}$

Estimate to the nearest whole number.

6. $2\frac{5}{6} - 1\frac{1}{16}$ 2

7. $6\frac{7}{16} + 3\frac{3}{8}$ 9

8. $5\frac{9}{10} - 2\frac{3}{4}$ 3

9. $8\frac{1}{3} + 7\frac{4}{5}$ 16

Rename each whole number.

10. $12 = 11\frac{\blacksquare}{16}$ 16

11. $6 = 5\frac{\blacksquare}{9}$ 9

12. $9 = 8\frac{\blacksquare}{10}$ 10

13. $15 = 14\frac{\blacksquare}{20}$ 20

Find the LCD.

14. $\frac{3}{4}$ $\frac{1}{5}$ 20

15. $\frac{1}{2}$ $\frac{2}{3}$ 6

16. $\frac{7}{10}$ $\frac{2}{15}$ $\frac{1}{6}$ 30

17. $\frac{11}{12}$ $\frac{5}{8}$ 24

18. $\frac{7}{20}$ $\frac{3}{5}$ 20

Add. Write the answers in lowest terms.

19. $1\frac{1}{3}$
    $+2\frac{1}{4}$ $3\frac{7}{12}$

20. $\frac{3}{16}$
    $+\frac{5}{16}$ $\frac{1}{2}$

21. $5\frac{1}{2}$
    $+6\frac{2}{5}$ $11\frac{9}{10}$

22. $2\frac{5}{8}$
    $+6\frac{3}{8}$ 9

23. Stock ABC went up $3\frac{7}{8}$. If it was at $13\frac{1}{4}$ before, what is the new price? $17\frac{1}{8}$

24. Brad worked $2\frac{1}{4}$ hours on Monday and $1\frac{1}{5}$ hours on Tuesday. How many hours did he work? $3\frac{9}{20}$ hours

List the first five multiples.

25. 11
26. 17
27. 21
28. 25
29. 50

Add or subtract. Write the answers in lowest terms.

30. $\frac{1}{12} + \frac{1}{2}$ $\frac{7}{12}$

31. $5\frac{9}{10} - 2\frac{3}{10}$ $3\frac{3}{5}$

32. $\frac{9}{10} + \frac{2}{3}$ $1\frac{17}{30}$

33. $\frac{5}{6} - \frac{1}{4}$ $\frac{7}{12}$

Answers

25. 11 22 33 44 55
26. 17 34 51 68 85
27. 21 42 63 84 105
28. 25 50 75 100 125
29. 50 100 150 200 250

Adding and Subtracting Fractions and Mixed Numbers **171**

T171

Career Focus Activity

Materials: pencils, paper

Procedure: Organize students into four groups. Students arrange to have a panel of professionals speak to the class.

• The first group writes an invitation to a chef, a school cafeteria employee, a nutritionist, and a waiter/waitress to visit the classroom.

• The second group compiles a list of questions to ask the individuals about the job, activities the job entails, level of difficulty, required education, rewards of the job, how math skills are utilized on the job, etc.

• During the visit, members of the third group ask the questions and record the responses.

• Members of the fourth group compose a thank you note to be sent within three days of the visit.

• All students evaluate the experience.

Use customary measurements to find

• the distance a football is thrown.

• the weight of a book bag.

• the amount for a recipe.

What are some other ways to use customary measurement?

Chapter 8

Customary Measurement

A *chef prepares food.*

- Chefs work in restaurants, hotels, schools, hospitals, cruise ships, and for caterers.

- To be a chef, the individual should enjoy cooking, be creative, and be able to work under pressure.

- A chef reads recipes, measures ingredients, creates menus, keeps a record of supplies, and prices the food.

- To become a chef, an individual can work his or her way up through the ranks of the kitchen staff or go to a culinary institute.

- Some other careers in the food industry include kitchen staff, managers, nutritionists, and teachers.

CAREER

CHEF

PORTFOLIO PROJECT: *Create a meal for 10 people.*

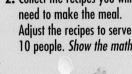

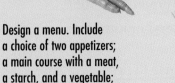

2. Collect the recipes you will need to make the meal. Adjust the recipes to serve 10 people. *Show the math.*

1. Design a menu. Include a choice of two appetizers; a main course with a meat, a starch, and a vegetable; and a choice of three desserts.

3. Determine how much you will charge per person. You need to make a profit yet be competitive. *Show the math.*

Career Focus Activity

Materials: pencils, paper

Procedure: Organize students into four groups. Students arrange to have a panel of professionals speak to the class.

- The first group writes an invitation to a chef, a school cafeteria employee, a nutritionist, and a waiter/waitress to visit the classroom.
- The second group compiles a list of questions to ask the individuals about the job, activities the job entails, level of difficulty, required education, rewards of the job, how math skills are utilized on the job, etc.
- During the visit, members of the third group ask the questions and record the responses.
- Members of the fourth group compose a thank you note to be sent within three days of the visit.
- All students evaluate the experience.

About the Portfolio Project

This could be done in conjunction with the panel discussion. Students should be prepared to present their new creations and recipe choices.prior to the discussion. Prepare some of the items ahead and serve at the end of the panel discussion.

Assessment: The individual scoring rubric on page 161 of the Teacher's Resource Binder can be reproduced and used for assessment. Include the following information in the last two boxes. Students should have:

- designed a menu, including all the requirements.
- accurately converted the measurements of the recipe to feed ten people.

8.1 Introduction to the Customary System

Miles Feet Pounds Months Degrees

You use the customary system of measurement all the time. In fact, you use it often to describe facts about yourself. Take Mark as an example.

Quarts Inches

Mark is 5 feet, $6\frac{1}{2}$ inches tall and weighs 145 pounds. He is 14 years, 3 months, and 12 days old. His normal body temperature is 98.6° Fahrenheit, and his body contains about 5 quarts of blood. He lives $5\frac{1}{2}$ miles from downtown Chicago. Mark works 20 hours a week and earns $6 an hour.

1. List the units of measurement that you recognize in the description of Mark.

2. List some units of measurement that were not included in the description of Mark.

3. Which of the following types of measurement are included in the description of Mark?

   capacity   height   temperature   time   weight

4. Write a description of yourself using several units of measurement.

5. What types of measurement would you use to describe a baseball game?

6. What types of measurement do you use each day?

► Express Yourself

You are familiar with many customary measurement terms already. Use the glossary and a dictionary to write definitions for the following terms.

7. capacity **8.** length **9.** temperature **10.** weight

List all the units of customary measure you can think of that describe the following types of measurement.

11. distance **12.** time **13.** weight **14.** height **15.** capacity

For each description in Column A, find the appropriate unit of measurement listed in Column B.

Column A

16. The distance from your home to Yellowstone National Park

17. The amount of milk used for a cake recipe

18. The height of a box of cereal

19. The time it takes to run a 100-yard dash

20. The amount you weigh

21. The temperature outside

Column B

a. degrees Fahrenheit
b. inches
c. miles
d. cups
e. seconds
f. pounds

► Practice What You Know

You may remember that the metric system is based on powers of 10. The division of measurements in the customary system is not so regular. The most common numbers you must work with in converting from one customary unit to another are multiples of 4, such as 8, 12, 16, 24, 36, and 60. Other numbers you might have to work with are 3, 1760, and 5280.

Solve.

22. $3\frac{1}{2} \times 12$ **23.** 4×60 **24.** $78 \div 36$ **25.** $500 \div 1760$

26. 4×8 **27.** $25{,}000 \div 5280$ **28.** 17×3 **29.** $92 \div 12$

Express Yourself Answers

7. the ability to receive, hold, or absorb; volume

8. measurement of the extent of something along its greatest dimension; distance; amount of time between moments

9. the degree of hotness or coldness of a body or environment

10. the measure of the heaviness, or mass, of an object

11. inch, feet, yard, mile

12. second, minute, hour, day, week, month, year, decade, century

13. ounce, pound, ton

14. inch, foot, yard

15. cup, pint, quart, gallon

16. c **17.** d **18.** b

19. e **20.** f **21.** a

Practice What You Know Answers

22. 42

23. 240

24. 2 R6, $2.1\overline{6}$ or $2\frac{1}{6}$

25. 0 R500, 0.28, or $\frac{25}{88}$

26. 32

27. 4 R3880, 4.73, or $4\frac{97}{132}$

28. 51

29. 7 R8, $7.\overline{6}$, or $7\frac{2}{3}$

Project

Create a display of measuring tools. Include the following in your display: the tool or a picture of it, the name of the tool, the units of measurement used with each tool, and examples of things that are measured with each tool.

8.2 Converting Customary Units of Length

Objective

• To convert between customary units of length

Purpose

Being able to convert customary units of length is sometimes necessary when you are comparing lengths. For example, if you wanted to compare how far you could throw a baseball with how far you could throw a football, you might have measured the baseball distance in feet and the football distance in yards. You might convert the football measurement to feet to compare the two distances.

Introducing the Lesson

Review converting metric units of length (Lesson 4.2). Use the examples: Convert 47 millimeters to centimeters. (4.7 cm) Convert 3.2 kilometers to meters. (3200 m) Ask: What operation did you use to convert from millimeters to centimeters? (division) What operation did you use to convert from kilometers to meters? (multiplication) Elicit from students that to convert to a larger unit you divide and to convert to a smaller unit you multiply.

Alternative Examples

Example A—Convert 23 feet to inches. Multiply since you are converting to a smaller unit.
1 ft = 12 in., so
23 ft. = 23 × 12 = 276 in.
23 ft. = **276 in.**

Example B—Convert 7920 feet to miles. Divide since you are converting to a larger unit.
3 ft. = 1 yd., so
7920 ft. = 7920 ÷ 3 = 2640 yd.
1760 yd. = 1 mi., so
2640 yd. = 2640 ÷ 1760 = $1\frac{1}{2}$ mi.
7920 ft. = **$1\frac{1}{2}$ mi.**

Which roller coaster drops farther?

Examples

To convert customary units of length, first determine if you are converting to a larger or smaller unit.

Equivalents		Abbreviations	
12 inches = 1 foot		inch **in.**	yard **yd.**
3 feet = 1 yard		foot **ft.**	mile **mi.**
1760 yards = 1 mile			

A Convert 50 yards to feet.

Multiply since you are changing to a smaller unit.

1 yd. = 3 ft., so
50 yd. = 50 × 3 = 150 ft.
50 yd. = **150 ft.**

B Convert 456 inches to yards.

Divide since you are changing to a larger unit.

12 in. = 1 ft., so
456 in. = 456 ÷ 12 = 38 ft.
3 ft. = 1 yd., so
38 ft. = 38 ÷ 3 = $12\frac{2}{3}$ yd.
456 in. = **$12\frac{2}{3}$ yd.**

▶ Think and Discuss

1. Complete the table below.

   1 ft. = ___ in.   1 yd. = ___ ft.   1 mi. = ___ yd.
                          1 yd. = ___ in.   1 mi. = ___ ft.
                                                 1 mi. = ___ in.

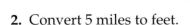

SKILLS

2. Convert 5 miles to feet.

3. Refer to the introduction to this lesson. Which roller coaster drops farther?

4. It takes Jan 8 minutes to run a mile. How many feet does she run in 1 minute?

5. Convert 5.1 feet to inches in two ways. First, round to the nearest foot and then convert. Second, convert and then round to the nearest inch. Which answer is a better estimate? Why?

6. Explain how you would order 35 yards, 1392 inches, and 114 feet from shortest to longest.

Exercises

Convert each measure. (See Example A.)

7. 4 ft. to in.
48 in.
8. 25 yd. to ft.
75 ft.
9. 2 mi. to ft.
10,560 ft.
10. 7 yd. to in.
252 in.
11. 20 ft. to in.
240 in.
12. 3 yd. to ft.
9 ft.
13. 10 yd. to in.
360 in.
14. 9 mi. to ft.
47,520 ft.

Convert each measure. (See Example B.)

15. 561 ft. to yd.
187 yd.
16. 540 in. to yd.
15 yd.
17. 15,840 ft. to mi.
3 mi.
18. 228 in. to ft.
19 ft.
19. 7040 yd. to mi.
4 mi.
20. 36,960 ft. to mi.
7 mi.

▶ Mixed Practice (For more practice, see page 425.)

Convert each measure.

21. 5 ft. to in.
60 in.
22. 108 in. to yd.
3 yd.
23. 297 ft. to yd.
99 yd.
24. 10 ft. to in.
120 in.
25. 1800 in. to ft.
150 ft.
26. 21,600 in. to yd.
600 yd.

▶ Applications

27. A marathon can be 26 miles 385 yards long. How many yards is that? 46,145 yd.

28. Bill told his mother he was going to race in the 440 this weekend. "Don't you usually run the $\frac{1}{4}$-mile race?" she asked. Was Bill running in a different race than usual? Explain.

▶ Review (Lessons 7.1, 7.3, 7.4)

Add.

29. $\frac{1}{6}$
$+ \frac{5}{6}$ 1

30. $2\frac{1}{2}$
$+ 1\frac{3}{4}$ $4\frac{1}{4}$

31. $\frac{3}{10}$
$+ \frac{1}{4}$ $\frac{11}{20}$

32. $\frac{4}{5} + \frac{1}{2}$ $1\frac{3}{10}$

33. $2\frac{2}{3} + 6\frac{1}{3}$ 9

Alternative Strategies

Show students that by memorizing some conversion facts, such as 1 yd. = 36 in., they can eliminate a step in the conversion process. For example, show students that by knowing that 1 yd. = 36 in., they can convert 5676 inches to yards as follows, eliminating a step in the conversion process:

5676 in. ÷ 36 = (157$\frac{2}{3}$ yd.)

▶ **Think and Discuss Answers**

1. 12; 3; 1760; 36; 5280; 63,360
2. 26,400 ft.
3. the roller coaster that drops 50 yards
4. 660 ft
5. 60 in.; 61 in.; the second answer, found by converting and then rounding, is a better estimate because 0.1 feet is about an inch and by rounding first you lost that inch
6. First convert each distance to the same unit and then compare them;
35 yd. = 105 ft., 1392 in. = 116 ft.;
35 yd. < 114 ft. < 1392 in.

Answers

28. no; a 440 is 440 yards, which is $\frac{1}{4}$ mile

★ **Error Alert**

Mistakes may reveal that students are dividing to convert to a smaller unit and multiplying to convert to a larger unit.

Reinforcement

Extra Practice, page 425
EP/MR Worksheet 61, TRB, page 61

Challenge

The distance around the earth at the equator is about 24,900 miles. Convert this distance to yards, feet, and inches. (43,824,000 yd.; 131,472,000 ft.; 1,577,664,000 in.)

Objectives

- To measure to the nearest inch, $\frac{1}{2}$ inch, and $\frac{1}{4}$ inch
- To choose reasonable units of length

Purpose

This lesson helps you practice using customary units of length to measure objects. For example, you measure length when making curtains, rearranging furniture, or determining the amounts of carpeting and wallpaper you need to buy.

Introducing the Lesson

Review measuring length with metric units (Lesson 4.3). Use the example: Measure the length of the word "Think" in the heading "Think and Discuss" in this lesson to the nearest centimeter. (The length is closer to 1 centimeter than 2 centimeters.)

Generate a discussion about choosing an appropriate unit of length to measure something. Compile a list of items that might be measured using inches (small objects such as paper clips and index cards), feet (room dimensions, boats), yards (playing fields, gardens), and miles (highway distances, rivers, ocean depths). Elicit from students some instances when precise measurements are needed rather than estimates. (when building something, determining costs if based on length)

Alternative Examples

Example A—Measure the length of a dictionary to the nearest inch, $\frac{1}{2}$ inch, and $\frac{1}{4}$ inch. (Answers may vary.)

Example B—Complete the following statement. Choose the more reasonable measure. The height of a bus is about ___ .
12 in.   12 ft.
The height of a 3-ring binder is about 12 inches.
The height of a basketball hoop is 10 feet.
The more reasonable measure is **about 12 feet.**

8.3 Measuring with Customary Units of Length

When Maury was at the doctor's office, the nurse measured his height and said, "5 feet $7\frac{3}{4}$ inches." Then she wrote 5 feet 8 inches on Maury's chart. What happened to the $\frac{1}{4}$ inch?

Examples

To measure length, line up the zero mark on a ruler with one end of an object. Depending on the precision you need, you can round to the nearest $\frac{1}{4}$ inch, $\frac{1}{2}$ inch, inch, foot, or yard.

A Measure the length of the pencil to the nearest inch, $\frac{1}{2}$ inch, and $\frac{1}{4}$ inch.

Nearest inch: $4\frac{9}{16}$ inches is closer to **5 inches** than 4 inches.

Nearest $\frac{1}{2}$ inch: $4\frac{9}{16}$ inches is closer to $4\frac{1}{2}$ **inches** than 5 inches.

Nearest $\frac{1}{4}$ inch: $4\frac{9}{16}$ is closer to $4\frac{1}{2}$ **inches** than $4\frac{3}{4}$ inches.

B Choose the more reasonable measure.

The height of a classroom is about ___ .   40 ft.   4 yd.

The height of a 4-story building is about 40 feet.
The height of a basketball rim is a little over 3 yards.

The more reasonable answer is **4 yards.**

▶ Think and Discuss

1. Measure the line segment below to the nearest inch, $\frac{1}{2}$ inch, and $\frac{1}{4}$ inch.

_____

2. Refer to the introduction to this lesson. If the nurse rounds to the nearest inch, someone listed as 5 feet 8 inches could be as short as ▨ feet ▨ inches tall.

3. What unit is used for distances between two cities? Why?

▶ Exercises

Measure each item to the nearest inch, $\frac{1}{2}$ inch, and $\frac{1}{4}$ inch.
(See Example A.)

4. the length of your shoe Answers may range from 8–11 inches.

5. the line segment at the right ___ 2 in.; 2 in.; $1\frac{3}{4}$ in. _____

Complete each statement. Choose the more reasonable measure.
(See Example B.)

6. The width of a classroom is about ___. 1500 in. (15 ft.)

7. The length of a golf club is about ___. 10 ft. (1 yd.)

▶ Mixed Practice (For more practice, see page 425.)

Measure each item to the nearest inch, $\frac{1}{2}$ inch, and $\frac{1}{4}$ inch.

8. the width of your desk
Answers will vary.

9. the length of your thumbnail
Answers will vary.

Complete each statement. Choose the more reasonable measure.

10. The length of a football field is ___. 30 yd. (360 ft.)

11. The height of a floor lamp is about ___. (60 in.) 6 yd.

▶ Applications

12. Measure the length and width of the comb shown to the nearest $\frac{1}{4}$ inch. $4\frac{3}{4}$ in.; $1\frac{1}{4}$ in.

13. Measure the length and width of this book's cover to the nearest $\frac{1}{4}$ inch. $7\frac{3}{4}$ in.; $9\frac{1}{2}$ in.

▶ Review (Lessons 7.1, 7.5, 7.7, 7.9)

Subtract.

14. $\frac{9}{10} - \frac{1}{2}$ $\frac{2}{5}$

15. $7 - 4\frac{1}{3}$ $2\frac{2}{3}$

16. $\frac{15}{16} - \frac{7}{16}$ $\frac{1}{2}$

17. $6\frac{3}{4} - 1\frac{1}{6}$ $5\frac{7}{12}$

SKILLS

Objectives

- To convert between customary units of weight
- To choose reasonable units of weight

Purpose

This lesson helps you convert and compare customary units of weight. Conversion is often necessary in comparison shopping in order to find the best buy. For example, to compare different-sized packages of a product, you may need to convert pounds to ounces.

Introducing the Lesson

Review measuring mass in the metric system (Lesson 4.5). Use the example: Convert 6000 grams to kilograms. Ask: Are you converting to a larger or smaller unit? (larger) What operation will you use to convert? (division) 1000 g = 1 kg, so 6000 kg = 6.000 kg or 6 kg. Remind students to divide when converting to a larger unit and to multiply when converting to a smaller unit.

Have students make a list of items sold by weight. (fresh fruits and vegetables, meats, nails, coal) Then have them discuss activities or occupations that involve using weight. (grocery clerk—weighing produce, truck driver—weighing loads, postal clerk—weighing mail, fitness instructor—using proper weights)

Alternative Examples

Example A—Convert 5 pounds 4 ounces to ounces. Multiply since you are changing to a smaller unit.
16 oz. = 1 lb., so
5 lb. = 5 × 16 = 80 oz.
5 lb. 4 oz. = **84 oz.**

Example B—Convert 140,300 pounds to tons. Divide since you are changing to a larger unit.
1 T. = 2000 lb., so
140,300 lb. = 140,300 ÷ 2000 = $70\frac{300}{2000}$ T.
140,330 lb. = **70 T. 300 lb.**

8.4 Customary Units of Weight

Abdul wanted to buy potato chips for a party. He preferred Stacko Chips, but the bag of Crunchy Chips looked larger. He decided to compare the net weights written on the packages. Is one package heavier?

Examples

To convert customary units of weight, first determine if you are converting to a larger or smaller unit.

Equivalents	Abbreviations
16 ounces = 1 pound	ounce **oz.** pound **lb.**
2000 pounds = 1 short ton	short ton **T.**

A Convert 3 pounds 2 ounces to ounces.

Multiply since you are changing to a smaller unit.

16 oz. = 1 lb., so
3 lb. = 3 × 16 = 48 oz.
3 lb. 2 oz. = 48 + 2 = **50 oz.**

B Convert 4500 pounds to tons.

Divide since you are changing to a larger unit.

1 T. = 2000 lb., so
4500 lb. = 4500 ÷ 2000 = $2\frac{500}{2000}$ T.

The numerator is the number of pounds.

4500 lb. = **2 T. 500 lb.**

C Choose the more reasonable measure.

Chris's hamburger weighs 3 ____.   lb.   oz.

A 3-pound hamburger could exist, but would be awfully big (and hard to handle).
A 3-ounce hamburger is a little less than a quarter-pounder.

The more reasonable measure is **ounces.**

▶ **Think and Discuss**

1. Convert 3 tons 248 pounds to pounds.

2. How much does a $\frac{1}{4}$-pound hamburger weigh in ounces?

3. Refer to the introduction to this lesson. Which container of potato chips weighs more?

4. How many pounds equal 0.25 ton? Explain.

Exercises

Convert each measure. (See Example A.)

5. 19 lb. to oz.
304 oz.

6. 33 lb. to oz.
528 oz.

7. 11 T. to oz.
352,000 oz.

8. 9 lb. 13 oz. to oz.
157 oz.

9. 21 lb. 8 oz. to oz.
344 oz.

10. 2 T. 850 lb. to lb.
4850 lb.

Convert each measure. (See Example B.)

11. 48 oz. to lb.
3 lb.

12. 176 oz. to lb.
11 lb.

13. 98 oz. to lb.
6 lb. 2 oz.

14. 119 oz. to lb.
7 lb. 7 oz.

15. 8000 lb. to T.
4 T.

16. 18,000 lb. to T.
9 T.

Complete each statement. Choose the more reasonable measure.
(See Example C.)

17. A newborn baby weighs about 8 ___. (lb.) oz.

18. A whale weighs about 10 ___. (T.) lb.

▶ Mixed Practice (For more practice, see page 426.)

Convert each measure.

19. 2 lb. 14 oz. to oz.
46 oz.

20. 13 T. to lb.
26,000 lb.

21. 47 oz. to lb.
2 lb. 15 oz.

22. 6321 lb. to T.
3 T. 321 lb.

23. 17,860 lb. to T.
8 T. 1860 lb.

24. 64,000 oz. to T.
2 T.

Complete each statement. Choose the more reasonable measure.

25. When Rafael was 14, he weighed about 100 ___. (lb.) oz.

26. A pair of blue jeans weighs about 14 ___. lb. (oz.)

▶ Applications

27. A farm supply company has 3 tons 756 pounds of seed on hand. How many 1-pound bags can they fill with the seed?
6756 bags

28. "On my diet, I've gone from weighing $\frac{1}{8}$ ton to $\frac{1}{10}$ ton!" Mrs. Lati exclaimed. How many pounds has Mrs. Lati lost?
50 lb.

▶ Review (Lessons 1.5, 1.6, 5.4)

Compare. Use >, <, or =.

29. $\frac{7}{8}$ ___ $\frac{5}{8}$ >

30. 6853 ___ 6935 <

31. 0.073 ___ 0.0076 >

32. 4.32 ___ 4.3200 =

33. 8.745 ___ 8.8 <

34. 343 ___ 334 >

*L*ucy weighs 100 pounds. She claims she can lose 15 pounds overnight. "It's easy," she remarked. "All I have to do is move to Venus!"

Lucy knows that weight depends on gravity.

The weight of an object varies from planet to planet because the force of gravity is different on different planets. The table below shows how the weights of Lucy and her dog vary on the planets and on the Moon.

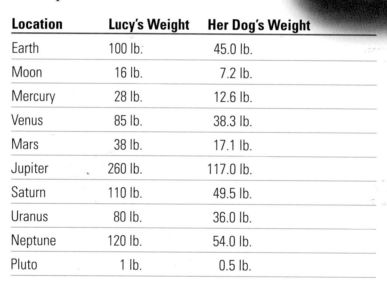

Location	Lucy's Weight	Her Dog's Weight
Earth	100 lb.	45.0 lb.
Moon	16 lb.	7.2 lb.
Mercury	28 lb.	12.6 lb.
Venus	85 lb.	38.3 lb.
Mars	38 lb.	17.1 lb.
Jupiter	260 lb.	117.0 lb.
Saturn	110 lb.	49.5 lb.
Uranus	80 lb.	36.0 lb.
Neptune	120 lb.	54.0 lb.
Pluto	1 lb.	0.5 lb.

How much would a 200-pound man on Earth weigh on the Moon?

First find 100 pounds on Earth from the table. Then look down the column to see that this would equal 16 pounds on the Moon. Therefore, 1 pound on Earth is 0.16 pound on the Moon.

200 lb. on Earth × 0.16 = 32 lb. on the Moon.

PROBLEM SOLVING

Use the table on page 182 to answer the following questions.

1. Gina weighs 28 pounds on Mercury. How much does she weigh on Earth? 100 lb.

2. How much more does Lucy's dog weigh on Jupiter than on Venus? 78.7 lb.

3. If an object weighs 32 pounds on the Moon, how much will it weigh on Earth? 200 lb.

4. If a spacecraft weighs four tons on Earth, how much will it weigh on the Moon in pounds? 1280 lb.

5. How much will 1 pound of raisins on Earth weigh on Mars? 0.38 lb.

6. How much will 5 pounds of potatoes on Earth weigh on Jupiter? 13 lb.

Now suppose you move to Mars and want a weight conversion table for a 100-pound piece of lidanium crystal that you found. To do this, you can divide all entries from Lucy's Earth table by 0.38 on a calculator. Round your answers to the nearest pound. Fill in the table to the right.

Location	Rock's Weight
Mars	100 lb.
Moon	42 lb.
7. Mercury	74 lb.
8. Venus	224 lb.
9. Earth	263 lb.
10. Jupiter	684 lb.

Use the completed table to answer the following questions.

11. If a person weighs 150 pounds on Mars, how much will that person weigh on Earth? 394.5 lb. or 395 lb.

12. If a boulder weighs 1 ton on Mars, how many pounds will it weigh on Jupiter? 13,680 lb.

13. Next you move to Jupiter and adopt an interterrestrial cat that weighs 100 pounds. Complete a weight conversion table for your pet cat.

▶ **Review** (Lesson 3.8)

Write which operation you would use to solve each problem. Then solve.

14. Vito bought 5 large packs of gum for $0.69 each. How much was the gum (not including tax)? Multiplication; $3.45

15. Marty weighs 175 pounds. He gained 8 pounds by lifting weights. How much did he weigh before? Subtraction; 167 lb.

8.6 Customary Units of Capacity

Georgette helps prepare meals at a nursing home. She is constantly amazed at the amount of food consumed. She would like to figure out how many gallons of soup the cooking pot contains. The cook makes enough to give 60 patients each an 8-ounce serving.

Georgette needs to convert fluid ounces to gallons.

Examples

To convert customary units of capacity, first determine if you are converting to a larger or smaller unit.

Equivalents
8 fluid ounces = 1 cup
16 fluid ounces = 2 cups = 1 pint
32 fluid ounces = 2 pints = 1 quart
128 fluid ounces = 4 quarts = 1 gallon

Abbreviations
fluid ounce **fl. oz.**
cup **c.** pint **pt.**
quart **qt.** gallon **gal.**

A Convert 480 fl. oz. to gal.

Divide since you are changing to a larger unit.

1 gal. = 128 fl. oz., so
480 fl. oz. = 480 ÷ 128 = $3\frac{3}{4}$ gal.
480 fl. oz. = $3\frac{3}{4}$ **gal.**

B Convert 3 c. to fl. oz.

Multiply since you are changing to a smaller unit.

1 c. = 8 fl. oz., so
3 c. = 3 × 8 = **24 fl. oz.**

C Choose the more reasonable measure.

A small bottle of perfume holds 4 ___.   fl. oz.   c.   A pitcher would hold
The more reasonable measure is **fluid ounces.**   about 4 cups.

▶ Think and Discuss

1. Refer to the introduction to this lesson. How many gallons of soup does the cook make?

2. Convert 20 fluid ounces to cups.

3. Complete the table below.

1 cup = ___ fl. oz. 1 qt. = ___ pt. 1 gal. = ___ qt.
1 pt. = ___ c. 1 qt. = ___ c. 1 gal. = ___ pt.
1 pt. = ___ fl. oz. 1 qt. = ___ fl. oz. 1 gal. = ___ c.
  1 gal. = ___ fl. oz.

Exercises

Convert each measure. (See Example A.)

4. 32 fl. oz. to c.
4 c.

5. 28 c. to pt.
14 pt.

6. 42 pt. to qt.
21 qt.

7. 48 qt. to gal.
12 gal.

8. 70 fl. oz. to c.
8 c. 6 fl. oz.

9. 19 c. to pt.
9 pt. 1 c.

Convert each measure. (See Example B.)

10. 7 c. to fl. oz.
56 fl. oz.

11. 13 pt. to c.
26 c.

12. 28 qt. to pt.
56 pt.

13. 19 gal. to qt.
76 qt.

14. 19 c. to fl. oz.
152 fl. oz.

15. 9 gal. 2 qt. to qt.
38 qt.

Complete each statement. Choose the more reasonable measure.
(See Example C.)

16. A water cooler holds 10 ___ of water. fl. oz. (gal.)

17. A serving of orange juice is 6 ___. (fl. oz.) pt.

▶ Mixed Practice (For more practice, see page 426.)

Convert each measure.

18. 27 c. to pt.
13 pt. 1 c.

19. 5 pt. to fl. oz.
80 fl. oz.

20. 9 qt. to c.
36 c.

21. 8 pt. 1 c. to c.
17 c.

22. 7 gal. to c.
112 c.

23. 4 gal. 2 qt. to pt.
36 pt.

Complete each statement. Choose the more reasonable measure.

24. An automobile tank will hold 12 ___ of gasoline. qt. (gal.)

25. A large lemonade pitcher holds 1 ___ of liquid. c. (gal.)

▶ Applications

26. Kim needs five quarts of oil for her car. If the store sells only gallon containers of oil, how many gallons must she buy?
2 gal.

27. A 6-pack of 12-ounce cans and a $\frac{1}{2}$-gallon bottle each cost $1.19. Which is the better buy?
6-pack

▶ Review (Lessons 2.3, 2.7, 3.3)

Multiply or divide mentally.

28. $89.4 \div 10$
8.94

29. 500×80
40,000

30. $9013 \div 100$
90.13

31. 5.75×1000
5750

Objective

- To add and subtract customary units

Purpose

This lesson helps you to do calculations of sums and differences of lengths, periods of time, and quantities. For example, you can subtract your height last year from your present height to find how much you have grown in 1 year.

Introducing the Lesson

Review customary units of length, weight, and volume (Lessons 8.2, 8.4, 8.6). Write the following problem on the chalkboard: 1221 − 987 = (234). Ask: What must you do before subtracting? (regroup the hundreds, tens, and ones places) Help students see that regrouping digits when subtracting whole numbers is similar to regrouping customary units. Show how you can regroup 9 yards 2 feet.

Alternative Examples

Example A—Add.
12 hr. 25 min. + 16 hr. 52 min.
   12 hr. 25 min.
+ 16 hr. 52 min.
   28 hr. 77 min. Rename 77 min.
77 min. = 1 hr. 17 min., so
28 hr. 77 min. = **29 hr. 17 min.**

Example B—Subtract.
142 lb. 4 oz. − 39 lb. 7 oz.
Regroup 142 lb.
   142 lb. 4 oz. → 141 lb. 20 oz.
−   39 lb. 7 oz. →   39 lb. 7 oz.
                    102 lb. 13 oz.
142 lb. 4 oz. − 39 lb. 7 oz. = **102 lb. 13 oz.**

▶ Think and Discuss Answers

1. yes
2. 12 hr. 11 min., 5 sec.
3. 23 yd. 8 ft.

8.7 Computing with Customary Units

Elliot tapes comedy routines off the radio. Can he fit the three routines described here on the 15 minutes left on a tape?

Examples

To compute with customary units, add or subtract like units. Regroup if necessary.

A **Add.**   **4 min. 12 sec. + 3 min. 55 sec.**

    4 min. 12 sec.
+ 3 min. 55 sec.
    7 min. 67 sec.   Rename 67 sec. as 1 min. 7 sec. Add to 7 min.

4 min. 12 sec. + 3 min. 55 sec. = **8 min. 7 sec.**

B **Subtract.**   **12 yd. 1 ft. − 9 yd. 2 ft.**

  12 yd. 1 ft. →   11 yd. 4 ft.   Regroup 12 yd.
− 9 yd. 2 ft. →   9 yd. 2 ft.
                 2 yd. 2 ft.

12 yd. 1 ft. − 9 yd. 2 ft. = **2 yd. 2 ft.**

▶ Think and Discuss

1. Refer to the introduction to this lesson. Will the three routines (4 min. 12 sec., 3 min. 55 sec., and 5 min. 8 sec.) fit on Elliot's tape?

2. Add.   9 hr. 25 min. 55 sec. + 2 hr. 45 min. 10 sec.

3. Regroup 25 yards 2 feet so you could subtract 7 feet from it.

4. Explain why it is sometimes necessary to regroup when subtracting with customary units. Give an example.

Exercises

Add. (See Example A.)

5.
   1 hr. 19 min.
+ 2 hr. 32 min.
_____
   3 hr. 51 min.

6.
   16 lb. 7 oz.
+ 9 lb. 8 oz.
_____
   25 lb. 15 oz.

7.
   19 gal. 1 qt.
+ 13 gal. 2 qt.
_____
   32 gal. 3 qt.

8.
   18 ft. 5 in.
+ 6 ft. 9 in.
_____
   25 ft. 2 in.

9.
   13 hr. 32 min.
+ 6 hr. 39 min.
_____
   20 hr. 11 min.

10.
   27 lb. 13 oz.
+ 13 lb. 12 oz.
_____
   41 lb. 9 oz.

Subtract. (See Example B.)

11.
   3 hr. 28 min.
− 2 hr. 19 min.
_____
   1 hr. 9 min.

12.
   6 gal. 2 qt.
− 5 gal. 3 qt.
_____
   3 qt.

13.
   29 lb. 12 oz.
− 13 lb. 15 oz.
_____
   15 lb. 13 oz.

14.
   9 yd. 10 in.
− 5 yd. 5 in.
_____
   4 yd. 5 in.

15.
   19 hr. 23 min.
− 11 hr. 29 min.
_____
   7 hr. 54 min.

16.
   31 lb. 6 oz.
− 15 lb. 11 oz.
_____
   15 lb. 11 oz.

▶ Mixed Practice (For more practice, see page 427.)

Add or subtract.

17.
   13 min. 15 sec.
+ 26 min. 29 sec.
_____
   39 min. 44 sec.

18.
   9 yd. 2 ft. 3 in.
− 7 yd. 2 ft. 9 in.
_____
   1 yd. 2 ft. 6 in.

19.
   15 gal. 1 qt.
− 9 gal. 3 qt.
_____
   5 gal. 2 qt.

20.
   3 T. 843 lb.
− 1 T. 1650 lb.
_____
   1 T. 1193 lb.

21.
   9 yd. 2 ft.
+ 3 yd. 1 ft. 7 in.
_____
   13 yd. 7 in.

22.
   19 min.
− 6 min. 8 sec.
_____
   12 min. 52 sec.

▶ Applications

23. The winning time for the marathon was 2 hours 26 minutes 18 seconds. This time was 2 hours 36 minutes 53 seconds faster than that of the last finisher. What was the slowest time?
5 hr. 3 min. 11 sec.

24. An empty delivery truck weighs 6 tons 650 pounds. The truck weighs 8 tons when completely full. What is the weight of the truck's full load in pounds?
3350 lb.

25. A program manager wrote the list at the right for a 30-minute TV show. How much time is planned for commercials?
4 min. 15 sec.

TV 3

First Segment	2:30	Third Segment	9:00
Theme Song	1:30	Commercials	
Commercials		Closing Credits	0:30
Second Segment	12:15	Commercials	
Commercials			

▶ Review (Lesson 3.9)

Simplify.

26. $63 \div 7 + 8 \times 6$ 57

27. $9 \times (8 - 6) \times 7$ 126

28. $12 + 60 \div 10 \times 5$ 42

29. $56 \div 8 + 10 - 4$ 13

30. $28 \div 4 \times (95 + 4)$ 693

31. $45 \div (9 + 6) \times 7$ 21

▶ Think and Discuss Answers

(continued)

4. You regroup when the amount of a unit you are subtracting is larger than the amount of that unit you are subtracting from. Possible answers include: 2 lb. 10 oz. − 1 lb. 15 oz. and 5 hr. 16 min. − 3 hr. 35 min.

★ Error Alert

Errors may reveal that students are forgetting to use conversion facts when regrouping. For example, they may regroup 7 lb. 3 oz. as 6 lb. 13 oz., forgetting to use the fact that 1 lb. = 16 oz., not 10 oz.

Reinforcement

Extra Practice, page 427
EP/MR Worksheet 65, TRB, page 65

Puzzle

Work in a group with 2 other students. Each group should select an object in the classroom that the other groups must identify by asking 5 measurement questions. Each group should find out the following information for its object: length, width, distance around object, weight, volume. Use a ruler, scale, measuring cup, or other measuring tools to take the measurements. Let other groups, one at a time, take turns asking up to 5 questions about the unknown object. The group that identifies an object by asking the fewest number of questions wins. Example: How long is it? (5 inches long) How wide is it? (less than $\frac{1}{2}$ inch wide) What is the distance around it? (about $\frac{3}{4}$ inch around) How much does it weigh? (less than one ounce) What is it? (a pencil)

T187

Objective

• To determine temperatures on the Fahrenheit and Celsius scales

Purpose

Although temperature in the United States is usually measured in degrees Fahrenheit, in other countries and in science temperature is usually measured in degrees Celsius. This lesson helps you use both the Celsius and the Fahrenheit scales.

Introducing the Lesson

If necessary, review reading a metric ruler as practice for reading thermometers (Lesson 4.3). Display both Celsius and Fahrenheit thermometers in class. Measure the temperature of a cup of water with each. Record the temperatures on the chalkboard. Ask: Is the water at two different temperatures? (no) Explain that both thermometers measure the same water temperature but on different scales.

Alternative Exampes

Example A—Determine normal body temperature in degrees Celsius.
37°C

Example B—Determine the temperature of a hot day in Chicago in degrees Fahrenheit.
90°F

▶ Think and Discuss Answers

1. no; because 30°C is the temperature of a hot day and the ice would melt
2. no; it would be too cold
3. because the temperatures vary a lot between the two scales
4. It doesn't make sense to say that it is twice as warm because 20°F is about −7°C and 10°F is about −12°C, and −7 is not twice as much as −12. (Contrast with length: if one object is twice as long as another, that will be true no matter what unit is used.)

8.8 Measuring Temperature

Before leaving on a trip to France, Mr. Kuhn telephoned to find out about the weather there. The overseas operator told him the temperature was 30 degrees. Mr. Kuhn was surprised, but to be safe he wore his winter coat, boots, and gloves. When he got off the plane, Mr. Kuhn realized that what he really needed was his swimsuit. What caused the misunderstanding?

Mr. Kuhn assumed that the temperature scale was Fahrenheit, but it actually was Celsius.

Examples

To determine temperature on the Fahrenheit or Celsius scale, use the drawing of a thermometer on page 189.

A Determine the room temperature in degrees Fahrenheit (°F).

68°F

B Determine the temperature of a hot day in Los Angeles in degrees Celsius (°C).

32°C

▶ Think and Discuss

1. If you were going ice-skating outside, would you want the temperature to be 30 degrees Celsius? Explain your answer.

2. Would you want to swim outdoors if the temperature were 10 degrees Celsius? Explain your answer.

3. When a temperature is given, why is it important to know which scale is being used?

4. Explain why it is incorrect to say that 20°F is "twice as warm" as 10°F.

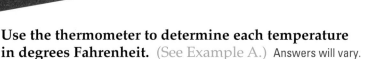

Exercises

Use the thermometer to determine each temperature in degrees Fahrenheit. (See Example A.) Answers will vary.

5. a cold winter day in Chicago 5° F

6. freezing point of water 32° F

7. normal body temperature 98.6° F

8. boiling point of water 212° F

Use the thermometer to determine each temperature in degrees Celsius. (See Example B.) Answers will vary.

9. room temperature 20° C

10. a cold winter day in Denver −15° C

11. normal body temperature 37° C

12. freezing point of water 0° C

▶ **Mixed Practice** (For more practice, see page 427.)

Use the thermometer to determine each temperature in degrees Fahrenheit and Celsius. Answers will vary.

13. a hot day in Miami 90° F   32° C

14. warm dinner rolls 176° F   80° C

15. a warm shower 125° F; 52° C

16. hot soup 194° F   90° C

▶ **Applications**

17. The high temperature for the day in Tucson was ninety-eight degrees Fahrenheit. What would the temperature be if it dropped nineteen degrees? 79° F

18. There is a 12-degree difference between 20 degrees Celsius and 32 degrees Celsius. What is the difference between the equivalent temperatures on the Fahrenheit scale? 22 degrees

▶ **Review** (Lessons 6.1, 6.2, 6.4, 6.6, 6.7)

Multiply or divide.

19. $\frac{7}{10} \times \frac{4}{5}$ $\frac{14}{25}$

20. $3\frac{1}{3} \div 6\frac{1}{4}$ $\frac{8}{15}$

21. $2\frac{2}{3} \times 9$ 24

22. $\frac{7}{8} \div 3$ $\frac{7}{24}$

23. $8 \div 1\frac{3}{4}$ $4\frac{4}{7}$

24. $5 \times 5\frac{3}{5}$ 28

25. $\frac{5}{8} \div \frac{5}{12}$ $1\frac{1}{2}$

26. $1\frac{1}{10} \times 3\frac{1}{5}$ $3\frac{13}{25}$

Reinforcement
Extra Practice, page 427
EP/MR Worksheet 66, TRB, page 66

Project
Use a temperature chart for selected cities found in a newspaper or the Internet to answer the following.

1. Find the city that had the highest temperature the previous day. Record the temperature.
2. Find the city that had the lowest temperature the previous day. Record the temperature.
3. What is the difference between the two temperatures?
4. Find the city you live in or the nearest one to your home city and record the temperature of the previous day.
5. Use the chart to list 10 cities in order from the warmest to the coldest.
(Answers to all questions depend on the cities selected.)

Objective

- To investigate elapsed time

Purpose

Computing elapsed time helps you to find how long it takes to complete a task or how much time must pass before an event takes place.

Introducing the Lesson

Review computing with customary units (Lesson 8.7).

Write the following time equivalencies on the chalkboard: 1 day = 24 hours; 1 hour = 60 minutes; 1 minute = 60 seconds.

Ask students to name some familiar events and estimate their elapsed time. (sample answers: a club meeting, 40 min.; an awards television program, 3 hr.; radio weather bulletin, 30 sec.)

Alternative Strategies

Explain to students that from any time a.m. to the same time p.m. is always 12 hours of elapsed time. Thus, another method of calculating elapsed time is to determine how many hours less or more than 12 have elapsed. For example, use this method for the times given in the text. Find the difference: 8:10 − 2:25 = 5:45. Subtract this difference from 12. 12 − 5:45 = 6:15, so 6 hours and 15 minutes have elapsed.

8.9 Investigating Elapsed Time

School begins at 8:10 in the morning and ends at 2:25 in the afternoon. How long is the school day?

1. Find the length of the school day. Discuss how you computed your answer.

You may find that people solve problems involving time in different ways. Did anyone in your class solve the problem using one of the methods shown below?

Method 1

8:10 to 12:10 → 4 hours
12:10 to 2:10 → 2 hours
2:10 to 2:25 → _____ 15 minutes _____   Add the times.
6 hours, 15 minutes

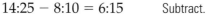

Method 2

8:10 to noon → 3 hours, 50 minutes
Noon to 2:25 → 2 hours, 25 minutes   Add the times.
5 hours, 75 minutes = 6 hours, 15 minutes

Method 3

Convert 2:25 to 14:25.   Add 12 hours and 2 hours.
14:25 − 8:10 = 6:15   Subtract.

In each case,
the total time is **6 hours, 15 minutes.**

No one of the three methods shown is always the best one to use. Other methods are also possible. Was any method used by your class different from those shown?

Solve each problem below using any method.

PROBLEM SOLVING

2. A baseball game began at 7:35 p.m. and ended at 10:42 p.m. How long was the game? 3 hours, 7 minutes

3. A woman began work at 9:15 a.m. and ended at 5:30 p.m. How long did she work? 8 hours, 15 minutes

4. Mr. Button came over to borrow some sugar at 10:45 a.m. He didn't leave until 4:20 p.m. How long did he stay? 5 hours, 35 minutes

5. The marathon race began at 6:30 a.m. The last runner crossed the finish line at 6:36 p.m. How long did this runner take? 12 hours, 6 minutes

6. A man began repeatedly singing "You Light Up My Life" at 8:12 a.m. on May 7. He did not stop singing until 3:21 p.m. on May 10. How long did he sing? 79 hours, 9 minutes

Knowing a variety of different ways to attack elapsed time problems helps you solve other problems involving time. Discuss and solve each problem below.

7. Can you find the elapsed time from 8:40 a.m. to 1:15 p.m. using Method 3? Discuss how this method is similar to subtracting decimals. How is it different?

8. Find the elapsed time from 1:10 a.m. to 12:55 a.m.

9. A concert begins at 8:00 p.m. It takes an hour and 15 minutes to get there. When should you leave if you want to be there an hour early?

10. You are taking an all-day exam. Your watch reads 10:48. The section you are on now ends at 11:06. How much time is left?

11. An opera begins at 7:00 p.m. and lasts $4\frac{1}{2}$ hours. You get home 20 minutes later. Are you home by midnight?

Copy and complete the table below.

Starting Time	Finishing Time	Elapsed Time	
12. 11:40 a.m.	6:42 p.m.	_____	7 hours, 2 minutes
13. _____	3:20 a.m.	6 hours, 7 minutes	9:13 p.m.
14. 6:30 p.m.	_____	17 hours, 5 minutes	11:35 a.m.
15. _____	4:11 p.m.	8 hours, 52 minutes	7:19 a.m.

▶ **Review** (Lesson 5.8)

Write as a repeating decimal.

16. $\frac{1}{6}$ 0.1$\overline{6}$ 17. $\frac{5}{6}$ 0.8$\overline{3}$ 18. $\frac{1}{3}$ 0.$\overline{3}$ 19. $\frac{2}{3}$ 0.$\overline{6}$ 20. $\frac{2}{9}$ 0.$\overline{2}$ 21. $\frac{3}{11}$ 0.$\overline{27}$

Answers

7. yes; change 1:15 p.m. to 13:15 and then subtract 8:40 to get 4 hours 35 minutes; this is similar to decimals since you would regroup as you do with decimals; this is different from decimals since you would have to regroup based on 60 instead of 10

8. 23 hours 45 minutes; a possible method would be to figure out how much time less than 24 hours the elapsed time would be (in this case it would be 15 minutes less than 24 hours)

9. 5:45 p.m.; one possible method is to subtract 2 hours and 15 minutes from 8:00

10. 18 minutes; one possible method is to determine how many minutes until 11:00 and then add 6 minutes

11. yes; one possible method is to add 4 hours and 30 minutes to 7:00 (11:30) and then add 20 minutes (11:50)

★ **Error Alert**
Mistakes may indicate that students are incorrectly regrouping.

Reinforcement
EP/MR Worksheet 67, TRB, page 67

Challenge
If the number of lily pads on a pond doubles every day until the pond is covered on March 15, on what day was the pond half-covered with lily pads? (March 14)

Objectives

- To read and interpret time cards
- To compute gross earnings

Purpose

Many workers use time cards to record the number of hours they work. This lesson helps you use a time card to compute your earnings and to check that your wages are being computed correctly.

Introducing the Lesson

Review addition of hours and minutes (Lesson 8.7) and multiplication of decimals (Lesson 2.8). Use the examples: Add—10 hr. 30 min. + 8 hr. 45 min. = (19 hr. 15 min.); multiply—12.50 × 19 = (237.5).

Alternative Examples

Example A—Determine the number of hours you worked.

Monday	4–6	2 hours
Thursday	5–9	4 hours
Sunday	12–5	+ 5 hours

You worked ▃▃ **11 hours.**

Example B—Determine your gross earnings if you make $10.50 per hour.

Multiply your earnings per hour by the number of hours you worked (Example A).

$10.50 ← rate per hour
× 11 ← hours worked
$115.50 ← gross earnings

You earned **$115.50.**

8.10 Calculating Earnings

Maria and Jessie recently began weekend jobs. Maria earns $6.50 an hour and Jessie earns $5.75 an hour. On their first payday, Maria was surprised that her paycheck was smaller than Jessie's. Jessie remarked, "Remember, you worked a short day last Sunday."

Maria and Jessie could compare their gross earnings, or earnings before taxes, by reading their weekly timecards.

Name: Maria Cabrera	In	Out	In	Out	Total Hours
Sat.	10:00	12:00	1:00	5:00	
Sun.	12:00	3:00			

Name: Jessie Martin	In	Out	In	Out	Total Hours
Sat.	10:00	12:00	1:00	5:00	
Sun.	12:00	6:00			

Examples

To determine gross earnings, first figure the number of hours worked. Then multiply by the hourly rate.

A **Determine the number of hours Maria worked.**

Maria worked **9 hours.**

Saturday:	10 –12	2 hours
	1–5	4
Sunday:	12–3	+ 3
		9 hours

B **Determine Maria's gross earnings.**

Maria earned **$58.50.**

Multiply Maria's hourly rate by the number of hours she worked.

$6.50 ← rate per hour
× 9 ← hours worked
$58.50 ← gross earnings

▶ Think and Discuss

1. Determine the total weekly earnings for 20 hours at $7 an hour.

2. Refer to the introduction to this lesson. How much greater was Jessie's gross pay than Maria's?

SKILLS

3. Jean works 35 hours a week for $6.25 an hour. How much does she earn in 2 weeks?

4. Fran earns $11 an hour and works 20 hours a week. Her brother Rogelio earns $5.50 an hour. How many hours must Rogelio work to earn as much as Fran in a week? Solve mentally.

Exercises

Use the timecards below.

Determine the total hours worked each week. (See Example A.)

5.
Day	Mon.	Tue.	Wed.	Thu.	Fri.
Hours Worked	$5\frac{1}{2}$	$7\frac{3}{4}$	$6\frac{3}{4}$	9	$8\frac{1}{2}$

6.
Day	Mon.	Tue.	Wed.	Thu.	Fri.
Hours Worked	$3\frac{1}{2}$	2	$3\frac{1}{4}$	$6\frac{1}{2}$	$7\frac{1}{4}$

Determine the gross earnings for both timecards.
(See Example B.)

7. Rate: $6.35 an hour $238.13; $142.88

8. Rate: $7.10 an hour $266.25; $159.75

▶ Mixed Practice (For more practice, see page 428.)

Copy and complete the chart below. Then find the gross earnings.

Mergenthal Pharmacy, Inc. Employee Timecard		Name: Eric Obenza Hourly Wage: $ 7.25			
Date	In	Out	In	Out	Hours
9. 1-3	8:30	12:00	12:30	5:00	
10. 1-4	8:45	12:30	1:15	4:45	
11. 1-5	8:30	12:15	1:00	5:00	
12. 1-6	8:30	12:30	1:00	5:15	
13. 1-7	9:00	1:30			
14. 1-8	12:00	5:45			
15. Total Hours					
16. Gross Earnings					

▶ Review (Lesson 2.3)

Multiply mentally.

17. 8000×50
400,000

18. 30×700
21,000

19. 300×100
30,000

20. 600×9000
5,400,000

21. $10 \times 60,000$
600,000

22. 400×500
200,000

23. 6000×70
420,000

24. 25×300
7500

Chapter 8 Review

REVIEW

Complete each statement. (Lesson 8.1)

1. The four basic units of length in the customary system are the ___, the ___, the ___, and the ___. Inch; foot; yard; mile

2. The Fahrenheit and Celsius scales measure ___. Temperature

Convert each measure. (Lessons 8.2, 8.4, 8.6)

3. 7 ft. to in.
   84 in.

4. 75 yd. to ft.
   225 ft.

5. 99 in. to ft.
   8 ft. 3 in.

6. 87 in. to yd.
   2 yd. 1 ft. 3 in.

7. 35 oz. to lb.
   2 lb. 3 oz.

8. 10 qt. to gal.
   2 gal. 2 qt.

Complete each statement. Choose the more reasonable measure.
(Lessons 8.3, 8.4, 8.6)

9. During practice, the athlete swam ___.   30 yd. (3 mi.)

10. The cake recipe called for 1 ___ of corn oil. (c.)   gal.

11. Laura's new bracelet weighed 4 ___. (oz.)   lb.

Measure each line segment below to the nearest inch, $\frac{1}{2}$ inch, $\frac{1}{4}$ inch.
(Lesson 8.3)

12. $\underline{\quad}$ 1 in.; $\frac{1}{2}$ in.; $\frac{1}{2}$ in.

13. $\underline{\qquad\qquad\qquad\qquad}$ 2 in.; $2\frac{1}{2}$ in.; $2\frac{1}{4}$ in.

14. $\underline{\qquad\qquad}$ 2 in.; $1\frac{1}{2}$ in.; $1\frac{3}{4}$ in.

Use the table to solve the following. (Lesson 8.5)

15. If you buy 6 roses, how much does each rose cost? $2.50

16. If you buy 6 roses one day and 2 roses the next, how much did you spend on the flowers? $21

Number	Cost
1	$3
2	$6
6	$15
12	$25

Add or subtract. (Lesson 8.7)

17.   7 yd. 2 ft. 8 in.
   + 9 yd. 2 ft. 9 in.
   _____
   17 yd. 2 ft. 5 in.

18.   1 gal. 2 qt.
   −   3 qt.
   _____
   3 qt.

19.   20 lb. 5 oz.
   − 5 lb. 15 oz.
   _____
   14 lb. 6 oz.

Determine the temperature of the following. (Lesson 8.8)

20. The normal body temperature is about 98.6° Fahrenheit, which is about ___. (37°C) 100°C 0°C

Chapter 8 Test

TEST

Add or subtract.

1. 2 gal. 3 qt. 1 pt.
    + 4 gal. 2 qt. 1 pt.
    _____
    7 gal. 1 qt.

2. 8 yd. 1 ft. 8 in.
    − 6 yd. 2 ft. 9 in.
    _____
    1 yd. 1 ft. 11 in.

3. 36 lb. 14 oz.
    + 25 lb. 13 oz.
    _____
    62 lb. 11 oz.

Complete each statement.

4. To convert pounds to ounces, you would multiply by ____.
    16

5. There are ____ inches in a foot and ____ feet in a yard.
    12; 3

Convert each measure.

6. 67 oz. to lb.
    4 lb. 3 oz.

7. 13 gal. to c.
    208 c.

8. 28 yd. to ft.
    84 ft.

Use the table to answer the following.

Number of calls	Length of calls	Cost per call
2	3 min.	$1.80
1	6 min.	3.30
5	4 min.	2.30
1	18 min.	9.30

9. Which is the highest-priced call?
    18-minute call

10. Which is the lowest priced call?
    3-minute call

11. What is the difference in cost between these two calls?
    $7.50

Complete each statement. Choose the more reasonable unit of measurement.

12. A newborn kitten weighs about 6 ____. (oz.) lb.

13. A caterpillar is about 3 ____ long. (in.) ft.

14. Room temperature is about 20 degrees ____.
    (Celsius) Fahrenheit

Measure each line segment to the nearest inch, $\frac{1}{2}$ inch, $\frac{1}{4}$ inch.

15. _____
    3 in.; 3 in.; $3\frac{1}{4}$ in.

16. _____
    3 in.; 3 in.; $2\frac{3}{4}$ in.

Chapter Tests
Short Answer, Forms A and B, TRB, pages
  295–296, 297–298
Multiple Choice, Forms A and B, TRB, pages
  363–364, 365–366

Teaching Aids
Answer sheet
TA 8, TRB, page 161a
Teaching suggestions precede the Teaching
  Aids worksheets.

Cumulative Tests
Short Answer, Forms A and B, TRB, pages
409–411, 412–414
Multiple Choice, Forms A and B, TRB, pages
433–435, 436–438

Teaching Aids
Answer sheet
TA 8, TRB, page 161a
Teaching suggestions precede the Teaching
Aids worksheets.

Cumulative Test Chapters 1–8

▶ **Choose the letter that shows the correct answer.**

1. $3\frac{1}{8} \times 2\frac{2}{5}$

  a. $2\frac{29}{48}$
  b. 15
  c. $7\frac{1}{2}$
  d. not given

2. $\frac{3}{4} + \frac{7}{8}$

  a. $1\frac{1}{4}$
  b. $1\frac{5}{8}$
  c. $\frac{10}{32}$
  d. not given

3. $13 - 4\frac{5}{12}$

  a. $8\frac{7}{12}$
  b. $9\frac{7}{12}$
  c. $8\frac{5}{12}$
  d. not given

4. $4\frac{1}{2} \div \frac{2}{9}$

  a. 1
  b. $4\frac{1}{2}$
  c. $\frac{18}{4}$
  d. not given

5. $6\frac{3}{5} \div 3\frac{2}{3}$

  a. $1\frac{4}{5}$
  b. $24\frac{3}{5}$
  c. $1\frac{1}{5}$
  d. not given

6. $6\frac{5}{6} + 3\frac{3}{4}$

  a. $10\frac{1}{2}$
  b. $9\frac{7}{12}$
  c. $10\frac{7}{12}$
  d. not given

7. $5\frac{1}{2} - 2\frac{9}{10}$

  a. $2\frac{2}{5}$
  b. $3\frac{3}{5}$
  c. $3\frac{3}{4}$
  d. not given

8. $\frac{8}{9} \times \frac{4}{5}$

  a. $\frac{6}{7}$
  b. $\frac{32}{45}$
  c. $1\frac{1}{7}$
  d. not given

9.   9 yd. 1 ft. 4 in.
   − 3 yd. 2 ft. 10 in.

  a. 5 yd. 1 ft. 6 in.
  b. 6 yd. 1 ft. 4 in.
  c. 6 yd. 2 ft. 6 in.
  d. not given

10.   7 gal. 1 qt.
   − 4 gal. 3 qt.

  a. 3 gal. 2 qt.
  b. 4 gal. 1 qt.
  c. 3 gal. 1 qt.
  d. not given

11.   28 lb. 14 oz.
   + 35 lb. 11 oz.

  a. 63 lb. 9 oz.
  b. 53 lb. 25 oz.
  c. 64 lb. 9 oz.
  d. not given

▶ **Convert each measure.**

12. 127 in. to ft.

  a. $10\frac{7}{12}$ ft.
  b. $42\frac{1}{12}$ ft.
  c. $12\frac{7}{12}$ ft.
  d. not given

13. 35 c. to qt.

  a. $17\frac{1}{4}$ qt.
  b. $4\frac{3}{4}$ qt.
  c. $8\frac{3}{4}$ qt.
  d. not given

14. 8 lb. 9 oz. to oz.

  a. 105 oz.
  b. 137 oz.
  c. 17 oz.
  d. not given

15. 3 hr. 39 min. to min.

  a. 159 min.
  b. 42 min.
  c. 219 min.
  d. not given

► **Complete each statement.**

16. Water boils at 100 degrees ___.

    a. Fahrenheit
    c. Fahrenheit and Celsius
    b. Celsius
    d. not given

17. The metric system is organized by powers of ___.
    a. 5
    b. 100
    c. 12
    d. not given

18. A(n) ___ is one of a pair of numbers whose product is 1.
    a. difference
    b. sum
    c. reciprocal
    d. not given

19. A fraction with a numerator that is greater than or equal to the denominator is called a(n) ___ fraction.
    a. improper
    b. LCD
    c. GCF
    d. not given

20. 0.3333333 . . . is called a(n) ___ decimal.
    a. terminating
    b. repeating
    c. nonrepeating
    d. not given

► **Use Guess and Check to solve.**

21. Alfonso has $10 and wants to buy an equal number of pounds of oranges and bananas. Oranges cost $1.59 for 3 pounds. Bananas cost $0.39 for 3 pounds. what is the largest number of pounds he can buy?
    a. 5 pounds of each
    b. 10 pounds of each
    c. 15 pounds of each
    d. not given

22. Some tape storage boxes hold 10 tapes and some hold 16. What kinds of boxes should Anne get if she wants all of her 46 tapes to be stored?
    a. 2 large
    b. 1 large and 3 small
    c. 4 small
    d. not given

► **Round each number to the nearest**

23. tenth.
    9.638
    a. 10
    b. 9.65
    c. 9.7
    d. not given

24. hundred.
    25,251
    a. 25,200
    b. 25,600
    c. 25,300
    d. not given

25. cent.
    $13.7973
    a. $13.79
    b. $13.80
    c. $14.00
    d. not given

26. million.
    11,499,105
    a. 11,000,000
    b. 12,000,000
    c. 11,500,000
    d. not given

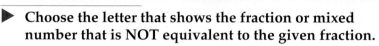

▶ Choose the letter that shows the fraction or mixed number that is NOT equivalent to the given fraction.

27. $\frac{3}{4}$

a. $\frac{8}{9}$ ⟵

b. $\frac{12}{16}$

c. $\frac{75}{100}$

d. not given

28. $\frac{17}{4}$

a. $3\frac{5}{4}$

b. $\frac{34}{8}$

c. $4\frac{1}{4}$

d. not given ⟵

29. $\frac{2}{16}$

a. $\frac{1}{8}$

b. $\frac{4}{36}$ ⟵

c. $\frac{8}{64}$

d. not given

30. $\frac{10}{50}$

a. $\frac{20}{100}$

b. $\frac{2}{5}$ ⟵

c. $\frac{1}{5}$

d. not given

▶ Compare. Use <, >, or =.

31. $\frac{5}{6}$ ▇ $\frac{11}{18}$

a. <

b. > ⟵

c. =

d. not given

32. $2\frac{1}{4}$ ▇ $\frac{15}{4}$

a. < ⟵

b. >

c. =

d. not given

33. $\frac{8}{16}$ ▇ $\frac{10}{20}$

a. <

b. >

c. = ⟵

d. not given

34. $3\frac{5}{8}$ ▇ $3\frac{7}{12}$

a. <

b. > ⟵

c. =

d. not given

▶ Solve.

35. How many $1\frac{1}{2}$-foot pieces of wood can Sheila cut from a $9\frac{3}{4}$-foot board?

a. 14 pieces

b. 7 pieces

c. 6 pieces ⟵

d. not given

36. Cans of juice are packed 24 to a box. How many full boxes can be packed from 836 cans?

a. 34 cases ⟵

b. 30 cases

c. 340 cases

d. not given

37. In a Chicago snowstorm the north side of town received $8\frac{1}{4}$ inches of snow. The south side received $2\frac{5}{8}$ inches. How much more snow fell on the north side?

a. $10\frac{7}{8}$ in.

b. $6\frac{3}{8}$ in.

c. $5\frac{5}{8}$ in. ⟵

d. not given

38. Mark wants to triple his chili recipe. The recipe calls for $2\frac{3}{4}$ teaspoons of chili powder. How much chili powder should he use for the larger recipe?

a. 6 teaspoons

b. $8\frac{1}{4}$ teaspoons ⟵

c. $\frac{1}{12}$ of a teaspoon

d. not given

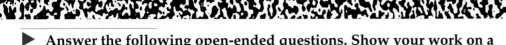

► **Answer the following open-ended questions. Show your work on a separate sheet of paper.**

39. This recipe makes 48 oatmeal cookies. A baker wants to make only 16 cookies. Rewrite the recipe for 16 cookies. Explain how you found your answer. Show your work. Skills used—multiplying and dividing fractions and mixed numbers

OATMEAL COOKIES	
$4\frac{1}{2}$ cups flour	$1\frac{1}{2}$ cups butter
$2\frac{1}{4}$ cups white sugar	3 eggs
$1\frac{1}{2}$ cups brown sugar	3 cups chopped nuts
24 oz. oatmeal	$1\frac{1}{2}$ tsp. vanilla
	1 tsp. salt

40. Amine is making costumes for the class play. He needs these materials for each costume.

$3\frac{3}{4}$ yards blue felt $1\frac{3}{4}$ yards gold braid trim

$2\frac{1}{2}$ yards red felt $\frac{7}{8}$ yards satin trim

If he needs to make 7 costumes, how much of each material does he need? If the class needs to save money, which trim should they eliminate? Explain how you found your answer. Show your work. Skills used—adding and subtracting fractions and mixed numbers

41.

Bus Schedule			
Binghamton to Monticello		**Monticello to New York**	
Leave	**Arrive**	**Leave**	**Arrive**
9:00 A.M.	11:45 A.M.	12:30 A.M.	1:40 P.M.
10:15 A.M.	12:30 P.M.	12:45 A.M.	2:55 P.M.
11:10 A.M.	1:35 P.M.	1:50 P.M.	4:00 P.M.

You live in Binghamton. You have scheduled a job interview at 2:45 P.M. in New York City. It takes you 12 minutes to walk from your home to the bus station. You must switch buses in Monticello to catch the bus to New York. It takes 15 minutes for you to walk from the bus station in New York City to the interview.

At what time would you leave home? What other factors may influence when you leave home? If you could reschedule your interview so that you would spend less time waiting for the bus or for the interview, what time would you schedule it? Which bus would you take? Write a paragraph explaining how you found your answer. Show your work. Skills used—adding and subtracting customary units, computing elapsed time

Career Focus Activity

Materials: pencils, papers, computer with Internet access

Procedure: Organize students into four groups. Students write a letter to an air traffic controller or a related professional.
- All students brainstorm interview-type questions to place in the letter. The categories of questions should include those in the job description: what an air traffic controller does, the attributes necessary in the performance of duties, where one could work, what education is necessary to qualify for this type of work, related careers, and how math is used on the job.
- The first group compiles the best questions.
- The second group researches on the Internet for possible businesses to which the class can send the letter.
- The third group actually composes the letter, including a return address.
- The fourth group reviews responses and reports on the results to the class.

Use graphs to

- show the results of an opinion poll.
- compare team scores.
- record weather information such as temperature or rain amounts over time.
- show how the school day is divided into class periods.

What are some other ways to use graphs?

Graphs

An air traffic controller directs airplanes as they near airports, take off and land, and taxi at the airport.

- Air traffic controllers work at airports or nearby facilities, directing commercial and private air traffic.

- An air traffic controller should have good eyesight, good communication skills, and quick-thinking skills.

- An air traffic controller relays weather-related data to pilots; reads and interprets maps and graphs; and understands the relationships among speed, altitude, and direction.

- To become an air traffic controller, an individual can complete a course of study in a four-year college or train as a commercial or a military pilot. Then he or she receives specialized training by the Federal Aviation Administration.

- Related careers include pilots, flight attendants, airport security officers, and airport service personnel such as baggage handlers and ticket agents.

CAREER

AIR TRAFFIC CONTROLLER

PORTFOLIO PROJECT: *Graph the number of an airline's departures and arrivals at a nearby airport.*

1. Choose an airline that flies into a nearby commercial airport.

2. Use reference materials such as an airline travel guide available from a library or an on-line source. Find out how many flights the airline has scheduled into and out of the airport every day of the week.

3. Graph the number of daily arrivals and departures. Show *Days of the Week* on the horizontal scale and *Number of Flights* on the vertical scale. *Show the math.*

About the Portfolio Project

Supply each student with graph paper (which can be found on page 160 of the Teacher's Resource Binder) and flight schedules donated by local travel agencies or airline companies. The Internet may offer an abundance of different schedules. Students should realize that they are to graph two different pieces of information.

Assessment: The individual scoring rubric on page 161 of the Teacher's Resource Binder can be reproduced and used for assessment. Include the following information in the last two boxes. Students should have:
- used at least two references to confirm data.
- correctly graphed both arrivals and departures from one major airport.

Objectives

- To determine what the horizontal and vertical scales of a graph show
- To determine the intervals on the scales of a graph

Purpose

Often in the newspapers or in books, you'll see graphs. Once you learn the different kinds of graphs and how they are used, you'll be able to understand the information that graphs represent.

Introducing the Lesson

Review using and making tables (Lessons 4.7, 4.8). Read students a short paragraph of information. Then express the same information by putting numbers into a chart or table on the board. Ask: Which one is easier to understand? Why? (the chart; the information is easier to obtain)

Review multiplying fractions and whole numbers (Lesson 6.1).

Use the examples: $\frac{1}{2} \times 250$ (125); $\frac{1}{4} \times 500$ (125); $\frac{2}{3} \times 150$ (100).

Alternative Strategies

Although the same information is pictured in the bar graph, circle graph, and pictograph on page 202 of the student text, there are advantages and disadvantages to each. What do all the graphs allow you to do? (Compare data quickly.) Which graph do you prefer and why? (Get several responses to this question. Accept any reasonable explanations.) What does a circle graph show? (parts of a whole)

9.1 Introduction to Graphs

This chapter is about graphs and graphing. A *graph* is a drawing or diagram that displays information. Although graphs cannot always show information as accurately as tables can, they can give a "snapshot view" of complex situations.

Sometimes graphs show information broken into groups. For example, the **bar graph** below shows how test scores were distributed among As, Bs, Cs, and Ds. The same information can also be shown in a **circle graph** or a **pictograph**.

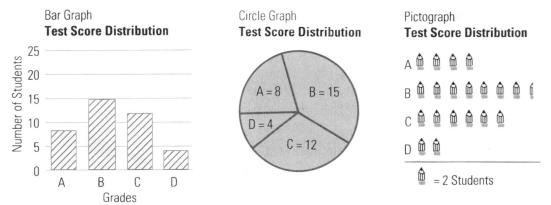

Line graphs are used to show trends, or changes over time. The line graph below shows how the average price of farmland in the United States changed between 1978 and 1987.

▶ Express Yourself

You read a line graph or bar graph by first examining the title. Then you examine the **vertical scale** and the **horizontal scale** of the graph. The scales of a graph often show numerical information such as years, dollar amounts, or numbers of people.

Title

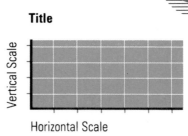

Horizontal Scale

1. What does the vertical scale of the line graph on the opposite page show?

2. What does the horizontal scale of the bar graph on the opposite page show?

3. Examine the title, and vertical and horizontal scales of the line graph on the opposite page. Describe what is shown.

When a scale shows numerical information, it is usually divided into **equal intervals.** For example, the interval on the vertical scale of the bar graph on the opposite page is 5—the difference between marks on the scale is always 5.

4. What is the interval on the vertical scale of the line graph on the opposite page?
   $100

5. What is the interval on the horizontal scale of the line graph?
   1 year

▶ Practice What You Know

Often, when you read a graph, you must estimate values. For example, in the line graph on the opposite page the highest point is about one-quarter of the way between $800 and $900.

6. What is the difference between $800 and $900? $100

7. What is one-quarter of this difference? $25

8. Add the answer you found in Question 7 to $800 to find the approximate value of the highest point in the line graph. $825

Estimate each of the following.

9. a value one-half of the way between $500 and $1000 $750

10. a value three-quarters of the way between 400 and 500 475

11. a value four-fifths of the way between $1000 and $2000 $1800

12. a value one-quarter of the way between 20 and 40 25

Express Yourself Answers
1. the price of farmland per acre
2. test grades
3. It shows that the price of farmland rose and then fell over the period 1978–1987, with the highest prices being in 1982.

★ **Error Alert**
Errors may occur because students do not know the meanings of the words *horizontal* and *vertical*.

Project
Have students collect five graphs from newspapers or magazines. Graphs should include three of the four kinds presented in this lesson. Ask them to write a sentence describing what is shown in each graph.

9.2 Reading Bar Graphs

If there's one thing Matthew loves, it's cars. He reads about cars every chance he gets. To compare all the statistics, Matthew especially likes to read the graphs.

Examples

To read a bar graph, first read the labels to see what is being studied.

Acceleration, 0 – 60 MPH

Capella 2000
Pollux DS
Crucis
Sirius M2

0 1 2 3 4 5 6 7 8 9 10 11
Seconds

A Find how long it takes the Pollux DS to accelerate from 0 to 60 miles per hour.

Find the bar for the Pollux DS. Go to the end of the bar and, with your finger, drop straight down to the horizontal scale. The number on the scale is a 7.

It takes **7 seconds** for the Pollux DS to accelerate from 0 to 60 miles per hour.

B Find the cost of the Crucis.

Find the bar for the Crucis. Go to the top of the bar and trace a line straight across to the vertical scale. The number on the scale is halfway between $10,000 and $20,000, or $15,000.

The Crucis costs **about $15,000.**

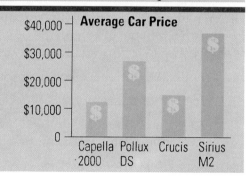

Average Car Price

$40,000
$30,000
$20,000
$10,000
0

Capella 2000   Pollux DS   Crucis   Sirius M2

▶ Think and Discuss

1. Refer to Example A. How long does it take the Sirius M2 to accelerate from 0 to 60 miles per hour?

2. Refer to Example B. Estimate the cost of the Capella 2000.

3. Refer to Example B. About how much less is the cost of the Crucis than the Sirius M2?

★ **Error Alert**

Errors may occur if students do not read "straight across" or "straight down" to the appropriate scale.

Exercises

Use the graph below to answer each question.
(See Example A.)

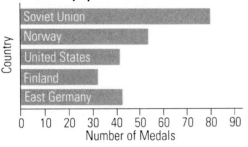

Winter Olympic Gold Medals, 1932 – 1988

Soviet Union
Norway
United States
Finland
East Germany

Country

0 10 20 30 40 50 60 70 80 90
Number of Medals

4. Which country won the second most gold medals in the Winter Olympic Games? Norway

5. Which country won about 45 gold medals? East Germany

6. About how many more gold medals did the Soviet Union win than the United States? about 40 gold medals

Use the graph to the right to answer each question. (See Example B.)

7. Which country won the most gold medals in hockey? Soviet Union

8. How many more gold medals in hockey did Canada win than the U.S.? 4 gold medals

9. How many gold medals were awarded in hockey between 1932 and 1998? 17 gold medals

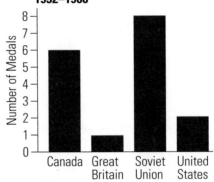

Olympic Gold Medals in Hockey, 1932–1988

Number of Medals

8
7
6
5
4
3
2
1
0

Canada Great Britain Soviet Union United States

► **Mixed Practice** (For more practice, see page 428.)

Use the graphs above to answer each question.

10. Which country has won the fewest gold medals in hockey?
Great Britain

11. Which country has won the fewest gold medals in all sports?
Finland

12. Which country has won 6 gold medals in hockey?
Canada

► **Applications**

13. Find a bar graph in a newspaper or magazine. Write a paragraph describing the contents of the graph.

Answers

13. Answers may vary depending on the graphs students select.

► **Review** (Lessons 2.6, 3.4)

Estimate.

14. $436 \div 3$
150

15. 8911×5
45,000

16. $922 \div 20$
45

17. 348×19
7000

18. 1987×8
16,000

19. $4321 \div 7$
600

20. $791 \div 82$
10

21. 22×4723
100,000

22. $8471 \div 9$
900

23. 13×1111
13,000

Reinforcement

Extra Practice, page 428
EP/MR Worksheet 69, TRB, page 69

Project

Work in small groups. Select a bar graph from another source and write five questions pertaining to that graph. Exchange graphs and questions with another group. Let them answer the questions and return to your group for corrections.

Objective

- To read double bar graphs

Purpose

Sometimes comparisons between two sets of data are expressed in the form of a double bar graph. For example, information for two groups or two years might be shown. This lesson shows you how to read double bar graphs.

Introducing the Lesson

Choose three types of pets; for example, dogs, cats, and birds. Take a class survey to determine how many girls and boys have each kind of pet. Then, draw two bar graphs on the board, one for the girls and one for the boys. On the first graph, express the number of boys who have each type of pet; on the other, express the same information for girls. Ask students questions that call for comparisons between the two groups. Then ask them if there is any way to combine the information into a more readable form. With a little coaxing, they may come up with a double bar graph.

Alternative Example

Find the difference between the number of boys who play or watch sports after school and the number of girls who do the same.
Boys: about 100
Girls: about 40
$100 - 40 = 60$
About 60 more boys than girls play or watch sports after school.

9.3 Reading Double Bar Graphs

Mr. Jay's sociology class surveyed the sophomores to find out about after-school activities. The students then constructed graphs. Marty made a double bar graph to show how the boys and the girls differed.

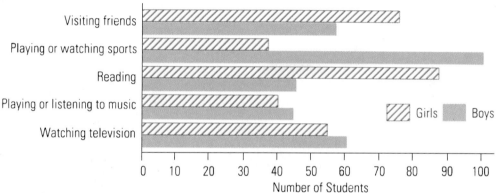

Examples

To read a double bar graph, read each bar separately.

Find the difference in the number of boys and girls who enjoy reading after school.

First, find the 2 bars for the reading category. According to the key, the ▨ bar corresponds to boys and the ▨ bar corresponds to girls. Determine the value for each bar.

Boys: 45   Girls: 86 $86 - 45 = 41$

41 more girls than boys said that they enjoy reading after school.

▶ **Think and Discuss**

1. Which activity is most popular among boys? Which is most popular among girls?

2. Which activity is least popular overall? How did you find it?

SKILLS

3. Describe how the information shown in Marty's graph could be represented on two single bar graphs. Could it be shown in one single bar graph?

4. When is a double bar graph useful?

Exercises
(For more practice, see page 429.)

Use the graph to the right to answer the following questions.

5. In which city was the median house price highest in 1987?
San Francisco

6. Approximately how much more did a house in Chicago cost in 1997 than in 1987?
≈$55,000

7. Estimate the difference in house prices between Los Angeles and Chicago in 1997.
≈$17,500

8. In which city did house prices nearly double between 1987 and 1997?
Chicago

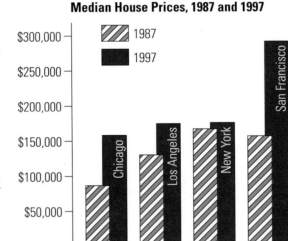

Median House Prices, 1987 and 1997

▶ Applications

9. You are doing a report on public land in the United States and plan to summarize the bar graph shown below in a paragraph. What will you write?

U.S. National Parklands

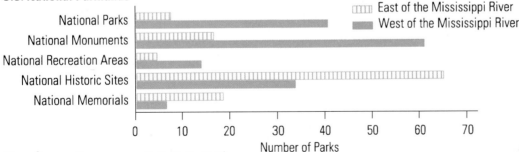

▶ Review (Lessons 2.3, 2.7, 3.3)

Divide or multiply.

10. 3797 ÷ 10
379.7

11. 0.9 × 3000
2700

12. 72.3 × 100
7230

13. 88 ÷ 400
0.22

14. 2.5 × 8000
20,000

15. 0.6211 ÷ 100
0.006211

16. 109 × 1000
109,000

17. 44.36 × 2000
88,720.00

Objective

- To construct bar graphs

Purpose

You've learned how to read single and double bar graphs. This lesson shows you how to construct them.

Introducing the Lesson

Review reading single and double bar graphs (Lessons 9.2, 9.3). On the board write a list showing the number of CDs different students have purchased. Ask: What kind of bar graph would be best for this information? (single bar graph) Would a horizontal or vertical graph be best? (either) Explain that making the graph would require several more decisions. Because of this, graphs that show the same set of facts do not always look the same.

Answers

1. yes; one label could be activities, the other could be calories burned
2. horizontal: activities; vertical: calories
3. Check student graphs. See answer for Exercise 11.
4. Check student graphs. See answer for Exercise 11.
5. 922; the value of the longest bar must be included on the scale
6. 1000 can be divided into intervals of 100, which are easy to work with.
7. Check student graphs. See answer for Exercise 11.
8. 1000 is a large number. Too many numbers on the scale make it difficult to read or very long or both.
9. Check student graphs. See answer for Exercise 11.
10. Check student graphs. See answer for Exercise 11.

(continued on page T216)

9.4 Constructing Bar Graphs

Erica works at the Get Fit Gym. People often ask her how many calories they burn doing various activities. Erica has decided to draw a bar graph that shows the information.

Erica gathers and arranges the information in a chart as shown below.

Activity	Calories Burned Per Hour
Aerobic Dance	778
Basketball	564
Jumping Rope	922
Racquetball	732
Running	786
Swimming	320
Weight Training	294

Then Erica must decide how to set up the scales of her graph.

1. Look at the headings in Erica's chart. Could these headings be made into the labels for the vertical and horizontal scales? Explain how.

2. Erica decides to make a vertical bar graph. What will the horizontal scale show? What will the vertical scale show?

3. Draw the scales, making each about 4 inches long.

4. Decide on a reasonable bar width. Then divide the horizontal scale and label each bar.

Now the vertical scale must be labeled and divided.

5. First, look at the information given. Find the greatest number in the "Calories Burned" column. The top of the vertical scale must be greater than this number. Why?

6. Erica decides to use 1000 as the top of the scale. Why would 1000 be easier to work with than a number such as 925?

PROBLEM SOLVING

The vertical scale must now be divided into equally spaced intervals. The scale covers 1000 units, from 0 to 1000. For Erica's graph, an interval of 100 is appropriate.

7. Divide and label the intervals of the vertical scale.

8. Why would an interval of 1 or 10 be inappropriate?

Finally, the bars must be drawn. Since the vertical scale has an interval of 100, the height of each bar must be estimated. Start with the bar for aerobic dance: 778 is about $\frac{3}{4}$ of the distance between 700 and 800.

9. On the vertical scale, find a point that is $\frac{3}{4}$ of the distance between 700 and 800. Draw a vertical bar for aerobic dance that goes as high as this point. Color the bar.

10. Playing basketball burns 564 calories per hour: 564 is slightly greater than $\frac{1}{2}$ the distance between 500 and 600. On the vertical scale, estimate where 564 lies. Now draw a vertical bar for basketball and color it.

11. Complete the graph.

▶ **Think and Discuss** (For more practice, see page 429.)

12. Describe the graph you constructed. Compare your graph to the list of numbers you started with. How are they different? How are they the same?

13. Refer to the introduction to this lesson. Erica organized her information by listing the activities in alphabetical order. How else might she have organized the information? Describe how the look of the graph would change if she reorganized the information.

14. How is the bar graph more helpful than the original table? Discuss.

▶ **Review** (Lessons 4.2, 4.5, 4.6)

Convert each measure.

15. 9.9 cm to m
0.099 m

16. 337 mL to L
0.337 L

17. 0.48 kg to g
480 g

18. 1650 m to km
1.650 km

19. 543 mm to cm
54.3 cm

20. 75 g to kg
0.075 kg

21. 43 L to mL
43,000 mL

22. 9.7 km to m
9700 m

23. 157 g to kg
0.157 kg

24. 47.8 m to mm
47,800 mm

25. 0.6 L to mL
600 mL

26. 92 kg to g
92,000 g

9.5 Reading Line Graphs

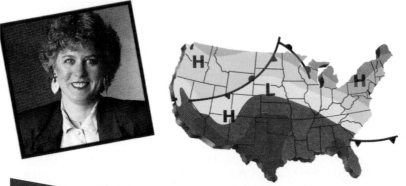

Sallie is a meteorologist in Minneapolis. Part of her job involves graphing weather data. She often uses line graphs because they show trends, or changes over a period of time.

Examples

To read a line graph, first read the scale labels to see what is being studied. The line graph below shows the average monthly temperatures for Minneapolis, Minnesota.

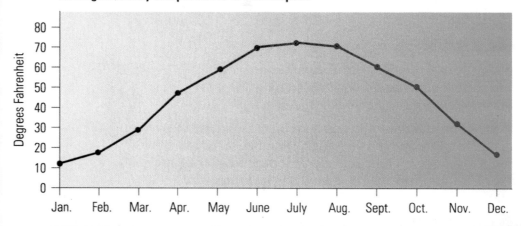

Average Monthly Temperatures in Minneapolis

Find the average temperature for May in Minneapolis.

Find May on the horizontal scale. Move straight up to the graph. Then trace a line straight across to the vertical scale.

The average temperature in May in Minneapolis is **about 59°.**

▶ Think and Discuss

1. Describe how to find the average temperature for February in Minneapolis.

2. What is the average temperature in Minneapolis in August?

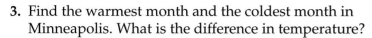

3. Find the warmest month and the coldest month in Minneapolis. What is the difference in temperature?

4. How is the information on the horizontal scale organized? Would it be reasonable to alphabetize these labels? Why?

5. "That graph is wrong. I was in Minneapolis last March and it was 10° outside," one cynic said. Why is he mistaken?

Exercises (For more practice, see page 430.)

Use the graph to the right to answer the following questions.

6. Describe briefly what the graph shows. About how many days it rains each month in San Francisco

7. Which month has the greatest number of rainy days? January

8. According to this graph, when is the rainy season in San Francisco? When is the dry season? Winter; summer

9. About how many days a year does it rain in San Francisco? 62 days

Average Number of Days with Rain in San Francisco

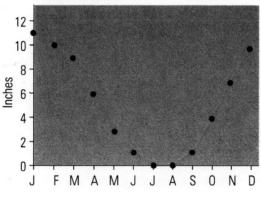

▶ **Applications**

Average Monthly Temperature and Rainfall in Honolulu

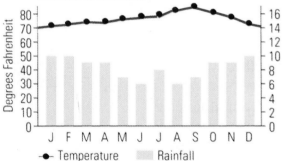

10. Use the graph to the left to describe the climate of Honolulu, Hawaii.

11. Compare the graphs for Honolulu and Minneapolis (opposite page). Describe how the two cities differ in temperature.

▶ **Review** (Lessons 2.2, 2.3, 2.4, 2.8, 2.10)

Multiply.

12.	13.	14.	15.	16.
327	0.894	88	0.7	606
× 62	× 0.9	× 37	× 0.54	× 509
20,274	0.8046	3256	0.378	308,454

17.	18.	19.	20.	21.
9.07	600	6398	0.004	0.49
× 7.6	× 80	× 5	× 0.05	× 3
68.932	48,000	31,990	0.0002	1.47

▶ **Think and Discuss Answers**

1. Find February on the horizontal scale; move straight up the graph; then trace a line horizontally to vertical scale (about 18°F)

2. about 70°

3. July is warmest. January is coldest; the difference in temperature is about 60°.

4. It is organized chronologically; it would not be reasonable to organize the months alphabetically because variation over time is what matters in this case.

5. the graph shows average temperatures, so there could be a lot of variation in any given month.

10. The temperatures are warm year round. It rains all year long, but more in the winter.

11. Honolulu: high temperatures with little variation; Minneapolis: temperatures vary greatly; generally much cooler in Minneapolis

★ **Error Alert**

Errors may occur if the lines students trace (from points on the graph to the scales) are not vertical or horizontal.

Reinforcement
Extra Practice, page 430
EP/MR Worksheet 72, TRB, page 72

Project
Find several line graphs showing changes over time, some of which express information other than weather data. Write an explanation of what each graph shows, using terms like *trend* or *change over a period of time* for each graph.

Objective

• To construct line graphs

Purpose

In the last lesson, you learned to read line graphs. This lesson shows you how to construct this type of graph.

Introducing the Lesson

Review constructing bar graphs (Lesson 9.4). Review the purpose of line graphs. (A line graph shows trends, or changes over a period of time.) Discuss with students the kinds of things that are easily expressed in the form of a line graph. The discussion might include: yearly school enrollment, daily attendance, hourly readings on a gauge, and weekly income for a worker paid an hourly rate.

Answers

1. Years should go on the horizontal scale.
2. in 20-year periods (1821–1840, 1841–1860, etc.); there will be 8 divisions; decision is based on the information given
3. 10,000, 20,000, 30,000, 40,000
4. 15 million; 15
5. divide into intervals of 1 million (or perhaps 2 million or 5 million)
6. Check students' graphs. See answer for Exercise 8.

9.6 Constructing Line Graphs

For a history project, you are studying immigration to the United States. You decide to present information for 1821–1980 in a line graph, to show the trend of immigration over time.

First you arrange your information in a table.

Immigration to the United States, 1821—1980

1821—1840	0.8 million
1841—1860	4.3 million
1861—1880	5.1 million
1881—1900	8.9 million
1901—1920	14.4 million
1921—1940	4.7 million
1941—1960	3.7 million
1961—1980	7.3 million

Line graphs and vertical bar graphs are constructed in similar ways. The previous lessons in this chapter can help you decide how to divide the scales for the immigration graph.

1. What information goes on the horizontal scale?

2. Describe how the scale should be divided. How many divisions are there? Explain how you decided.

Often in graphs, when the numbers are very large, the scales can be labeled with "abbreviated" numbers.

3. Look at the sample scale at the right. Write the numbers that the "abbreviated" numbers stand for.

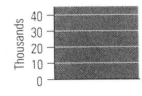

4. What should the greatest number on your vertical scale be? Write this number as an "abbreviated" number.

5. Describe how the vertical scale should be divided. What interval did you select? Why?

6. Draw, divide, and label the horizontal and vertical scales.

Constructing a line graph is similar to constructing a bar graph. For the period 1821–1840, for example, you start by finding the mark on the horizontal scale that is labeled 1821–1840. Lightly pencil in a line that rises vertically from this point.

Next find the point on the vertical scale that corresponds to 0.8 million. Lightly pencil in a line that extends horizontally from this point. Where the 2 penciled-in lines cross, place a point. This is the first point on your line graph.

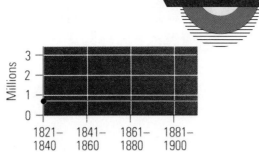

7. Continue to find the points for each 20-year period.

8. When you have found all the points, use a line to connect each point in order. Your line graph is now complete.

9. Describe in a few sentences the pattern of immigration to the United States since 1821.

U.S. Life Expectancy
(average expected lifespan)

1920	54.1
1930	59.7
1940	62.9
1950	68.2
1960	69.7
1970	70.8
1980	73.7
1990	75.4

Exercises

(For more practice, see page 430.)

10. Construct a line graph from the table at the right. Then describe the pattern in life expectancy since 1920.

▶ Applications

11. The two graphs below show the rise in a bank account balance over a 4-year period. Notice that the first graph gives an impression of a sharp increase, while the second graph gives an impression of a slow increase. Why? What is similar about the two graphs? What is different?

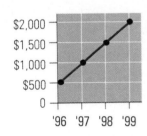

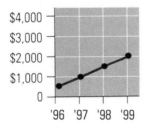

12. Draw a graph that gives an impression of a sharper increase in the bank account than the two graphs here do. Answers may vary.

▶ Review (Lesson 1.7)

Round to the nearest hundred.

13. 9647 9600   14. 11,557 11,600   15. 32,976 33,000 16. 48,339 48,300 17. 57,151 57,200

Answers (continued)

7. Check students' graphs. See answer for Exercise 8.

8. A sample line graph is shown below.

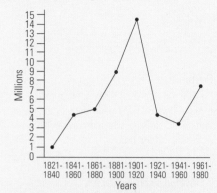

9. Discussion should include the fact that immigration was at its lowest in 1821–1840; it was at its high point in the period 1901–1920, after which it dropped sharply; then there was an increase in 1961–1980.

Answers

(see page T221)

★ Error Alert

Errors may occur if students are not accurate in graphing the point for each time period, or if they do not connect points in chronological order.

Reinforcement
Extra Practice, page 430
EP/MR Worksheet 73, TRB, page 73

Teaching Aids
Quarter-inch grid
TA 7, TRB, page 160
Teaching suggestions precede the Teaching Aids worksheets.

Project
Use your daily newspaper for a week to chart the high temperatures for your city or town and for three other cities. Make <u>one</u> graph for your data using four different colored pencils, one for each city.

Objective

• To read pictographs

Purpose

You have learned about several different types of graphs. This lesson shows you how to read pictographs, which use symbols to represent information.

Introducing the Lesson

Review the purpose of tables, charts, and graphs. (sample answer: to display complex information in a simple graphic form) Explain that sometimes a graph uses simple drawings to represent a large number of objects. For example, if a store sells 5000 CDs during one year, what object might you use to represent sales? (CDs) Ask: Why wouldn't you draw one CD for each sale? (because you would have to draw 5000 CDs) How many sales would you let each CD stand for? (Answers may vary, but 1000 is a good answer.) How many CDs must you draw for 5000 sales? (5) for 5500? ($5\frac{1}{2}$)

▶ **Think and Discuss Answers**

1. 10

2. 15

3. 35

4. He would have one picture equal more than 10 computers, since many more computers would be sold over the course of a year.

9.7 Constructing and Reading Pictographs

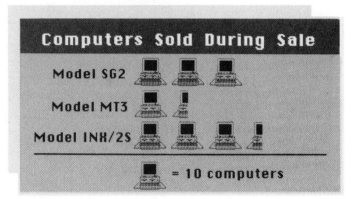

Neil works at the Computer Source, where a three-day sale has just ended. Neil must make a report on the sale to the store manager. He decided to construct a pictograph to show how many computers were sold.

Examples

To read a pictograph, determine what each symbol represents. An incomplete symbol represents a fractional part of the symbol's value.

Find the total number of computers sold at the sale.

Each computer symbol represents 10 computers sold. Count the number of whole computers pictured and multiply by 10. $7 \times 10 = 70$

Count the number of half-computers pictured and multiply by 5. $2 \times 5 = 10$

Add. $70 + 10 = 80$

Approximately 80 computers were sold.

▶ Think and Discuss

1. How many computers does the symbol 🖥 represent?

2. How many model MT3 computers were sold?

3. How many Model INX/2S computers were sold?

4. If Neil made a graph showing total sales for the entire year, would he still have one picture equal 10 computers? Explain.

Exercises

(For more practice, see page 431.)

Refer to the introduction to this lesson. Use Neil's graph to answer the following questions.

5. Model SG2 costs $1500. What were the total sales in dollars for this model? $45,000

6. Model MT3 costs $2000. Model INX/2S costs $1000. What were the combined total sales in dollars for these models? $65,000

7. Using "$" to represent $5000, construct a pictograph to represent total sales in dollars for each computer model.

▶ Applications

Use the graph below to answer the following questions.

Rural and Urban United States Population, 1950 – 1980

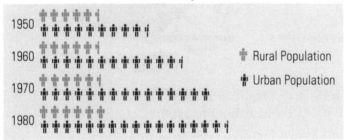

Each symbol represents 10 million people

8. What does the symbol 👤👤👤 represent?

9. About how many people lived in cities in 1950? In 1980?

10. Approximately how much greater was the rural population in 1980 than in 1950? ≈5 million people

11. Examine the growth of urban and rural populations over the period 1950–1980. Predict the 1990 populations. Explain your predictions.

12. Could this information be shown in a bar graph? Could it be shown in a line graph? Which method do you think would be most effective? Why?

▶ Review (Lessons 1.9, 1.10, 1.11)

Add or subtract.

13.	8.096	14.	6	15.	0.8	16.	9007	17.	27,375
	+ 3.897		− 3.153		+ 12.4		− 3268		+ 46,786
	11.993		2.847		13.2		5739		74,161

Answers

7. A sample pictograph is shown below.

Total Sales in Dollars	
Model SG2	$ $ $ $ $ $ $ $ $
Model MT3	$ $ $ $ $ $
Model INX/25	$ $ $ $ $ $ $
	$=$5,000

8. 30 million people
9. 95 million; 165 million

11. The urban population grew significantly, whereas the rural population remained fairly static; the 1990 rural population will probably be about 60 million (no or little growth); the 1990 urban population will probably be about 175 million (growth has slowed since 1950 but is still significant).
12. It could be shown in both a double bar graph and a double line graph; all three methods are effective; the pictograph, through the use of picture symbols, is very evocative of the rural/urban dichotomy; the line graph might give a more vivid sense of the change over time.

★ **Error Alert**

Errors may occur if students do not understand what complete or partial symbols represent in a pictograph.

Reinforcement

Extra Practice, page 431
EP/MR Worksheet 74, TRB, page 74

Project

Divide into groups of four. Decide on and gather information that could be represented in a pictograph. Select a symbol that is both meaningful and easy to draw. Provide a "key" to explain what the symbol stands for and draw all complete symbols exactly the same. Make the pictograph. Show your pictograph to the other groups.

T215

9.8 Reading Circle Graphs

Objective

• To read circle graphs

Purpose

So far in this chapter you have learned about three types of graphs: bar graphs, line graphs, and pictographs. This lesson covers the circle graph, which is a widely used type of graph.

Introducing the Lesson

Review multiplying fractions and whole numbers (Lesson 6.1). Use the examples: $\frac{1}{3}$ of 360 (120); $\frac{1}{9}$ of 360 (40). Draw a circle on the board. Divide it into quarters and shade in one quarter. Ask students how much of the circle is shaded. ($\frac{1}{4}$) Ask students what value is represented by one quarter if the whole circle represents 100? (25) Ask what value is represented by three quarters if the whole circle represents 500? (375)

Answers

(continued from page T208)

A sample bar graph is shown below.

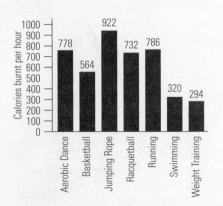

Carol sometimes wonders where all her money goes, so she decided to keep track of her expenditures. In June she wrote down her expenses in 6 categories. Then she made a circle graph to show the results.

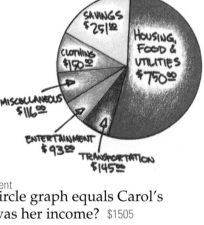

1. In which category did Carol spend the most money? How did you find an answer? Housing, Food, Utilities; largest sector

2. In which category did Carol spend the least money? Entertainment

3. List Carol's expense categories in order from most money spent to least money spent. Housing, Savings, Clothing, Transportation, Miscellaneous, Entertainment

4. The sum of all the amounts in the circle graph equals Carol's total income for the month. What was her income? $1505

5. About what fraction of Carol's income went into savings? about $\frac{1}{6}$

6. About what fraction of Carol's income went for transportation? about $\frac{1}{10}$

7. What might the Miscellaneous category include? Magazine subscriptions, insurance, medical bills, etc.

 **Exercises** (For more practice, see page 431.)

Thom decided to show in a graph how his time was divided up. Use his graph to answer the following questions.

8. How many hours does Thom spend eating or studying each day? $3\frac{1}{2}$ hours

9. Which activity is the second most time consuming? School

10. What fractional part of his day does Thom spend sleeping? $\frac{1}{3}$

11. What fractional part of his day does Thom spend in school? $\frac{1}{4}$

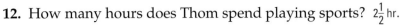

PROBLEM SOLVING

12. How many hours does Thom spend playing sports? $2\frac{1}{2}$ hr.

13. What fractional part of Thom's school day is his study time equal to? $\frac{1}{4}$

14. What might the Miscellaneous category include? Shopping; TV

▶ **Applications**

The graph below shows the proposed U.S. budget for 1988.

15. What is the total U.S. budget in billions of dollars? $1141.7 billion

16. List the budget categories in order from least to greatest.
Interest; Miscellaneous; Defense; Social Security

17. Estimate the fractional part of the total budget that goes to social security, pensions, and health. $\frac{1}{2}$

18. Estimate the fractional part of the total budget that goes to interest on the national debt. How many billions of dollars is this? $\frac{1}{7}$; $151.8 billion

19. Estimate the fractional part of the total budget that goes to defense. How many billions of dollars is this? $\frac{1}{4}$; 294 billion

20. There are about 250 million U.S. citizens. Use a calculator to estimate how much is spent on defense per American. ≈$1100

▶ **Review** (Lessons 3.3, 3.5, 3.6, 3.12)

Divide. 11 R56

21. $81)\overline{947}$ 390

22. $3)\overline{5876}$ 1958 R2 52 R88

23. $500)\overline{6000}$ 12 2830

24. $1.2)\overline{10.8}$ 9 38 R13

25. $0.004)\overline{1.56}$

26. $90)\overline{4768}$

27. $0.006)\overline{16.98}$

28. $25)\overline{963}$

29. $42{,}287 \div 7$ 6041

30. $39.48 \div 2$ $19.74

31. $1.176 \div 49$ 0.024

32. $0.182 \div 2.8$ 0.065

9.9 Choosing the Appropriate Graph

Shelby works at the Vistaville Teen Center raising money for the Center's programs. The Center has become so popular since it was founded in 1995 that Shelby thinks it's time to expand its programs. He is now preparing a presentation to convince the Center's board of directors of the need for more programs.

Shelby wants to use graphs in his presentation, but he's not sure just how. His goal is to show the rapid growth of the Center, especially in the past two years. He has experimented with one table, making four different graphs from it. The table and Shelby's graphs are shown below.

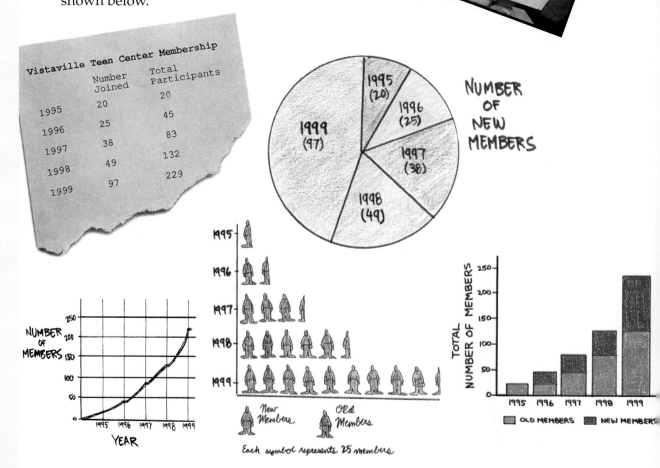

Vistaville Teen Center Membership

	Number Joined	Total Participants
1995	20	20
1996	25	45
1997	38	83
1998	49	132
1999	97	229

Each symbol represents 25 members

▶ Think and Discuss

1. In which graph is it easiest for you to see how fast total membership has grown? Why? Discuss.

2. In which graph is it easiest for you to see how fast new membership has grown? Why? Discuss.

3. In which graph is it most difficult for you to see how fast total membership has grown? Why? Discuss.

4. In which graph is it most difficult for you to see how fast new membership has grown? Why? Discuss.

5. In which graph is growth during 1999 made most clear? Why?

6. Reread the first part of this lesson. If you were Shelby, which graph would you use? How does it do the job better than the others? Discuss.

As treasurer of the Elevator Racing Society, you know that there is a crisis—the Society is running out of money! To convince the members that dues must be increased, you have made the table shown below. Now you want to make graphs from the table. Work with a classmate on the problems below.

7. Study the table and discuss ways to present your case to the Society. Draw the graph that will best convince the members.

8. Compare your graph with those drawn by others in your class. Discuss as a group the advantages and disadvantages of each.

Year 1998	Dues Income	Expenses	Year 1999	Dues Income	Expenses
Jan.–Mar.	$105	$ 97	Jan.–Mar.	$110	$132
Apr.–June	115	84	Apr.–June	100	147
July–Sept.	120	123	July–Sept.	125	156
Oct.–Dec.	100	104	Oct.–Dec.	105	148
1998 Total	**$440**	**$408**	**1999 Total**	**$440**	**$583**

▶ Review (Lesson 6.8)

9. Find the total cost for making 100 baseball pennants, based on the following table.

Materials and Costs for Making 2 Baseball Pennants

Materials	Unit Cost	Materials	Unit Cost
$\frac{1}{2}$ yard blue felt	$1.59/yd.	$1\frac{1}{4}$ yards yellow cord	$0.89/yd.
$\frac{1}{4}$ yard yellow satin	$8.99/yd.	$6\frac{1}{2}$ feet of $\frac{1}{4}$-inch doweling	$0.75/ft.

---

4. the line graph, because it does not differentiate between old and new membership

5. The slope of the line graph shows that growth was fairly rapid; the large section in the circle graph shows that the greatest number of new members joined in 1999.

6. The line graph shows the rate of growth best, but the bar graph shows the breakdown of membership and is almost as effective in showing the rate of growth, so it is perhaps best for Shelby's purpose; accept any answer that is adequately supported.

7. Possible options are 2 circle graphs (one for income, one for expenses), a double line graph, a double bar graph, and a double pictograph, accept any answer that is adequately supported.

8. Discussion should focus on the characteristics of each type of graph and the usefulness of different graphs for different purposes.

★ **Error Alert**

Errors may occur if students just guess which graph form is most appropriate. Have them support their choice.

Answer

9. blue felt: $ 39.75
   yellow satin: 112.38
   yellow cord: 55.63
   doweling   243.75
   TOTAL $451.51

Note that stated costs are for making two pennants; thus, each product quantity and unit cost must be multiplied by 50.

Reinforcement

EP/MR Worksheet 76, TRB, page 76

Project

Divide into groups of four. Read an encyclopedia article to find information that can be expressed in graph form. Find four different ways to graph the information. Describe the strengths and weaknesses of each graph for the given type of information.

Answers

4. A sample single bar graph is shown below.

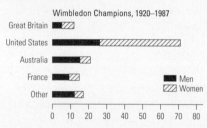

Wimbledon Champions, 1920–1987

7. A sample single line graph is shown below.

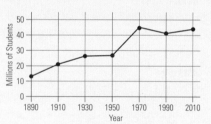

Chapter 9 Review

Use Graph A to answer Questions 1–4. (Lessons 9.2, 9.3, 9.4)

1. What country had the second highest number of winners? Australia

2. What country had the highest number of female winners? United States

3. How many more American women than American men have won? about 10

4. Construct a single bar graph based on this double graph.

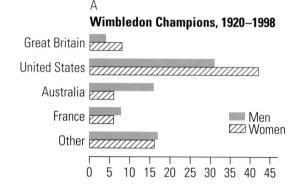

A
Wimbledon Champions, 1920–1998

Use Graph B to answer Questions 5–7. (Lessons 9.5, 9.6)

5. Estimate the number of students enrolled in grades Kindergarten–8 in 1930. 22 million students

6. About what was the greatest number of students enrolled in grades 9–12 during the period shown on the graph? What year was that? about 13 million, 1995

7. Construct a single line graph based on this double line graph.

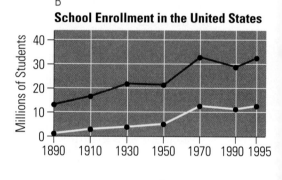

B
School Enrollment in the United States

— Kindergarten – Grade 8
— Grades 9 – 12

Answer the following question. (Lesson 9.7)

8. If the symbol 📺 stands for 50 TV sets, what does the symbol ⊏ stand for? 25 sets

Use Graph C to answer Questions 9–10. (Lesson 9.8)

9. Approximately what fractional part of the total budget goes to printed materials? $\frac{1}{4}$

10. How much money is spent on salaries, building and maintenance costs, and other expenses? $1,019,500

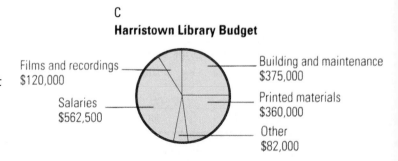

C
Harristown Library Budget

Films and recordings $120,000

Building and maintenance $375,000

Salaries $562,500

Printed materials $360,000

Other $82,000

Chapter 9 Test

TEST

Use Graph A to answer Questions 1–3.

1. Which magazine has the most readers? *TV Preview*

2. Which two magazines together have about the same number of readers as *Sports View*? *Music Scene* and *Teen Image*

3. About how many readers do the sports, teen, and music magazines have all together? 5.2 million

Use Graph B to answer Questions 4–7.

4. When did U.S. farms have the most cattle? The most dairy cattle? 1975; 1960

5. About how many more cattle were there in 1975 than in 1985? 20,000

6. Do you predict that in 2005 there will be fewer or more dairy cattle than in 1985? Why? Fewer; trend shows a decline

7. Construct a single line graph showing the number of non-dairy cattle.

Use Graph C to answer Questions 8–10.

8. What does the symbol ☎ stand for? ☎? 10 phones
   5 phones

9. How many telephones are there in Poland for every 100 people? Great Britain? Israel? 12; 50.5; 46

10. Compare the number of phones per 100 people in the United States and Mexico. U.S. has 69.5; Mexico has 12

A

Readership of Six Popular Magazines

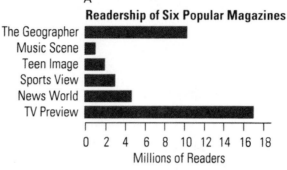

The Geographer
Music Scene
Teen Image
Sports View
News World
TV Preview

0 2 4 6 8 10 12 14 16 18
Millions of Readers

B

Cattle on Farms, 1960 – 1995

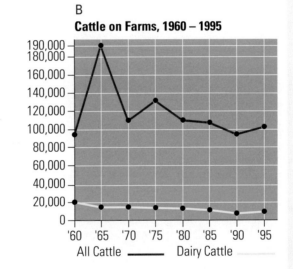

190,000
180,000
160,000
140,000
120,000
100,000
80,000
60,000
40,000
20,000
0

'60 '65 '70 '75 '80 '85 '90 '95

All Cattle ——— Dairy Cattle

C

Telephones per 100 People, 1995

Mexico

Poland

Israel

Great Britain

United States

 ☎ = 10 phones

Chapter Tests
Short Answer, Forms A and B, TRB, pages 229–300, 301–302
Multiple Choice, Forms A and B, TRB, pages 367–368, 369–370

Teaching Aids
Answer sheet
TA 8, TRB, page 161a
Teaching suggestions precede the Teaching Aids worksheets.

7. A sample single line graph is shown below.

Cattle on Farms, 1945 – 1985

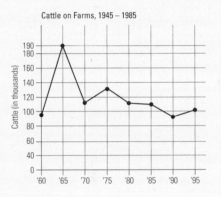

Cattle (in thousands)

190
180
160
140
120
100
80
60
40
0

'60 '65 '70 '75 '80 '85 '90 '95

Answers

(from page T213)
10. Life expectancy has increased steadily since 1920; in 1990, it was more than 20 years greater than in 1920.
11. The interval of the first graph is larger, so the increase appears sharper. The two graphs show the same information. The vertical scale is what makes the difference—the interval on the first graph is $1000; on the second graph it is $500.

Materials: pencils, paper

Procedure: Organize students into four groups. Students arrange to have a statistician speak to the class. Some places to contact are universities, insurance companies, and government agencies.

• The first group writes an invitation to a statistician to visit the classroom.

• The second group compiles a list of questions to ask the individual about the job, activities the job entails, level of difficulty, required education, rewards of the job, how math skills are utilized on the job, etc.

• During the visit, members of the third group ask the questions and record the responses.

• Members of the fourth group compose a thank-you note to be sent within three days of the visit.

• All students evaluate the experience.

Use statistics to describe

• how classmates spend their free time.

• the win-lose record of a school team and players' performances.

• average test scores in a class.

• the favorite television programs, movies, or books of friends.

What are some other ways to use statistics?

Statistics

A *statistician* collects, organizes, and interprets numerical data.

- Statisticians work in a formal environment such as a business, corporation, or government agency.

- A statistician must possess an interest in numbers, patience, and the ability to pay attention to detail.

- A statistician calculates frequency and averages, graphs data, and summarizes the results.

- To become a statistician, an individual must complete a course of study in a four-year college.

- Related careers include accountants, economists, market researchers, graphic artists, and pollsters.

CAREER

STATISTICIAN

PORTFOLIO PROJECT: *Keep statistics about yourself.*

1. List three activities you perform each day for which statistics can be collected. Such activities may include time spent sleeping, time spent doing homework, or the number of laps you run in track.

2. Collect and list statistics for each activity for one week.

3. Summarize your data, display it in a visual way, and compare it to the data collected by your classmates. *Show the math.*

About the Portfolio Project

Students clearly state the three activities for which they are compiling data on a daily basis. They may record time spent on each activity in any number of ways: time started to time ended; number of hours and minutes; or in fractional parts of hours. However, they should only use one method and be consistent, for ease of summation.

Assessment: The individual scoring rubric on page 161 of the Teacher's Resource Binder can be reproduced and used for assessment. Include the following information in the last two boxes. Students should have:
- listed all three activities with time spent daily for each.
- accurately figured totals for each activity for a week and creatively displayed the final results.

10.1 Introduction to Statistics

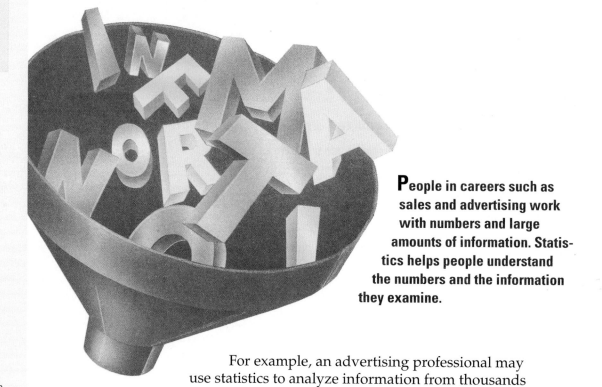

People in careers such as sales and advertising work with numbers and large amounts of information. Statistics helps people understand the numbers and the information they examine.

For example, an advertising professional may use statistics to analyze information from thousands of consumers to determine what type of soft drink people prefer.

In this chapter you will learn how to organize and display large amounts of information.

▶ Express Yourself

Many terms used in statistics are a part of everyday language, as you will see from the following exercises.

1. A teacher told her class that the mean score on last week's test was 48. "That's a pretty mean score," responded one student. What did the teacher mean by *mean*? Use a dictionary to help you identify the different definitions.

2. What is a highway *median*?

3. How is the word *average* used in everyday speech?

4. Look up each of the terms below in a dictionary. Write a math-related definition for each word.

   average   **data**   **frequency**

THE RESULTS ARE IN!

Taste tests prove that Apple Sparkle is the best.

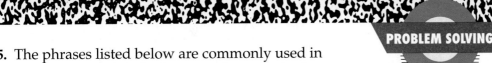

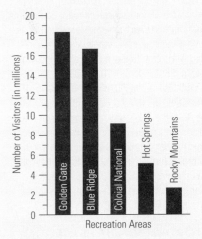

PROBLEM SOLVING

5. The phrases listed below are commonly used in advertising. For each phrase, write a short advertisement for a product you are familiar with.
"Four out of five"
"Laboratory tests prove"
"Number-one-selling"

6. Look in a newspaper for examples of news stories or reports that use statistics. The sports and business sections are good places to look. Bring in examples to show the class.

▶ **Practice What You Know**

Order each set of numbers from least to greatest.

7. 19 20 53 6 17 206 85 21 12
   6 12 17 19 20 21 53 85 206

8. 3.5 18.0 35.0 28.6 1001.1 10.1
   3.5 10.1 18.0 28.6 35.0 1001.1

9. 30 7 1200 800 9 54 98 706
   7 9 30 54 98 706 800 1200

10. 112 88 16 91 57 47 31 306 80
    16 31 47 57 80 88 91 112 306

11. $22,000 $18,500 $56,000 $2500 $10,600
    $2500 $10,600 $18,500 $22,000 $56,000

12. $1465 $20,683 $108,675 $200,031 $18,563
    $1465 $18,563 $20,683 $108,675 $200,031

Round each decimal to the nearest tenth.

13. 14.06 14.1   14. 106.531 106.5   15. 2.75 2.8   16. 47.31 47.3   17. 206.99 207.0

18. Complete a bar graph using the information shown here.

National Park Service Recreation Areas	Number of Visitors
Golden Gate National Recreation Area	18.4 million
Blue Ridge Parkway	16.7 million
Colonial National Historical Park	9.1 million
Hot Springs National Park	5.3 million
Rocky Mountain National Park	2.6 million

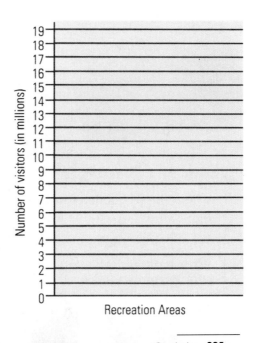

Number of visitors (in millions)

Recreation Areas

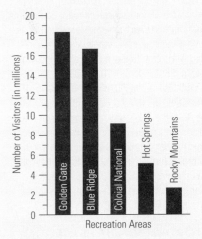

Express Yourself Answers
(continued)
5. Sample answers include: "Four out of five dentists recommend Dazzle Toothpaste"; "Laboratory tests prove that Baby Face Shampoo is gentler on baby's skin and eyes"; "Growl Dog food is the number-one-selling brand nationwide."
6. Particular words to look for in news stories or reports that the students bring to class should include *mean*, *average*, *median*, *range*, and *data*.

Practice What You Know Answers

18. Sample bar graph shown below.

Number of Visitors (in millions)

Recreation Areas

Golden Gate · Blue Ridge · Coloial National · Hot Springs · Rocky Mountains

★ **Error Alert**

Errors may indicate that students change the number in the place they are rounding to when rounding down. For example, 13.74 to the nearest tenth becomes 13.7, not 13.6. Or students forget that in rounding up, they sometimes need to change more places. For example, 3.95 to the nearest tenth becomes 4.0, not 3.0.

Project

Use a news story or a magazine article that you collected for Question 6 to prepare a questionnaire that you might use in a survey to gather similar information. Report the purpose of your study and who will be surveyed using the questionnaire.

10.2 Making a Frequency Table

Rita is starting a business to care for the pets and plants of people who are on vacation. She is preparing a flyer to distribute around the neighborhood and she needs to figure out how much to charge for each visit.

Rita decides to find out what other businesses charge for a similar service. She calls 16 services advertised in the yellow pages and makes a list of their fees.

Rita makes a plan for analyzing the fees. First she has to organize her information.

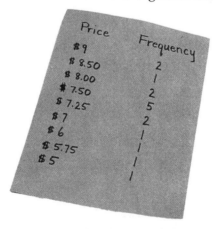

Rita uses her data to make a **frequency table.** She writes the prices in order and counts how often each price appears. The number of times each price appears is called its **frequency.** Rita can see from her table that she should charge between $5 and $9 if she wants to be competitive. She decides to charge the price that appears most often in her list, $7.50.

▶ **Think and Discuss**

1. Check the frequencies in Rita's list. Does $7.50 seem like a reasonable price for Rita to charge? Discuss.

2. What price would you charge? Why? Discuss.

3. Write a paragraph explaining how organizing the data helped Rita determine her fee.

Exercises

(For more practice, see page 432.)

4. Make a frequency table for the following data on the size of men's shoes sold during one work day.

   9   10   11   12   8   10   11   9   7   10   11

   10   8   9   9   8   12   9   10   8   10   9

Use the frequency table you made for Question 4 to answer the following questions.

5. How many pairs of shoes were sold? 22 pairs

6. Which shoe size was sold most often? 9 and 10

7. How many pairs of shoes larger than size 10 were sold? 5 pairs

8. How could a shoe store use the kind of information shown here? Discuss. It would help them to know what sizes to stock.

9. Make a frequency table for the following scores on a 15-point quiz. Use your table to answer Questions 10, 11, and 12.

   14   12   10   14   9   10   12   10   9   15   13   12

   9   10   12   12   8   11   12   10   12   14   12   14

10. How many students took the quiz? 24 students

11. Which was the most common score? 12

12. How many scores were 12 or less? 18 scores

▶ Applications

13. Conduct a survey of your class. Ask about such topics as favorite musical group or favorite brand of cereal. Construct a frequency table that shows the results of your survey.

14. Write a summary of the results of your survey. Questions 5–8 and 10–12 may help you analyze your table.

▶ Review (Lessons 1.10, 1.11)

Subtract.

15. $42 - 9.76$
    32.24

16. $602 - 399$
    203

17. $4.79 - 2.182$
    2.608

18. $234 - 176$
    58

19. $88.8 - 0.172$
    88.628

20. $0.75 - 0.705$
    0.045

21. $1472 - 595$
    877

22. $2.93 - 1.09$
    1.84

Answers

4.

Size	Tally	Number
12	II	2
11	III	3
10	JHT I	6
9	JHT I	6
8	IIII	4
7	I	1

9.

Score	Tally	Number of Students
15	I	1
14	IIII	4
13	I	1
12	JHT III	8
11	I	1
10	JHT	5
9	III	3
8	I	1

13. Answers will depend on the number of students and what is surveyed.

14. Answers will depend on surveys.

★ Error Alert

While students are usually able to construct a frequency table without problems, they often skip one of the items in the list of data. They should count the number of items in the list of data and add the numbers in the frequency table to be sure they are equal.

Reinforcement

Extra Practice, page 432
EP/MR Worksheet 77, TRB, page 77

Project

Work in small groups to make a frequency table for the letters in selected paragraphs from a book or magazine. Each group will use different paragraphs. Identify the ten most common letters. Compare your tables and answers with those of the other groups. What conclusions can you draw? (Answers may vary.)

10.3 Finding the Range, Mode, and Median

Mr. Barnes has 21 students in his class. When he gives a test, he examines the class's performance by finding the range, mode, and median of the test scores.

Examples

To find the range, mode, and median of a set of numbers, first write the numbers in order.

range the difference between the greatest and the least numbers
mode the number or numbers that occur most often
median the middle number in an ordered set of data

A Find the range of the test scores.

  9 9   Subtract the least number from the greatest number in the set.
− 7 4
  2 5   The range of the scores is **25**.

B Find the mode of the test scores.

Find the number of numbers that occur most often. 78 occurs 6 times.
The mode of the test scores is **78**.

C Find the median of the test scores.

Find the middle number. There are 21 scores. 10 scores are above 83. 10 scores are below 83.
The median is **83**.

D Find the median.   **76, 80, 81, 83, 87, 90**

83 + 81 = 164   Add the two middle numbers.
164 ÷ 2 = 82   Divide by 2.
The median is **82**.

▶ Think and Discuss

1. Order the set from least to greatest.
   7   9   4   8   3   0   10   5   8   5

2. Find the mode: 1   2   3   1   2   1   2.   Discuss.

3. Refer to the introduction to this lesson. If the score of 99 was erased from Mr. Barnes's list, would the range, mode, or median change? Explain.

4. Which of the following—range, mode, or median—would a frequency table be particularly useful for finding? Explain.

Exercises

Find the range. (See Example A.)

5. 3.2   2.7   4.1   6.5   3.8   4.9 3.8

6. 19   23   17   24   20   29   16   18 13

Find the mode. (See Example B.)

7. $1.25   75¢ $1.49 $2.35 $1.25
   $2.10 $1.10   80¢ $1.25 $1.89 $1.25

8. 98   87   78   88   91   90   88   92
   91   88   78   91   87   86   88   82 88

Find the median. (See Example C.)

9. $12,500 $9600 $21,000 $5500
   $24,000 $14,700 $18,200 $14,700

10. $24.20 $47.50 $31.74 $26.15
    $25.70 $35.90 $40.53 $31.74

Find the median. (See Example D.)

11. 4   9   7   6   2   9   3   5 5.5

12. $4.50 $5.00 $6.60 $9.25 $5.80

▶ Mixed Practice (For more practice, see page 432.)

Use this set of data for Questions 13–15.

76   73   80   82   77   77   69   82   75   79   70   71   80   77   76   77

13. Find the range. 13   14. Find the mode. 77   15. Find the median. 77

▶ Applications

16. Elroy's lunches for two weeks cost: $3.52, $2.06, $4.16, $3.52 $2.25, $3.05, $6.15, $2.06, $3.76, and $3.52. Find the range, the median, and the mode.

17. The prices and weights for running shoes are listed here. Find the median price. Find the median weight. Find the range of prices and of weights.

Price	Weight (oz.)
$53	24
$80	20
$59	22
$57	19

▶ Review (Lessons 3.2, 3.5)

Divide.

18. 36 ÷ 9 4   19. 150 ÷ 5 30   20. 372 ÷ 3 124   21. 1025 ÷ 5 205   22. 562 ÷ 18 31 R4

Alternative Examples (continued)

Example D—Find the median.   20, 4, 15, 2, 13, 19 Write the numbers in order:
2, 4, 13, 15, 19, 20.
13 + 15 = 28   *Add the two middle numbers.*
28 ÷ 2 = 14   *Divide by 2.*
The median is **14**.

▶ Think and Discuss Answers

1. 0 3 4 5 5 7 8 8 9 10
2. There are two modes: 2 and 1; both 2 and 1 occur three times.
3. The range would become 18 and the median would become 82; the mode would not change. Discussion might include the fact that the score of 99 was higher than the other scores. If it was omitted, the range and median would decrease.
4. mode; the frequency table tells at a glance which score is most common

Answers

16. range: $4.09; median: $3.52; mode: $3.52
17. median price: $58; median weight: 21 oz.; range of prices: $27; range of weights: 5 oz.

★ Error Alert

Errors may reveal that students are not putting the numbers in order before finding the median.

Reinforcement

Extra Practice, page 432
EP/MR Worksheet 78, TRB, page 78

Project

Go to a grocery store and make a list of prices and weights of similar items, such as loaves of bread. Order your data set from least to greatest. Find the range, mode, and median for your data set. (sample data for bread: $1.05, $0.99, $1.05; 16 oz., 16 oz., 18 oz.; price range: $0.06; weight range: 2 oz.; price mode: $1.05; weight mode: 16 oz.; price median: $1.05; weight median: 16 oz.)

Objective

- To find the mean of a set of numbers

Purpose

Finding the mean of a set of numbers is another tool you can use to help you interpret a set of data. This is useful, for example, if you want to find the average distance you can kick a football.

Introducing the Lesson

Review adding whole numbers and decimals and dividing by 1-digit and 2-digit divisors (Lessons 1.9, 3.2, 3.5). Use the examples: Add—15 + 12 + 16.5 + 25 + 19.8 = (88.3); divide—973 ÷ 7 = (139); 297 ÷ 12 = (24.75)

Write the word *mean* on the chalkboard. Ask students to state as many definitions as they can for the word. You might wish to have a student read definitions of the word *mean* from a dictionary. Tell students that in this lesson they will use *mean* in connection with mathematics.

Alternative Example

Example—Find the mean weight of the team's bowling balls. The balls weigh 14 lb., 12 lb., 10 lb., 10 lb., 16 lb., 16 lb., 8 lb., 12 lb., and 10 lb.

Find the sum.
```
   14 lb.
   12
   10
   10
   16
   16
    8
   12
 + 10
  108 lb.
```
108 ÷ 9 = 12   *Divide the sum by 9, the number of bowling balls.*

The mean is **12 lb.**

10.4 Finding the Mean

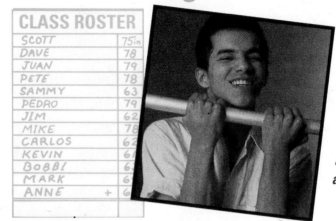

CLASS ROSTER

SCOTT	75in
DAVE	78
JUAN	79
PETE	78
SAMMY	63
PEDRO	79
JIM	62
MIKE	78
CARLOS	62
KEVIN	61
BOBBI	6
MARK	6
ANNE	+ 6

Southside High is building a new gym, and Coach Charles wants to determine the best height for the chin-up bar. To do this, he decides to find the mean, or average, height of his students and then add 11 inches.

Examples

To find the mean of a set of numbers, first find the sum of the numbers. Then divide the sum by the number of items.

Find the mean height in Coach Charles's survey.

Find the sum.
```
   7 5
   7 8
   7 9
   7 8
   6 3
   7 9
   6 2
   7 8
   6 2
   6 1
   6 3
   6 4
 + 6 1
   9 0 3
```

```
         6 9.4 6 1
    13)9 0 3.0 0 0
        7 8
        1 2 3
        1 1 7
          6 0
          5 2
            8 0
            7 8
             2 0
             1 3
```

Divide the sum by 13, the number of students.

You might want to use a calculator in this problem.

The mean is **about 69.46 inches.**

▶ Think and Discuss

1. Find the mean.   29   55   43   37   52.

2. Refer to the introduction to this lesson. If Coach Charles uses his original plan, how high will he position the chin-up bar?

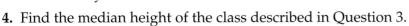

3. If a class of 14 has five people 65 inches tall and nine people 74 inches tall, is the mean height nearer to 65 inches or 74 inches? Why?

4. Find the median height of the class described in Question 3.

5. If a class of 12 has six people 65 inches tall and six people 74 inches tall, are the mean and the median equal? Explain.

6. Should you write a set of numbers in order before computing their mean? Explain.

Exercises

(For more practice, see page 433.)

Find the mean.

7. 12   16   4   25   10   13.4   8. 16   38   71   82   91   71   61.5

9. 375   902   434   182   473.25   10. 284   267   225   213   247.25

11. $15,000 $22,000 $18,500 $12,250 $24,400 $18,430

12. 23   19   22   25   22   21   24   20   23   21   22

13. 78   67   93   82   88   56   84   86   90   79   80.3

14. $4.15 $3.75 $5.10 $4.50 $5.40 $3.80 $7.95 $6.25 $5.00 $5.10

15. 176   181   167   202   195   186   158   198   211   170   169   205   184.8̄3

▶ Applications

16. Ana's math grade is actually the mean of her test scores for the term. Ana's test scores were 89, 74, 67, 83, 73, 91, and 85. What will her final grade be?   ≈ 80.3

17. Last week Morgan ran 6.5 miles, 7.25 miles, 8 miles, 4 miles, 12.5 miles, 14 miles, and 7.5 miles. What was his mean daily distance?   ≈ 8.5 miles

18. Greg wants a B in English class. He has three test scores of 86, 78, and 76. What score does he need on the final test to end up with a mean score of 80?   80

▶ Review (Lessons 6.7, 7.1, 7.3, 7.4)

Solve. Write the answers in lowest terms.

19. $1\frac{3}{4} \div 2\frac{7}{8}$ 20. $1\frac{1}{8} \div 3\frac{3}{8}$ 21. $2\frac{5}{8} \div 1\frac{3}{4}$ $1\frac{1}{2}$ 22. $2\frac{1}{2} \div 3\frac{3}{4}$ $\frac{2}{3}$ 23. $3\frac{1}{5} \div 1\frac{1}{5}$ $2\frac{2}{3}$

24. $\frac{4}{9} + \frac{7}{9}$ $1\frac{2}{9}$ 25. $\frac{5}{6} + \frac{4}{5}$ $1\frac{19}{30}$ 26. $\frac{9}{10} + \frac{7}{20}$ $1\frac{1}{4}$ 27. $3\frac{1}{8} + 6\frac{7}{8}$ 10   28. $8\frac{3}{4} + 5\frac{11}{16}$ $14\frac{7}{16}$

▶ Think and Discuss Answers

1. 43.2
2. At about $80\frac{1}{2}$ inches, or 6 feet $8\frac{1}{2}$ inches
3. The mean height is closer to 74 inches because there are more people who are 74 inches tall than 65 inches tall.
4. 74 inches
5. Yes; the median height is the average of 65 and 74; since the numbers of students in each group are the same, the mean height is also the average of 65 and 74 (69.5)
6. It is not necessary to order the numbers; the relevant facts are the sum of numbers and the number of numbers in the set.

★ Error Alert

Mistakes may indicate that students are confusing *mean* and *median*.

Reinforcement

Extra Practice, page 433
EP/MR Worksheet 79, TRB, page 79

Challenge

Ana's test grades in Mr. Ramirez's class were 89, 99, 94, 10, 92. Which of the four concepts that you've learned in the last lesson and in this one do teachers usually use to figure out grades? (mean) What is Ana's mean score? (76.8) Is this the best way to figure out Ana's grade? (Students may answer yes or no.) If so, why? (A sample answer is that the mean gives the average of all her scores.) If not, why not? (A sample answer is that the score of 10 is much lower than her other scores.) What is the mean if Mr. Ramirez drops the lowest score? (93.5) What conclusion can you draw? (Sample answers may include: the mean of a set of numbers is greatly affected when one number is very different from the others.)

T231

10.5 Investigating Averages

Luisa just got a job. When she interviewed she was told that her division's average salary was a little over $21,290. Then a co-worker told her the average salary was $13,600. Luisa decided to do her own calculations. She found the average salary to be $14,090. Why do you think these figures are different?

Luisa's company consists of 3 managers and 12 clerks. Their salaries are shown below.

Salaries (in dollars)

50,000	50,000	50,000	15,325	15,060	15,000	14,125	14,090
14,000	13,750	13,600	13,600	13,600	13,600	13,600	

Find the mean salary. Total payroll is $319,350.
Mean = $319,350 ÷ 15 = $21,290

Find the median salary. There are 15 salaries: 7 are greater than $14,090, 7 are less than $14,090.
Median = $14,090

Find the mode of the salaries. Five people earn $13,600.
Mode = $13,600

The mean, median, and mode can be different numbers. Yet each is sometimes called an average, just as in the above case.

1. Find the median and the mean salaries of the 12 clerks. Discuss why the mean of this group of salaries is different from the mean of the original group of salaries.

2. Suppose two of the managers in Luisa's department leave their jobs. What are the mean, median, and mode salaries now? Explain how changing one or two figures can affect the mean, median, and mode differently.

PROBLEM SOLVING

3. Now suppose one of the three managers earns $120,000 instead of $50,000. What are the mean, median, and mode salaries now? Discuss how each changes.

4. Which average—the mean, the median, or the mode—most accurately describes the typical salary in Luisa's division? Justify your answer.

5. Suppose you wanted to study average income in the United States as part of a history project. Would you use median or mean income in your study? Justify your choice.

Read the following example:

According to a recent study, half of Newark Community College's students are over 24 years old. The average age of the students is 29.

Based on the information in this lesson, use the word *mean* or *median* to complete each statement.

6. The ___ age of Newark Community College students is 29. Mean

7. The ___ age of Newark Community College students is 24. Median

Sometimes finding the mean, median, or mode is not enough to help you understand a situation.

Planet	Approximate Length of a Day in Earth Hours
Mercury	1416
Venus	5832
Earth	24
Mars	24.6
Jupiter	9.9
Saturn	10.2
Uranus	22
Neptune	19
Pluto	144

8. What is the mean length of one day in our solar system? ≈ 833.5 Earth hours

9. What is the median length of one day in our solar system? 24 hours

10. Is the use of mean or median helpful in understanding day length in our solar system? Discuss.
Answers will vary.

▶ **Review** (Lesson 9.4)

11. Use the following data to make a bar graph.

National League Pennant Winners (through 1998)
Cubs—4 years   Cardinals—1 year
Tigers—10 years   Yankees—34 years

Answers (continued)

4. median; the mean is unrepresentative because the 3 managers' salaries are so much higher; the mode just shows the most common salary; therefore, the median, which gives the number in the middle, is the best description of the typical salary

5. median; for the same reasons as in Question 4

11. A sample bar graph is shown.

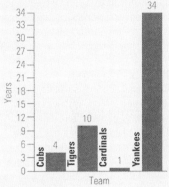

★ **Error Alert**

Errors may indicate that when students are calculating the mean, they are not using a divisor that is equal to the number of addends.

Reinforcement

EP/MR Worksheet 80, TRB, page 80

Challenge

Copy the following tables on your paper and compute the batting averages for each player. Then find the sum of the times at bat and the sum of hits, and compute the overall batting average for each player. Note: RH means right-handed and LH means left-handed.

SPARKY

Pitcher	At Bat	Hits	Avg.
RH	573	90	(.157)
LH	15	2	(.133)
Totals	(588)	(92)	(.156)

SPEEDY

Pitcher	At Bat	Hits	Avg.
RH	81	12	(.148)
LH	43	16	(.372)
Totals	(124)	(28)	(.226)

Objective

- To construct a histogram

Purpose

You can use graphs to present a great amount of information in a small space. This lesson shows you how to construct histograms, bar graphs that show frequencies.

Introducing the Lesson

Conduct a small poll with students, asking them how many soft drinks they drank the previous day. Write the information on the chalkboard. Tell students that this lesson shows how to express the information they have just gathered in a meaningful graphic form.

After teaching the lesson you may wish to have students construct a histogram using the information above.

▶ Think and Discuss Answers

1. Histogram will look like the one shown here.

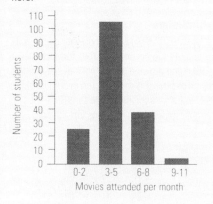

2. no; because the frequencies for each member of the category are grouped together

3. no; only bar graphs that show frequencies of categories are histograms

How often do you go to the movies? A high school newspaper staff conducted a survey concerning freshman movie attendance. The results are shown here. The editors decided to present the results in a histogram to attract attention to the information.

Movies attended per month	0	1	2	3	4	5	6	7	8	9	10	11
Numbers of students	3	9	15	29	43	35	18	14	8	3	0	2

Histograms are bar graphs that show the frequency of events, prices, or scores. Histograms condense and organize large amounts of information.

Examples

To construct a histogram, follow these steps:

1. Draw and label the horizontal and vertical axes.
2. Label the numbers along the axes.
3. Draw the bars to their proper heights.
4. Write a title for the histogram.

Use the information above to construct a histogram.

Follow these steps:

1. Organize the movie survey results into 6 categories.
2. Find the frequency for each category.
3. Label the horizontal axis to show the 6 categories.
4. Label the vertical axis to show the frequencies.
5. Construct the histogram bars.

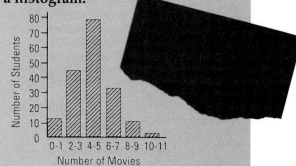

▶ Think and Discuss

1. Use the movie survey results above to construct another histogram that shows 4 movie attendance categories.

2. Can you tell exact frequencies from a histogram? Explain.

3. Are all histograms bar graphs? Discuss.

Exercises

(For more practice, see page 433.)

Use the information in each table to construct a histogram.

4. Number of states visited by Miss Lal's math students (besides home state)

States visited	0	1	2	3	4	5	6	7	8	9	10	11+
Number of students	4	6	8	6	5	4	0	3	2	0	0	1

Divide the states visited into categories, 0–2, 3–5, and so on.

5. Torino Bicycle Shop sales (number of bicycles sold per month)

Month	Jan.	Feb.	Mar.	Apr.	May	June	July	Aug.	Sept.	Oct.	Nov.	Dec.
Number of bicycles	10	12	24	31	58	72	103	69	32	12	9	94

Divide the months into 6 categories.

6. Ages of Slocumville Symphony Orchestra members

Age	22	27	31	38	44	46	49	52	53	55	57	58	59	62	66	70
Number of members	1	1	2	1	3	4	8	10	14	9	18	15	20	14	7	3

Divide the ages into 20s, 30s, and so on.

▶ Applications

7. You work for a movie production studio. You want to design a graph showing the studio's income over the past year, using the data below.

The studio president wants the information shown by quarters (3-month periods). Construct a histogram. Describe what the histogram tells about the studio's income.

Studio Income (in thousands of dollars)

Jan.	Feb.	Mar.	Apr.	May	June	July	Aug.	Sept.	Oct.	Nov.	Dec.
12	25	30	42	28	59	78	107	94	61	24	37

▶ Review (Lessons 7.1, 7.5, 7.7, 7.9)

Subtract. Write the answers in lowest terms.

8. $\frac{11}{20} - \frac{3}{20}$ $\frac{2}{5}$

9. $2\frac{2}{3} - 1\frac{1}{4}$ $1\frac{5}{12}$

10. $3\frac{1}{2} - 1\frac{2}{3}$ $1\frac{5}{6}$

11. $\frac{8}{9} - \frac{1}{3}$ $\frac{5}{9}$

12. $4\frac{5}{6} - 4\frac{1}{2}$ $\frac{1}{3}$

13. $\frac{7}{12} - \frac{1}{3}$ $\frac{1}{4}$

14. $9\frac{5}{9} - 7\frac{1}{6}$ $2\frac{7}{18}$

15. $\frac{13}{16} - \frac{11}{16}$ $\frac{1}{8}$

16. $\frac{7}{8} - \frac{2}{5}$ $\frac{19}{40}$

17. $5 - 2\frac{3}{5}$ $2\frac{2}{5}$

Answers

4.

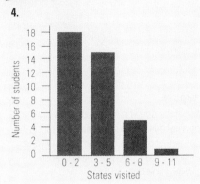

5.

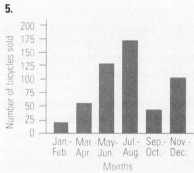

(continued on page T238)

★ **Error Alert**

Mistakes may occur if students confuse the single categories of a bar graph with the intervals of a histogram.

Reinforcement

Extra Practice, page 433
EP/MR Worksheet 81, TRB, page 81

Teaching Aids

Quarter-inch grid
TA 7, TRB, page 160
Teaching suggestions precede the Teaching Aids worksheets.

Project

Find a histogram in a magazine, a book of facts and records, or an encyclopedia. Sketch the histogram and answer these questions: What information does the histogram show? What information is presented on each axis? Write a paragraph that summarizes the information presented.

10.7 Statistics: A Career Application

Graphic artists illustrate statistics that apply to the nation, finances, and our lives. They organize data in ways that are interesting and informative.

The artist chooses a type of graph that is appropriate to the set of data. For example, the artist might choose a pictograph to illustrate the population of the five largest cities in the United States. To illustrate changes in the stock market, the artist might choose a line graph.

▶ **Think and Discuss**

1. What do you find interesting about the graphs on these pages? What things make a graph informative or interesting? Discuss.

2. What type of graph is used to report the fuel consumption of motor vehicles in the United States?

3. Why do you think a line graph is used for hurricanes instead of a circle graph?

4. How do you think the graphic artist selected the colors for the map of U.S. population density shown on the next page?

5. Why is a map a better choice than a graph to represent U.S. population density?

What type of graph would you choose if you were a media artist and you were reporting:

6. the amounts of corn and wheat grown in the United States?

7. the stray dog population in Tulsa over the last 10 years?

8. the number of men and women who worked outside the home in 1940, 1950, 1960, 1970, 1980, and 1990?

U.S. Motor Vehicle Fuel Consumption
(1996 estimate)

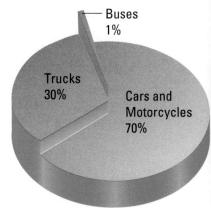

Source: Dept. of Transportation, Federal Highway Administration

Total number of Hurricanes in U.S., 1871 – 1996

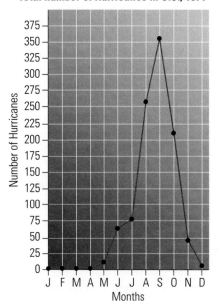

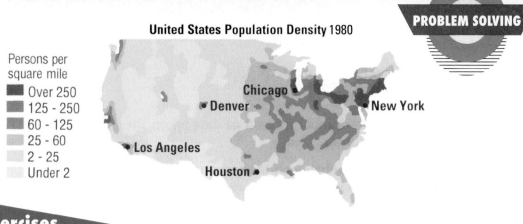

United States Population Density 1980

Persons per square mile
- Over 250
- 125 - 250
- 60 - 125
- 25 - 60
- 2 - 25
- Under 2

Chicago • Denver • New York • Los Angeles • Houston •

Exercises

A national teen magazine surveyed 600 employed students. The results are shown below:

Type of Job	Freshmen	Sophomores	Juniors	Seniors
Pizza delivery person	0	0	34	36
Waiter/waitress (fast food)	0	18	68	74
Sales clerk (department store)	0	5	26	38
Stock person	1	8	22	30
Babysitter	47	31	20	4
Lawn mower	42	27	12	6
Other	10	11	18	12

Now you are a graphic artist. Choose the type and style of graph that would best represent the information.

9. Draw a graph that shows the decline of babysitting employment throughout the four high school years.

10. Draw a graph that shows the types of jobs held by juniors.

11. Draw a graph that shows the findings of the entire survey.

▶ Review (Lesson 3.8)

Write which operation you would use to solve each problem. Then solve.

12. The Thompson family spends an average of $350 a month on food. Estimate the average cost of food for each week.
Division; $87.50

13. Jenny's car averages 24.7 miles per gallon. How much does Jenny spend to purchase 13.5 gallons of gas at $0.98 a gallon?
Multiplication; $13.23

Answers

9. $2   6
   $3   5
   $4   4

Range: $2   Median: $3
Mean: $2.87   Mode: $2

10.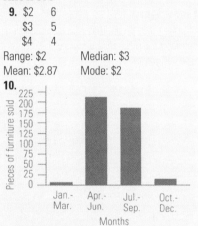

11. Answers may vary. Sample answers may include: to show cost of living changes for last five years.
12. circle graph

Answers

(continued from page T235)

6.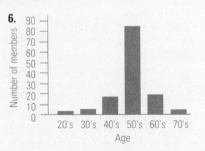

7. Check students' histograms for these totals: Jan.–Mar., 67; Apr.–June, 129; July–Sept., 279; and Oct.–Dec., 122. The greatest income was in the summer months (July–Sept.); the least was in the winter months (Jan.–Mar.); spring and autumn have similar incomes.

Chapter 10 Review

REVIEW

Complete each statement. (Lessons 10.3, 10.4)

1. Another word for mean is ___. Average

2. The ___ is the middle number in set of data when the numbers are listed in order. Median

3. The ___ is the difference between the largest and the smallest numbers in a set of numbers. Range

Find the range, mean, median, and mode for each set of numbers. (Lessons 10.3, 10.4)

4. 84   68   81   76
   Range: 16; mean: 77.25; median: 78.5; mode: all

5. 74   79   91   74   91
   Range: 17; mean: 81.8; median: 79; modes: 74, 91

Use these salaries of Winsome baseball team members to answer the following questions. (Lesson 10.5)

6. What is the mean salary? $585,000

7. What is the mean salary of the first 4 players? $231,250

8. Which mean salary describes the salary situation better? Why?
   $231,250; 4 of the 5 are closer to this average than to $585,000

Player	Salary
Spitball Harry (pitcher)	$230,000
Sturdy Al (shortstop)	$185,000
Traveling Troy (1st base)	$315,000
Lightning Sol (3rd base)	$195,000
Stop'em Joe (catcher)	$2,000,000

Make a frequency table for the set of data below. Then find the range, mean, median, and mode. (Lessons 10.2, 10.3, 10.4)

9. Cost of a package of pens at local stores
   $2 $2 $2 $3 $4 $2 $2 $3 $4 $3 $4 $3 $2 $4 $3

Use the information below to construct a histogram. (Lesson 10.6)

10. Last year's sales of lawn furniture at Kelly's Patio Shoppe

Month	Jan.	Feb.	Mar.	Apr.	May	June	July	Aug.	Sept.	Oct.	Nov.	Dec.
Number of pieces	0	0	3	6	85	119	97	53	37	8	0	0

Divide the year into 3-month periods.

Answer the following questions. (Lesson 10.7)

11. Describe a situation when a graphic artist might choose a line graph to illustrate data.

12. What kind of graph would you choose to show a family's budget for one year?

Chapter 10 Test

TEST

Find the range, mean, median, and mode for each set of numbers.

1. $25 $23 $25 $30 $32 $28
Range: $9; mode: $25; median: $26.50; mean: $27.17

2. 4 9 3 8 5 8 6
Range: 6; mode: 8; median: 6; mean: 6.14

Make a frequency table for the data below. Then find the range, mean, median, and mode.

3. Hourly charge of 20 child-care workers
$4.50 $5 $4.75 $5 $4.50 $5.50 $4.25 $4.50 $4.75 $4.50
$5.50 $4.75 $5 $4.50 $5.50 $4.50 $4.50 $5 $6 $4.25

Use the information in the table below to construct a histogram.

4. African-violet sales, Hooper Florists

Month	Jan.	Feb.	Mar.	Apr.	May	June	July	Aug.	Sept.	Oct.	Nov.	Dec.
Number of plants sold	17	25	15	12	8	10	6	4	9	18	28	33

Divide the year into 2-month periods.

Complete each statement.

5. The number that appears most often in a set of numbers is called the ___. Mode

6. A graph that shows the frequency of events, prices, or scores is called a(n) ___. Histogram

7. The ___, ___, and ___ are all sometimes called the average. Mode, median, mean

Use the table below to answer the following questions.

8. What is the mean distance?
41,960 mi.

9. What is the median distance?
30,700 mi.

10. What is the range of distances?
73,800 mi.

Annual Driving Distances of Salespeople, Acme Distributors

Tom	21,700 mi.
Bette	33,900 mi.
Walt	95,500 mi.
Carmen	28,000 mi.
Bob	30,700 mi.

Chapter Tests
Short Answer, Forms A and B, TRB, pages 303–304, 305–306
Multiple Choice, Forms A and B, TRB, pages 371–372, 373–374

Teaching Aids
Answer sheet
TA 8, TRB, page 161a
Teaching suggestions precede the Teaching Aids worksheets.

Answers

3.

$4.25	2
$4.50	7
$4.75	3
$5.00	4
$5.50	3
$6.00	1

Range: $4.75
Mean: $4.84
Median: $4.75
Mode: $4.50

4.

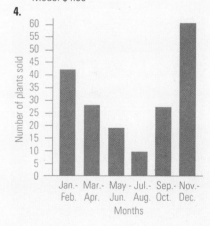

Career Focus Activity

Materials: pencils, paper

Procedure: Organize students into four groups. Students arrange to have a nutritionist speak to the class.

• The first group writes an invitation to a nutritionist to visit the classroom.

• The second group compiles a list of questions to ask the individual about the job, activities the job entails, level of difficulty, required education, rewards of the job, how math skills are utilized, etc.

• During the visit, members of the third group ask the questions and record responses.

• Members of the fourth group compose a thank-you note to be sent within three days of the visit.

• All students evaluate the experience.

Use ratio and proportion to

• assess nutrient content in foods.

• compare quantities.

• scale maps and drawings.

What are some other ways to use ratio and proportion?

Ratio and Proportion

A *nutritionist* educates people about how to have a healthy lifestyle.

- Nutritionists work in hospitals, in schools, in health clinics, and for corporations.

- A nutritionist should have an interest in health and enjoy working with people to help them remain or become healthy.

- A nutritionist calculates the nutritional needs of a person based on age and medical condition, writes reports, and prepares budgets.

- A nutrition degree requires four years of study in a college or university.

- Other careers related to nutrition include dietitian, hotel and restaurant management, consultant for athletic teams and personal trainers, and writers for books and magazines.

CAREER

NUTRITIONIST

PORTFOLIO PROJECT: *Create well-balanced meals.*

1. Record the different foods, including beverages, you eat each day for one week. Look up the nutritive value of these foods (proteins, fats, carbohydrates, calcium, etc.).

2. Research the Recommended Daily Allowances (RDAs) for the amount of protein, vitamins, and minerals that a person of your age and gender requires. Compare the results of Steps 1 and 2. What are you missing? *Show the math.*

3. Plan three meals and two snacks for one day which will meet the RDAs for your age and gender.

About the Portfolio Project

Supply students with a copy of an almanac or a nutritive guide and an RDA chart. The students should keep an honest record of what they eat per day for one week, creating charts for ease of both recording and accessing information.

When they create their own meals, they should include the nutritive value and RDA in separate columns.

Assessment: The individual scoring rubric on page 161 of the Teacher's Resource Binder can be reproduced and used for assessment. Include the following information in the last two boxes. Students should have:
- recorded all the suggested information in a readable way.
- created a balanced diet to include all recommendations.

Purpose

This lesson helps you to write ratios so that you can compare two quantities. For example, you can determine the quantities of fuel and of oil you need to mix for a lawn mower engine that specifies 8 parts of gasoline to 1 part of oil.

Introducing the Lesson

Review finding equivalent fractions (Lesson 5.2).

Take a poll of the class to find how many students write with their left hand and how many students write with their right hand. Record the results on the chalkboard. Make a statement like this: "In our class there are 25 right-handed students to 4 left-handed students." Tell students that in this lesson they will learn how to express such relationships as *ratios*.

Alternative Examples

Example A—Write the ratio of 210 kilometers per 19 liters of diesel fuel 3 different ways.
The ratio of 210 kilometers per 19 liters of diesel fuel can be written as **210 to 19**, $\frac{210}{19}$, and **210:19**.

Example B—Find 3 ratios equivalent to $\frac{16}{24}$. Use the same method as Example B. Three ratios equivalent to $\frac{16}{24}$ are $\frac{8}{12}$, $\frac{32}{48}$, and $\frac{4}{6}$.

▶ **Think and Discuss Answers**

1. 3 to 2; $\frac{3}{2}$; 3:2
2. sample answers to include: $\frac{14}{18}$, $\frac{21}{27}$, $\frac{28}{36}$
3. $\frac{10}{24}$ or $\frac{5}{12}$; $\frac{24}{10}$ or $\frac{12}{5}$; no, because the order of a ratio is important
4. sample answers may include determining speed (miles to hours) or a team's won-lost record (wins to losses).

11.1 Writing Ratios and Rates

Bill stopped his friend Ravi while they were selling tee shirts on the Fourth of July. "You told me we'd sell just as many small as large shirts. I'm selling 3 large for every 2 small. What happened?"

Bill is using a **ratio,** which is a comparison of two numbers by division.

Examples

To write ratios, use the word *to*, a colon, or a fraction bar.
To find equivalent ratios, multiply or divide each term of the given ratio by the same number.

A Write the ratio of 100 miles to 4 gallons of gasoline in 3 different ways.

With the word *to*: 100 to 4
As a fraction: $\frac{100}{4}$
With a colon: 100 : 4
The ratio of 100 miles to 4 gallons of gasoline can be written as **100 to 4,** $\frac{100}{4}$, and **100 : 4.**

B Find 3 ratios equivalent to $\frac{6}{8}$.

$$\frac{6}{8} = \frac{6 \div 2}{8 \div 2} = \frac{3}{4}$$
$$\frac{6}{8} = \frac{6 \times 2}{8 \times 2} = \frac{12}{16}$$
$$\frac{6}{8} = \frac{6 \times 7}{8 \times 7} = \frac{42}{56}$$

Three ratios equivalent to $\frac{6}{8}$ are $\frac{3}{4}$, $\frac{12}{16}$, and $\frac{42}{56}$.

▶ **Think and Discuss**

1. Refer to the introduction to this lesson. Write the given ratio in three different ways.

2. Write three ratios equivalent to $\frac{7}{9}$.

3. Ten girls and twenty-four boys are enrolled in a class. Find the ratio of girls to boys and the ratio of boys to girls. Are these ratios equivalent? Explain.

4. Name two situations in which you could use ratios.

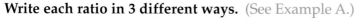

Exercises

Write each ratio in 3 different ways. (See Example A.)

5. 55 miles per hour

6. 12 laps in 15 minutes

7. 10-pound loss in 5 weeks

8. 8 quarters for 2 dollars

9. $1.56 for 4 pounds of bananas

10. $4.56 for 3 light bulbs

Find 3 ratios equivalent to each ratio. (See Example B.)

11. 10 prizes for 5 games

12. 250 desks for 10 classrooms

13. 3 hours of homework in 4 classes

14. 500 miles traveled in 10 hours

▶ Mixed Practice (For more practice, see page 434.)

Write each ratio in 3 three different ways. Find 3 ratios equivalent to each ratio.

15. 7 records broken in 2 years

16. 52 passengers per bus

17. $10 for 8 gallons of gas

18. 5 hits in 8 times at bat

19. 7 games won out of 9 games played

20. $1.09 for 12 eggs

21. 200 seats for 10 rows

22. $5.99 for 2 tapes

▶ Applications

23. Marcy got three hits in five times at bat. Write her ratio of hits to times at bat and three ratios equivalent to it. If she continues to hit this way, how many hits will she have after thirty times at bat? $\frac{3}{5}, \frac{6}{10}, \frac{9}{15}, \frac{12}{20}$; 18 hits

24. Ricardo took a 3-minute typing test. He typed 105 words. His are results shown here. Find the number of words he typed per minute. 35 words per minute

▶ Review (Lessons 2.4, 2.7, 2.8, 2.10)

Multiply.

25. 5.7×3
17.1

26. $\begin{array}{r} 36 \\ \times 15 \\ \hline 540 \end{array}$

27. 254×481
122,174

28. $\begin{array}{r} 0.83 \\ \times 1.6 \\ \hline 1.328 \end{array}$

29. $\begin{array}{r} 420 \\ \times 0.02 \\ \hline 8.40 \end{array}$

30. 9.11×0.32
2.9152

31. $\begin{array}{r} 3.57 \\ \times 12.5 \\ \hline 44.625 \end{array}$

32. 1.225×50
61.250

33. $\begin{array}{r} 683 \\ \times 475 \\ \hline 324,425 \end{array}$

34. 5.39×4.2
22.638

35. 8.54×9.7
82.838

36. $\begin{array}{r} 294 \\ \times 0.78 \\ \hline 229.32 \end{array}$

11.2 Finding Proportions

Marty usually charges $5 an hour to do odd jobs. After a bad snowstorm, one of the local merchants asked him to shovel the sidewalk around his store for $20. He finished the task in 3 hours. How did the money earned on this job compare with his usual fee?

Marty could compare ratios by using a **proportion,** a mathematical statement that two ratios are equivalent.

Examples

To tell whether a statement is a proportion, find the cross products.

A Tell whether the statement is a proportion. Use = or ≠.

$\frac{2}{7}$ ▨ $\frac{6}{21}$

$\frac{2}{7} \bowtie \frac{6}{21}$ Find the cross products.

$2 \times 21 = 42$
$7 \times 6 = 42$ ⟩ Cross products

$42 = 42$, so $\frac{2}{7} = \frac{6}{21}$.

The statement is **a proportion.**

B Tell whether the statement is a proportion. Use = or ≠.

$\frac{12}{5}$ ▨ $\frac{7}{3}$

$\frac{12}{5} \bowtie \frac{7}{3}$ Find the cross products.

$12 \cdot \times 3 = 36$
$5 \times 7 = 35$ ⟩ Cross products

$36 \neq 35$, so $\frac{12}{5} \neq \frac{7}{3}$.

The statement is **not a proportion.**

▶ Think and Discuss

1. Tell whether the statement is a proportion. $\frac{6}{3}$ ▨ $\frac{4}{2}$

2. Tell whether the statement is a proportion. $\frac{1}{3}$ ▨ $\frac{6}{2}$
   Explain how you found your answer.

3. One student claimed that $\frac{2}{3} = \frac{6}{4}$ is a proportion. Do you agree? Why?

4. Refer to the introduction to this lesson. Write the two ratios involved. Do they form a proportion?

5. Write a proportion using the numbers 1, 18, 6, and 3. Compare your answers with other students' answers. Is there more than one correct answer?

6. Some ratios, such as 40 miles per hour, are called rates. What are some other rates you have seen?

Exercises

Tell whether each statement is a proportion. Use = or ≠.
(See Example A.)

7. $\frac{1}{2}$ ▦ $\frac{4}{8}$ =   8. $\frac{2}{5}$ ▦ $\frac{4}{9}$ ≠   9. $\frac{1}{11}$ ▦ $\frac{3}{32}$ ≠   10. $\frac{4}{7}$ ▦ $\frac{3}{5}$ ≠

11. $\frac{7}{8}$ ▦ $\frac{21}{25}$ ≠   12. $\frac{1}{24}$ ▦ $\frac{3}{72}$ =   13. $\frac{3}{12}$ ▦ $\frac{12}{50}$ ≠   14. $\frac{6}{9}$ ▦ $\frac{8}{12}$ =

15. $\frac{5}{7}$ ▦ $\frac{15}{21}$ =   16. $\frac{4}{9}$ ▦ $\frac{8}{16}$ ≠   17. $\frac{7}{12}$ ▦ $\frac{13}{24}$ ≠   18. $\frac{9}{12}$ ▦ $\frac{15}{20}$ =

Tell whether each statement is a proportion. Use = or ≠.
(See Example B.)

19. $\frac{5}{2}$ ▦ $\frac{3}{1}$ ≠   20. $\frac{7}{4}$ ▦ $\frac{21}{12}$ =   21. $\frac{13}{2}$ ▦ $\frac{17}{3}$ ≠   22. $\frac{14}{6}$ ▦ $\frac{7}{3}$ =

23. $\frac{8}{5}$ ▦ $\frac{12}{9}$ ≠   24. $\frac{20}{3}$ ▦ $\frac{60}{9}$ =   25. $\frac{15}{4}$ ▦ $\frac{50}{16}$ ≠   26. $\frac{100}{7}$ ▦ $\frac{700}{56}$ ≠

27. $\frac{19}{2}$ ▦ $\frac{95}{10}$ =   28. $\frac{37}{6}$ ▦ $\frac{187}{30}$ ≠   29. $\frac{52}{8}$ ▦ $\frac{416}{64}$ =   30. $\frac{125}{4}$ ▦ $\frac{350}{12}$ ≠

▶ Mixed Practice (For more practice, see page 434.)

Tell whether each statement is a proportion. Use = or ≠.

31. $\frac{6}{11}$ ▦ $\frac{18}{38}$ ≠   32. $\frac{8}{2}$ ▦ $\frac{20}{5}$ =   33. $\frac{4}{3}$ ▦ $\frac{60}{45}$ =   34. $\frac{12}{15}$ ▦ $\frac{20}{25}$ =

35. $\frac{20}{9}$ ▦ $\frac{100}{45}$ =   36. $\frac{10}{15}$ ▦ $\frac{12}{16}$ ≠   37. $\frac{47}{50}$ ▦ $\frac{107}{120}$ ≠   38. $\frac{12}{7}$ ▦ $\frac{84}{49}$ =

39. $\frac{89}{100}$ ▦ $\frac{44}{50}$ ≠   40. $\frac{90}{5}$ ▦ $\frac{36}{2}$ =   41. $\frac{168}{171}$ ▦ $\frac{56}{57}$ =   42. $\frac{120}{7}$ ▦ $\frac{1200}{77}$ ≠

▶ Applications

43. Mati did 12 sit-ups in 15 seconds one day. Another day she did 36 sit-ups in 45 seconds. Are her rates the same? Yes

44. Alice swam fifteen laps in ten minutes. Then she swam twenty laps in fifteen minutes. Are her rates the same? No

▶ Review (Lesson 5.6)

Rewrite each fraction in lowest terms.

45. $\frac{18}{2}$ $\frac{9}{1}$ 46. $\frac{5}{7}$ $\frac{5}{7}$ 47. $\frac{24}{13}$ $\frac{24}{13}$ 48. $\frac{4}{12}$ $\frac{1}{3}$ 49. $\frac{42}{14}$ $\frac{3}{1}$

▶ Think and Discuss Answers

1. yes
2. no; the cross products are (1 × 2 and 3 × 6) and 2 ≠ 18
3. no; because the cross products (2 × 4 and 3 × 6) are not equal
4. $\frac{5}{1}$ and $\frac{20}{3}$; no
5. Sample answers include: $\frac{1}{6} = \frac{3}{18}$, $\frac{1}{3} = \frac{6}{18}$, $\frac{3}{1} = \frac{18}{6}$, and $\frac{6}{1} = \frac{18}{3}$; yes
6. Sample answers include: miles per gallon; words per minute; and meters per second.

★ Error Alert

Incorrect answers may reveal that students are not cross multiplying, but are multiplying numerator by numerator and denominator by denominator.

Reinforcement

Extra Practice, page 434
EP/MR Worksheet 84, TRB, page 84

Challenge

One week Matt drove at the following rates:
Monday: 255 miles in 5 hours
Tuesday: 371 miles in 7 hours
Wednesday: $331\frac{1}{2}$ miles in 6 hours
Thursday: $487\frac{1}{4}$ miles in $9\frac{1}{4}$ hours
Friday: $514\frac{1}{4}$ miles in $10\frac{1}{2}$ hours
Determine the average rate per day to the nearest mile per hour. Which days are the same? (answer: 51 mph, 53 mph, 55 mph, 53 mph, 49 mph; Tuesday and Thursday are the same)

Purpose

This lesson shows you how to solve proportions. This is a way you can determine, for example, the cost of five items that sell at the rate of three for $1.99.

Introducing the Lesson

Review finding proportions (Lesson 11.2). Use the examples: Tell whether the statement is a proportion (use = or ≠)— $\frac{12}{7}(\;=\;)\frac{36}{21}, \frac{4}{3}(\;=\;)\frac{84}{63}, \frac{6}{11}(\;\neq\;)\frac{36}{55}, \frac{7}{13}(\;=\;)\frac{28}{52}$. Display an empty bottle of children's pain reliever, and a container of yogurt. Assist students in listing the ratios used in each. (medicine—dosage to child's weight or age; yogurt—number of calories per serving). Tell students that this lesson shows them how to increase or decrease amounts expressed by any of these ratios at the same rate—or proportionally.

Alternative Examples

Example A—Solve the proportion.
$\frac{\blacksquare}{5} = \frac{171}{45}$
$\frac{\blacksquare}{5} \boxtimes \frac{171}{45}$ *Find the cross products.*
Cross products are $\underline{\blacksquare} \times 45$ and 855.
Set the cross products equal.
$\underline{\blacksquare} \times 45 = 855$
Divide both sides by 45.
$\underline{\blacksquare} \times 45 \div 45 = 855 \div 45$
$\underline{\blacksquare} = \mathbf{19}$

Example B—Solve the proportion.
$\frac{3}{8} = \frac{\blacksquare}{7}$
$\frac{3}{8} \boxtimes \frac{\blacksquare}{7}$ *Find the cross products.*
Cross products are 21 and $8 \times \underline{\blacksquare}$.
Set the cross products equal.
$8 \times \underline{\blacksquare} = 21$
Divide both sides by 8.
$8 \times \underline{\blacksquare} \div 8 = 21 \div 8$
$\underline{\blacksquare} = \frac{21}{8}$, **or** $2\frac{5}{8}$

11.3 Solving Proportions

The art teacher wants to use Wesley's cartoon in the school paper. He asks Wesley to reduce the cartoon so that it is 6 inches tall.

How wide will the reduced cartoon be? You can use a proportion to find the width: $\frac{\blacksquare}{6} = \frac{10}{15}$.

Examples

To solve proportions, first find the cross products. Then set the cross products equal. Use division to solve.

A Solve the proportion. $\frac{\blacksquare}{6} = \frac{10}{15}$

$\frac{\blacksquare}{6} \boxtimes \frac{10}{15}$ Cross products are $\underline{\blacksquare} \times 15$ and 60.

$\underline{\blacksquare} \times 15 = 60$ Set the cross products equal.
$\underline{\blacksquare} \times 15 \div 15 = 60 \div 15$ Divide both sides by 15.
$\underline{\blacksquare} = 4$

B Solve the proportion. $\frac{3}{7} = \frac{\blacksquare}{10}$

$\frac{3}{7} \boxtimes \frac{\blacksquare}{10}$ Cross products are 30 and $7 \times \underline{\blacksquare}$.

$7 \times \underline{\blacksquare} = 30$ Set the cross products equal.
$7 \times \underline{\blacksquare} \div 7 = 30 \div 7$ Divide both sides by 7.
$\underline{\blacksquare} = \frac{30}{7}$, or $4\frac{2}{7}$

▶ **Think and Discuss**

1. Explain why $16 \times 3{,}147{,}878 \div 3{,}147{,}878 = 16$.

2. Solve the proportion $\frac{4}{9} = \frac{\blacksquare}{36}$.

3. Solve the proportion $\frac{1}{2} = \frac{\blacksquare}{6}$ mentally.

4. Write three different proportions involving $\frac{6}{7}$.

5. Can you solve the proportion $\frac{0}{3} = \frac{0}{\blacksquare}$? Explain.

6. When you have solved a proportion, how can you check to see that your answer is correct?

7. Refer to the introduction to this lesson. How wide will Wesley's cartoon be?

▶ Think and Discuss Answers

1. Multiplying a number and then dividing by the same number has no effect on the original number.

2. 16

3. 3

4. Sample answers include: $\frac{6}{7} = \frac{12}{14}, \frac{18}{21}, \frac{24}{28}$.

5. yes; any number will work because the cross products are both 0 no matter what number is put in the box

6. Substitute the answer into the original problem and see if the ratios are equal.

7. 4 inches

Exercises

Solve each proportion. (See Example A.)

8. $\frac{\blacksquare}{8} = \frac{9}{12}$ 6

9. $\frac{\blacksquare}{10} = \frac{4}{5}$ 8

10. $\frac{\blacksquare}{16} = \frac{15}{24}$ 10

11. $\frac{\blacksquare}{18} = \frac{20}{45}$ 8

12. $\frac{\blacksquare}{20} = \frac{21}{14}$ 30

13. $\frac{18}{\blacksquare} = \frac{12}{9}$ $13\frac{1}{2}$

14. $\frac{24}{\blacksquare} = \frac{8}{3}$ 9

15. $\frac{78}{\blacksquare} = \frac{18}{12}$ 52

16. $\frac{40}{\blacksquare} = \frac{12}{21}$ 70

17. $\frac{\blacksquare}{12} = \frac{7}{5}$ $16\frac{4}{5}$

Solve each proportion. (See Example B.)

18. $\frac{10}{15} = \frac{\blacksquare}{6}$ 4

19. $\frac{15}{3} = \frac{\blacksquare}{1}$ 5

20. $\frac{13}{39} = \frac{\blacksquare}{12}$ 4

21. $\frac{28}{4} = \frac{\blacksquare}{15}$ 105

22. $\frac{9}{4} = \frac{36}{\blacksquare}$ 16

23. $\frac{15}{8} = \frac{60}{\blacksquare}$ 32

24. $\frac{15}{4} = \frac{75}{\blacksquare}$ 20

25. $\frac{4}{6} = \frac{57}{\blacksquare}$ $85\frac{1}{2}$

▶ Mixed Practice (For more practice, see page 435.)

Solve each proportion.

26. $\frac{\blacksquare}{11} = \frac{12}{132}$ 1

27. $\frac{\blacksquare}{9} = \frac{12}{27}$ 4

28. $\frac{13}{10} = \frac{52}{\blacksquare}$ 40

29. $\frac{15}{9} = \frac{55}{\blacksquare}$ 33

30. $\frac{18}{27} = \frac{\blacksquare}{9}$ 6

31. $\frac{14}{\blacksquare} = \frac{3}{20}$ $93\frac{1}{3}$

32. $\frac{12}{5} = \frac{30}{\blacksquare}$ $12\frac{1}{2}$

33. $\frac{\blacksquare}{21} = \frac{8}{12}$ 14

34. $\frac{53}{100} = \frac{\blacksquare}{600}$ 318

35. $\frac{\blacksquare}{12} = \frac{5}{20}$ 3

36. $\frac{41}{5} = \frac{369}{\blacksquare}$ 45

37. $\frac{7}{16} = \frac{\blacksquare}{192}$ 84

▶ Applications

38. Jerome drove an average of fifty-two miles per hour on a trip. About how many miles did he go in three hours of nonstop driving? 156 mi.

39. Ruth missed 12 problems on a 75-question test. If each problem was worth the same amount, how many points did she earn out of 100 points? 84 points

▶ Review (Lessons 1.7, 1.8)

Round to the nearest tenth.

40. 4.871 4.9

41. 0.135 0.1

42. 2.092 2.1

43. 19.9842 20.0

44. 25.64 25.6

Round to the nearest hundred.

45. 1879 1900

46. 58 100

47. 44,326 44,300

48. 27,647 27,600

49. 39,961 40,000

★ Error Alert

Errors may indicate that students are not dividing both sides by the same number or that they are cross multiplying incorrectly.

Reinforcement

Extra Practice, page 435
EP/MR Worksheet 85, TRB, page 85

Puzzle

A proportion can be used to change one unit of measure to another. For example, you can change $2\frac{1}{2}$ feet to inches. You know that one foot equals 12 inches; write this as the ratio $\frac{1\,\text{ft.}}{12\,\text{in.}}$. Now write the proportion $\frac{1\,\text{ft.}}{12\,\text{in.}} = \frac{2\frac{1}{2}\,\text{ft.}}{\blacksquare\,\text{in.}}$ and solve. Since $\blacksquare = 30$, $2\frac{1}{2}$ ft. = 30 in. Use a proportion to change each amount from one unit of measure to the other. Write your answers in the puzzle.

Across	Down
1. $7\frac{1}{3}$ ft. to in.	1. 8.75 m to cm
4. $24\frac{2}{3}$ yd. to ft.	2. $3\frac{1}{2}$ days to hr.
6. .873 kg to g	3. $3\frac{1}{2}$ gal. to qt.
7. $13\frac{1}{2}$ yr. to mo.	5. $10\frac{3}{4}$ lb. to oz.
	6. $21\frac{1}{2}$ qt. to cups

1. (8)	**2.** (8)		**3.** (1)
4. (7)	(4)		(4)
(5)		**5.** (1)	
	6. (8)	(7)	(3)
7. (1)	(6)	(2)	

- To find the unit price of an item
- To determine the better buy using unit prices

Purpose

This lesson shows you how to determine unit prices. This will help you do comparison shopping by finding, for example, the unit price of an individual can of a soft drink and comparing it to the price of a 6-pack that costs $2.49.

Introducing the Lesson

If necessary, review solving proportions (Lesson 11.3). Use the examples: Solve the proportions— $\frac{\blacksquare}{47} = \frac{15}{141}, \frac{13}{52} = \frac{3}{\blacksquare}$. (5, 12) Assist students in making a list on the chalkboard of items they purchase that are sold in various units. (Sample answers include: cereal; snack foods; laundry soap; socks.) Ask: What do you look for when looking for the better buy of something? (Sample answers include: lowest cost; good quality.) Explain that in this lesson they will learn how to evaluate items by finding the unit price to help them comparison shop.

Alternative Examples

Example A—Find the unit price of a 64 oz. bottle of ketchup which costs $1.94.
$\frac{\$1.94}{64 \text{ oz.}} = \frac{\blacksquare}{1 \text{ oz.}}; 64 \times \underline{\quad} = 1.94 \times 1$
$64 \times \underline{\quad} \div 64 = 1.94 \div 64$
$\underline{\quad} \approx \$0.0303$, or $0.03 rounded to the nearest cent.
The unit price of the ketchup is **$0.03 per ounce.**

Example B—Determine the better buy: $2.99 for 6 cans of soft drinks or $6.99 for a 12-can carton of soft drinks.
$\frac{\$2.99}{6 \text{ cans}} = \frac{\blacksquare}{1 \text{ can}}$ $\frac{\$6.99}{12 \text{ cans}} = \frac{\blacksquare}{1 \text{ can}}$
$\underline{\quad} = \frac{\$2.99}{6}$ $\underline{\quad} = \frac{6.99}{12}$
$\underline{\quad} \approx \$0.4983$ $\underline{\quad} = \$0.5825$
or $0.50   or $0.58
per can   per can

6 cans for $2.99 is the better buy.

11.4 Unit Pricing

Tamara wanted to try a new type of shampoo. She selected the brand shown here. Which bottle is the better value?

$1.98
8 oz.

$2.75
12 oz.

Unit pricing is a way to compare values. The **unit price** tells you how much a product costs for a given unit. The unit could be an ounce, a pound, a gallon, a quart, or some other unit.

Examples

To find the unit price of an item, first identify the appropriate unit. Then set up a proportion and solve.

$$\frac{\text{Price paid}}{\text{Quantity bought in units}} = \frac{\text{Unit price}}{\text{Unit}}$$

A Find the unit price of the smaller bottle of shampoo.

$\frac{\$1.98}{8 \text{ oz.}} = \frac{\blacksquare}{1 \text{ oz.}}$ Let the unit be an ounce. Set up the proportion.

$8 \times \blacksquare = 1.98 \times 1$

$8 \times \blacksquare \div 8 = 1.98 \div 8$

$\blacksquare = \$0.2475$, or $0.25 rounded to the nearest cent.

The unit price is **$0.25 per ounce**.

B Determine the better buy: **$9 for 6 tape rentals or $8 for 5 tape rentals.**

The appropriate unit is 1 rental.

$\frac{\blacksquare}{1 \text{ rental}} = \frac{\$9}{6 \text{ rentals}}$ $\frac{\blacksquare}{1 \text{ rental}} = \frac{\$8}{5 \text{ rentals}}$

$\underline{\quad} = \frac{9}{6}$ $\underline{\quad} = \frac{8}{5}$

$\underline{\quad} = \$1.50 \text{ per tape rental}$ $\underline{\quad} = \$1.60 \text{ per tape rental}$

Since its unit price is less, **$9 for 6 tape rentals is the better buy.**

▶ **Think and Discuss**

1. Solve the proportion. $\frac{3}{4} = \frac{\blacksquare}{1}$

2. Find the unit price if 10 pens cost $19.99. Solve mentally.

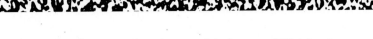
3. Refer to the introduction to this lesson. Which size bottle is the better buy?

4. Is buying a larger quantity at a lower unit price always the better buy? Explain your answer.

5. When could you use unit pricing? Discuss.

Exercises

Find the unit price. (See Example A.)

6. $3.75 for 4 light bulbs $0.94

7. $3 for 30 trash bags $0.10

8. $2 for 24 oz. of BBQ sauce $0.08

9. $1.99 for 20 pencils $0.10

10. $5 for 12 cans of soda $0.42

11. $1.50 for 200 sheets of paper $0.0075

Determine the better buy. (See Example B.)

12. $9.54 for 6 power bars or $8.25 for 5 power bars

13. $7.12 for 4 batteries or $5.70 for 3 batteries

14. $2.20 for 12 prints or $6 for 36 prints

▶ Mixed Practice (For more practice, see page 435.)

Find the better buy.

15. $4 for 2 pairs of socks or $3.50 for a pair of socks

16. $0.89 for a quart of milk or $3.16 for a gallon of milk

17. $1.08 for a dozen eggs or $1.71 for 18 eggs

18. $1.26 for an 18-ounce bottle of soy sauce or $2.08 for a 32-ounce bottle of soy sauce

▶ Applications

19. Which pack of film shown is the better buy? 3-pack of 24 prints

20. Mr. Blaine buys a woodworking magazine every month for $2.25. A one-year subscription to the magazine costs $19.20. How much would he save each month by subscribing? $0.65

▶ Review (Lessons 2.3, 2.7)

Multiply mentally.

21. 60 × 700
42,000

22. 8.4 × 1000
8400

23. 90 × 9000
810,000

24. 500 × 500
250,000

25. 0.053 × 100
5.3

26. 10 × 0.967
9.67

27. 100 × 4.486
448.6

28. 6000 × 400
2,400,000

▶ **Think and Discuss Answers**
1. 0.75
2. $2.00 (rounded to the nearest cent)
3. 12-ounce bottle for $2.75
4. no, because if you won't use the whole amount or the product spoils before you can use all of it, the larger quantity at a lower price may not be the better buy
5. Sample answers include: buying an item that is sold in different quantities; comparing the values of sale items.

★ **Error Alert**
Incorrect answers may reveal that students are dividing incorrectly.

Reinforcement
Extra Practice, page 435
EP/MR Worksheet 86, TRB, page 86

Challenge
Determine the unit price (to the nearest cent) of each of the following bottles of mouthwash. Which is the best buy?

Size and Price	Answer
4 fl. oz. for $2.54	(64¢)
6 fl. oz. for $1.49	(25¢)
8 fl. oz. for $1.99	(25¢)
12 fl. oz. for $2.19	(18¢)
18 fl. oz. for $2.93	(16¢)
24 fl. oz. for $3.17	(13¢)
32 fl. oz. for $4.49	(14¢)

(Since its unit price is less, 24 fluid ounces for $3.17 is the best buy.)

T249

Objectives

- To find actual lengths from information about scale drawings
- To find scale lengths on scale drawings

Purpose

Being able to use scale drawings allows you to find actual distances and lengths from maps, floor plans, and other diagrams that use scales. For example, you can find the actual length of a room that is 2 inches long on a drawing if you know that in the drawing $\frac{1}{2}$ inch = 3 feet.

Introducing the Lesson

Review solving proportions (Lesson 11.3). Use the examples: Solve the proportions—$\frac{1}{2} = \frac{5}{\blacksquare}$; $\frac{4}{5} = \frac{6}{\blacksquare}$. (10; $7\frac{1}{2}$)

$\frac{20}{\blacksquare} = \frac{10}{1}$ ($\blacksquare = 2$)

$\frac{\blacksquare}{2} = \frac{7\frac{1}{2}}{1}$ ($\blacksquare = 15$)

$\frac{\frac{1}{2}}{4} = \frac{6}{\blacksquare}$ ($\blacksquare = 48$)

$\frac{\blacksquare}{2} = \frac{2}{16}$ ($\blacksquare = \frac{1}{4}$)

Display a map in the classroom. Locate the scale and copy it on the chalkboard. Tell students that in this lesson they will learn how to work with scale drawings. Elicit from students other examples of scale drawings they may be familiar with.

Alternative Examples

Copy the two diagrams shown below on the chalkboard.
Example A—Find the actual length of side b in the figure below.

scale: $\frac{1}{4} = 7$ yd.

$\frac{\frac{1}{4} \text{ in.}}{7 \text{ yd.}} = \frac{2 \text{ in.}}{\blacksquare}$

$\frac{1}{4} \times \blacksquare = 7 \times 2$

$\blacksquare = 14 \div \frac{1}{4}$

$\blacksquare = 56$

The actual length of side b is **56 yards.**

11.5 Using Scale Drawings

A *fashion designer uses scale drawings like the one shown to illustrate dress designs. The designer then works from scale drawings to make the designs into actual-size clothing. Proportions are used when working with scale drawings.*

Examples

To find lengths from scale drawings, set up and solve proportions.

A Find the actual length of side b.

scale: $\frac{1}{2}$ in. = 4 ft.

$\frac{\frac{1}{2} \text{ in.}}{4 \text{ ft.}} = \frac{1\frac{1}{4} \text{ in.}}{\blacksquare}$

$\frac{1}{2} \times \blacksquare = 4 \times 1\frac{1}{4}$

$\frac{1}{2} \times \blacksquare \div \frac{1}{2} = 5 \div \frac{1}{2}$

$\blacksquare = 10$

$b = 1\frac{1}{4}$ in.

The actual length of side b is **10 feet**.

B Find the scale length for side f.

scale: $\frac{1}{4}$ in. = 8 ft.

actual length of $f = 56$ ft.

$\frac{\frac{1}{4} \text{ in.}}{8 \text{ ft.}} = \frac{\blacksquare}{56 \text{ ft.}}$

$8 \times \blacksquare = \frac{1}{4} \times 56$

$8 \times \blacksquare \div 8 = 14 \div 8$

$\blacksquare = \frac{14}{8}$ or $1\frac{3}{4}$

f

The scale length for side f is $1\frac{3}{4}$ **inches**.

▶ **Think and Discuss**

1. Solve. $\frac{5}{8} = \frac{10}{\blacksquare}$

2. Solve. $\frac{1}{2} \div 6 = \frac{\blacksquare}{3}$

3. Find the actual length of a side if its scale length is 2 inches.
   scale: $\frac{1}{8}$ in. = 3 ft.

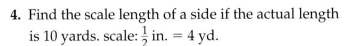

SKILLS

4. Find the scale length of a side if the actual length is 10 yards. scale: $\frac{1}{2}$ in. = 4 yd.

5. Name some other professions that might use scale drawings. How are scale drawings helpful?

Exercises

Find the actual length for each scale length given.
(See Example A.)

6. 3 in. scale: 1 in. = 25 mi. 75 mi.

7. $1\frac{1}{4}$ in. scale: $\frac{1}{4}$ in. = 12 ft. 60 ft.

8. $5\frac{1}{2}$ in. scale: $\frac{1}{2}$ in. = 5 yd. 55 yd.

9. $\frac{3}{4}$ in. scale: $\frac{1}{2}$ in. = 2 ft. 3 ft.

Find the scale length for each actual length given.
(See Example B.)

10. 45 ft. scale: 1 in. = 12 ft. $3\frac{3}{4}$ in.

11. 120 mi. scale: 1 in. = 24 mi. 5 in.

12. 75 yd. scale: $\frac{1}{2}$ in. = 15 yd. $2\frac{1}{2}$ in.

13. $6\frac{1}{2}$ ft. scale: $\frac{1}{2}$ in. = 1 ft. $3\frac{1}{4}$ in.

▶ **Mixed Practice** (For more practice, see page 436.)

Find the unknown length.

14. scale length = $3\frac{1}{2}$ in.
    scale: $\frac{1}{4}$ in. = 9 ft. Actual length = 126 ft.

15. actual length = 90 ft.
    scale: 1 in. = 12 ft.
    Scale length = $7\frac{1}{2}$ in.

16. actual length = 144 mi.
    scale: $\frac{3}{4}$ in. = 12 mi. Scale length 9 in.

17. scale length = 9 in.
    scale: $\frac{1}{2}$ in. = 5 ft.
    Actual length = 90 ft.

18. scale length = $4\frac{1}{4}$ in.
    scale: $\frac{1}{2}$ in. = 5 mi. Actual length $42\frac{1}{2}$ mi.

19. actual length = 100 yd.
    scale: $\frac{3}{4}$ in. = 15 yd.
    Scale length = 5 in.

▶ **Applications**

20. The actual dimensions of a stage are twelve feet by twenty feet. Using a scale of three inches equals two feet, what will be the dimensions of a scale drawing of the stage? 18 in. × 30 in.

21. Melanie starts a trip with a full tank of gas. Her car gets 375 miles to a tank of gas. On the map, her trip covers $3\frac{3}{4}$ inches. Does she have enough gas?
    Yes

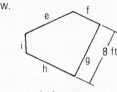

▶ **Review** (Lesson 3.9)

Simplify.

22. $105 \div 5 \times 4$
    84

23. $(8 + 4) \times 8 + 11$
    107

24. $50 - 7 \times 4 + 16$
    38

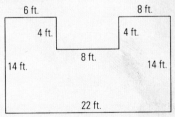

Alternative Examples (continued)

Example B—Find the scale length for side g in the figure below.
scale: 2 in. = 3 ft.
$\frac{2 \text{ in.}}{3 \text{ ft.}} = \frac{\blacksquare}{8 \text{ ft.}}$
$2 \times 8 = 3 \times \blacksquare$
$16 \div 3 = \blacksquare$
$5\frac{1}{3} = \blacksquare$

The scale length for side g is **$5\frac{1}{3}$ inches.**

▶ **Think and Discuss Answers**

1. 16
2. $\frac{1}{4}$
3. 48 ft.
4. $1\frac{1}{4}$ in.
5. sample answers include: architects; real estate agents; sculptors; map makers.

★ **Error Alert**

Mistakes may reveal that students are setting up proportions incorrectly.

Reinforcement
Extra Practice, page 436
EP/MR Worksheet 87, TRB, page 87

Teaching Aids
Quarter-inch grid
TA 7, TBR, page 160
Teaching suggestions precede the Teaching Aids worksheets.

Project
Note to the teacher: Copy the figure below on the chalkboard.

Draw this figure to scale using the measurements and a scale of $\frac{1}{2}$ in. = 2 ft. (dimensions of scale drawing: 6 ft. side should be $1\frac{1}{2}$ in.; 4 ft. sides should be 1 in.; 8 ft. sides should be 2 in.; 14 ft. sides should be $3\frac{1}{2}$ in.; 22 ft. side should be $5\frac{1}{2}$ in.)

T251

Objective

- To interpret and make scale drawings

Purpose

This lesson shows you how to use a scale drawing in planning a house. You will determine the actual size of a room from a drawing and make a drawing to show how several pieces of furniture can be arranged in one room.

Introducing the Lesson

Review using scale drawings (Lesson 11.5). Use the example: Find the actual length of side b.

scale: $\frac{1}{2}$ in. = 10 ft.

Side b is drawn as $3\frac{1}{2}$ inches.

$\left(\frac{\frac{1}{2} \text{ in.}}{10 \text{ ft.}} = \frac{3\frac{1}{2} \text{ in.}}{\blacksquare} \right)$

(The actual length of side b is 70 feet.)

11.6 Planning a House

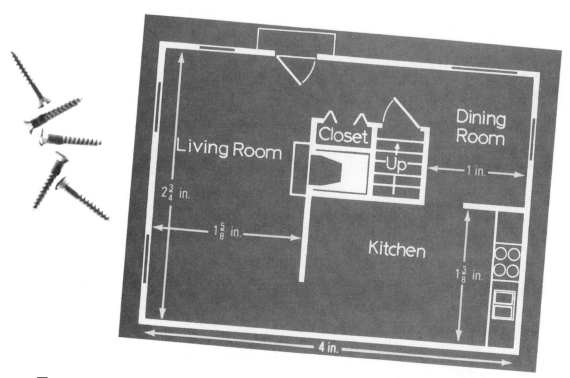

The Brandjords used the drawing shown here to get an idea of the amount of space they might have when their new house is built. According to the architect, 1 inch represents 10 feet.

If the depth of a closet measures $\frac{3}{8}$ inch on the diagram, how deep will the actual closet be?

To find the actual depth of the closet, set up a proportion.

$$\frac{\text{Drawing in inches}}{\text{Actual size in feet}} \; \begin{array}{c} \rightarrow \\ \rightarrow \end{array} \; \frac{1}{10} = \frac{\frac{3}{8}}{\blacksquare} \; \begin{array}{c} \leftarrow \\ \leftarrow \end{array} \; \frac{\text{Closet (drawing)}}{\text{Closet (actual size)}}$$

$1 \times \blacksquare = 10 \times \frac{3}{8}$ Find cross products.

$1 \times \blacksquare \div 1 = \frac{30}{8} \div 1$

$\blacksquare = \frac{30}{8} = \frac{15}{4} = 3\frac{3}{4}$ **feet, or 45 inches**

Refer to the introduction to this lesson.

1. What is the actual width (the shorter dimension) of the dining room in feet? 10 ft.

2. What is the actual width of the kitchen in feet? $13\frac{3}{4}$ ft.

3. What is the actual length of the living room in feet? $27\frac{1}{2}$ ft.

4. If the living room, from one corner diagonally to another, measures about $3\frac{1}{4}$ inches on the drawing, what proportion would you use to find the actual measurement in feet? $\frac{1}{10} = \frac{3\frac{1}{4}}{\blacksquare}$

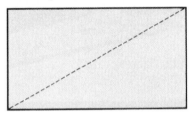

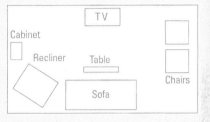

5. Find the actual measure of the diagonal of the living room. $32\frac{1}{4}$ ft.

6. If the diagonal of the kitchen measures $2\frac{5}{8}$ inches on the drawing, what is the actual measurement in feet? $26\frac{1}{4}$ ft.

7. Will a 91-inch couch fit in the living room? yes

8. A kitchen wall that is $1\frac{1}{4}$ inches long on the drawing is to be covered with cabinets 18 inches wide. How many cabinets will fit across? 8 cabinets

The Brandjords would like to use the following furniture in their living room: an 88-inch sofa that is 36 inches deep, two chairs each 32 inches wide and 34 inches deep, a table that is 42 inches wide and $11\frac{1}{4}$ inches deep, a recliner that is $41\frac{1}{2}$ inches wide and 39 inches deep, a cabinet that is 25 inches wide and 13 inches deep, and a television set that is 43 inches wide and 22 inches deep.

9. Make a scale drawing of each piece of furniture and the living room. Show a possible arrangement of the furniture.

▶ **Review** (Lesson 8.9)

Copy and complete the table below.

	Starting Time	Finishing Time	Elapsed Time	
10.	6:15 p.m.	12:01 a.m.	_____	5 hours, 46 minutes
11.	▨	9:25 a.m.	15 hours	6:25 p.m.
12.	11:47 a.m.	_____	6 hours, 35 minutes	6:22 p.m.

Answers

9. The living room should be 2 inches by $1\frac{1}{8}$ inches. The furniture would have the following approximate measurements:
sofa, 0.73 in. ($\frac{3}{4}$ in.) by 0.30 in. ($\frac{5}{16}$ in.);
chairs, 0.27 in. ($\frac{1}{4}$ in.) by 0.28 in. ($\frac{1}{4}$ in.);
table 0.35 in. ($\frac{3}{8}$ in.) by 0.09 in. ($\frac{1}{16}$ in.);
recliner, 0.35 in. ($\frac{3}{16}$ in.) by 0.335 in. ($\frac{5}{16}$ in.);
cabinet, 0.21 in. ($\frac{3}{16}$ in.) by 0.11 in. ($\frac{1}{8}$ in.);
and TV, 0.36 in. ($\frac{3}{8}$ in.) by 0.18 in. ($\frac{3}{16}$ in.).
A possible arrangement is given below.

Cabinet		TV
Recliner	Table	
	Sofa	Chairs

★ **Error Alert**

Errors may occur if students set up the proportions incorrectly.

Reinforcement

EP/MR Worksheet 88, TRB, page 88

Teaching Aids

Quarter-inch grid
TA 7, TRB, page 160
Teaching suggestions precede the Teaching Aids worksheets.

Project

Make a scale drawing of a floor plan of a house with the room dimensions listed below.
scale: 1 inch = 12 feet
The actual dimensions are:
Kitchen: 12 ft. × 26 ft. (1 in. × $2\frac{1}{6}$ in.)
Hall: 3 ft. × 14 ft. ($\frac{1}{4}$ in. × $1\frac{1}{6}$ in.)
Living room: 21 ft. × 14 ft. ($1\frac{3}{4}$ in. × $1\frac{1}{6}$ in.)
Dining room: 14 ft. × 9 ft. ($1\frac{1}{6}$ × $\frac{3}{4}$ in.)
Deck: 12 ft. × 9 ft. (1 in. × $\frac{3}{4}$ in.)
Each door is 3 ft. wide. ($\frac{1}{4}$ in.)

T253

11.7 Using Similar Figures

Marius wants to enlarge a picture to fit the frame shown here. He brought the picture and the negative to a photo processor and told the clerk the dimensions of the frame.

$2\frac{1}{2}$ in.

$3\frac{1}{2}$ in.

7 in.

5 in.

The photo and the frame are **similar figures**. Their corresponding dimensions form the proportion $2\frac{1}{2} : 3\frac{1}{2} = 5 : 7$.

Examples

To find unknown lengths for similar figures, set up and solve a proportion.

Find the length of the unknown side for these similar triangles.

$\frac{3 \text{ in.}}{4 \text{ in.}} = \frac{7 \text{ in.}}{\blacksquare}$

$3 \times \blacksquare = 4 \times 7$

$3 \times \blacksquare \div 3 = 28 \div 3$

$\blacksquare = \frac{28}{3}, \text{ or } 9\frac{1}{3}$

3 in.

5 in.

4 in.

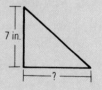

7 in.

?

The length of the unknown side is **$9\frac{1}{3}$ inches.**

▶ Think and Discuss

1. Refer to the introduction to this lesson. Could the photo be enlarged to fit a 9 × 12 frame? Explain.

2. The pentagons shown to the right are similar. Find the length of the unknown side.

3. One rectangle measures 12 inches by 15 inches. Is it similar to a 4-inch by 5-inch rectangle?

4. Are all squares similar? Explain your answer.

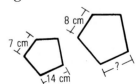

8 cm

7 cm

14 cm

?

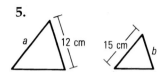

Exercises

(For more practice, see page 436.)

Each pair of polygons is similar. Find the length of the unknown sides.

5.

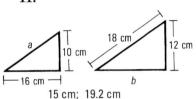

a   12 cm   15 cm   b

16 cm   10 cm

24 cm; 7.5cm

6.

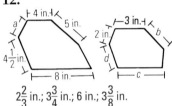

22 cm   a   b   18 cm
9 cm   c
15 cm   20 cm

16.5 cm; 13.5 cm; 12 cm

7.

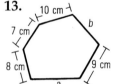

3 in.   5 in.
2 in.   3 in.
7 in.   a   b
6 in.   e   c
4 in.   d

$4\frac{1}{2}$ in.; $7\frac{1}{2}$ in.; $10\frac{1}{2}$ in.; 6 in.; 9 in.

8. Rectangles
$w = 2$ in.; $l = 7$ in.
$w = 5$ in.; $l = $ ___
$l = 17\frac{1}{2}$ in.

9. Rectangles
$w = 7$ cm; $l = $ ___
$w = 25.2$ cm; $l = 32.4$ cm
$l = 9$ cm

10. Rectangles
$w = 5\frac{1}{4}$ in.; $l = 6\frac{1}{2}$ in.
$w = $ ___ in.; $l = 13$
$w = 10\frac{1}{2}$ in

11.

a   18 cm   12 cm
10 cm
16 cm   b

15 cm; 19.2 cm

12.

4 in.   5 in.
a   3 in.   b
2 in.
$4\frac{1}{2}$ in.   d
8 in.   c

$2\frac{2}{3}$ in.; $3\frac{3}{4}$ in.; 6 in.; $3\frac{3}{8}$ in.

13.

10 cm   b
7 cm
8 cm   c   9 cm   d
a

4 cm   6 cm
e
8 cm

20 cm; 15 cm; 2.8 cm;
3.2 cm; 3.6 cm

14. Rectangles
$w = 5$ in.; $l = 6$ in.
$w = $ ___ ; $l = 18$ in.
$w = 15$ in.

15. Rectangles
$w = $ ___ ; $l = 4$ m
$w = 19.5$ cm; $l = 3$ cm
$w = 26$ cm

16. Rectangles
$w = 20$ in.; $l = $ ___
$w = 12\frac{1}{2}$ in.; $l = 10$ in.
$l = 16$ in.

▶ Applications

17. Kevin wanted to enlarge a six-inch by four-inch picture to fit a fourteen-inch by ten-inch frame. Is this possible? Explain.
No; a proportion is not formed

18. Mandisa made a kite like the one shown. Her next kite had dimensions $1\frac{1}{2}$ times as large. What were the second kite's dimensions? $27\frac{3}{4}$ in.; $39\frac{3}{4}$ in.

$18\frac{1}{2}$ in.

$26\frac{1}{2}$ in.

▶ Review (Lesson 10.4)

Find the mean of each set of numbers.

19. 32   25   10   41   27

20. 121   115   136   128   125

21. 92   88   79   95   86   88

▶Think and Discuss Answers

1. no, because their corresponding dimensions do not form a proportion:
$\frac{2\frac{1}{2}}{3\frac{1}{2}} \neq \frac{9}{12}$

2. 16 cm

3. yes

4. yes, because the ratio of the length to the width of any square is $\frac{1}{1}$

★ Error Alert

Mistakes may reveal that students are incorrectly determining which side of one figure is the corresponding side of the similar side of the other figure.

Reinforcement
Extra Practice, page 436
EP/MR Worksheet 89, TRB, page 89

Challenge
Note to the Teacher: Copy the figures shown below on the chalkboard.

3   5
4   4
3   2   2

a   g
b   f
c   d   e

The figures are similar. If $a = 1$, find the value of $b, c, d, e, f,$ and g by setting up and solving proportions. ($b = \frac{4}{3}, c = 1, d = \frac{2}{3},$ $e = \frac{2}{3}, f = \frac{4}{3}$ and $g = \frac{5}{3}$)

T255

11.8 Using Proportions to Solve Problems

As part of a geography project, you are to paint a scale map of the United States on one of the school walls. You will need mathematics to figure out how far apart cities should be placed.

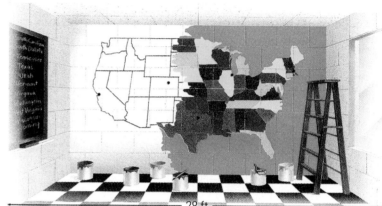

— 28 ft. —

Start with the cities shown in the table and use rounded distances as shown. The wall is 28 feet wide, so make the distance between Boston and San Francisco 25 feet. The real distance between these two cities is 3100 miles.

	Boston	Chicago	Dallas	Denver	San Francisco
Boston	——	1000	1750	2000	3100
Chicago		——	900	1000	2200
Dallas			——	800	1750
Denver				——	1250

How many feet should the distance between Boston and Chicago be on your map? To make the map look right, you have to consider the distances you used for Boston and San Francisco. Since these cities are 3100 miles apart, and you chose to draw them 25 feet apart, the scale of $\frac{25 \text{ feet}}{3100 \text{ miles}}$ must be used for the rest of the map. To find the distance from Boston to Chicago, use a proportion.

$$\frac{\text{Distance on map}}{\text{Actual distance}} = \frac{\text{Boston to San Francisco on map}}{\text{Actual Boston to San Francisco distance}}$$

$$\frac{\text{Distance on map}}{\text{Actual distance}} = \frac{25}{3100}$$

$$\frac{\text{Distance on map}}{1000} = \frac{25}{3100} \quad \text{Find Boston to Chicago on the table above.}$$

$3100 \times \text{Distance on map} = 1000 \times 25$

$\text{Distance on map} = 25{,}000 \div 3100$

$\text{Distance on map} = 8\frac{2}{31} \text{ feet} \approx 8 \text{ feet}$

Draw Boston and Chicago about 8 feet apart on your map.

Exercises

1. What is the distance from Chicago to Denver? 1000 mi.

2. How many feet apart will Chicago and Denver be on the map? About 8 ft.

3. What is the distance from Denver to Boston? 2000 mi.

4. How many feet apart will Denver and Boston be on the map? About 16 ft.

5. Set up a ratio comparing map measurements to real distances for Chicago/Dallas and Boston/Dallas. Solve a proportion for each pair of cities using $\frac{25}{3100}$. $\frac{25}{3100} \cdot \frac{\blacksquare}{900} = \frac{25}{3100}, \frac{\blacksquare}{1750} = \frac{25}{3100}$; ≈7 ft.; ≈14 ft.

6. Use proportions to find the four map measurements that you have not yet found: Chicago/San Francisco, Denver/Dallas, Dallas/San Francisco, and Denver/San Francisco. ≈18 ft.; ≈$6\frac{1}{2}$ ft.; ≈14 ft.; ≈10 ft.

Write a proportion for each problem. Then solve.

7. There were 400 people at last week's football game. They ate 250 frankfurters. This week 650 people are expected. About how many frankfurters should be prepared? $\frac{400}{250} = \frac{650}{\blacksquare}$; about 400 frankfurters

8. A car uses 5 gallons of gas to travel 115 miles. How far can it travel on 12 gallons of gas? $\frac{5}{115} = \frac{12}{\blacksquare}$; 276 mi.

F K H

9. A plane travels 900 miles in $1\frac{1}{2}$ hours. How far will it travel in 5 hours if it continues at the same rate? $\frac{900}{1\frac{1}{2}} = \frac{\blacksquare}{5}$; 3000 mi.

▶ Applications

For the following exercises, state whether a proportion can be used to solve the problem. If it can, use it to solve the problem. If a proportion cannot be used, explain why not.

10. If a child is 3 feet tall at age 2, how tall will she be at age 10? No; children grow at different rates

11. If a car travels 160 miles in 3 hours on the open road, about how far will it travel in 7 hours on the open road? Yes; $\frac{160}{3} = \frac{\blacksquare}{7}$; $373\frac{1}{3}$ mi. or ≈370 mi.

12. If a car travels 1 mile in 30 minutes during rush hour, how long will it take to go 5 miles? No; cars do not travel at a steady pace during rush hour

▶ Review (Lesson 3.3)

Divide.

13. 95 ÷ 100 0.95
14. 600 ÷ 20 30
15. 49,000 ÷ 70 700
16. 8.431 ÷ 10 0.8431
17. 64,000 ÷ 800 80
18. 4500 ÷ 50 90
19. 3.13 ÷ 100 0.0313
20. 2067 ÷ 1000 2.067

★ **Error Alert**
Mistakes may occur if students simplify large numbers before finding the cross products. For example, they might simplify the numerator of one ratio and the denominator of the other ratio. The proportion

$\frac{\blacksquare}{1000} = \frac{25}{3100}$ is not $\frac{\blacksquare}{40} = \frac{1}{3100}$.

However, the proportion can be simplified as $\frac{\blacksquare}{1000} = \frac{1}{124}$.

Reinforcement
EP/MR Worksheet 90, TRB, page 90

Challenge
On their part-time jobs, Lori, Doug, and Brian have each earned $108 this year for every $100 they each earned last year. Set up proportions to find how much each person earned this year if they earned the following amounts last year. Round your answers to the nearest dollar.

Lori: $3500   ($3780)
Doug: $2900   ($3132)
Brian: $3800   ($4104)

T257

Chapter 11 Review

REVIEW

Write each ratio in 3 different ways. (Lesson 11.1)

1. 60 pins in 7 pincushions
60 to 7; $\frac{60}{7}$; 60 : 7

2. 10 shoes for 5 feet
10 to 5; $\frac{10}{5}$; 10 : 5

3. 63 bills for 18 wallets
63 to 18; $\frac{63}{18}$; 63 : 18

4. 45 students to 5 chaperones
45 to 5; $\frac{45}{5}$; 45 : 5

Find 3 ratios equivalent to each ratio. (Lesson 11.1)

5. $1.25 for 3 stamps
$\frac{\$2.50}{6}$, $\frac{\$3.75}{9}$, $\frac{\$5}{12}$

6. 200 miles in 4 hours
$\frac{50}{1}$, $\frac{100}{2}$, $\frac{600}{12}$

7. $25 for 2 shirts
$\frac{\$50}{4}$, $\frac{\$75}{6}$, $\frac{\$100}{8}$

Tell whether each statement is a proportion. Use = or ≠.
(Lesson 11.2)

8. $\frac{4}{99}$ ___ $\frac{8}{198}$
=

9. $\frac{30}{50}$ ___ $\frac{5}{3}$
≠

10. $\frac{19}{20}$ ___ $\frac{39}{40}$
≠

11. $\frac{5}{9}$ ___ $\frac{6}{9}$
≠

Solve each proportion. (Lesson 11.3)

12. $\frac{\blacksquare}{5} = \frac{9}{15}$ 3

13. $\frac{8}{12} = \frac{\blacksquare}{3}$ 2

14. $\frac{13}{\blacksquare} = \frac{52}{84}$ 21

15. $\frac{600}{50} = \frac{144}{\blacksquare}$ 12

Find the unit price. (Lesson 11.4)

16. $28.74 for 3 pairs of earrings $9.58

17. $19.95 for 5 tapes $3.99

Determine the better buy. (Lesson 11.4)

18. $1.09 for 3 pounds of apples or ($1.55 for 5 pounds of apples)

19. ($34.50 for 6 ounces of cologne) or $9.95 for 1.5 ounces of cologne

Write a proportion for each problem. Then solve.
(Lessons 11.5, 11.6, 11.7, 11.8)

20. A roll of film contains 36 exposures. How many rolls of film must you buy to have 324 exposures?

21. On a map, 1 inch represents 64 miles. Find the actual distance that is represented by 4.5 inches on the map.

22. The distance between two cities in Europe is 840 kilometers. On a map, the distance is 6 centimeters. How many kilometers does each centimeter represent on the map?

23. Mr. Burbank is making a sketch of his garden on paper. On his scale, one inch equals $1\frac{1}{2}$ feet. The sketch is 9 inches by 7 inches. What are the actual dimensions of his garden?

Answers
20. $\frac{1}{36} = \frac{\blacksquare}{324}$; 9 rolls
21. $\frac{1}{64} = \frac{4.5}{\blacksquare}$; 288 mi.
22. $\frac{6}{840} = \frac{1}{\blacksquare}$; 140 km
23. $\frac{1}{1\frac{1}{2}} = \frac{9}{\blacksquare}$; $\frac{1}{1\frac{1}{2}} = \frac{7}{\blacksquare}$; $13\frac{1}{2}$ ft. by $10\frac{1}{2}$ ft.

Chapter 11 Test

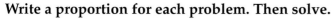

TEST

Chapter Tests
Short Answer, Forms A and B, TRB pages
  307–308, 309–310
Multiple Choice, Forms A and B, TRB, pages
  375–376, 377–378

Teaching Aids
Answer sheet
TA 8, TRB, page 161a
Teaching suggestions precede the Teaching
  Aids worksheets.

Write a proportion for each problem. Then solve.

1. There are 993 students at Highland High School. Two out of every three students are on a sports team. How many students are on sports teams?

2. Fourteen girls made the softball team. One out of every six girls made the team. How many girls tried out?

Answers
1. $\frac{2}{3} = \frac{\blacksquare}{993}$; 662 students
2. $\frac{1}{6} = \frac{14}{\blacksquare}$; 84 girls

Find the unit price.

3. $49.95 for 2 sweaters $24.98

4. $19.88 for 8 pairs of socks $2.49

Write each ratio in 3 different ways.

5. 9 miles in 4 hours
   9 to 4; $\frac{9}{4}$; 9 : 4

6. 1 egg to 70 calories
   1 to 70; $\frac{1}{70}$; 1 : 70

7. 9 pies for 72 pieces
   9 to 72; $\frac{9}{72}$; 9 : 72

Tell whether each statement is a proportion. Use = or ≠.

8. $\frac{6}{4}$ ____ $\frac{12}{10}$ ≠

9. $\frac{1}{7}$ ____ $\frac{7}{56}$ ≠

10. $\frac{96}{16}$ ____ $\frac{60}{10}$ =

11. $\frac{5}{65}$ ____ $\frac{1}{13}$ =

Find 3 ratios equivalent to each ratio.

12. 5 boxes for 50 cans
    $\frac{1}{10}$, $\frac{2}{20}$, $\frac{3}{30}$

13. 70 miles in 9 days
    $\frac{140}{18}$, $\frac{210}{27}$, $\frac{280}{36}$

14. $15 for 4 books
    $\frac{\$3.75}{1}$, $\frac{\$7.50}{2}$, $\frac{\$11.25}{3}$

Determine the better buy.

15. ($1.54 for 9 pencils) or $0.90 for 5 pencils

16. ($34.45 for 5 pairs of gloves) or $41.40 for 6 pairs of gloves

Solve.

17. The drawing of a room is 3 inches by $2\frac{1}{2}$ inches. One inch represents 12 feet. What are the actual dimensions of the room?
    36 ft. by 30 ft.

18. Sharon shot twelve rolls of film and took 288 photos. How many photos were there from each roll of film? 24 photos

19. Jenny drew a plan for a bookcase. The plan uses $1\frac{1}{2}$ inches to represent 9 inches. The bookcase is 6 inches by $2\frac{1}{2}$ inches on the plan. What are the actual measurements of the bookcase? 36 in.; 15 in.

20. Mrs. Smith's garden measures 45 feet by 39 feet. What is the size of her garden on paper if she uses a scale where $\frac{1}{2}$ inch represents 3 feet? $7\frac{1}{2}$ in. by $6\frac{1}{2}$ in.

Use percents to

• describe a test or quiz score.

• show the increase or decrease in a price.

• determine the amount of tip to leave a food server.

• describe a favorite team's winning record.

What are some other ways to use percents?

fashionables

10% off

20% off

Percents

An inventory manager controls the amount of product that a business has available.

- Inventory managers work in businesses that maintain, hold, and/or sell products. Examples of these businesses include grocery stores, retail stores, automobile dealerships, and warehouses.

- An inventory manager should be organized and enjoy paying attention to details.

- An inventory manager counts and organizes inventory, identifies unit cost, and determines the value of unused inventory.

- Some inventory managers establish prices and schedule delivery of merchandise.

- To become an inventory manager, an individual can often learn from other inventory specialists or work his or her way up from a stock or sales clerk.

- Related careers include order processors, store product stockers or inventory counters, store or warehouse managers, and auditors.

CAREER

INVENTORY MANAGER

SALE PRICE

PORTFOLIO PROJECT: *Create an inventory of a collection.*

1. Identify something that you or a member of your family collects. Examples of collectibles include stuffed animals, trading cards, CDs, computer software programs, and books.

2. Create a list of the collection. Make your list as efficient and organized as possible.

3. Count the number of items in your inventory. Determine the percent of increase in the total number of items if you add 4, 9, or 15 items to your collection. Show the percent decrease if you sell 2, 3, and 6 items of your collection. *Show the math.*

About the Portfolio Project

Students must be precise about the inventory of their collection: baseball cards, crystal figurines, fountain pens, or other item. Each item in the collection should be identified and listed. Size, color, or shape may be categories in which to inventory the items. Students need to make an accurate count of their inventory items and determine the total. Students use this total to figure each of the math problems in step 3. Be sure students label all their work.

Assessment: The individual scoring rubric on page 161 of the Teacher's Resource Binder can be reproduced and used for assessment. Include the following information in the last two boxes. Students should have:

- created an accurate list, by category, of inventoried items.
- accurately solved all math problems.

12.1 Introduction to Percents

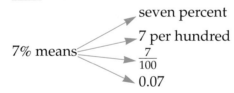

The sale sign shown and others like it are a common sight in most shopping areas. The signs are meaningful only if you understand the meaning of percent and how to use the % symbol.

▶ Express Yourself

Here are some terms that will help you in this chapter.

%   symbol for percent

7% means
- seven percent
- 7 per hundred
- $\frac{7}{100}$
- 0.07

of   in percent statements, another word for "times"

For example, 8% of 200 means 8% × 200.

is   in mathematics, another word for "equals"

You already know a lot about percents just by being a consumer.

1. A sports store is having a 30%-off sale. The price of a tennis racket is usually $60. If you buy the tennis racket on sale, will you pay more or less than $60? Can you find how much less? Discuss.

2. Look at the sign in the store window above. What percent off are the tennis shoes? How much would you have to pay for the shoes? How did you arrive at your answer? Explain.

PROBLEM SOLVING

3. Give an example of a percent that you have come across outside of school.

4. What is the meaning of the word *of* in the following sentence? **Ten percent of 60 is 6.**

5. What is the meaning of the word *is* in the sentence above?

6. You work with percents every time you pay sales tax. If the sales tax is 6% on every dollar, how much tax would you pay on a $5 purchase? Explain how you would compute the answer.

Percents can be illustrated in numerous ways. Here are some ways to represent 25%.

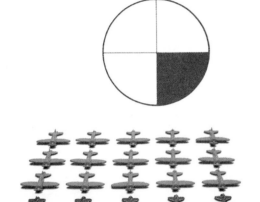

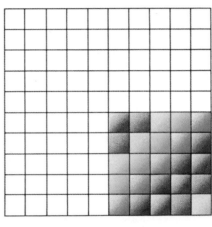

▶ Practice What You Know

As you work with percents in this chapter, you will be multiplying and dividing by 10 and by 100. You already know that to multiply by 10, you move the decimal point 1 place to the right. To multiply by 100, you move the decimal point 2 places to the right.

$$6.2 \times 10 = 62 \qquad 6.2 \times 100 = 620$$

Remember that to divide by 10, you move the decimal point 1 place to the left. To divide by 100, you move the decimal point 2 places to the left.

$$6.2 \div 10 = 0.62 \qquad 6.2 \div 100 = 0.062$$

Multiply or divide mentally.

7. 0.37×10 3.7   8. $13 \div 10$ 1.3   9. $47.2 \div 100$ 0.472   10. 4.5×100 450

11. $8.7 \div 10$ 0.87   12. 0.276×100 27.6   13. $343 \div 100$ 3.43   14. 56.3×10 563

Answers (continued)

3. Examples might include bank interest, sales tax, income tax, results of opinion polls, sales commission.

4. *Of* means times.

5. *Is* means equals.

6. $0.30; multiply $5 by 0.06

★ **Error Alert**

Errors may occur if students confuse percents and decimals. Impress upon them that *percent* means "per hundred" and that, for percents, one hundred is always the number of parts in the whole.

Project

Write a report that gives 5 real-life examples of percents. You may use sources such as magazines, newspaper ads, or local businesses. For example, you might telephone a local bank to find what the current interest rate is on a passbook savings account. Share your report with the class.

Objectives

- To write a decimal as a percent
- To write a percent as a decimal

Purpose

When you want to find a percent of something, expressing the percent as a decimal before doing the calculation may make solving the problem easier. This lesson shows you how to write percents as decimals and decimals as percents.

Introducing the Lesson

Review reading and writing decimals (Lesson 1.2). Use the examples: Write the following as decimals—75 hundredths, 9 hundredths, and 100 hundredths. (0.75, 0.09, 1.00)

Write the fraction $\frac{5}{100}$ on the chalkboard. Ask students to name 3 equivalent fractions and a decimal for $\frac{5}{100}$. (sample answers: $\frac{1}{20}$, $\frac{10}{200}$, $\frac{20}{400}$; 0.05) Ask: Are each of these equal to $\frac{5}{100}$? (yes) When might you use an equivalent fraction instead of the fraction $\frac{5}{100}$? (sample answer: to do calculations with like denominators) When might you use 0.05 instead of $\frac{5}{100}$? (sample answer: to multiply 3.5 by $\frac{5}{100}$) Explain that learning how to convert decimals to percents and percents to decimals makes certain calculations easier.

Alternative Examples

Example A—Write 0.7 as a percent. *Move the decimal point two places to the right. Add a zero as a placeholder.*
0.7 = 0.70.
Write a % sign.
0.7 = **70%**

Example B—Write 15% as a decimal. *Move the decimal point two places to the left.*
15% = .15.
Add zeros as placeholders and omit the percent sign.
15% = **0.15**

12.2 Decimals and Percents

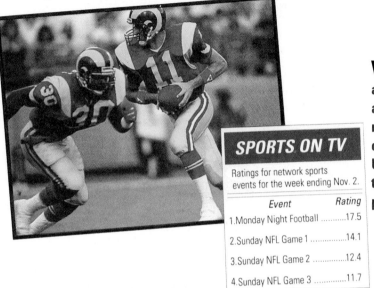

Weekly ratings reports tell us about television viewing. Such a report is shown here. Each rating point is equivalent to 1% of the television sets in the United States. You can express the rating of each program as a percent or as a decimal.

SPORTS ON TV

Ratings for network sports events for the week ending Nov. 2.

Event	Rating
1.Monday Night Football	17.5
2.Sunday NFL Game 1	14.1
3.Sunday NFL Game 2	12.4
4.Sunday NFL Game 3	11.7

Examples

To write a decimal as a percent, multiply the decimal by 100 and write a percent sign after it.

To write a percent as a decimal, divide the percent by 100 and omit the percent sign.

A Write 0.375 as a percent.

0.375 = 0.37.5   Move the decimal point two places to the right.
     = **37.5%**   Write a % sign.

B Write 4% as a decimal.

4% = .04.   Move the decimal point two places to the left.
   = **0.04**   Add zeros as placeholders and omit the percent sign.

▶ Think and Discuss

1. Write 13% as a decimal. How many places and in what direction did you move the decimal point?

2. Refer to the introduction to this lesson. Write the rating of the fourth-rated program as a percent and as a decimal.

3. Write 67.3 as a percent.

4. Refer to the introduction to this lesson. What percent of the television sets were not tuned to Monday Night Football? Explain how you found your answer.

5. What does 0% mean? How do you change it to a decimal?

6. Jason bought a used car for $1250 and had to pay 7% sales tax. He decided to figure the tax on his calculator, but it doesn't have a percent key. How would he write 7% as a decimal so that he could calculate the answer?

Exercises

Write each decimal as a percent. (See Example A.)

7. 0.65 65%   8. 0.05 5%   9. 0.5 50%   10. 0.73 73%   11. 1.00 100%

12. 0.09 9%   13. 0.215 21.5%   14. 0.9 90%   15. 0.075 7.5%   16. 0.11 11%

Write each percent as a decimal. (See Example B.)

17. 8% 0.08   18. 32% 0.32   19. 11.4% 0.114   20. 15% 0.15   21. 13.5% 0.135

22. 25% 0.25   23. 44.5% 0.445   24. 81% 0.81   25. 66.5% 0.665   26. 100% 1

Mixed Practice (For more practice, see page 437.)

Write each percent as a decimal and each decimal as a percent.

27. 0.2 20%   28. 0.16 16%   29. 75% 0.75   30. 1.25% 0.0125   31. 16.5% 0.165

32. 0.08 8%   33. 0.135 13.5%   34. 9.6% 0.096   35. 0.505 50.5%   36. 3.6% 0.036

37. 0.01 1%   38. 99% 0.99   39. 78% 0.78   40. 0.12 12%   41. 0.021 2.1%

Applications

42. Outfielder Ted Williams, the "Splendid Splinter," hit 0.406 in 1941. Write his batting average as a percent. 40.6%

43. A bank pays the interest advertised below. Write the interest rate as a decimal. 0.078

7.8% ON LONG TERM DEPOSITS

Review (Lesson 5.7)

Convert each fraction to a decimal.

44. $\frac{4}{5}$ 0.8   45. $\frac{1}{2}$ 0.5   46. $\frac{2}{3}$ 0.6̄   47. $\frac{15}{20}$ 0.75   48. $\frac{3}{4}$ 0.75   49. $\frac{7}{8}$ 0.875

Convert each decimal to a fraction in lowest terms.

50. 0.4 $\frac{2}{5}$ 51. 0.33 $\frac{33}{100}$ 52. 0.95 $\frac{19}{20}$ 53. 0.056 $\frac{7}{125}$ 54. 0.04 $\frac{1}{25}$ 55. 0.125 $\frac{1}{8}$

12.3 Writing Fractions as Percents

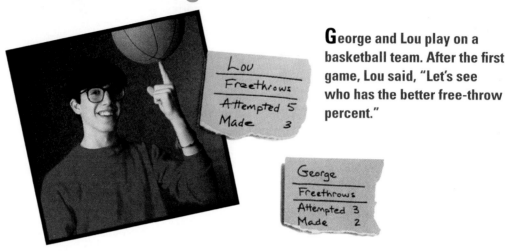

George and Lou play on a basketball team. After the first game, Lou said, "Let's see who has the better free-throw percent."

Lou
Freethrows
Attempted 5
Made 3

George
Freethrows
Attempted 3
Made 2

To find who had the better free-throw percent, you can write each fraction as a percent and then compare.

Examples

To write a fraction as a percent, first convert the fraction to a decimal. Then write the decimal as a percent.

A Write $\frac{3}{5}$ as a percent.

$\frac{3}{5} = 0.6$ ←
$= \mathbf{60\%}$

$$\begin{array}{r} 0.6 \\ 5\overline{)3.0} \\ -3\,0 \\ \hline 0 \end{array}$$

B Write $\frac{2}{3}$ as a percent.

$\frac{2}{3} = 0.66\frac{2}{3}$ ←
$= \mathbf{66\frac{2}{3}\%}$

$$\begin{array}{r} 0.66\frac{2}{3} \\ 3\overline{)2.00} \\ -1\,8 \\ \hline 20 \\ -1\,8 \\ \hline 2 \end{array}$$

▶ Think and Discuss

1. Which part of the fraction is the divisor when you convert a fraction to a decimal?

2. Write $\frac{3}{4}$ as a percent.

3. Refer to the introduction to this lesson. Which player had the higher percent of successful free throws?

4. Can you determine if $\frac{5}{6}$ is larger than $\frac{2}{3}$ without converting to percents?

Exercises

SKILLS

Write as a percent. (See Example A.)

5. $\frac{1}{5}$ 20%   **6.** $\frac{1}{2}$ 50%   **7.** $\frac{3}{4}$ 75%   **8.** $\frac{3}{10}$ 30%   **9.** $\frac{17}{25}$ 68%   **10.** $\frac{23}{50}$ 46%

11. $\frac{3}{100}$ 3%   **12.** $\frac{9}{36}$ 25%   **13.** $\frac{4}{20}$ 20%   **14.** $\frac{12}{12}$ 100%   **15.** $\frac{3}{20}$ 15%   **16.** $\frac{9}{15}$ 60%

Write as a percent. (See Example B.)

17. $\frac{1}{3}$ $33\frac{1}{3}$%   **18.** $\frac{1}{6}$ $16\frac{2}{3}$%   **19.** $\frac{5}{6}$ $83\frac{1}{3}$%   **20.** $\frac{17}{40}$ $42\frac{1}{2}$%   **21.** $\frac{1}{8}$ $12\frac{1}{2}$%   **22.** $\frac{3}{16}$ $18\frac{3}{4}$%

23. $\frac{11}{16}$ $68\frac{3}{4}$%   **24.** $\frac{9}{16}$ $56\frac{1}{4}$%   **25.** $\frac{7}{21}$ $33\frac{1}{3}$%   **26.** $\frac{8}{12}$ $66\frac{2}{3}$%   **27.** $\frac{1}{15}$ $6\frac{2}{3}$%   **28.** $\frac{7}{56}$ $12\frac{1}{2}$%

▶ Mixed Practice (For more practice, see page 437.)

Write as a percent.

29. $\frac{3}{8}$ $37\frac{1}{2}$%   **30.** $\frac{7}{8}$ $87\frac{1}{2}$%   **31.** $\frac{2}{5}$ 40%   **32.** $\frac{7}{10}$ 70%   **33.** $\frac{1}{16}$ $6\frac{1}{4}$%   **34.** $\frac{15}{75}$ 20%

35. $\frac{9}{12}$ 75%   **36.** $\frac{19}{20}$ 95%   **37.** $\frac{11}{66}$ $16\frac{2}{3}$%   **38.** $\frac{37}{50}$ 74%   **39.** $\frac{15}{16}$ $93\frac{3}{4}$%   **40.** $\frac{4}{15}$ $26\frac{2}{3}$%

▶ Applications

41. Seven-tenths of the earth is covered by water. Write this as a percent. 70%

42. Two out of every nine people in the world are Chinese. Write this as a percent. $22\frac{2}{9}$%

43. Jeremy attended seven of his school's eleven home games. What percent of the home games did Jeremy attend? $63\frac{7}{11}$%

44. Refer to the introduction to this lesson. Together Lou and George attempted 8 free throws in the first game. What was their combined free-throw percent? 62.5%

45. A 1-hour aerobic exercise class is divided into the categories shown here. Write each as a percent.

Warm-up exercises	15 minutes
Abdominal exercises	10 minutes
Leg exercises	9 minutes
Hip exercises	6 minutes
Arm exercises	5 minutes
Aerobic exercises	12 minutes
Cool-down exercises	3 minutes

▶ Applications (Lesson 5.6)

Rewrite each fraction in lowest terms.

46. $\frac{8}{100}$ $\frac{2}{25}$ **47.** $\frac{12}{200}$ $\frac{3}{50}$ **48.** $\frac{355}{1000}$ $\frac{71}{200}$ **49.** $\frac{57}{300}$ $\frac{19}{100}$ **50.** $\frac{12.5}{100}$ $\frac{1}{8}$ **51.** $\frac{31}{200}$ $\frac{31}{200}$ **52.** $\frac{82}{300}$ $\frac{41}{150}$

Objective

- To express percents as fractions

Purpose

This lesson shows you how to convert percents to fractions. This is useful if, for example, you want to know what fraction of questions you must answer correctly to get a score of 80%.

Introducing the Lesson

Write the following percents on the chalkboard: 75%, 90%, 23%. Ask: What does *percent* mean? (per hundred) If you write the percents as fractions, what denominator could you choose for all three percents? (100) Explain that in this lesson students will learn to convert percents to fractions.

Alternative Examples

Example A—Write 45% as a fraction in lowest terms.

$45\% = \frac{45}{100} = \frac{9}{20}$

Example B—Write $7\frac{3}{8}\%$ as a fraction in lowest terms.

First rewrite as fractions. Then multiply by the reciprocal.

$7\frac{3}{8}\% = \frac{7\frac{3}{8}}{100} = \frac{\frac{59}{8}}{\frac{100}{1}} = \frac{59}{8} \times \frac{1}{100} = \frac{59}{800}$

$7\frac{3}{8}\% = \frac{59}{800}$

Example C—Write 13.6% as a fraction in lowest terms.

Multiply the numerator and denominator by 10 to move the decimal point.

$13.6\% = \frac{13.6}{100} = \frac{13.6 \times 10}{100 \times 10} = \frac{136}{1000} = \frac{17}{125}$

$13.6\% = \frac{17}{125}$

12.4 Writing Percents as Fractions

Torrez wins election with 52.5% of vote!

In St. Louis, 67% of the families subscribe to cable television.

62% of all downtown commuters *use* PUB-TRANS

90% of all dentists polled recommended Happy Smile toothpaste to help prevent cavities.

SALE 33⅓% OFF!

Percents can be found in newspapers, television advertisements, and magazines. Often it is easier to understand the situation if you write the percent as a fraction. Remember, percent means *per hundred*.

Examples

To write a percent as a fraction, first write the percent as the numerator without the percent sign. Use 100 as the denominator. Then write the fraction in lowest terms.

A Write 30% as a fraction in lowest terms.

$30\% = \frac{30}{100} = \frac{3}{10}$

B Write $12\frac{1}{2}\%$ as a fraction in lowest terms.

$12\frac{1}{2}\% = \frac{12\frac{1}{2}}{100} = \frac{\frac{25}{2}}{\frac{100}{1}} = \frac{25}{2} \times \frac{1}{100} = \frac{25}{200} = \frac{1}{8}$

First rewrite as fractions. Then multiply by the reciprocal of $\frac{100}{1}$.

$12\frac{1}{2}\% = \frac{1}{8}$

C Write 20.5% as a fraction in lowest terms.

$20.5\% = \frac{20.5}{100} = \frac{20.5 \times 10}{100 \times 10} = \frac{205}{1000} = \frac{41}{200}$

Multiply the numerator and denominator by 10 to move the decimal point.

$20.5\% = \frac{41}{200}$

▶ Think and Discuss

1. Write $\frac{6}{1000}$, $\frac{20}{100}$, and $\frac{50}{100}$ in lowest terms.

2. Write 58% as a fraction in lowest terms.

3. How could 40.5% be written as a percent in another way?

4. Refer to the introduction to this lesson. If 50 different dentists are polled tomorrow, how may do you think will recommend Happy Smile toothpaste? Discuss.

5. Why would a store choose "$33\frac{1}{3}$% off" for a sale?

Exercises

Write as a fraction in lowest terms. (See Example A.)

6. 26% $\frac{13}{50}$ 7. 75% $\frac{3}{4}$ 8. 48% $\frac{12}{25}$ 9. 99% $\frac{99}{100}$ 10. 5% $\frac{1}{20}$ 11. 4% $\frac{1}{25}$

12. 40% $\frac{2}{5}$ 13. 24% $\frac{6}{25}$ 14. 57% $\frac{57}{100}$ 15. 73% $\frac{73}{100}$ 16. 85% $\frac{17}{20}$ 17. 10% $\frac{1}{10}$

18. 12% $\frac{3}{25}$ 19. 55% $\frac{11}{20}$ 20. 2% $\frac{1}{50}$ 21. 64% $\frac{16}{25}$ 22. 3% $\frac{3}{100}$ 23. 25% $\frac{1}{4}$

Write as a fraction in lowest terms. (See Example B.)

24. $7\frac{1}{2}$% $\frac{3}{40}$ 25. $37\frac{1}{2}$% $\frac{3}{8}$ 26. $6\frac{1}{4}$% $\frac{1}{16}$ 27. $41\frac{2}{3}$% $\frac{5}{12}$ 28. $3\frac{1}{2}$% $\frac{7}{200}$ 29. $50\frac{1}{3}$% $\frac{151}{300}$

Write as a fraction in lowest terms. (See Example C.)

30. 1.25% $\frac{1}{80}$ 31. 19.5% $\frac{39}{200}$ 32. 22.75% $\frac{91}{400}$ 33. 12.5% $\frac{1}{8}$ 34. 6.25% $\frac{1}{16}$ 35. 9.75% $\frac{39}{400}$

▶ Mixed Practice (For more practice, see page 438.)

Write as a fraction in lowest terms.

36. 25% $\frac{1}{4}$ 37. $33\frac{1}{3}$% $\frac{1}{3}$ 38. 22.5% $\frac{9}{40}$ 39. 44% $\frac{11}{25}$ 40. 9.5% $\frac{19}{200}$ 41. 57.5% $\frac{23}{40}$

42. 1% $\frac{1}{100}$ 43. 14% $\frac{7}{50}$ 44. 95% $\frac{19}{20}$ 45. $16\frac{2}{3}$% $\frac{1}{6}$ 46. 30.5% $\frac{61}{200}$ 47. 87.5% $\frac{7}{8}$

48. 66% $\frac{33}{50}$ 49. 54% $\frac{27}{50}$ 50. 5.75% $\frac{23}{400}$ 51. $6\frac{1}{2}$% $\frac{13}{200}$ 52. 11% $\frac{11}{100}$ 53. 62% $\frac{31}{50}$

▶ Applications

54. A shirt is 60% cotton and 40% polyester. Write the percents as fractions. $\frac{3}{5}$, $\frac{2}{5}$

55. If the sales tax is five percent, what fraction of an item's price must you add to the price? $\frac{1}{20}$

▶ Review (Lesson 11.3)

Solve each proportion.

56. $\frac{6}{9} = \frac{12}{\blacksquare}$ 18

57. $\frac{2}{1} = \frac{1}{\blacksquare}$ $\frac{1}{2}$

58. $\frac{8}{3} = \frac{\blacksquare}{24}$ 64

▶ Think and Discuss Answers

1. $\frac{3}{500}$; $\frac{1}{5}$; $\frac{1}{2}$
2. $\frac{29}{50}$
3. $40\frac{1}{2}$%
4. 45; 90% of 50 is 0.90 × 50, which is 45; this assumes the dentists polled are a representative sample of all dentists
5. because it is $\frac{1}{3}$ off the original sale price

★ Error Alert

Errors may indicate that students are calculating incorrectly as they express the fraction in lowest terms.

Reinforcement

Extra Practice, page 438
EP/MR Worksheet 93, TRB, page 93

Challenge

Ocean water is about 97% pure water. The rest consists of dissolved minerals. The percentages of elements that make up the dissolved minerals in ocean water are shown in the table. Round the percents in the table to the nearest 5%. Then convert each percent to a fraction and answer the following questions.

Element	%	Rounded %	Fraction
Chlorine	55%	(55%)	$(\frac{11}{20})$
Sodium	30%	(30%)	$(\frac{3}{10})$
Magnesium	4%	(5%)	$(\frac{1}{20})$
Sulfur	3%	(5%)	$(\frac{1}{20})$
Other	8%	(10%)	$(\frac{1}{10})$

1. About what percent of ocean water is composed of minerals? (3%)
2. What element makes up about $\frac{1}{2}$ of all the minerals in ocean water? (chlorine)
3. What element makes up about $\frac{1}{3}$ of all the minerals in ocean water? (sodium)
4. What two elements together make up about $\frac{1}{10}$ of the minerals in ocean water? (magnesium and sulfur)

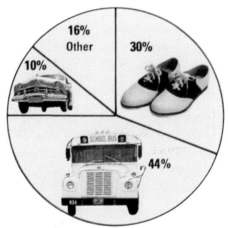

- To represent percents in the form of circle graphs

Purpose

In this lesson you use percents on circle graphs. You can use circle graphs to show percents that add up to 100% because they are part of a whole, such as the national budget, or the results of a survey. In this way you can see how the parts relate to the whole and how the parts compare to each other.

Introducing the Lesson

Review reading circle graphs (Lesson 9.8). Then draw a circle graph on the chalkboard. Divide the graph into the following sections. Put the category heading in each section of the graph, but do not write in the percent values: Food—≈25%; Rent—≈20%; Clothes—≈13%; Transportation—≈9%; Phone, Gas, Electric—≈8%; Entertainment—≈10%; Other expenses—≈10%; Savings—≈5%. Tell students that this graph represents a family's yearly expenses. Elicit from students what information they can discern about each category by seeing what part of the whole each category occupies without knowing actual dollar values. (sample answers: the most money was spent on food; entertainment and other expenses cost about the same as rent)

Answers

4. yes; because the size of the graph is proportional to the percent it represents
6. because the percents must add up to 100% in order to show that all categories are accounted for; bicycle, train, motorcycle

12.5 Using Percents and Circle Graphs

You probably have heard someone say, "Back in the good old days I used to walk to school 3 miles through rain, sleet, and snow . . . "

You can use circle graphs like the ones shown here to compare how high school students traveled to school in the 1950s with how they got to school in the 1980s. The circle in a circle graph represents the whole group, or 100%. Each slice of the circle represents a portion of the whole.

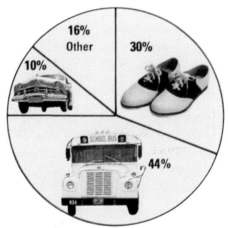

Methods of transportation to high schools in 1950s

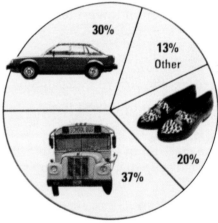

Methods of transportation to high schools in 1980s

1. What percent of students walked to school in the 1950s? What percent walked in the 1980s? 30%; 20%

2. Which mode of transportation did students use most in the 1950s? Which did they use most in the 1980s? bus; bus

3. What percent of students drove in the 1980s? What fraction does that represent? How much of the circle is this slice? 30%; $\frac{3}{10}$; 30% or $\frac{3}{10}$

4. Suppose there were no numbers on the circle graphs. Could you still get any information from them? Explain.

5. What is the sum of the percents in each circle graph? 100%

6. Discuss why the "Other" category is important, even though you may not know exactly what it includes. What are some modes of transportation that might be included in the category "Other"?

PROBLEM SOLVING

A survey was given to people in three age groups: those under 21, those 21 to 50, and those over 50. Each group was asked to choose its favorite type of car. The results are shown below:

Vehicle	Under 21	21 – 50	Over 50
Sports car	200	12	10
Van	125	12	8
Economy	100	60	20
Full size	50	30	40
Other	25	6	2
Total number surveyed	**500**	**120**	**80**

$\frac{1}{13} \times 360$

$2\pi r \times 360$

7. What fraction of persons under 21 prefers sports cars? How would you write this as a percent? $\frac{2}{5}$; 40%

8. What fraction of persons 21 to 50 prefers vans? How would you write this as a percent? $\frac{1}{10}$; 10%

9. Convert the figures in the table above for each group to fractions and then to percents.

10. Use your answers from Question 9 to select the graph that represents each group. Copy the graphs and label each one. Then label each slice with the type of car it represents and its percent.

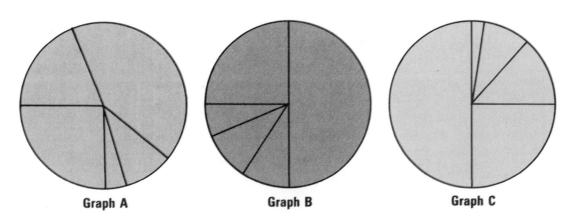

Graph A   Graph B   Graph C

▶ **Review** (Lesson 1.12)

Estimate.

11.	335 + 467 ≈800 or ≈810	12	1119 + 5880 ≈7000	13.	3852 + 4439 ≈8000 or ≈8300	14.	523 + 1991 ≈2500 or ≈3000

Percents **271**

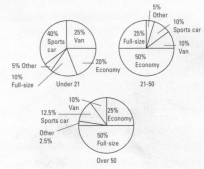

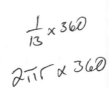

Objectives

• To express numbers greater than 1 and less than 0.01 as percents
• To express percents less than 1% as fractions and decimals

Purpose

Some information is commonly expressed as percents that are less than 1%, such as monthly inflation rates, and percents that are greater than 100%, such as an increase in car sales. This lesson helps you to understand and work with percents less than 1% and greater than 100%.

Introducing the Lesson

Draw a number line on the chalkboard like the one below. Assist students in naming the percents for the fractional amounts on the number line. Then extend the number line beyond 100% and circle the area on the number line that is less than 1% but greater than 0%. Tell students that this lesson gives them practice writing these percents.

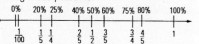

Alternative Examples

Example A—Write 12.84 as a percent.
Move the decimal point 2 places to the right.
12.84 = **1284%**

Example B—Write $\frac{2}{5000}$ as a percent.
Change the fraction to a decimal.
$\frac{2}{5000} = 0.0004$
Move the decimal point 2 places to the right.
$\frac{2}{5000} = \textbf{0.04\%}$

Example C—Write $\frac{3}{8}\%$ as a fraction and as a decimal.
Multiply by the reciprocal.

$\frac{3}{8}\% = \dfrac{\frac{3}{8}}{\frac{100}{1}} = \frac{3}{8} \times \frac{1}{100} = \frac{3}{800} = 0.00375$

$\frac{3}{8}\% = \frac{3}{800} = \textbf{0.00375}$

12.6 Percents Less Than One and Greater Than One Hundred

At the right are the prizes and chances of winning in a $1 instant state lottery game. The chances of winning $1000 are 1 in 7,692. Do you realize that this is less than a 1% chance of winning?

LOTTERY	
Prize *	Chance
$1,000	1 in 7,692
$500	1 in 4,170
$100	1 in 912
$50	1 in 496

Examples

To work with percents less than one or greater than one hundred, follow the rules you have already learned about percents in this chapter.

A Write 9.8 as a percent.

9.8 = **980%**   Move the decimal point 2 places to the right.

B Write $\frac{1}{400}$ as a percent.

$\frac{1}{400} = 0.0025$ Change the fraction to a decimal.

$= \textbf{0.25\%}$ Move the decimal point 2 places to the right.

C Write $\frac{1}{2}\%$ as a fraction and as a decimal.

$\frac{1}{2}\% = \dfrac{\frac{1}{2}}{\frac{100}{1}} = \frac{1}{2} \times \frac{1}{100} = \frac{1}{200} = 0.005$

Multiply by the reciprocal. Fraction Decimal

$\frac{1}{2}\% = \frac{1}{200} = \textbf{0.005}$

▶ Think and Discuss

1. Divide $\frac{3}{4}$ by 100.

2. Write 0.008 as a percent.

3. Convert the following percents to decimals.   100%   125%

4. Convert the following to percents. $\frac{1}{10}$ $\frac{1}{1000}$ 1 $1\frac{1}{4}$

5. Arrange the following percents in order from least to greatest.

0.3%   0.35%   0.5%   1%   3.5%   0.53%

6. A sign reads "SALE $\frac{1}{2}$% off!" Is the sign accurate? Explain.

Exercises

Write each decimal as a percent. (See Example A.)

7. 1.7 170%   **8.** 3.6 360%   **9.** 4 400%   **10.** 5.75 575%   **11.** 0.7 70%

12. 0.009 0.9%   **13.** 0.001 0.1%   **14.** 0.0052 0.52%   **15.** 0.0075 0.75%   **16.** 0.0019 0.19%

Write each fraction as a percent. (See Example B.)

17. $\frac{1}{200}$ 0.5%   **18.** $\frac{11}{10}$ 110%   **19.** $\frac{7}{1000}$ 0.7%   **20.** $\frac{29}{20}$ 145%   **21.** $\frac{17}{4}$ 425%

22. $\frac{5}{2000}$ 0.25%   **23.** $\frac{4000}{8}$ 50,000%   **24.** $\frac{8}{8000}$ 0.1%   **25.** $\frac{900}{4}$ 22,500%   **26.** $\frac{12}{2400}$ 0.5%

Write each percent as a fraction and as a decimal. (See Example C.)

27. $\frac{1}{4}$% $\frac{1}{400}$; 0.0025   **28.** 175% $\frac{7}{4}$; 1.75   **29.** $\frac{5}{8}$% $\frac{1}{160}$; 0.00625   **30.** $\frac{9}{10}$% $\frac{9}{1000}$; 0.009   **31.** 324% $\frac{81}{25}$; 3.24

32. 156% $\frac{39}{25}$; 1.56   **33.** $220\frac{1}{2}$% $\frac{441}{200}$; 2.205   **34.** 433% $\frac{13}{3}$; 4.33   **35.** $\frac{5}{16}$% $\frac{1}{320}$; 0.003125   **36.** $\frac{3}{8}$% $\frac{3}{800}$; 0.00375

▶ Mixed Practice (For more practice, see page 438.)

Write each fraction or decimal as a percent.

37. $\frac{3}{400}$ 0.75%   **38.** $1\frac{1}{5}$ 120%   **39.** 4.25 425%   **40.** $\frac{13}{6}$ $216\frac{2}{3}$%   **41.** $\frac{1}{250}$ 0.4%

42. 5.3 530%   **43.** $\frac{3}{1000}$ 0.3%   **44.** 9 900%   **45.** $3\frac{7}{8}$ $387\frac{1}{2}$%   **46.** $\frac{4}{3}$ $133\frac{1}{3}$%

47. 7.08 708%   **48.** $\frac{5}{8}$ $62\frac{1}{2}$%   **49.** $6\frac{1}{4}$ 625%   **50.** 0.085 8.5%   **51.** $7\frac{5}{12}$ $741\frac{2}{3}$%

52. $\frac{11}{12}$ $91\frac{2}{3}$%   **53.** 0.0003 0.03%   **54.** $3\frac{8}{9}$ $388\frac{8}{9}$%   **55.** 10 1000%   **56.** $11\frac{19}{20}$ 1195%

▶ Applications

57. Refer to the introduction to this lesson. Express your chances of winning $50 as a percent. Round to the nearest hundredth of a percent. 0.20%

58. The price of mailing a letter rose 1150% from 1920 to 1988. Express the price rise as a fraction and a decimal. $\frac{23}{2}$; 11.5

▶ Review (Lessons 2.8, 6.1, 6.2)

Multiply.

59. 0.7×8 5.6   **60.** $\frac{3}{4} \times 16$ 12   **61.** 5.83×17 99.11   **62.** $\frac{19}{20} \times 55$ $52\frac{1}{4}$

Objective

• To find the percent of a number

Purpose

This lesson shows you how to find the percent of a number. Using this method you will be able to find, for example, how many free throws a basketball player made if you know how many he attempted and the percent that he made.

Introducing the Lesson

Review the mathematical meanings of *percent, of,* and *is* (Lesson 12.1). Make sure students understand that *of* means "times." Then ask students what the percent sales tax is in their locality. (sample answer: 5%) Elicit from students that a 5% sales tax means that 5% of every dollar they spend is added to the total bill. Tell students that this lesson shows them how to find the sales tax, which is a percent, on any amount.

Alternative Examples

Example A—Find 42% of $156.
42% = 0.42
42% of $156 = 0.42 × 156
42% of $156 = 62.52
42% of $156 is **$65.52.**

Example B—Find $12\frac{1}{2}$% of $450.
$12\frac{1}{2}$% = $\frac{1}{8}$
$12\frac{1}{2}$% of $450 = $\frac{1}{8}$ × $450
$12\frac{1}{2}$% of $450 = $\frac{450}{8}$ = 56.25
$12\frac{1}{2}$ of $450 is **56.25.**

▶ **Think and Discuss Answers**

1. *of* means "times"; *is* means "equals"
2. 8
3. 8; yes, by moving the decimal two places to the left
4. 12,800
5. 105

12.7 Finding the Percent of a Number

Wilma works as a volunteer for the election campaign of a local politician. Her job is to see that all citizens are registered to vote. So far, 80% of the 16,000 citizens of voting age are registered. How many people are registered?

Examples

To find **the percent of a number,** first convert the percent to a decimal or fraction. Then multiply.

A Find 80% of 16,000.

80% = 0.80
80% of 16,000 = 0.80 × 16,000
80% of 16,000 = 12,800
80% of 16,000 is **12,800.**

B Find $33\frac{1}{2}$% of $75.

$33\frac{1}{3}$% = $\frac{1}{3}$
$33\frac{1}{3}$% of 75 = $\frac{1}{3}$ × 75
$33\frac{1}{3}$% of 75 = $\frac{75}{3}$ = 25
$33\frac{1}{3}$% of $75 is **$25.**

▶ **Think and Discuss**

1. What do *of* and *is* mean in "30% of 200 is 60"?

2. Find 20% of 40.

3. Find 1% of 800. Can you do it mentally?

4. Refer to the introduction to this lesson. How many of the 16,000 citizens are registered?

5. Suppose $12\frac{1}{2}$% of a class of 120 students went to a soccer game. How many students did not attend?

6. When might you need to find the percent of a number?

7. Write $33\frac{1}{2}$% as a fraction. How would you enter $33\frac{1}{3}$% on your calculator? Discuss.

Exercises

Find each number. (See Example A.)

8. 12% of $75 $9   **9.** 32% of $110 $35.20   **10.** 9% of $80 $7.20   **11.** 125% of 16 20

12. 50% of 120 60   **13.** 5% of 15.6 0.78   **14.** 0.5% of 126 0.63   **15.** 275% of 56 154

Find each number. (See Example B.)

16. $12\frac{1}{2}$% of 24 3   **17.** $66\frac{2}{3}$% of 36.6 24.4   **18.** $87\frac{1}{2}$% of 64 56   **19.** $66\frac{2}{3}$% of 90 60

20. $33\frac{1}{3}$% of 900 300   **21.** $37\frac{1}{2}$% of 40 15   **22.** $33\frac{1}{3}$% of 96 32   **23.** $62\frac{1}{2}$% of 700 437.5

▶ Mixed Practice (For more practice, see page 439.)

Find each number.

24. 40% of 250 100   **25.** 35.5% of 100 35.5   **26.** 50% of 51 25.5   **27.** $33\frac{1}{3}$% of 54 18

28. 75% of 40 30   **29.** 35% of 60 21   **30.** 0.4% of 85 0.34   **31.** 10% of $70 $7

32. $37\frac{1}{2}$% of 8.8 3.3   **33.** 15% of $25 $3.75   **34.** $16\frac{2}{3}$% of 72 12   **35.** 0.1% of 210 0.21

36. 175% of 60 105   **37.** 95% of 1122 1065.9   **38.** 19.5% of 46 8.97   **39.** 2.5% of 17 0.425

▶ Applications

40. During the Great Depression, the unemployment rate went as high as 25%. The work pool was 52 million people. Find 25% of 52 million. 13 million

41. The sales tax in New York City is $8\frac{1}{4}$%. How much sales tax must New Yorkers pay when purchasing the automobile below? $2,062.50

42. Dinah ordered a hamburger for $3.75 and iced tea for $0.75. The tax was 6%. If she gave the waitress 20% of the bill (before taxes) as a tip, how much did she spend altogether? $5.67

$25,000

▶ Review (Lesson 1.8)

Round to the nearest tenth.

43. 7.19 7.2   **44.** 18.64 18.6   **45.** 99.92 99.9   **46.** 3.0518 3.1   **47.** 2.1745 2.2   **48.** 6.268 6.3

Round to the nearest hundredth.

49. 0.873 0.87   **50.** 4.285 4.29   **51.** 1.964 1.96   **52.** 2.996 3.00   **53.** 8.3435 8.34   **54.** 9.0572 9.06

▶ **Think and Discuss Answers**
(continued)

6. Answers might include: to figure a sales commission, to find out a sales tax or income tax, and to determine bank interest.

7. $\frac{1}{3}$; you could touch 1, the division key, and 3

★ **Error Alert**

Mistakes may indicate that students are multiplying the percent times the number without first changing the percent to a decimal or a fraction.

Reinforcement

Extra Practice, page 439
EP/MR Worksheet 96, TRB, page 96

Challenge

Find the following:

1. 3% of 0.90   (0.027)
2. $\frac{1}{2}$% of 48   (0.24)
3. $10\frac{1}{2}$% of 36   (3.78)
4. 125% of 6.75   (8.4375)
5. Danny got an 8% raise. If he had been earning $6.50 per hour, how much was his raise and how much does he now make per hour? ($0.52, $7.02 per hour)

Objective

• To find what percent one number is of another

Purpose

This lesson shows you how to find what percent one number is of the other. You can use this, for example, to find what percent your discount was if you bought a shirt for $16 that originally sold for $25.

Introducing the Lesson

Write the following on the chalkboard: 20% of 40 = ▓ ? (8) After students have found the answer, rewrite the problem using the same information: 8 is what percent of 40? Students should see that the answer is 20% because 20% of 40 is 8. Tell students that in this lesson they will answer questions like the second one without having to answer a question like the first.

Alternative Examples

Example A—7 is what percent of 560?
Write the number that represents the whole as the denominator.
Write the number that represents the part of the whole as the numerator.
$\frac{7}{560}$
Convert the fraction to a decimal.
$\frac{7}{560} = 0.0125$
Write the decimal as a percent.
$0.0125 = 1.25\%$
7 is **1.25%** of 560.

Example B—What percent of $30 is $10?
Convert the fraction to a decimal.
$\frac{10}{30} = \frac{1}{3} = 0.33\frac{1}{3}$
Write the decimal as a percent.
$0.33\frac{1}{3} = 33\frac{1}{3}\%$
$10 is **$33\frac{1}{3}$%** of $30.

12.8 Finding What Percent One Number Is of Another

Sheri's boss gave her cab fare so that she could make a quick delivery to a customer's store. "The fare is $16, and give the driver a $2 tip," the boss said. Sheri knew that her parents left a 15% tip in restaurants and she wondered what percent she tipped the driver.

Sheri must answer the question "What percent of $16 is $2?"

Examples

To find what percent one number is of another, use division to get a decimal. Then convert the decimal to a percent.

A 12 is what percent of 60?

$\frac{12}{60}$ 12   Write the number that represents the whole as the denominator.
       60   Write the number that represents part of the whole as the numerator.

$\frac{12}{60} = 0.20$ Convert the fraction to a decimal.

$0.20 = 20\%$ Write the decimal as a percent.

12 is **20%** of 60.

B What percent of $16 is $2?

$\frac{2}{16} = 0.125$ Convert the fraction to a decimal.

$0.125 = 12.5\%$ Write the decimal as a percent.

$2 is **12.5%** of $16.

$$\begin{array}{r} 0.125 \\ 16\overline{)2.000} \\ \underline{1\ 6} \\ 40 \\ \underline{32} \\ 80 \\ 80 \end{array}$$

▶ Think and Discuss

1. Find 20% of 60. Explain how this is a check for Example A.

2. Twelve is what percent of 120?

SKILLS

3. What is 100% of 7?

4. Refer to the introduction to this lesson. What percent of the fare was Sheri's tip? Is it more or less than 15%?

5. Name 2 situations in which you might want to find what percent one number is of another.

Exercises

Find each percent. (See Example A.)

6. 14 is what percent of 25? 56%   7. 33 is what percent of 44? 75%

8. 12 is what percent of 75? 16%   9. 31 is what percent of 62? 50%

10. 1 is what percent of 50? 2%   11. 129 is what percent of 300? 43%

Find each percent. (See Example B.)

12. What percent of 200 is 65? 32.5%   13. What percent of 400 is 170? 42.5%

14. What percent of 15 is 18? 120%   15. What percent of 82 is 10.25? 12.5%

16. What percent of 84 is 7? $8\frac{1}{3}$%   17. What percent of 150 is 2? $1\frac{1}{3}$%

▶ **Mixed Practice** (For more practice, see page 439.)

Find each percent.

18. 7 is what percent of 70? 10%   19. 25 is what percent of 75? $33\frac{1}{3}$%

20. 3 is what percent of 4? 75%   21. 28 is what percent of 80? 35%

22. What percent of 25 is 5? 20%   23. What percent of 240 is 6? 2.5%

24. 7 is what percent of 35? 20%   25. 56 is what percent of 128? 43.75%

26. What percent of 3 is 7? $233\frac{1}{3}$%   27. 62 is what percent of 62? 100%

▶ **Applications**

28. Jeanne wanted a one-hundred-fifty-dollar coat and put down a thirty-dollar deposit in order to place the coat on layaway. What percent did she put down? 20%

29. The Recommended Daily Allowance of calcium for young people is 1200 milligrams. What percent of the RDA is 1800 milligrams? 150%

▶ **Review** (Lessons 2.3, 2.7, 3.3)

Multiply or divide.

30. 6.5 × 1000   31. 98.7 ÷ 1000   32. 400 × 500   33. 900 ÷ 30
    6500   0.0987   200,000   30

34. 0.34 ÷ 1000   35. 60 × 9000   36. 0.017 ÷ 100   37. 0.671 × 100
    0.0034 0.00034   540,000   0.00017   67.1

12.9 Finding a Number When a Percent of It Is Known

Fifty freshmen were asked about their favorite books. If 8% of the freshmen chose George Orwell's *1984,* how many students chose this book? You can write this as

8% of 50 is ? .

What percent of the 50 students chose *1984* if 4 students chose this book? You can write this as

?% of 50 is 4 .

These types of questions were solved in Lessons 12.7 and 12.8.

How would you solve the following problem: how many students were asked about their favorite books, if 4 students are 8% of the total?

Examples

To find a number when a percent of it is known, first convert the percent to a decimal. Then divide.

A 8% of what number is 4?

This sentence translates into
8% of ? is 4, which becomes
8% × ? = 4.
0.08 × ? = 4   Write the percent as a
$\frac{0.08}{0.08} \times ? = \frac{4}{0.08}$ decimal. Divide.
? = 50

8% of **50** is 4.

B 15 is 6% of what number?

This sentence translates into
15 = 6% of ?, which becomes
15 = 6% × ?.
15 = 0.06 × ?   Write the percent as
$\frac{15}{0.06} = \frac{0.06}{0.06} \times ?$ a decimal. Divide.
250 = ?

15 is 6% of **250**.

▶ Think and Discuss

1. What is 10% of 170?

2. 17 is 10% of what number?

3. Refer to the introduction to this lesson. Describe the pattern for the three types of percent problems. What are some ways you can remember how to solve each type of percent problem?

4. Look at Example B. Convert 6% to a fraction instead of a decimal. Then solve the problem. Is your answer the same?

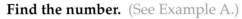
Exercises

Find the number. (See Example A.)

5. 40% of what number is 22? 55.

6. 95% of what number is 38? 40

7. $33\frac{1}{3}$% of what number is 15? 45

8. 0.8% of what number is 2? 250

9. 5% of what number is 25.75? 515

10. $166\frac{2}{3}$% of what number is 65? 39

Find the number. (See Example B.)

11. 16 is 4% of what number? 400

12. 66 is 75% of what number? 88

13. 36 is 50% of what number? 72

14. 0.8 is 0.4% of what number? 200

15. 125 is 12.5% of what number? 1000

16. 9 is $1\frac{1}{3}$% of what number? 675

▶ Mixed Practice (For more practice, see page 440.)

17. 30% of what number is 81? 270

18. 13 is 2% of what number? 650

19. 17 is $33\frac{1}{3}$% of what number? 51

20. 25% of what number is 30? 120

21. 200% of what number is 50 25

22. 40 is 20% of what number? 200

23. 2% of what number is 40? 2000

24. 40 is 1% of what number? 4000

▶ Applications

25. A box of cereal states that a 1-ounce serving contains 0.36 milligram of iron. This is 2% of the Minimum Daily Requirement for teenagers. What is the Minimum Daily Requirement? 18 mg

26. Workers at a telethon for a local charity raised the amount shown. One hundred twenty-five percent of the goal was raised. What was the goal? $40,000

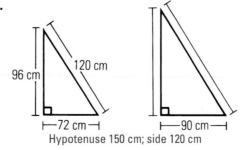

▶ Review (Lesson 11.7)

Find the length of the missing sides in these similar drawings.

27.

5 in.

4 in.

2 in.

2.5 in.

28.

96 cm   120 cm

72 cm   90 cm

Hypotenuse 150 cm; side 120 cm

► **Think and Discuss Answers**
1. 17   **2.** 170
3. In each case you have two known quantities and one unknown quantity. Set up the same kind of statement and substitute a question mark or the unknown quantity. Use the statement 8% × 200 = 16 as an example. To find the third element, multiply. To find either of the other two, divide.
4. yes

★ **Error Alert**
Errors may reveal that students are confusing the types of percent problems they have learned and are using an incorrect procedure to solve for the unknown value.

Reinforcement
Extra Practice, page 440
EP/MR Worksheet 98, TRB, page 98

Project
Find an article or an advertisement in a newspaper or magazine that uses percents. Write a paragraph that explains how percents are used. Then write 3 different mathematical sentences about percents using the information in the article.

Purpose
This lesson shows you how to find the percent of change from one number to another. This is useful, if, for example, you want to express the increase or decrease in a store's sales as a percent.

Introducing the Lesson
Describe the following situation to students: Andrea worked at the Fratinellis' grocery store for $5 per hour. The next week, she got a raise, and now made $6 per hour. How much more money did she earn per hour after her raise? ($1 per hour) Have students compare this increase to her starting amount. Tell students that this lesson shows how to express the increase in her rate of pay as a percent.

Alternative Examples

Example A—Find the percent of increase from 300 to 400.
Subtract to find the amount of increase.
400 − 300 = 100
Divide the amount of increase by the original amount.
$\frac{100}{300} = 0.33\frac{1}{3}$
Write the decimal as a percent.
$0.33\frac{1}{3} = 33\frac{1}{3}\%$
The percent of increase is **$33\frac{1}{3}\%$**.

Example B—Find the percent of decrease from $1400 to $1299.
Subtract to find the amount of decrease.
$1400 − $1299 = $101
Divide the amount of decrease by the original amount.
$\frac{101}{1400} = 0.07\frac{3}{14}$
Write the decimal as a percent.
$0.07\frac{3}{14}\% = 7\frac{3}{14}\%$
The percent of decrease is **$7\frac{3}{14}\%$**.

12.10 Finding the Percent of Change

Anderson's Department Store is offering $15 shirts for $12. What percent off is that?

SALE
Originally $15.00
Now only $12.00

Examples

> **To find the percent of change**, first subtract to find the amount of change. Then use division to find the percent of change.

A Find the percent of increase from 24 to 30.

30 − 24 = 6	Subtract to find the amount of increase.
$\frac{6}{24} = 0.25$	Divide the amount of increase by the original amount.
0.25 = 25%	Write the decimal as a percent.

The percent of increase is **25%**.

B Find the percent of decrease from $15 to $12.

$15 − $12 = $3
$\frac{3}{15} = 0.20$
0.20 = 20%

The percent of decrease is **20%**.

▶ **Think and Discuss**

1. An item's price rose from $40 to $50. To find the percent of change, would you divide 10 by 40 or by 50?

2. A price fell from $50 to $40. To find the percent of change, would you divide 10 by 40 or by 50?

3. Refer to the introduction to this lesson. What was the percent off?

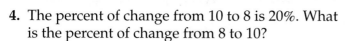

4. The percent of change from 10 to 8 is 20%. What is the percent of change from 8 to 10?

5. Explain why the two percents in Question 4 are not the same.

6. What is the percent of change

Exercises

Find the percent of increase. (

7. $4 to $5
25%

8. $3 to
100%

.50

11. 4000 to 10,000
150%

12. 1000
0.3%

Find the percent of decrease.

15. 5 to 3
40%

16. $25
70%

19. 12 to 11
$8\frac{1}{3}$%

20. $600
25%

P. 281

7-37 all

▶ Mixed Practice (For more

Find the percent of change.

23. 50 to 57
14% increase

24. 48 to 36
25% decrease

25. 60 to 36
40% decrease

o $9.30
7% decrease

27. 1000 to 1001
0.1% increase

28. 575 to 690
20% increase

29. 18 to 15
$16\frac{2}{3}$% decrease

30. $125 to $100
20% decrease

31. $3.90 to $2.73
30% decrease

32. 216 to 189
12.5% decrease

33. $25 to $25.50
2% increase

34. $50 to $200
300% increase

▶ Applications

35. After taking a walk, Andrea's pulse rate rose from 70 beats per minute to 77 beats per minute. What percent of increase is this? 10%

36. A house was originally listed as shown here. After six months, the seller dropped the price to $175,000. By what percent did the seller reduce the price? $12\frac{1}{2}$%

37. Over a 30-year period the number of people living in New York City dropped from 7.9 million to 7.1 million. What is the percent of change? ≈10.13% decrease

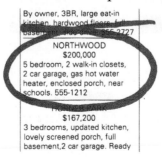

By owner, 3BR, large eat-in kitchen, hardwood floors, full basement. $300 or best 555-2727

NORTHWOOD
$200,000
5 bedroom, 2 walk-in closets, 2 car garage, gas hot water heater, enclosed porch, near schools. 555-1212

$167,200
3 bedrooms, updated kitchen, lovely screened porch, full basement, 2 car garage. Ready

▶ Review (Lesson 1.12)

Estimate.

38. $119.33 − $79.80
≈$40 or $39

39. $66.78 + $39.15
≈$110 or $106

40. $243.88 − $96.25
≈$140 or $148

41. $412.51 + $385.95
≈$900 or $899

42. $489.50 + $103.10
≈$600, $590, or $593

43. $931.98 − $629.57
≈$300 or $302

Purpose

This lesson applies what you've learned about percents to computing sale prices when buying items in a store.

Introducing the Lesson

Write the word "off" on the chalkboard. Ask students to give definitions for the word. Focus the discussion on the meaning as it relates to sale prices. Explain that in this lesson students will be computing sale prices based on a percent off the original price.

12.11 Applying Percents

Charlotte has a job at Grand Canyon National Park. She hopes to find time next summer for some hiking and camping. She has been looking at catalogs for clothes and equipment. Her selections are shown below.

Sun Visor
Reg. $6
10% off

Item No.: A2847

Hiking Boots
Reg. $80
20% off

Item No.: B1134

Thermos Bottle
Reg. $19.90
10% off

Item No.: C3098

Binoculars
Reg. $36
15% off

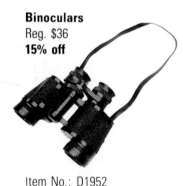

Item No.: D1952

Flashlight
Reg. $5.55
20% off

Item No.: E4204

Knee-Length Socks
Reg. $5.00
5% off

Item No.: F8866

The sale price of Item No. A2847 can be found in two steps:

Step 1. Compute the discount.
   10% of $6 = 0.10 × 6 = 0.60 = $0.60
Step 2. Subtract the discount price from the regular price.
   $6.00 = $0.60 = $5.40
   The sale price of the sun visor is $5.40
Another way to solve this problem is as follows:
Compute the sale price as a percent of the regular price (100% − 10% = 90%).
90% of $6 = 0.90 × 6 = 5.40 = $5.40

PROBLEM SOLVING

▶ Think and Discuss

1. What percent of the regular price is the discount for hiking boots? What percent do you actually pay?
2. What is the sale price of the hiking boots? Use both methods shown to solve.
3. Which of the two methods would you use to estimate? Why would the method you chose help you check your answer?
4. How much sales tax would be charged on the sale price of the hiking boots if the tax rate were 6%?
5. Look at the shipping and handling chart below. What would be the final total if the subtotal (the total of all items before tax and shipping and handling are added) were $25?

Exercises

Copy this order blank and complete it. Order one of each item. You will need the information on shipping and handling that appears below the order blank.

Catalog #	Qty.	Description	Reg. Price	Sale Price Each	Total
A2847	1	Sun visor	6. $ 6.00	7. $ 5.40	8. $ 5.40
B1134	1	Hiking boots	9. 80.00	10. 64.00	11. 64.00
C3098	1	Thermos bottle	12. 19.90	13. 17.91	14. 17.91
D1952	1	Binoculars	15. 36.00	16. 30.60	17. 30.60
E4204	1	Flashlight	18. 5.55	19. 4.44	20. 4.44
F8866	1	Socks	21. 5.00	22. 4.75	23. 4.75
				24. Subtotal	$127.10
				25. Sales Tax: add 6%	7.63
				26. Shipping and Handling	20.00
				27. Total	154.73

Shipping and Handling

Subtotal	
Up to $15	$2.75
$15.01 – $35	$4.50
$35.01 – $55	$6.25
$55.01 – $75	$8.00
$75.01 – $95	$10.00
$95.01 – $120	$20.00
Over $120	$20.00

▶ Review (Lesson 11.1)

Write 3 ratios equivalent to each ratio.

28. 25 students to 1 teacher
29. 150 freshmen to 140 sophomores
30. 75 campers to 10 counselors
31. 52 cards to 4 players

▶ Think and Discuss Answers

1. 20%; 80%
2. $64
3. the second method; you could check using the other method
4. $3.84
5. $31

★ Error Alert

Mistakes may occur if students do not change the percent to a decimal before multiplying.

Answers

28. Sample answers include $\frac{50}{2}, \frac{75}{3}, \frac{100}{4}$
29. Sample answers include $\frac{15}{14}, \frac{30}{28}, \frac{45}{42}$
30. Sample answers include $\frac{150}{20}, \frac{15}{2}, \frac{30}{4}$
31. Sample answers include $\frac{13}{1}, \frac{26}{2}, \frac{39}{3}$

Reinforcement

EP/MR Worksheet 100, TRB, page 100

Challenge

Before the 1929 stock market crash, a share of telephone stock sold for $\$15\frac{1}{4}$. During the crash, the stock dropped 12%. In 1987, the same stock sold for $\$137\frac{3}{4}$. After the 1987 meltdown, it, too, had dropped 12%. By how many more dollars did the stock drop in 1987 than in 1929? ($\$14\frac{7}{10}$)

Chapter 12 Review

REVIEW

Complete each statement. (Lesson 12.1)

1. Percent means per ▇. hundred

2. Six percent ▇ 50 means 6% × 50. of

Write each decimal as a percent and each percent as a decimal. (Lesson 12.2)

3. 0.175 17.5%   4. $33\frac{1}{3}$% 0.33   5. 0.4 40%   6. 7% 0.07   7. 0.875 87.5%

Write each fraction as a percent. (Lesson 12.3)

8. $\frac{3}{10}$ 30%   9. $\frac{5}{8}$ 62.5%   10. $\frac{1}{4}$ 25%   11. $\frac{1}{20}$ 5%   12. $\frac{2}{3}$ $66\frac{2}{3}$%

Write each percent as a fraction in lowest terms. (Lesson 12.4)

13. 48% $\frac{12}{25}$ 14. 50% $\frac{1}{2}$ 15. 37.5% $\frac{3}{8}$ 16. 2% $\frac{1}{50}$ 17. $41\frac{2}{3}$% $\frac{5}{12}$

Write each fraction or decimal as a percent. (Lesson 12.6)

18. $\frac{1}{400}$ 0.25%   19. 5 500%   20. 8.2 820%   21. $\frac{7}{1000}$ 0.7%   22. $\frac{4}{3}$ $133\frac{1}{3}$%

Write each percent as a fraction and as a decimal. (Lesson 12.6)

23. $\frac{3}{4}$% $\frac{3}{400}$; 0.0075   24. $\frac{1}{10}$% $\frac{1}{1000}$; 0.001   25. $\frac{7}{8}$% $\frac{7}{800}$; 0.00875   26. $\frac{7}{4}$% $\frac{7}{400}$; 0.0175   27. $\frac{3}{5}$% $\frac{3}{500}$; 0.006

Find each number or percent. (Lessons 12.7, 12.8, 12.9)

28. 65% of 480 312   29. 2% of $56 $1.12   30. 580% of 25 145   31. $\frac{1}{2}$% of 44 0.22

32. 77.5 is what percent of 775? 10%   33. 15 is what percent of 300? 5%

34. 594 is what percent of 600? 99%   35. 224 is what percent of 28? 800%

36. 40% of what number is 24? 60   37. 3% of what number is 27? 900

38. 225% of what number is 72? 32   39. 50.5% of what number is 6.06? 12

Find the percent of change (Lesson 12.10)

40. 75 to 100 $33\frac{1}{3}$% increase   41. 30 to 24 20% decrease

Find the sale price of each item. (Lesson 12.11)

42. Mittens, regularly $25, now 10% off $22.50   43. Camera, was $278, marked down 35% $180.70

4. The percent of change from 10 to 8 is 20%. What is the percent of change from 8 to 10?

5. Explain why the two percents in Question 4 are not the same.

6. What is the percent of change from 40 to 60? Solve mentally.

Exercises

Find the percent of increase. (See Example A.)

7. $4 to $5
25%

8. $3 to $6
100%

9. $2 to $3
50%

10. $4.50 to $8.50
$88\frac{8}{9}$%

11. 4000 to 10,000
150%

12. 1000 to 1003
0.3%

13. 30 to 90
200%

14. $32 to $38
18.75%

Find the percent of decrease. (See Example B.)

15. 5 to 3
40%

16. $25 to $7.50
70%

17. $235 to $205
$12\frac{36}{47}$%

18. $45 to $36
20%

19. 12 to 11
$8\frac{1}{3}$%

20. $600 to $450
25%

21. 38 to 19
50%

22. 21 to 14
$33\frac{1}{3}$%

Mixed Practice (For more practice, see page 440.)

Find the percent of change.

23. 50 to 57
14% increase

24. 48 to 36
25% decrease

25. 60 to 36
40% decrease

26. $10.00 to $9.30
7% decrease

27. 1000 to 1001
0.1% increase

28. 575 to 690
20% increase

29. 18 to 15
$16\frac{2}{3}$% decrease

30. $125 to $100
20% decrease

31. $3.90 to $2.73
30% decrease

32. 216 to 189
12.5% decrease

33. $25 to $25.50
2% increase

34. $50 to $200
300% increase

Applications

35. After taking a walk, Andrea's pulse rate rose from 70 beats per minute to 77 beats per minute. What percent of increase is this? 10%

36. A house was originally listed as shown here. After six months, the seller dropped the price to $175,000. By what percent did the seller reduce the price? $12\frac{1}{2}$%

37. Over a 30-year period the number of people living in New York City dropped from 7.9 million to 7.1 million. What is the percent of change? ≈10.13% decrease

> By owner, 3BR, large eat-in kitchen, hardwood floors, full basement. 303-317-3. 555-2727
>
> NORTHWOOD
> $200,000
> 5 bedroom, 2 walk-in closets, 2 car garage, gas hot water heater, enclosed porch, near schools. 555-1212
>
> HOMER MARK
> $167,200
> 3 bedrooms, updated kitchen, lovely screened porch, full basement, 2 car garage. Ready

Review (Lesson 1.12)

Estimate.

38. $119.33 − $79.80
≈$40 or $39

39. $66.78 + $39.15
≈$110 or $106

40. $243.88 − $96.25
≈$140 or $148

41. $412.51 + $385.95
≈$900 or $899

42. $489.50 + $103.10
≈$600, $590, or $593

43. $931.98 − $629.57
≈$300 or $302

▶ **Think and Discuss Answers**
1. 40
2: 50
3. 20%
4. 25%
5. The original amount forms the divisor and, in each case, the original amount is different.
6. 50%

★ **Error Alert**
Errors may reveal that students are using the final amount instead of the original amount when dividing.

Reinforcement
Extra Practice, page 440
EP/MR Worksheet 99, TRB, page 99

Challenge
Calculate the percent increase or decrease in the following problems. Round your answers to the nearest tenth.

1. Suzanne went on a diet and lost 12 pounds. If she originally weighed 158 pounds, figure out the percent change in her weight. (7.6% decrease)

2. Brian grew $5\frac{1}{2}$ inches between the summer after eighth grade and his high school graduation. If he was 5 feet $9\frac{1}{4}$ inches when he graduated, what was the percent change in his height? (8.6% increase)

3. During the first semester of school, Maria Luisa bought 14 CDs. During the second semester, however, her classes at school were more difficult so she quit her job. As a result, she only bought 1 CD. What was the percent change in the number of CDs that Maria Luisa bought? (92.9% decrease)

Objective

• To apply your knowledge of percents to real-life situations

Purpose

This lesson applies what you've learned about percents to computing sale prices when buying items in a store.

Introducing the Lesson

Write the word "off" on the chalkboard. Ask students to give definitions for the word. Focus the discussion on the meaning as it relates to sale prices. Explain that in this lesson students will be computing sale prices based on a percent off the original price.

12.11 Applying Percents

Charlotte has a job at Grand Canyon National Park. She hopes to find time next summer for some hiking and camping. She has been looking at catalogs for clothes and equipment. Her selections are shown below.

Sun Visor
Reg. $6
10% off

Item No.: A2847

Hiking Boots
Reg. $80
20% off

Item No.: B1134

Thermos Bottle
Reg. $19.90
10% off

Item No.: C3098

Binoculars
Reg. $36
15% off

Item No.: D1952

Flashlight
Reg. $5.55
20% off

Item No.: E4204

Knee-Length Socks
Reg. $5.00
5% off

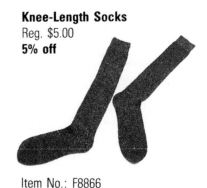

Item No.: F8866

The sale price of Item No. A2847 can be found in two steps:

Step 1. Compute the discount.
10% of $6 = 0.10 × 6 = 0.60 = $0.60

Step 2. Subtract the discount price from the regular price.
$6.00 = $0.60 = $5.40
The sale price of the sun visor is $5.40
Another way to solve this problem is as follows:
Compute the sale price as a percent of the regular price (100% − 10% = 90%).
90% of $6 = 0.90 × 6 = 5.40 = $5.40

▶ Think and Discuss

PROBLEM SOLVING

1. What percent of the regular price is the discount for hiking boots? What percent do you actually pay?

2. What is the sale price of the hiking boots? Use both methods shown to solve.

3. Which of the two methods would you use to estimate? Why would the method you chose help you check your answer?

4. How much sales tax would be charged on the sale price of the hiking boots if the tax rate were 6%?

5. Look at the shipping and handling chart below. What would be the final total if the subtotal (the total of all items before tax and shipping and handling are added) were $25?

Exercises

Copy this order blank and complete it. Order one of each item. You will need the information on shipping and handling that appears below the order blank.

Catalog #	Qty.	Description	Reg. Price	Sale Price Each	Total
A2847	1	Sun visor	**6.** $ 6.00	**7.** $ 5.40	**8.** $ 5.40
B1134	1	Hiking boots	**9.** 80.00	**10.** 64.00	**11.** 64.00
C3098	1	Thermos bottle	**12.** 19.90	**13.** 17.91	**14.** 17.91
D1952	1	Binoculars	**15.** 36.00	**16.** 30.60	**17.** 30.60
E4204	1	Flashlight	**18.** 5.55	**19.** 4.44	**20.** 4.44
F8866	1	Socks	**21.** 5.00	**22.** 4.75	**23.** 4.75

24. Subtotal	$127.10
25. Sales Tax: add 6%	7.63
26. Shipping and Handling	20.00
27. Total	154.73

Shipping and Handling

Subtotal

Up to $15 . . . . $2.75
$15.01 – $35 . . . . $4.50
$35.01 – $55 . . . . $6.25
$55.01 – $75 . . . . $8.00

$75.01 – $95 . . . . $10.00
$95.01 – $120 . . . . $20.00
Over $120 . . . . $20.00

▶ Review (Lesson 11.1)

Write 3 ratios equivalent to each ratio.

28. 25 students to 1 teacher

29. 150 freshmen to 140 sophomores

30. 75 campers to 10 counselors

31. 52 cards to 4 players

Chapter 12 Review

REVIEW

Complete each statement. (Lesson 12.1)

1. Percent means per ___. hundred

2. Six percent ___ 50 means 6% × 50. of

Write each decimal as a percent and each percent as a decimal. (Lesson 12.2)

3. 0.175 17.5%   4. $33\frac{1}{3}$% 0.33   5. 0.4 40%   6. 7% 0.07   7. 0.875 87.5%

Write each fraction as a percent. (Lesson 12.3)

8. $\frac{3}{10}$ 30%   9. $\frac{5}{8}$ 62.5%   10. $\frac{1}{4}$ 25%   11. $\frac{1}{20}$ 5%   12. $\frac{2}{3}$ $66\frac{2}{3}$%

Write each percent as a fraction in lowest terms. (Lesson 12.4)

13. 48% $\frac{12}{25}$ 14. 50% $\frac{1}{2}$ 15. 37.5% $\frac{3}{8}$ 16. 2% $\frac{1}{50}$ 17. $41\frac{2}{3}$% $\frac{5}{12}$

Write each fraction or decimal as a percent. (Lesson 12.6)

18. $\frac{1}{400}$ 0.25%   19. 5 500%   20. 8.2 820%   21. $\frac{7}{1000}$ 0.7%   22. $\frac{4}{3}$ $133\frac{1}{3}$%

Write each percent as a fraction and as a decimal. (Lesson 12.6)

23. $\frac{3}{4}$% $\frac{3}{400}$; 0.0075   24. $\frac{1}{10}$% $\frac{1}{1000}$; 0.001   25. $\frac{7}{8}$% $\frac{7}{800}$; 0.00875   26. $\frac{7}{4}$% $\frac{7}{400}$; 0.0175   27. $\frac{3}{5}$% $\frac{3}{500}$; 0.006

Find each number or percent. (Lessons 12.7, 12.8, 12.9)

28. 65% of 480 312   29. 2% of $56 $1.12   30. 580% of 25 145   31. $\frac{1}{2}$% of 44 0.22

32. 77.5 is what percent of 775? 10%   33. 15 is what percent of 300? 5%

34. 594 is what percent of 600? 99%   35. 224 is what percent of 28? 800%

36. 40% of what number is 24? 60   37. 3% of what number is 27? 900

38. 225% of what number is 72? 32   39. 50.5% of what number is 6.06? 12

Find the percent of change (Lesson 12.10)

40. 75 to 100 $33\frac{1}{3}$% increase   41. 30 to 24 20% decrease

Find the sale price of each item. (Lesson 12.11)

42. Mittens, regularly $25, now 10% off $22.50   43. Camera, was $278, marked down 35% $180.70

Chapter 12 Test

TEST

Find each number or percent.

1. 2 is what percent of 8? 25%

2. 2% of 50 1

3. $33\frac{1}{3}$% of what number is 284? 852

4. 98% of what number is 343? 350

5. 78% of 650 507

6. 195 is what percent of 39? 500%

7. 145 is 50% of what number? 290

8. $12\frac{1}{2}$% of 86 10.75

Find the percent of change.

9. 8 to 24 200% increase

10. 48 to 60 25% increase

11. 300 to 270 10% decrease

12. What is the total of all the percents in a circle graph? 100%

Write each decimal as a fraction and as a percent.

13. 0.06 $\frac{3}{50}$; 6%

14. 0.625 $\frac{5}{8}$; 62.5%

15. 0.001 $\frac{1}{1000}$; 0.1%

Write each percent as a fraction and as a decimal.

16. 80% $\frac{4}{5}$; 0.8

17. 450% $\frac{9}{2}$; 4.5

18. 4% $\frac{2}{50}$; 0.04

Write each fraction as a decimal and as a percent.

19. $\frac{2}{5}$ 0.4; 40%

20. $\frac{3}{20}$ 0.15; 15%

21. $\frac{81}{9}$ 9.0; 900%

Solve.

22. A watch is marked down 25% from $19.96. How much is the sale price? $14.97

23. Jose left a 15% tip. The bill came to $29. How much was his tip? $4.35

Chapter Tests
Short Answer, Forms A and B, TRB, pages 311–312, 313–314
Multiple Choice, Forms A and B, TRB, pages 379–380, 380–382

Teaching Aids
Answer sheet
TA 8, TRB, page 161a
Teaching suggestions precede the Teaching Aids worksheets.

Use probability to find the likelihood of

• being born on a Saturday.

• having a telephone number that ends with zero.

• getting heads in a coin toss.

• being in the same math class as a friend.

What are some other ways to use probability?

Probability

A geneticist studies and researches heredity, the passing of characteristics from one generation to the next.

- Geneticists work in laboratories, hospitals, and universities.

- A geneticist must be able to work on a project that may take years of research and should enjoy working with plants, animals, and people.

- A geneticist measures small quantities, analyzes experimental data, writes reports, and reads research journals. The individual measures the similarities and differences of related organisms and determines the probability of them displaying certain characteristics.

- To become a geneticist, an individual usually needs an advanced degree, such as a doctorate, from a university.

- Related careers include research assistants, medical personnel, biologists, horticulturists, and laboratory technicians.

CAREER

GENETICIST

PORTFOLIO PROJECT: *Make a tree diagram for a pea-plant characteristic.*

1. To be short, a pea plant has to inherit two genes for being short. Otherwise, it will be tall. Suppose you have two parent pea plants—each has one gene for being tall and one for being short.

2. Make a tree diagram to show the possible combinations of pea plants that could result from the two parent pea plants. *Show the math.*

3. Use your tree diagram to tell what the probability is for the plant to be tall and for it to be short. *Show the math.*

About the Portfolio Project

Students should create a tree diagram, labeling the parts as short genes or tall genes. They then draw and label each possible combination. Under the diagrams, students should calculate for each possibility.

Assessment: The individual scoring rubric on page 161 of the Teacher's Resource Binder can be reproduced and used for assessment. Include the following information in the last two boxes. Students should have:
- properly drawn the tree diagram to illustrate the disbursement of genes.
- accurately figured the probability of being tall and of being short.

13.1 Introduction to Probability

If you flip a coin into the air, the chance of it landing heads is 50%. The chance of it landing tails is also 50%. In mathematics, chance is called probability. You could say, then, that the probability of a tossed coin landing heads is 50%. Fifty percent is the same as 0.5, $\frac{1}{2}$, and 1 out of 2.

▶ **Express Yourself**

Here are some terms you will become familiar with:

chance or **probability**   the likelihood of a particular result

outcome   the result of one experiment

event   an outcome or a group of outcomes

favorable outcome   the desired outcome

Complete each statement.

1. The desired outcome is a(n) ____ . Favorable outcome
2. Another word for chance is ____ . Probability
3. A group of outcomes is a(n) ____ . Event

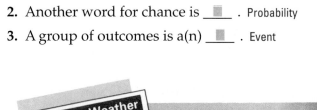

Today's Weather Outlook

Partly cloudy
30% chance of rain
High 77° F /Low 55° F

▶ Practice What You Know

Probability involves using fractions or ratios. You are familiar with fractions, so you already know something about probability.

Look at the concert tickets below and find the following.

4. the ratio of the number of Row A tickets to the total number of tickets $\frac{4}{20}$

5. the ratio of the number of Row A tickets to the number of Row B tickets $\frac{4}{4}$

6. the ratio of the number of tickets marked "D2" to the total number of tickets $\frac{1}{20}$

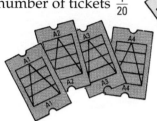
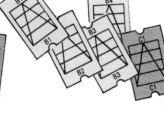

7. the ratio of the number of tickets in rows A through E to the total number of tickets $\frac{20}{20}$

8. the ratio of tickets in Row F to the total number of tickets $\frac{0}{20}$

Answer the following questions.

9. How would you write the ratio for Question 4 as a fraction in lowest terms? $\frac{1}{5}$

10. What whole number is equal to the ratio you found for Question 7? 1

Probability also involves making choices.

11. How many choices do you have if you are asked to pick a letter of the alphabet? 26 choices

12. How many choices do you have if you are asked to choose a whole number from 1 to 50? 50 choices

13. How many choices do you have if you are asked to pick a whole number from 10 to 50? 41 choices

14. How many choices do you have if you are asked to pick a month from the months in a year? 12 choices

15. How many choices do you have if you are asked to pick a date in April? 30 choices

Teaching Aids
Patterns: Number cube, spinners, protractor
TA 3, TRB, page 156
Teaching suggestions precede the Teaching Aids worksheets.

Challenge
Work in groups of five. You will each have a number cube and a tally sheet with the labels 1, 2, 3, 4, 5, and 6. Now roll the cube, put a tally mark under the appropriate number, and repeat these steps for a total of 50 times. Total your marks for each digit. Do your totals follow a pattern? (Answers depend on results of experiment.) Now add your six totals to the totals for each digit that others have in your group. Did the experiments show each digit about the same number of times? (Totals should show outcomes that are fairly close.) Now add the totals from each group in the class. What conclusions can you draw? (Students should see that the results are usually more evenly distributed when the experiment is performed hundreds of thousands of times.)

Objective

- To find the probability of a given event when all outcomes are equally likely.

Purpose

Understanding how to find probabilities can help you determine how likely it is that an event, such as the probability of picking a winning ticket from a set of 20 tickets, will happen.

Introducing the Lesson

Review the definition of *probability* (Lesson 13.1). (Probability, or chance, is the likelihood of a particular result.)

Review *outcomes* and *favorable outcome.* (An outcome is a result. A favorable outcome is a desired result.) Ask: Suppose you want to pick a multiple of five from a stack of cards marked with the numbers 1 through 20. What are the favorable outcomes? (5, 10, 15, 20) How many possible outcomes are there when you choose a card from the stack? (20)

Alternative Examples

Example A—Find the probability of spinning an even number if the spinner has equal sections marked 3, 6, 9, 12, 15.

There are 5 possible outcomes; 2 outcomes are favorable: 6, 12. The probability you will spin an even number is $\frac{2}{5}$.

Example B—Find the probability of picking a month that starts with the letter *M* from the months of the year. All outcomes are equally likely.

There are 12 possible outcomes; 2 outcomes are favorable: March, May. The probability of picking March or May is $\frac{2}{12}$ or $\frac{1}{6}$.

13.2 Finding Simple Probability

One student from the list shown here will be selected to be an extra in a new film. If everyone has an equal chance, what is the probability that Alexis will be selected?

Examples

To find the probability of a given event, use the formula

$$\text{Probability of an event} = \frac{\text{Number of favorable outcomes}}{\text{Total number of possible outcomes}}$$

Outcomes with equal chances of occurring are called **equally likely outcomes**.

A Find the probability that Alexis will be selected.

There are 30 possible outcomes; 1 outcome is favorable.
The probability that Alexis will be selected is $\frac{1}{30}$.

B Find the probability of picking a Friday from the dates shown. (All outcomes are equally likely.)

4 favorable outcomes: 7, 14, 21, 28; 28 possible outcomes
The probability of picking a Friday is $\frac{4}{28}$, or $\frac{1}{7}$.

▶ Think and Discuss

1. You are picking a whole number from 0 to 30 out of a jar. You want to know the probability that the number picked is evenly divisible by 7. List the favorable outcomes.

2. Find the probability in Question 1.

3. List the favorable outcomes of rolling a number less than 3 with a number cube.

4. Refer to the introduction to this lesson. What is the probability that Alexis will be selected? Liz is a friend of Alexis. Find the probability that Alexis or Liz will be chosen.

Exercises

Find the probability of choosing each of the following from the list shown at the right. (See Example A.)

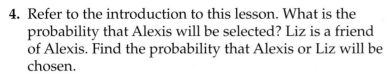

FRESHMEN | SOPHOMORE
EVELYN | JEANNE
MONTGOMERY | MARK
JOY | ABDUL
JEFFERY
MARY

5. a freshman $\frac{5}{8}$ 6. a name that begins with A $\frac{1}{8}$

7. a girl $\frac{1}{2}$

APRIL calendar

Find the probability of choosing each of the following from the dates shown. (All outcomes are equally likely.) (See Example B.)

8. a Thursday $\frac{2}{15}$ 9. a date that has a 5 in it $\frac{1}{10}$

10. a Monday $\frac{2}{15}$ 11. a date that ends in 0 $\frac{1}{10}$

▶ **Mixed Practice** (For more practice, see page 441.)

Find the probability of choosing each of the following from the zip code list shown here. (All outcomes are equally likely.)

60922
60901
60106
92753
93421

12. 60922 $\frac{1}{5}$

13. a zip code with a digit of 6 $\frac{3}{5}$

14. a zip code containing an even digit $\frac{5}{5}$ 15. a zip code with a last digit of 1 $\frac{2}{5}$

16. a zip code with a 9 in it $\frac{4}{5}$ 17. a zip code evenly divisible by 3 $\frac{0}{5}$

▶ **Applications**

18. Mark has 6 pairs of white socks, 3 pairs of black socks, and 1 pair of red socks in his drawer. If he closes his eyes, what is the probability that Mark will pick the red pair? $\frac{1}{10}$

19. The weather forecast predicts a forty percent chance of rain. What is the probability of rain? $\frac{2}{5}$; 40%

▶ **Review** (Lesson 11.1)

Write each as a ratio in 3 different ways.

20. 1 prize: 10 people 1 to 10; 1 : 10; $\frac{1}{10}$

21. 5 boys: 8 girls 5 to 8; 5 : 8; $\frac{5}{8}$

22. 2 vases: 12 roses 2 to 12; 2 : 12; $\frac{2}{12}$

1. Favorable outcomes are 7, 14, 21, and 28.
2. $\frac{4}{31}$
3. Favorable outcomes are 1 and 2.
4. probability is $\frac{1}{30}$; probability is $\frac{2}{30}$, or $\frac{1}{15}$

★ **Error Alert**

Errors may occur because students count the number of favorable and/or possible outcomes incorrectly.

Reinforcement

Extra Practice, page 441
EP/MR Worksheet 101, TRB, page 101

Teaching Aids

Patterns: Number cube, spinners, protractor
TA 3, TRB, page 156
Teaching suggestions precede the Teaching Aids worksheets.

Project

When you toss a penny, the probability of its landing either heads or tails is 1 out of 2 or $\frac{1}{2}$, assuming there are no imbalances in the penny to make one outcome more likely than another. Do you think that the results will be the same if you spin a penny as they are when you toss a penny? Take a penny and spin it so that it rotates for a large number of turns. Observe how the penny lands. Repeat the spin for a total of 50 times and record the number of heads. Is the number of heads about 25 (one half of 50)? (Answers may vary; some students' results may not be very close to 25.) Now compile the results of all the students. What conclusions can you draw? (sample answer: spinning the coins hundreds of times produces about the same results as tossing them)

13.3 Computing Odds

John felt pretty good after he learned about probability in mathematics class. "What are my chances of getting this job?" he asked on an interview at the department store that afternoon. "I'd say the odds are 1 to 3 that you will be hired," the manager replied.

John expected a probability and got odds instead. The two ideas are related.

Examples

To find odds, use the appropriate formula.

Odds of an event happening = $\dfrac{\text{Number of favorable outcomes}}{\text{Number of unfavorable outcomes}}$

Odds against an event = $\dfrac{\text{Number of unfavorable outcomes}}{\text{Number of favorable outcomes}}$

Odds can be stated in different ways: $\frac{1}{3}$, 1 : 3, and 1 to 3.

A **Find the odds of a license plate starting with a number rather than a letter. (Assume all outcomes are equally likely.)**

The number of favorable outcomes is 10 (digits 0 to 9).
The number of unfavorable outcomes is 26 (letters A to Z).
The odds of a license plate starting with a number are 10 to 26, or **5 to 13**.

B **Find the odds against being elected class president if 4 other people are running. (All outcomes are equally likely.)**

The number of unfavorable outcomes is 4.
The number of favorable outcomes is 1.
The odds against being elected president are **4 to 1**.

▶ Think and Discuss

1. What are two other ways of writing the odds $\frac{6}{7}$?

2. What are the odds against rolling a 2 on a number cube?

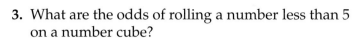
3. What are the odds of rolling a number less than 5 on a number cube?

4. Refer to the introduction to this lesson. What was the probability of John getting the job?

5. What do you get if you multiply the odds of an event occurring by the odds that the event will not occur?

Exercises

Find the odds of drawing each of the following from this list of names. (See Example A.)

Sue Barr
Mark Foreman
Judy Steinberg
Bill Wilson
Amanda Myer
Melissa Jones
Jackson Smith

6. a woman's name 4 to 3   7. a man's name 3 to 4   8. Sue Barr's name 1 to 6

9. a name with the initials JS 2 to 5   10. a name that begins with A 1 to 6

What are the odds against pulling each of the following from the pile shown here? (See Example B.)

11. a red sweat shirt 3 to 2

12. a number less than 20 3 to 2

13. a white sweat shirt 2 to 3

14. a number with a 5 in it 2 to 3

▶ Mixed Practice (For more practice, see page 441.)

A new company has telephone extensions 1 through 20. The numbers are assigned randomly. Find the following odds.

15. of having extension number 15
    1 to 19

16. against having an even extension
    1 to 1

17. of having an extension number greater than 10 1 to 1

18. against having an extension that is a multiple of 5 4 to 1

▶ Applications

19. Nine out of ten dentists recommend Nofuss floss. What are the odds that your dentist will recommend this floss? 9 to 1

20. The names of the 50 states are placed in a bag. What are the odds of choosing 1 of the 19 states that border the Pacific Ocean or the Atlantic Ocean? 19 to 31

▶ Review (Lesson 5.6)

Write in lowest terms.

21. $\frac{5}{15}$ $\frac{1}{3}$
22. $\frac{16}{20}$ $\frac{4}{5}$
23. $\frac{35}{60}$ $\frac{7}{12}$
24. $\frac{12}{48}$ $\frac{1}{4}$
25. $\frac{56}{90}$ $\frac{28}{45}$
26. $\frac{78}{100}$ $\frac{39}{50}$
27. $\frac{225}{375}$ $\frac{3}{5}$

▶ **Think and Discuss Answers**
1. 6 to 7, 6:7
2. 5 to 1
3. 4 to 2, 2 to 1
4. $\frac{1}{4}$
5. 1

★ **Error Alert**
Errors may occur because students still use the total number of possible outcomes as the denominator of the fraction (as in probability) instead of the number of favorable or unfavorable outcomes.

Reinforcement
Extra Practice, page 441
EP/MR Worksheet 102, TRB, page 102

Teaching Aids
Patterns: Number cube, spinners, protractor
TA 3, TRB, page 156
Teaching suggestions precede the Teaching Aids worksheets.

Challenge
In a class of 30 students, 11 are boys and 19 are girls. The seats are assigned randomly, and only one student is nearest the door. What are the odds that the person nearest to the door will be a girl? (19 to 11) Now pretend you are one of the 30 students. What are the odds against the person nearest the door being you? (29 to 1). Now find the odds against your sitting nearest the door in your own math class. (Answer depends upon the size of the class.)

T293

Objectives

- To distinguish probability from odds
- To find odds given the probability
- To find the probability given the odds

Purpose

Probability and odds are two different things. In this lesson you determine how probability and odds are alike and how they are different. Then you will not confuse the odds of winning a contest with the probability of winning.

Introducing the Lesson

Use the following exercises to review the terms: *possible outcomes, favorable outcomes,* and *unfavorable outcomes.* Suppose you are selecting a marble from a bag that contains 3 red, 4 blue, and 6 yellow marbles. What is the total number of possible outcomes? (13) Determine the number of favorable outcomes if you want a red marble (3), a blue marble (4), or a yellow marble (6). Determine the number of unfavorable outcomes if you want a red marble (10), a blue marble (9), or a yellow marble (7).

Reviewing finding simple probability (Lesson 13.2) and computing odds (Lesson 13.3). On the chalkboard, write the formulas for finding the probability of, odds of, and odds against an event.

Have students answer the following questions. If you have a bag of marbles containing 3 red, 4 blue, and 6 yellow marbles, what is the probability of picking a red marble? (3 to 13) What are the odds that you will pick a red marble? (3 to 10) What are the odds that you will not pick a red marble? (10 to 3) Point out that the denominator is always the larger number in a probability ratio but not in an odds ratio.

Answers

1. The odds can be thought of as fractions also. They are alike because they all have 1 as the numerator or denominator. They are different because the fractions are all different values.

13.4 Relating Odds to Probability

"**T**he key in your hand starts one of the five cars in front of you," Skip Basil, the game show host, told the nervous contestant. "That makes the odds 1 to 5 that you will be driving home in luxury tonight."

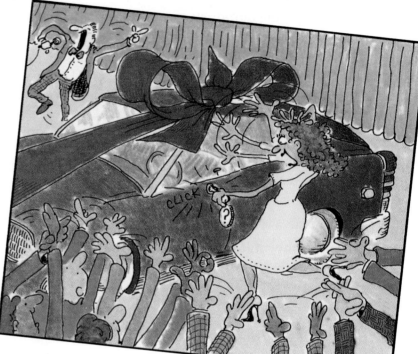

What is wrong with Skip's statement?

People often confuse probability and odds. Examine the situation of the contestant and you can see how odds and probability are related. On the game show, there are five cars in all. The key will start one car, but won't start the other four cars. So,

$$\text{Probability of starting} = \tfrac{1}{5}$$
$$\text{Odds of starting} \quad = 1 \text{ to } 4$$
$$\text{Odds against starting} = 4 \text{ to } 1$$

1. Compare the answers given above for probability and odds. How are they alike? How are they different?

If you know the probability of an event occurring, you can find the odds of and against the event occurring. For example, the probability of the contestant starting the car is $\frac{1}{5}$.

Probability		Odds Of	Odds Against
$\dfrac{1}{5}$	Numerator remains the same. Subtract numerator from denominator	$\dfrac{1}{4}$	Reverse. $\dfrac{4}{1}$

If you know the odds of (or against) any event occurring, you can find the probability of the event.

Odds Against		Odds Of		Probability
$\frac{4}{1}$	Reverse.	$\frac{1}{4}$	Numerator stays the same.	$\frac{1}{5}$
			Add numerator and denominator.	

2. Find the probability of the contestant starting the car if the key could start 2 cars out of 6. $\frac{2}{6}$ or $\frac{1}{3}$

3. Find the odds of the contestant starting the car if the key could start 2 cars out of 6. $\frac{2}{4}$ or $\frac{1}{2}$

4. Find the odds against the contestant starting the car if the key could start 2 cars out of 6. $\frac{4}{2}$ or $\frac{2}{1}$

5. According to a poll, Cleaver is considered a 3-to-2 favorite to win the election. Does the ratio $\frac{3}{2}$ represent the probability of Cleaver winning, the odds of Cleaver winning, or the odds against Cleaver winning? Odds of Cleaver winning

6. A computer selects 10 names to receive prize notices out of 1000 different names on its list. Your name is on the list. What is the probability that you will receive a notice? What are the odds of receiving a notice? What are the odds against receiving a notice? $\frac{10}{1000}$ or $\frac{1}{100}$; $\frac{10}{990}$ or $\frac{1}{99}$; $\frac{990}{10}$ or $\frac{99}{1}$

7. Tricia claimed, "The odds are 100 to 1 against me winning the contest." If her statement is correct, find the probability that she will win the contest. $\frac{1}{101}$

8. The weather announcer states that there is a 40% chance of rain tomorrow. Find the probability that it will rain, the odds that it will rain, and the odds that it will not rain. $\frac{40}{100}$ or $\frac{2}{5}$; $\frac{40}{60}$ or $\frac{2}{3}$; $\frac{60}{40}$ or $\frac{3}{2}$

People use phrases involving probability loosely. Often they confuse probability and odds. State what is wrong with each statement below and rewrite each correctly.

9. Madelyn has a 50–50 chance.

10. The odds are 1 in a million.

11. The probability of winning is 2 to 1.

▶ **Review** (Lesson 6.5)

Estimate each product.

12. $\frac{8}{17} \times 20$ ≈ 10   13. $\frac{19}{21} \times 4\frac{1}{3}$ ≈ 4   14. $\frac{4}{15} \times 28$ ≈ 7   15. $\frac{17}{19} \times 6\frac{2}{29}$ ≈ 12

Answers (continued)

9. Chance means probability and a $\frac{50}{50}$ probability would mean that she would definitely win. Madelyn's odds of winning are $\frac{50}{50}$ (that is, she has a 50% chance of winning).

10. The statement should be "The probability is 1 in a million." Odds are always expressed in terms of favorable (or unfavorable) outcomes to unfavorable (or favorable) outcomes, not in terms of the total number of outcomes, which the word "in" suggests.

11. A probability can never be greater than 1. The statement should be "The odds of winning are 2 to 1" (or "the probability of winning is $\frac{2}{3}$").

★ **Error Alert**

Incorrect answers may mean that students are confusing odds with probability, or odds for with odds against.

Reinforcement

EP/MR Worksheet 103, TRB, page 103

Teaching Aids

Patterns: Number cube, spinners, protractor TA 3, TRB, page 156
Teaching suggestions precede the Teaching Aids worksheets.

Challenge

Probability, or chance, is often expressed as a percent. A weatherman predicts a 30% chance of snow. What is the probability of having snow, expressed as a fraction? (30% = $\frac{30}{100}$ = $\frac{3}{10}$) What are the odds in favor of snow? ($\frac{3}{7}$) What are the odds against having snow? ($\frac{7}{3}$) How are the ratios for the odds related? (They are reciprocals.)

13.5 Using a Tree Diagram

Tyrone was planning his classes for the following school year. He could not decide between speech and literature for his English requirement, and among art, music, and typing for one elective. How many different pairs of classes could he choose?

A situation involving more than one decision or set of outcomes is called a **multiple event**.

Examples

To show all outcomes of a multiple event, draw a tree diagram.

A **Draw a tree diagram that shows Tyrone's different choices.**

Tree Diagram

English Requirement	Electives	Class Choices (Outcomes)
speech	art	speech and art
	music	speech and music
	typing	speech and typing
literature	art	literature and art
	music	literature and music
	typing	literature and typing

Tyrone has **6** possible pairs of classes.

B **Find the probability of two heads, if a coin is tossed twice.**

Draw a tree diagram.

1st Toss	2nd Toss	Outcomes	
heads	heads	heads	heads
	tails	heads	tails
tails	heads	tails	heads
	tails	tails	tails

There are 4 possible outcomes. One outcome is favorable.

The probability of tossing two heads is $\frac{1}{4}$.

▶ Think and Discuss

1. Find the probability of 6 and heads, if a number cube is rolled and a coin is tossed. Draw a tree diagram.

2. Refer to the introduction to this lesson. What are Tyrone's possible choices?

3. Where do you think the tree diagram got its name?

Exercises

Draw a tree diagram listing all possible outcomes for each of the following. (See Example A.)

4. rolling a number cube twice

5. tossing a coin three times

6. making a ham, cheese, or tuna sandwich with white, whole wheat, or rye bread

7. choosing a boy and a girl from Ann, Betty, Cathy, David, Ed, and Fred

If these two sets of letters are placed face down, what is the probability of drawing the following? (See Example B.)

8. a T and an A $\frac{1}{14}$ 9. a T and an M $\frac{1}{28}$ 10. an E and an A $\frac{1}{7}$

▶ Mixed Practice (For more practice, see page 442.)

Draw a tree diagram and find the probability of the underlined event.

11. a coin is tossed and a number cube is rolled; <u>heads and 3</u>

12. a number cube is rolled twice; <u>1 and 5</u>, in that order

▶ Applications

13. Draw a tree diagram of all possible outcomes if you have a choice of ordering a pepperoni, sausage, or vegetarian pizza with a thin, thick, or deep-dish crust. How many possible pizzas are there?

14. In the 1976 World Series, the Reds beat the Yankees in four games. What are some of the other ways those four games could have ended? Draw a tree diagram to show how the four games could have ended.

▶ Review (Lessons 6.1, 6.2, 6.4)

Multiply. Write the answers in lowest terms.

15. $\frac{3}{5} \times \frac{1}{2}$ $\frac{3}{10}$ 16. $1\frac{1}{2} \times \frac{4}{9}$ $\frac{2}{3}$ 17. $\frac{7}{8} \times \frac{6}{7}$ $\frac{3}{4}$ 18. $2\frac{2}{3} \times 1\frac{1}{5}$ $3\frac{1}{5}$ 19. $\frac{5}{15} \times \frac{18}{21}$ $\frac{2}{7}$

Alternative Examples (continued)

Example B—Spin a game spinner 2 times. Find the probability of getting red and then green if the spinner is $\frac{1}{3}$ red, $\frac{1}{3}$ green, and $\frac{1}{3}$ blue.

Draw a tree diagram as in Example B.

There are 9 possible outcomes. One outcome is favorable. The probability of spinning red and then green is $\frac{1}{9}$.

▶ Think and Discuss Answers

1. The probability is $\frac{1}{12}$. Outcomes: 1, h; 1, t; 2, h; 2, t; 3, h; 3, t; 4, h; 4, t; 5, h; 5, t; 6, h; 6, t.
2. speech and art, speech and music, speech and typing, literature and art, literature and music, literature and typing
3. The diagram looks like the branches of a tree.

Answers

(see page T304)

★ Error Alert

Errors may occur if students don't recognize the importance of order in multiple events. They may think an outcome such as 2, 3 is the same as 3, 2 and count them as one possible outcome instead of two.

Reinforcement
Extra Practice, page 442
EP/MR Worksheet 104, TRB, page 104

Teaching Aids
Patterns: Number cube, spinners, protractor
TA 3, TRB, page 156
Teaching suggestions precede the Teaching Aids worksheets.

Quarter-inch grid
TA 7, TRB, page 160
Teaching suggestions precede the Teaching Aids worksheets.

Challenge
Draw a tree diagram to determine the birth order of boys and girls in a family of three children. (possible outcomes: BBB, BBG, BGB, BGG, GBB, GBG, GGB, GGG)

Objectives

- To find the number of possible outcomes of a multiple event, using the counting principle
- To find the probability of a multiple event, using the counting principle

Purpose

Tree diagrams, while helpful, are sometimes impractical when there are a large number of possible choices. To determine the possible outcomes for a multiple event without drawing a diagram, you can use the counting principle, which is the topic of this lesson.

Introducing the Lesson

Review multiplying fractions (Lessons 6.1, 6.2). Use the examples: $\frac{1}{2} \times \frac{1}{3} \left(\frac{1}{6}\right)$; $\frac{2}{3} \times \frac{5}{9} \left(\frac{10}{27}\right)$; $\frac{3}{5} \times \frac{7}{9} \left(\frac{7}{15}\right)$. Review using a tree diagram (Lesson 13.5).

Alternative Examples

Example A—There are 16 sandwiches and 14 beverages listed on the menu. How many possible combinations exist for your lunch?

You have 16 choices for the first event (choosing a sandwich) and 14 choices for the second event (choosing a beverage).

There are 16×14, or **224**, possible combinations.

Example B—A number cube is rolled. A number from 1 to 9 is drawn from a hat. Find the probability of rolling a 5 and drawing a 5. The probability of rolling a 5 is $\frac{1}{6}$. The probability of drawing a 5 is $\frac{1}{9}$.

The probability of both rolling and drawing a 5 is $\frac{1}{6} \times \frac{1}{9}$ or $\frac{1}{54}$.

13.6 Using the Counting Principle

Patty and Paula are going to dinner and a movie. If they have 5 movies and 4 restaurants to choose from, how many different combinations are possible? You could use a tree diagram to find out, but there's a faster method.

Examples

To find the number of possible outcomes of a multiple event, use the Counting Principle, as shown below.

$$\begin{array}{ccc} \text{Total number of} \\ \text{possible outcomes} \end{array} = \begin{array}{c} \text{Number of outcomes} \\ \text{for first event} \end{array} \times \begin{array}{c} \text{Number of outcomes} \\ \text{for second event} \end{array}$$

To find the probability of a multiple event, multiply the probabilities of each event together.

A **How many possible outcomes exist for Patty and Paula's evening?**

First event: 5 choices   Second event: 4 choices
There are $5 \times 4 = \mathbf{20}$ possible outcomes.

B **A number cube is rolled. Then a coin is tossed. Find the probability of getting a 5 and tails.**

Probability of rolling a 5: $\frac{1}{6}$ Probability of tossing tails: $\frac{1}{2}$

The probability of getting a 5 and tails is $\frac{1}{6} \times \frac{1}{2} = \frac{1}{12}$.

▶ Think and Discuss

1. How many outcomes are possible if you spin a spinner with 4 different sections and roll a number cube?

2. Refer to the introduction to this lesson. How many different combinations of movies and restaurants are possible?

SKILLS

3. How is the counting principle related to drawing a tree diagram? How are these methods different? Discuss.

4. Which method do you prefer, the counting principle or a tree diagram? Why? Discuss.

Exercises

Find the number of possible outcomes for each of the following events. (See Example A.)

5. tossing a coin 3 times 8 outcomes

6. rolling a number cube 4 times 1296 outcomes

7. rolling a number cube once and tossing a coin twice 24 outcomes

8. tossing a coin twice and rolling a number cube 3 times 864 outcomes

If a number cube is rolled twice, what is the probability of rolling each of the following? (See Example B.)

9. two 4s $\frac{1}{36}$

10. two odd numbers $\frac{1}{4}$

11. an even number and a 1, in that order $\frac{1}{12}$

12. an even and an odd number, in that order $\frac{1}{4}$

▶ **Mixed Practice** (For more practice, see page 442.)

Find the number of possible outcomes. What is the probability that a computer would randomly select each of the underlined events?

13. a city and mode of transportation are chosen from 25 cities and bus, plane, train, or car; <u>New Orleans by plane</u> 100; $\frac{1}{100}$

14. a blouse and skirt are chosen from 5 white blouses, 3 red blouses, 4 blue blouses, 2 black skirts, 3 gray skirts, and 2 white skirts; <u>a red blouse and a white skirt</u> 84; $\frac{1}{14}$

▶ **Applications**

15. Luke has five ties and three shirts. How many shirt and tie combinations can he wear? 15 pairs

16. Each day the cafeteria offers 2 soups, 4 kinds of sandwiches, 3 drinks, and 4 desserts. How many different meal combinations are possible? 96 combinations

▶ **Review** (Lessons 6.6, 6.7)

Divide. Write the answers in lowest terms.

17. $\frac{7}{8} \div \frac{3}{4}$ $1\frac{1}{6}$

18. $2\frac{1}{5} \div \frac{2}{3}$ $3\frac{3}{10}$

19. $\frac{3}{8} \div 12$ $\frac{1}{32}$

20. $4\frac{5}{6} \div 1\frac{5}{7}$ $2\frac{59}{72}$

21. $\frac{5}{8} \div 2\frac{1}{3}$ $\frac{15}{56}$

Objective

• To draw correct conclusions in situations involving independent and dependent events

Purpose

After winning money in a state lottery, your chances of winning the next time are no better and no worse. But sometimes an outcome does affect the probabilities of outcomes after that. This lesson is to help you understand both situations better.

Introducing the Lesson

Have students consider closing their eyes and picking a shirt from a plaid shirt, a solid shirt, and a striped shirt. Ask: How many shirt choices do you have? (3) What are they? (plaid, solid, striped) How many choices do you have the next time if you want to wear a different shirt each day? (2) Explain: Your random selection on the first day affects your choices on the second day. What is the probability of wearing a solid shirt first? ($\frac{1}{3}$) What is the probability of wearing a plaid shirt next? ($\frac{1}{2}$) a solid shirt? ($\frac{0}{2}$) a striped shirt? ($\frac{1}{2}$) Tell students that just as an earlier event can affect a later choice, one event can affect the probability of another.

Answers

1. disagree because the chances are still 1 out of 2

3. It does not matter; the chances are still 1 out of 2.

4. yes, but only if the card was placed back in the hat

5. The information is not given. It matters because the probabilities are different when the card is replaced than they are when it is not.

13.7 Investigating Probability

At the start of each football game, the referee tosses a coin. The captain of the team that wins the toss can choose whether to kick or to receive.

The captain of Central High is unhappy. "I lost the toss again!" he complained. "That's 4 weeks in a row." "Relax," replied the water boy. "You're almost sure to guess right next week. The laws of probability are on your side. You can't possibly guess wrong 5 times in a row!"

1. Do you agree or disagree with the water boy's statement? Why?

2. What is the probability that the captain will win the toss next week? $\frac{1}{2}$

3. Suppose the captain called "heads" 4 weeks in a row and lost each time. What should he call next week? Explain.

A coin cannot "remember" whether you won or lost last time. You can win (or lose!) 20 times in a row, and your chance of winning on the next toss is still $\frac{1}{2}$.

Sometimes, however, what happened earlier *can* affect probabilities.

At the freshman class party, the names of all the students are written on separate cards. The cards are then placed in a hat. A card is drawn to see who wins first prize. Then a card is drawn to see who wins the second prize.

4. Could the same student win both prizes? Discuss.

5. What happens to the card with the first winner's name after it is drawn? Does this matter?

Forty freshmen attend the party.

6. What is the probability that Carlos will win first prize? $\frac{1}{40}$

7. Suppose Carlos wins first prize. His card is put back in the hat. What is the probability that he will win second prize? $\frac{1}{40}$

8. Suppose Carlos wins first prize, and the card with his name on it is *not* put back in the hat. Can he win both prizes? What is the probability of Carlos winning second prize? no; 0

9. Explain why the following statement is true: Your chance of winning both prizes depends on the rules of the drawing.

We have discussed both *dependent* and *independent* events. If the first prize winner's card is not replaced, your chance of winning the second prize depends on whether or not you won the first prize. On the other hand, your chance of winning a coin toss is always $\frac{1}{2}$. It is *independent* of whether you won last time.

Sometimes it is not clear whether events are dependent or independent.

Complete each statement.
Explain your answer. Discuss.

10. Clevon Dribble sinks an average of 70% of his free throws. He has succeeded in his last 10 tries. If he makes the next shot, his team wins. His chance of making that shot is ▉ .

11. The Central High football team has won 9 games and lost 3 games. It rained during two of their games, and they lost them both. If it rains during their next game, their chance of winning is ▉ .

▶ **Review** (Lesson 5.7)

Write as a decimal.

12. $\frac{1}{9}$ 0.$\overline{1}$ 13. $\frac{1}{11}$ 0.$\overline{09}$ 14. $\frac{5}{6}$ 0.8$\overline{3}$ 15. $\frac{7}{9}$ 0.$\overline{7}$ 16. $\frac{6}{11}$ 0.$\overline{54}$ 17. $\frac{11}{12}$ 0.91$\overline{6}$

18. $4\frac{3}{8}$ 4.375   19. $7\frac{2}{3}$ 7.$\overline{6}$ 20. $8\frac{3}{5}$ 8.6   21. $9\frac{4}{11}$ 9.$\overline{36}$ 22. $5\frac{1}{6}$ 5.1$\overline{6}$ 23. $2\frac{19}{100}$ 2.19

Write as a fraction or mixed number in lowest terms.

24. 3.8 $3\frac{4}{5}$ 25. 9.04 $9\frac{1}{25}$ 26. 0.036 $\frac{9}{250}$ 27. 8.125 $8\frac{1}{8}$ 28. 5.72 $5\frac{18}{25}$ 29. 1.555 $1\frac{111}{200}$

Answers (continued)

9. If the card is replaced, the chance of winning both prizes is $\frac{1}{40} \times \frac{1}{40}$, or $\frac{1}{1600}$. If the card is not replaced, the chance of winning both prizes is 0.

10. The probability is $\frac{7}{10}$, but other factors such as the pressure of the game might affect Clevon either positively or negatively.

11. Based on their record for all games, the probability is $\frac{3}{4}$. Based on their record for games played in the rain, the probability is 0. However, other factors, such as the skill of their opponent, will influence the outcome.

★ **Error Alert**

Mistakes may result when students cannot correctly identify events as dependent or independent.

Reinforcement
EP/MR Worksheet 106, TRB, page 106

Challenge
A telephone solicitor has records showing that for every 200 telephone calls made, on the average there will be 44 orders, of which 39 are actually paid for. What is the probability that a solicitor, on any given call, will receive an order? ($\frac{11}{50}$) What is the probability that a call will result in a paid order? ($\frac{39}{200}$) What is the probability that an order he or she receives will be paid for? ($\frac{39}{44}$)

Answers

9. Shoes Socks Outcomes

black
- white black shoes, white socks
- blue black shoes, blue socks
- green black shoes, green socks

brown
- white brown shoes, white socks
- blue brown shoes, blue socks
- green brown shoes, green socks

red
- white red shoes, white socks
- blue red shoes, blue socks
- green red shoes, green socks

Chapter 13 Review

A card is drawn from a set of 15 cards numbered 1–15. Find the probability of drawing each of the following. (Lesson 13.2)

1. 15 $\frac{1}{15}$

2. an even number $\frac{7}{15}$

3. an odd number $\frac{8}{15}$

A number cube is rolled. List the favorable outcomes for rolling each of the following. (Lesson 13.2)

4. an odd number 1, 3, 5

5. a number less than 3 1, 2

6. a multiple of 4 4

A ticket is drawn from the set shown. Find the odds for and against drawing each of the following. (Lesson 13.3)

7. an orange ticket 5 to 7; 7 to 5

8. a pink ticket 3 to 9; 9 to 3

Draw a tree diagram of the following multiple event. (Lesson 13.5)

9. choosing a pair of shoes from 1 black pair, 1 brown pair, and 1 red pair, and a pair of socks from 1 white pair, 1 blue pair, and 1 green pair

Use the information from Question 9 to find the probability of each event. (Lesson 13.5)

10. red shoes with blue socks $\frac{1}{9}$

11. white socks $\frac{1}{3}$

Find the number of possible outcomes for each of the following events. (Lesson 13.6)

12. rolling a number cube and spinning a spinner with 4 sections 24 outcomes

13. tossing a coin and drawing a card from a set of 12 cards numbered 1–12 24 outcomes

A card is drawn from a set of 10 cards numbered 1–10 and a coin is tossed. Find the probability of each event. (Lesson 13.6)

14. 9 and heads $\frac{1}{20}$

15. an odd number and tails $\frac{1}{4}$

16. an even number and heads $\frac{1}{4}$

Marbles like the ones shown are drawn from a container without replacement. Find the probability of drawing each of the following in the order listed. (Lesson 13.7)

17. red red $\frac{1}{45}$

18. green blue $\frac{1}{6}$

19. blue blue blue $\frac{1}{12}$

Chapter 13 Test

A card is drawn from a set of 20 cards numbered 1–20. Find the odds for drawing each of the following.

1. 13   1 to 19   **2.** an even number   1 to 1   **3.** a multiple of 4   5 to 15 or 1 to 3

A number cube is rolled. Find the odds against rolling each of the following.

4. 3   5 to 1   **5.** an odd number   1 to 1   **6.** a number greater than 2   1 to 2

Draw a tree diagram of the following event.

7. choosing one boat from red, blue, green, and yellow boats, and one flag from white, purple, orange, and pink flags

Use the information above to find the probability of each event.

8. a red boat with an orange flag $\frac{1}{16}$ **9.** a purple flag $\frac{1}{4}$

Find the number of possible outcomes for each of the following.

10. tossing a coin and rolling a number cube   12 outcomes

11. choosing an elective from 6 choices and a required course from 4 choices   24 outcomes

A marble is picked from a set like the one shown. Find the probability of each event.

12. yellow marble $\frac{6}{11}$ **13.** green marble $\frac{2}{11}$ **14.** not a blue marble $\frac{8}{11}$

A card is drawn from a set of 8 cards numbered 13–20. List the favorable outcomes for each event.

15. drawing a number less than 15   13, 14

16. drawing an even number or a 17   14, 16, 17, 18, 20

A number cube is rolled and a letter is drawn from the letters P, E, S, T, and O. Find the probability of each of the following.

17. 6 and S $\frac{1}{30}$ **18.** an odd number and E $\frac{1}{10}$

Cards are drawn without replacement from a set of 10 cards numbered 1–10. Find the probability of drawing each of the following in the order listed.

19. 1   2 $\frac{1}{90}$ **20.** odd   10 $\frac{1}{18}$ **21.** even   odd   odd $\frac{5}{36}$

Probability **303**

Chapter Tests
Short Answer, Forms A and B, TRB,
   pages 315–316, 317–318
Multiple Choice, Forms A and B, TRB,
   pages 383–384, 385–386

Teaching Aids
Answer sheet
TA 8, TRB, page 161a
Teaching suggestions precede the
   Teaching Aids worksheets.

Answers

7.

Boat	Flag	Outcomes
red	white	red boat, white flag
	purple	red boat, purple flag
	orange	red boat, orange flag
	pink	red boat, pink flag
blue	white	blue boat, white flag
	purple	blue boat, purple flag
	orange	blue boat, orange flag
	pink	blue boat, pink flag
green	white	green boat, white flag
	purple	green boat, purple flag
	orange	green boat, orange flag
	pink	green boat, pink flag
yellow	white	yellow boat, white flag
	purple	yellow boat, purple flag
	orange	yellow boat, orange flag
	pink	yellow boat, pink flag

T303

Cumulative Tests

Short Answer, Forms A and B, TRB,
   pages 415–417, 418–420
Multiple Choice, Forms A and B, TRB,
   pages 439–441, 442–444

Teaching Aids

Answer Sheet
TA 8, TRB, page 161a
Teaching suggestions precede the Teaching
   Aids worksheets.

Answers (continued from page T297)

Tree diagrams now shown.
   4. Outcomes:
1, 1; 1, 2; 1, 3; 1, 4; 1, 5; 1, 6;
2, 1; 2, 2; 2, 3; 2, 4; 2, 5; 2, 6;
3, 1; 3, 2; 3, 3; 3, 4; 3, 5; 3, 6;
4, 1; 4, 2; 4, 3; 4, 4; 4, 5; 4, 6;
5, 1; 5, 2; 5, 3; 5, 4; 5, 5; 5, 6;
6, 1; 6, 2; 6, 3; 6, 4; 6, 5; 6, 6.
   5. Outcomes:
h, h, h; h, h, t; h, t, h; h, t, t;
t, h, h; t, h, t; t, t, h; t, t, t.
   6. Outcomes:
ham, white; ham, whole wheat;
ham, rye; cheese, white;
cheese, whole wheat; cheese, rye;
tuna, white; tuna, whole wheat;
tuna, rye
   7. Outcomes:
Ann, David; Ann, Ed;
Ann, Fred; Betty, David;
Betty, Ed; Betty, Fred;
Cathy, David; Cathy, Ed;
Cathy, Fred
   11. Outcomes:
h, 1; h, 2; h, 3; h, 4; h, 5; h, 6;
t, 1; t, 2; t, 3; t, 4; t, 5; t, 6.
The probability is $\frac{1}{12}$.
   12. Outcomes:
1, 1; 1, 2; 1, 3; 1, 4; 1, 5; 1, 6;
2, 1; 2, 2; 2, 3; 2, 4; 2, 5; 2, 6;
3, 1; 3, 2; 3, 3; 3, 4; 3, 5; 3, 6;
4, 1; 4, 2; 4, 3; 4, 4; 4, 5; 4, 6;
5, 1; 5, 2; 5, 3; 5, 4; 5, 5; 5, 6;
6, 1; 6, 2; 6, 3; 6, 4; 6, 5; 6, 6.
The probability is $\frac{1}{36}$.

(continued on page T305)

Cumulative Test Chapters 1–13

▶ **Choose the letter that shows the correct answer.**

1. 8% of 175 is
   a. 140
   b. 14 ⟵
   c. 1.4
   d. not given

2. 24 is what percent of 96?
   a. $33\frac{1}{3}$%
   b. 300%
   c. 25% ⟵
   d. not given

3. 65% of 480 is
   a. 31,200
   b. 312 ⟵
   c. 31.20
   d. not given

4. 348 is what percent of 116?
   a. 300% ⟵
   b. 30%
   c. $33\frac{1}{3}$%
   d. not given

5. $\frac{5}{6} = \frac{30}{\blacksquare}$
   a. 32
   b. 60
   c. 42
   d. not given ⟵

6. $\frac{\blacksquare}{25} = \frac{10}{2}$
   a. 100
   b. 250
   c. 125 ⟵
   d. not given

7. $\frac{15}{20} = \frac{\blacksquare}{12}$
   a. 9 ⟵
   b. 8
   c. 10
   d. not given

8. $\frac{8}{\blacksquare} = \frac{56}{14}$
   a. 1
   b. 2 ⟵
   c. 3
   d. not given

9. $37\frac{1}{2}\% = $ _____
   a. 0.375 ⟵
   b. 3.75
   c. 37.5
   d. not given

10. 0.005 = _____
   a. 50%
   b. 5%
   c. 500%
   d. not given ⟵

11. $0.08\overline{3}$ = _____
   a. $0.8\frac{1}{3}$%
   b. 83%
   c. $8\frac{1}{3}$% ⟵
   d. not given

12. 9.4 = _____
   a. 94%
   b. 0.094%
   c. 940% ⟵
   d. not given

▶ **Find the probability of choosing each of the following from a set of cards numbered 1–18.**

13. a 6
   a. $\frac{1}{18}$ ⟵
   b. $\frac{1}{3}$
   c. $\frac{1}{6}$
   d. not given

14. an even number
   a. $\frac{1}{9}$
   b. $\frac{9}{1}$
   c. $\frac{1}{2}$ ⟵
   d. not given

15. a multiple of 6
   a. $\frac{1}{3}$
   b. $\frac{1}{4}$
   c. $\frac{1}{9}$
   d. not given ⟵

16. a number less than 9
   a. $\frac{1}{6}$
   b. $\frac{1}{3}$
   c. $\frac{4}{9}$ ⟵
   d. not given

17. What are the odds of rolling a 1, 3, or 7 on a 12-sided number cube?
   a. $\frac{1}{3}$ ⟵
   b. $\frac{3}{1}$
   c. $\frac{1}{4}$
   d. not given

▶ **Use Jim's math scores for problems 18–21.**
83, 92, 91, 62, 83, 78, 83

18. The mode of the scores is
　a. 83　　　　**b.** 78　　　　**c.** 30　　　　**d.** not given

19. The median score is
　a. 83　　　　**b.** 78　　　　**c.** 30　　　　**d.** not given

20. The range of the scores is
　a. 83　　　　**b.** 78　　　　**c.** 30　　　　**d.** not given

21. The mean score is
　a. 83　　　　**b.** 78　　　　**c.** 30　　　　**d.** not given

▶ **Solve.**

22. A radio is on sale. The original price was $108. The new price is $75.60. What is the percent of decrease?
　a. 25%　　　　**b.** 40%
　c. 30%　　　　**d.** not given

23. The cost of dinner is $35.95. The sales tax is 6%. What is the total bill, to the nearest cent?
　a. $38.11　　　　**b.** $57.52
　c. $33.79　　　　**d.** not given

24. On a map scale 1 cm equals 65 km. The distance between two towns on the map is 5.5 cm. What is the actual distance?
　a. 11 km
　b. 325 km
　c. 357.5 km
　d. not given

25. Suki's room measures 15 feet by 13 feet. In a drawing she uses a scale of $\frac{1}{2}$ inch equals 1 foot. What is the size of her drawing?
　a. $7\frac{1}{2}$ inches by $6\frac{1}{2}$ inches
　b. 30 inches by 26 inches
　c. 10 inches by $4\frac{1}{3}$ inches
　d. not given

▶ **Compute.**

26. $3\frac{1}{5} \times \frac{5}{6}$
　a. $2\frac{1}{2}$
　b. $13\frac{1}{3}$
　c. $3\frac{21}{25}$
　d. not given

27. $6 - 2.094$
　a. 3.906
　b. 3.094
　c. 4.906
　d. not given

28. $8.4 \div 0.06$
　a. 1.4
　b. 14
　c. 140
　d. not given

29. $8\frac{3}{4} + 5\frac{2}{3}$
　a. $13\frac{5}{12}$
　b. $14\frac{5}{12}$
　c. $13\frac{2}{3}$
　d. not given

Open-Ended Questions

42. Scoring Rubric
4 gives a complete explanation of how to solve the problem; calculations are correct.
3 shows an understanding of how to solve the problem; makes some computational errors.
2 determines how many weeks it will take to save the money, but omits data given in the problem, such as the sales tax.
1 shows little or no understanding of how to solve the problem; computation is incorrect.

43. Scoring Rubric
4 finds the correct mean, median and mode; explanation shows understanding of how these measures of central tendency would change if the new data were a function of the given data.
3 finds the correct mean, median, and mode; explanation shows a limited understanding of how these measures of central tendency would change if the new data were a function of the given data.
2 finds the correct mean, median, and mode, but has no understanding of how these measures of central tendency would change if the new data were a function of the given data.
1 shows no understanding of the concepts of mean, median, and mode.

30. $1\frac{7}{8} \div 1\frac{3}{4}$

a. $1\frac{1}{14}$
b. $3\frac{9}{32}$
c. $2\frac{1}{7}$
d. not given

31. 8.14×2.6

a. 211.64
b. 2116.4
c. 2.1164
d. not given

32. $4587 \div 60$

a. 760 R27
b. 74 R47
c. 76 R27
d. not given

33. _____ are most effective for showing the parts of a whole.
a. bar graphs
b. circle graphs
c. pictographs

34. Temperature trends from January through December are best displayed in a _____ .
a. line graph
b. pictograph
c. circle graph

35. The values of imports and exports for 7 countries are best displayed in a _____ graph.
a. line
b. double bar
c. circle

36. In a pictograph, a _____ represents a quantity.
a. symbol
b. vertical axis
c. tally

37. On a vertical bar graph showing the average price of gasoline in 5 cities, the label "Price in $" will be on the _____ .
a. horizontal axis
b. vertical axis
c. not given

▶ **Solve.**

38. All ice skates are marked 25% off. The regular price is $85. What is the sale price?
a. $21.25
b. $68
c. $63.75
d. not given

39. In the last four games Dale scored 12, 19, 23, and 18 points. What was her average number of points per game?
a. 18 points
b. 72 points
c. 13.5 points
d. not given

40. Dionne works 15 hours a week and makes $6.85 an hour. How much does she make in 2 weeks?
a. $102.75
b. $205.50
c. $108.55
d. not given

41. Suki saved 40% on her new leotard, a savings of $9.80. What was the regular price?
a. $24.50
b. $14.50
c. $34.30
d. not given

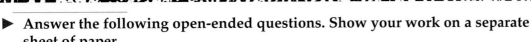

► **Answer the following open-ended questions. Show your work on a separate sheet of paper.**

42. Matt earns $80.00 a week at his job after school. He saves 10% of his earnings. How many weeks does Matt have to work to save enough money to buy a pair of sneakers that cost $72.00? There is a 5% sales tax in his state. Explain how you found your answer. Show your work. Skills used—dividing whole numbers and decimals

43. This chart shows the highest temperature recorded in each state during one year.

State	Temperature (in Degrees Fahrenheit)
Alaska	98
Arizona	118
Florida	106
Maine	97
Montana	101
Pennsylvania	98

What is the mean?
What is the median?
What is the mode?

If each temperature increased by 2 degrees Fahrenheit, then how would the mean, median, and mode change? Explain how you found your answer. Show your work Skills used—computing mean, median, and mode

44. Christina is comparing prices. Her usual brand of shampoo is $2.49 for 22.5 fluid ounces. The store brand is $3.20 for 40 fluid ounces. Tuesdays are Value Days at the store. All purchases made on this day are 10% off. Which shampoo is the better buy? How much does Christina pay if she shops on Tuesday? Show your work. Skills used—using proportions to calculate the unit price of an item, comparing values

45. There are two mountain bikes on sale, a black one and a red one. The black bike costs $289 with 30% off. The red bike costs $239 with 15% off. Which bike would you buy? Show your work and explain your reasoning. Skills used—converting percents to decimals, multiplication, comparing values

46. Maria is having a dress with trim made for the prom. She has six different colors to choose from and four different trims. She must also decide if she wants knee length or ankle length. How many possible selections does she have? Explain how you found your answer. Show your work. Skills used—applying the counting principle or drawing a tree diagram

Career Focus Activity

Materials: pencils, papers, computer with Internet access

Procedure: Organize students into four groups. Students write a letter to a painter or a related professional.
• All students brainstorm interview-type questions to place in the letter. The categories of questions should include those in the job description: what a painter does, the attributes necessary in the performance of duties, where one could work, what education is necessary to qualify for this type of work, related careers, and how math is used on the job.
• The first group compiles the best questions.
• The second group researches on the Internet for possible businesses to which the class can send the letter.
• The third group composes the letter, including a return address.
• The fourth group reviews responses and reports on the results to the class.

Use perimeter and area to find the

• length of a fence surrounding a yard.
• amount of carpet needed to cover a floor.
• distance around a playground.
• size of a garden.

What are some other ways to use perimeter and area?

Geometry: Perimeter and Area

A painter paints the interiors and exteriors of buildings.

- Painters work in business buildings or private homes. They may paint houses, office buildings, stores, hospitals, and schools.

- Painters should enjoy changing job locations regularly and working with their hands in a precise way.

- A painter determines the areas of surfaces to be painted, the amount of paint that will be required, and an estimate of the costs.

- To become a painter, an individual can learn from other painting professionals.

- Related careers include interior designers, carpet layers, window washers, and remodelers.

CAREER

PAINTER

PORTFOLIO PROJECT: *Determine the amount of paint required to paint a room.*

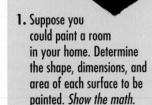

1. Suppose you could paint a room in your home. Determine the shape, dimensions, and area of each surface to be painted. *Show the math.*

2. Assume that one quart of paint covers 75 square feet and one gallon covers 300 square feet. How much paint will you need? *Show the math.*

3. Select the paint you will need for the ceiling, the walls, and the trim. Find the cost of the paint per quart or per gallon. Then find the cost to paint the room. *Show the math.*

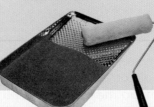

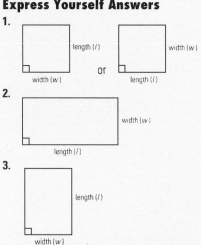
14.1 Introduction to 2-Dimensional Figures

Gary is studying for his driving test. He is learning what various road signs mean just by learning their shapes. Can you tell what some of these signs mean just by looking at their shapes?

These shapes and others like them are 2-dimensional figures. They have 2 dimensions—length and width. These figures are called **polygons**.

▶ Express Yourself

Here are some terms that will help you in this chapter.

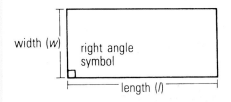
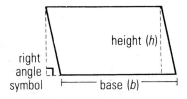
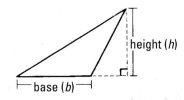

To test for a right angle, place the corner of a card or book on the drawing.

Copy the figures below. Label the length and width, and mark one angle as a right angle by using the symbol.

1.   2.    3.

4. Some polygons have names with a prefix that means the number of sides they have. For example, *tri-* in the word triangle means three. Look up the meanings of the following prefixes: *penta-, quad-, octa-, hexa-, deca-.*

Match each prefix in Question 4 to a figure below.

5. 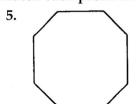 **6.**

7. 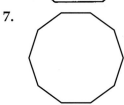 **8.** 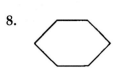 **9.**

The sides of a **regular polygon** are all equal in length and its angles are all the same size.

Tell whether the figures below are regular polygons or not.

10.  **11.**

12. 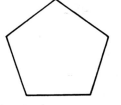 **13.**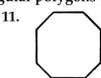

▶ ## Practice What You Know

You already know a lot about geometry because you know how to measure objects and how to add and multiply.

Add.

14. $15 + 29$ **15.** $20 + 30 + 50$ **16.** $2.3 + 3.1 + 8.5$

Multiply.

17. $21 \times 3 \times 9$ **18.** $16.3 \times 45.2 \times 3.1$ **19.** 125.8×333.3

In geometry you might see an expression such as $2 \times \pi \times r$.
Another way to write this is $2\pi r$.

Rewrite each expression below.

20. $b \times h$ **21.** $l \times w$ **22.** $\pi \times d$ **23.** $2 \times l$

24. Would you use the shorthand described above to rewrite 2×3? Explain your answer.

Project
Make a table for at least 6 different polygons. Include the name of the polygon, the number of sides it has, a drawing of the polygon, and examples of real objects with the same geometric shape. (A sample table is shown below.)

Name	Side	Sketch	Examples
triangle	3		road signs, building structures
quadri-lateral	4		kite
square	4		sidewalk, tile
rectangle	4		poster
pentagon	5		the Pentagon
hexagon	6		hex nut
octagon	8		stop sign

Purpose

This lesson helps you to find the perimeter of 2-dimensional figures. This is one way to calculate the distances around objects such as a room (because you are buying molding), or a field (because you are buying fencing).

Introducing the Lesson

Review adding whole numbers and decimals (Lesson 1.9). Use the examples:
Add—9 + 16 + 25 = (50);
2.6 + 3.3 + 1.2 + 3.8 = (10.9);
75.1 + 12.2 + 14.6 + 80.8 = (182.8).

Write the word *perimeter* on the board. Underline the letters *rim*. Tell students that remembering the word *rim* may help them remember that perimeter means "the distance around."

Alternative Examples

Example A—Find the perimeter of the pentagon. Add the lengths.

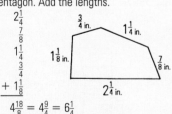

$4\frac{18}{8} = 4\frac{9}{4} = 6\frac{1}{4}$

The perimeter is **16$\frac{1}{4}$ inches.**

Example B—Find the perimeter of the rectangle.

$P = 2l + 2w$
$P = (2 \times 100) + (2 \times 60)$
$P = 200 + 120$
$P = 320$
The perimeter is **320 centimeters.**

14.2 Finding Perimeters of Polygons

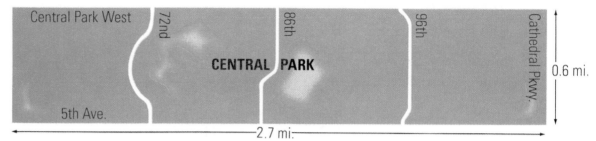

One Saturday Ed walked around the edge of Central Park. Ed could find how far he had walked by finding the distance around the park.

The distance around is called the **perimeter**.

Examples

To find the perimeter of a polygon, add the lengths of the sides.
To find the perimeter of a rectangle, use the formula $P = 2l + 2w$.

P = perimeter, l = length, w = width

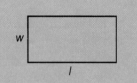

A Find the perimeter of the triangle.

Add the lengths

```
  4.5
  3.5
+ 7.5
  15.5
```

The perimeter is **15.5 meters.**

B Find the perimeter of the rectangle.
$P = 2l + 2w$
$P = (2 \times l) + (2 \times w)$
$P = (2 \times 12) + (2 \times 8)$
$P = 24 + 16$
$P = 40$
The perimeter is **40 feet.**

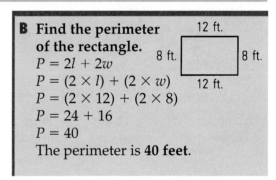

▶ **Think and Discuss**

1. How many sides does a rectangle have?

2. What is the name of a polygon that has three sides?

3. What is the perimeter of a triangle with sides that measure 3 meters, 4 meters, and 5 meters?

4. Refer to the introduction to this lesson. How far did Ed walk?

5. How do you find the perimeter of a square? Write a formula for finding the perimeter of a square.

Exercises

SKILLS

Find the perimeter of each polygon. (See Example A.)

6.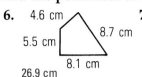
4.6 cm
8.7 cm
5.5 cm
8.1 cm
26.9 cm

7.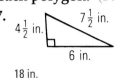
$4\frac{1}{2}$ in.
$7\frac{1}{2}$ in.
6 in.
18 in.

8.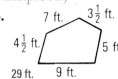
7 ft.
$3\frac{1}{2}$ ft.
$4\frac{1}{2}$ ft.
5 ft.
29 ft. 9 ft.

Find the perimeter of each rectangle. (See Example B.)

9. $l = 5$ in.
$w = 12$ in.
34 in.

10. $l = 175$ mm
$w = 225$ mm
800 mm

11. $l = 22$ ft.
$w = 41$ ft.
126 ft.

12. $l = 3.6$ m
$w = 2.4$ m
12 m

13. $l = 10$ cm
$w = 15$ cm
50 cm

14. $l = 5.5$ in.
$w = 20.5$ in.
52 in.

15. $l = 12.1$ cm
$w = 16.9$ cm
58 cm

16. $l = 33$ m
$w = 57$ m
180 m

▶ Mixed Practice (For more practice, see page 443.)

Find the perimeter of each polygon.

17.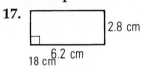
2.8 cm
6.2 cm
18 cm

18. Rectangle
$l = 5.7$ m
$w = 3.4$ m
18.2 m

19.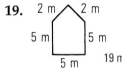
2 m 2 m
5 m 5 m
5 m 19 m

20.
7 in.
7 in. 7 in.
7 in. 28 in.

21. Rectangle
$l = 5.2$ cm
$w = 6$ cm
22.4 cm

22. Rectangle
$l = 2\frac{1}{2}$ in.
$w = 1\frac{1}{4}$ in. $7\frac{1}{2}$ in.

23. Rectangle
$l = 8.4$ m
$w = 9.5$ m
35.8 m

24. Rectangle
$l = 4\frac{2}{3}$ ft.
$w = 3\frac{1}{2}$ ft. $16\frac{1}{3}$ ft.

25.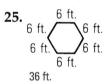
6 ft.
6 ft. 6 ft.
6 ft. 6 ft.
6 ft.
36 ft.

26.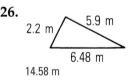
5.9 m
2.2 m
6.48 m
14.58 m

27. Rectangle
$l = 2$ cm
$w = 2.5$ cm
9 cm

28. Rectangle
$l = 14$ in.
$w = 21$ in.
70 in.

▶ Applications

29. A triangular-shaped garden has sides that measure $75\frac{3}{4}$ feet, $119\frac{1}{2}$ feet, and $98\frac{3}{4}$ feet. What is the perimeter of the garden? 294 ft.

30. A rectangular field is twenty feet wide and fifty-two feet long. How many times must you walk around the field to walk one mile? $\approx 36\frac{2}{3}$ or 37 times

▶ Review (Lesson 11.2)

Tell whether each statement is a proportion. Use = or ≠.

31. $\frac{6}{8}$ ___ $\frac{10}{12}$ ≠

32. $\frac{6}{20}$ ___ $\frac{3}{10}$ =

33. $\frac{4}{5}$ ___ $\frac{10}{8}$ ≠

34. $\frac{1}{5}$ ___ $\frac{8}{40}$ =

 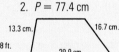

14.3 Estimating Lengths and Perimeters

In basketball, the free-throw line must be 15 feet from the basket. In baseball, the bases must be 90 feet apart. If you have played sports on an unmarked field, you know that being able to estimate lengths and perimeters is a useful skill.

1. Suppose you are playing each of the sports above. You have no ruler or other measuring tool with you. How would you decide where to place the free-throw line and the bases? Discuss and explain.

2. Suppose you have a 12-inch ruler. Now how would you decide where to place the free-throw line and the bases? Discuss and explain.

If you have a ruler, you can measure the length of your foot and the length of your stride.

Then you can walk toe to heel to estimate short distances and walk in even strides to estimate long distances.

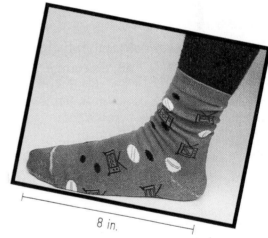

24 in.

8 in.

3. Bill's stride is 3 feet. How many strides from home plate will he place first base, if it should be 90 feet away?

4. Mary's stride is $2\frac{1}{2}$ feet. How many strides from home plate will she place third base?

5. Which method would you use to locate a free-throw line in basketball?

6. Where else might you use one of these methods to estimate lengths or perimeters? Discuss.

When a figure has an unusual shape, the problem of estimating its perimeter becomes more difficult. If a figure has curved sides, you cannot measure its perimeter with a ruler.

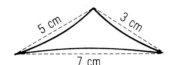

One way to estimate its perimeter is to first draw line segments that approximate the figure. Then measure the segments.

Draw line segments and measure each. Add the measures.
5 cm + 3 cm + 7 cm = 15 cm

The perimeter of the curved figure is **about 15 centimeters**.

Copy each figure below. Estimate the perimeters of each by drawing and measuring line segments. (For more practice, see page 443.)

7. 　　8. 　　9. 　　10.

Another method of estimating perimeters is to use a piece of string to trace the perimeter of the figure. Then you can use a ruler to measure the string.

Estimate the perimeter of each figure below using string.

11. 　　12. 　　13. 　　14.

15. Estimate the perimeter of the top of an aluminum can, or some other curved object in your classroom.

16. When would you use a tape measure?

▶ **Review** (Lessons 4.3, 4.6)

Choose the more reasonable measure.

17. The distance across the room is 9 _____ .　(m)　cm

18. Deanna and Crystal drank 1 _____ of orange juice.　mL　(L)

19. Chloe's new earrings are 2 _____ long.　m　(cm)

Geometry: Perimeter and Area **315**

Answers (continued)

For Questions 7–14, answers may vary.
7. 5 cm
8. 6 cm
9. 5 cm
10. 5 cm
11. 4–5 cm
12. 4–5 cm
13. 6–7 cm
14. 6–7 cm
15. Answers may vary. A sample answer is about 20 centimeters.
16. Answers may vary. Sample answers include measuring the length of an object, a height of a wall, or one's waistline.

★ **Error Alert**
Mistakes may reveal that students are not measuring all of the sides of a figure or are making errors when adding the measures.

Reinforcement
EP/MR Worksheet 108, TRB, page 108

Project
Estimate how far you walk and/or ride to school. Describe your starting and stopping points, and how you made your estimate of the distance. Suggest a possible method to find the exact distance. (Answers may depend on individual students' distances to school. A possible method of finding the exact distance includes using a measuring device such as a pedometer or an odometer.)

T315

14.4 Finding Circumference

Which do you think is greater, the height of a can of three tennis balls or the distance around the can? You can answer this question without measuring if you understand circumference.

Circumference is the distance around a circle.

Examples

To find circumference, use the appropriate formula.

$C = \pi \times d$, or πd $C = 2 \times \pi \times r$, or $2\pi r$
$C = $ circumference, $d = $ diameter, $r = $ radius

Use either 3.14 or $\frac{22}{7}$ for π,
or the π key on your calculator.

 radius

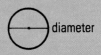 diameter

A Find the circumference.
  $d = 6.4$ centimeters

  $C = \pi \times d$
  $C \approx 3.14 \times 6.4$
  $C \approx 20.096$
  $C \approx 20.1$ **centimeters**

B Find the circumference.
  $r = 9\frac{1}{4}$ millimeters

  $C = 2 \times \pi \times r$
  $C \approx 2 \times \frac{22}{7} \times 9\frac{1}{4}$
  $C \approx 58\frac{1}{7}$
  $C \approx 58\frac{1}{7}$ **millimeters**

▶ **Think and Discuss**

1. Write $\frac{22}{7}$ as a decimal. Which is greater, $\frac{22}{7}$ or 3.14?

2. Find the circumference of a circle with a radius of 4.5 m.

3. Refer to the introduction to this lesson. A tennis ball has circumference $\pi \times d$. The height of the can is about $3 \times d$. Which is greater? Are you surprised?

4. If you know the radius of a circle, how can you find its diameter?

5. If you know the circumference of a circle, how can you find its diameter?

6. Press the key marked π on a calculator. What does it display? When you use 3.14 for π, do you get an exact answer? Why?

7. When is it easier to use $\frac{22}{7}$ instead of 3.14 for π? When is it easier to use 3.14?

Exercises

Find each circumference. Round answers to the nearest tenth. (See Example A.)

8. $d = 2.2$ cm
   ≈6.9 cm
9. $d = 8$ in.
   ≈25.1 in.
10. $d = 14$ m
    ≈44 m
11. $d = 4\frac{1}{2}$ ft.
    ≈$14\frac{1}{7}$ or 14.1 ft.

Find each circumference. Round answers to the nearest tenth. (See Example B.)

12. $r = 1.5$ m
    ≈9.4 m
13. $r = 5\frac{1}{4}$ in.
    ≈33 in.
14. $r = 0.8$ km
    ≈5.0 km
15. $r = 2$ in.
    ≈12.6 in.

▶ **Mixed Practice** (For more practice, see page 444.)

Find each circumference. Round answers to the nearest tenth.

16.
    3 m
    ≈18.8 m
17.
    1.6 km
    ≈5.0 km
18. $r = 7$ ft.
    ≈44.0 ft.
19.
    $d = 10$ yd.
    ≈ 31.4 yd.

20. $r = 6$ in.
    ≈37.7 in.
21. $d = 1$ m
    ≈3.1 m
22. $d = 9$ ft
    ≈28.3 ft.
23. $r = 1.9$ m
    ≈11.9 m

▶ **Applications**

24. The earth is about 93,000,000 miles from the sun and has a nearly circular orbit. Use a calculator to find how far the earth travels when it makes one orbit around the sun. Round to the nearest million. ≈584,000,000 miles

25. A bicycle wheel is 26 inches in diameter. How far forward will the bicycle move when the wheel makes one complete revolution? ≈ 81.7 in.

▶ **Review** (Lessons 6.1, 6.2, 6.4)

Multiply. Write your answers in lowest terms.

26. $\frac{7}{11} \times \frac{6}{7}$ $\frac{6}{11}$
27. $2\frac{1}{3} \times 5\frac{1}{4}$ $12\frac{1}{4}$
28. $\frac{1}{2} \times 6\frac{4}{5}$ $3\frac{2}{5}$

Objective

- To find the area of rectangles and parallelograms

Purpose

You can use the formulas in this lesson to find the area of any rectangle or parallelogram. This is useful if you need to find the area, for example, of ceilings, walls, or floors to help you determine how much paint, wallpaper, or carpeting to buy.

Introducing the Lesson

Introduce the concept of area by having students find the number of index cards it takes to cover their desk tops by laying index cards edge to edge to cover the entire top. Ask students to record how many index cards fit along the top edges of their desks and how many fit along the sides. Ask: How could you find the number of index cards without counting? (by multiplying) The units we usually use for area are square units. The area of a figure is the number of those units that it takes to cover it.

Alternative Examples

Example A—Find the area of the parallelogram: $b = 150$ yd., $h = 250$ yd.
$A = b \times h$
$A = 150 \times 250$
$A = 37{,}500$
The area is **37,500 square yards.**

Example B—Find the area of the rectangle: $l = 1\frac{1}{4}$ in., $w = \frac{3}{8}$ in.
$A = l \times w$
$A = 1\frac{1}{4} \times \frac{3}{8}$
$A = \frac{15}{32}$

The area is $\frac{15}{32}$ **square inches.**

14.5 Finding the Areas of Rectangles and Parallelograms

Kathi is a drummer for a band. She needs a place to practice where she won't disturb the neighbors, so she plans to cover an entire room with carpeting.

To find how much carpeting to buy, Kathi has to find areas.

Examples

To find the area of a parallelogram or a rectangle, use the appropriate formula.

parallel sides   two sides that are an equal distance apart at all points

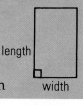
height
base

parallelogram   a four-sided figure whose opposite sides are equal and parallel

$A = b \times h$,   or bh
$A = $ area, $b = $ base, $h = $ height

rectangle   a parallelogram with four right angles

$A = l \times w$,   or lw
$A = $ area, $l = $ length, $w = $ width

length
width

A Find the area.

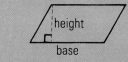
7 m
13 m

$A = b \times h$
$A = 13 \times 7$
$A = 91$

The area is **91 square meters.**

B Find the area.

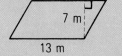
$7\frac{1}{2}$ ft.
9 ft.

$A = l \times w$
$A = 9 \times 7\frac{1}{2}$
$A = 67\frac{1}{2}$

The area is **$67\frac{1}{2}$ square feet.**

▶ Think and Discuss

1. Find the area of the parallelogram. $b = 15$ ft., $h = 5$ ft.

2. Refer to the introduction to this lesson. Kathi's drum room is 10 feet high, 10 feet wide, and 10 feet long. How much carpeting does she need to buy?

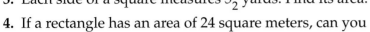

SKILLS

3. Each side of a square measures $5\frac{1}{2}$ yards. Find its area.

4. If a rectangle has an area of 24 square meters, can you find the lengths of the sides? Discuss.

Exercises

Find the area of each parallelogram. (See Example A.)

5.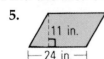
11 in.
├— 24 in. —┤

6.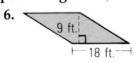
9 ft.
├—18 ft.—┤

7.
2 m
├—2.5 m—┤

8.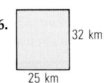
12 cm
4.5 cm

9. $b = 130$ m
$h = \ \ 50$ m

10. $b = 25$ in.
$h = 15$ in.

11. $b = 18$ yd.
$h = 18$ yd.

12. $b = 0.13$ km
$h = 0.28$ km

Find the area of each rectangle. (See Example B.)

13.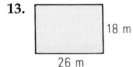
18 m
26 m

14. 19 ft.
17 ft.

15.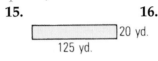
20 yd.
125 yd.

16. 32 km
25 km

17. $l = 12$ m
$w = \ \ 7$ m

18. $l = 29$ in.
$w = 36$ in.

19. $l = 20$ cm
$w = \ \ 9$ cm

20. $l = 7.2$ km
$w = 1.9$ km

▶ **Mixed Practice** (For more practice, see page 444.)

Find the area of each parallelogram or rectangle.

21.
5 m
5 m

22.
20 in.
├15 in.┤

23.
3.4 m
3 m

24.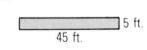
5 ft.
45 ft.

25. $b = 2.0$ cm
$h = 1.6$ cm

26. $l = 1.5$ m
$w = 3.2$ m

27. $b = 28$ in.
$h = 15$ in.

28. $l = 62$ yd.
$w = 31$ yd.

▶ **Applications**

29. A sheet of looseleaf paper is 11 inches long and $8\frac{1}{2}$ inches wide. Find its area. $93\frac{1}{2}$ sq. in.

30. A mile is 1760 yards long. An acre is 4840 square yards. How many acres are in a square mile? 640 acres

▶ **Review** (Lessons 12.7, 12.8, 12.9)

Solve each percent problem.

31. What is 2% of 3150? 63

32. What percent of 60 is 3? 5%

33. 45 is 15% of what number? 300

34. What is 87% of 500? 435

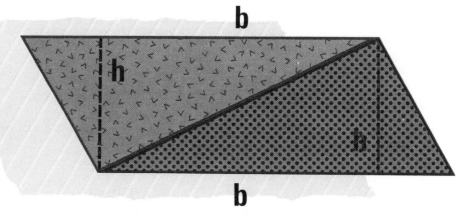

b

h

b

b

Draw a parallelogram like the one shown. Then cut the parallelogram so that two triangles are formed. By comparing the triangles, you can see that each has area half that of the original parallelogram.

Examples

To find the area of a triangle, use the formula

$A = \frac{1}{2} \times b \times h$, or $\frac{1}{2}bh$.

A = area, b = base, h = height

height

base

A Find the area of the triangle.

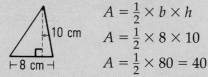

10 cm

8 cm

$A = \frac{1}{2} \times b \times h$

$A = \frac{1}{2} \times 8 \times 10$

$A = \frac{1}{2} \times 80 = 40$

The area is **40 square centimeters.**

B Find the area of the triangle.

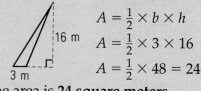

16 m

3 m

$A = \frac{1}{2} \times b \times h$

$A = \frac{1}{2} \times 3 \times 16$

$A = \frac{1}{2} \times 48 = 24$

The area is **24 square meters.**

▶ Think and Discuss

1. Write the formulas for the areas of a parallelogram and a triangle. How are they related?

2. The area of a triangle is 24 square inches. The base is 6 inches. What is its height?

3. How many bases does a triangle have? Explain.

4. What happens to the area of a triangle if both its base and its height are doubled?

Objective

• To find the area of a triangle

Purpose

This lesson shows you how to find the area of a triangle. Then you can determine the amount of paint needed to paint the walls on the two ends of an A-frame house.

Introducing the Lesson

Cut out two triangles of the same size and shape from a piece of poster board. Show how the triangles can be fit together to form a parallelogram. Ask students how the area of one of the triangles compares to the area of the parallelogram. (The area of the triangle is half the area of the parallelogram.)

Alternative Examples

Example A—Find the area of the triangle:
b = 12 in., h = 20 in.

$A = \frac{1}{2} \times b \times h$

$A = \frac{1}{2} \times 12 \times 20$

$A = \frac{1}{2} \times 240 = 120$

The area is **120 square inches.**

Example B—Find the area of the triangle
b = 36 cm, h = 72 cm.

$A = \frac{1}{2} \times b \times h$

$A = \frac{1}{2} \times 36 \times 72$

$A = \frac{1}{2} \times 2592 = 1296$

The area is **1296 square centimeters.**

▶ Think and Discuss Answers

1. for a parallelogram: $A = b \times h$; for a triangle: $A = \frac{1}{2} \times b \times h$; the area of a triangle is one-half that of a parallelogram with the same base and height.

2. 8 in.

3. 3; any side can be used as the base, but the height will vary according to which base is used (if the bases are different lengths)

4. The area is four times greater.

Exercises

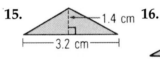 SKILLS

Find the area of each triangle. (See Example A.)

5. $b = 8.6$ cm
$h = 5.4$ cm

6. $b = 16$ ft.
$h = 12$ ft.

7. $b = 19$ m
$h = 9.5$ m

8. $b = 6$ in.
$h = 22$ in.

Find the area of each triangle. (See Example B.)

9.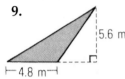
5.6 m
4.8 m

10.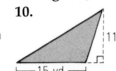
11 yd.
15 yd.

11.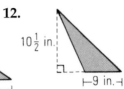
2.8 cm
1.9 cm

12.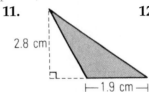
$10\frac{1}{2}$ in.
9 in.

▶ **Mixed Practice** (For more practice, see page 445.)

Find the area of each triangle.

13.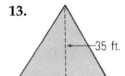
35 ft.
40 ft.

14.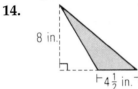
8 in.
$4\frac{1}{2}$ in.

15.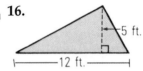
1.4 cm
3.2 cm

16.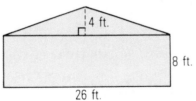
5 ft.
12 ft.

17. $b = 31$ m
$h = 25$ m

18. $b = 22$ in.
$h = 19$ in.

19. $b = 15$ ft.
$h = 24$ ft.

20. $b = 11$ mm
$h = 25$ mm

21. $b = 9.8$ cm
$h = 4$ cm

22. $b = 5\frac{1}{2}$ in.
$h = 7$ in.

23. $b = 7.2$ m
$h = 3.5$ m

24. $b = 6\frac{1}{2}$ in.
$h = 3\frac{3}{4}$ in.

▶ **Applications**

25. How many square inches of material are in the pennant below? **182 square inches**

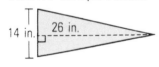
14 in.
26 in.

26. What is the area of the house wall shown below? **260 square feet**

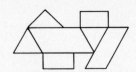
4 ft.
8 ft.
26 ft.

▶ **Review** (Lessons 1.9, 1.10, 1.11)

Add or subtract.

27.
$89.65
+ 37.87
$127.52

28.
5007
− 2348
2659

29.
13
− 6.91
6.09

30.
26.75
+ 9.856
36.606

Geometry: Perimeter and Area **321**

 **Answers**

5. 23.22 square centimeters
6. 96 square feet
7. 90.25 square meters
8. 66 square inches
9. 13.44 square meters
10. 82.5 square yards
11. 2.66 square centimeters
12. $47\frac{1}{4}$ square inches
13. 700 square feet
14. 18 square inches
15. 2.24 square centimeters
16. 30 square feet
17. 387.5 square meters
18. 209 square inches
19. 180 square feet
20. 137.5 square millimeters
21. 19.6 square centimeters
22. $19\frac{1}{4}$ square inches
23. 12.6 square meters
24. $12\frac{3}{16}$ square inches

★ **Error Alert**
Errors may indicate that students have forgotten to multiply by $\frac{1}{2}$ when computing the area of a triangle.

Reinforcement
Extra Practice, page 445
EP/MR Worksheet 111, TRB, page 111

Challenge
Note to the Teacher: Draw several figures on the chalkboard like the ones below. Make the figures combinations of triangles, parallelograms, and rectangles.

Work with a partner. Use a ruler to help you find the perimeter of each figure. Then find the area of each figure on the chalkboard. There may be more than one way of computing each area. Explain how you computed the area of each figure. Compare your results with the results of other groups.

Purpose

There are many other 4-sided figures that you may encounter in everyday life besides squares, rectangles, and parallelograms. This lesson helps you to find the area of 4-sided figures called trapezoids.

Introducing the Lesson

Draw a trapezoid on a large piece of paper. Ask how this figure differs from a rectangle or a parallelogram. (It only has one pair of parallel sides.) Cut out the trapezoid. Fold the paper so that the two parallel sides line up. Open the paper and cut the trapezoid along the fold. Arrange the two pieces together to form a parallelogram as shown below. Then, ask students how to find the area of a trapezoid by using what they already know. (Find the area of the parallelogram using $A = bh$. This is also the area of the original trapezoid.)

Alternative Examples

Example A—Find the area of the trapezoid: $h = 12$ in., $a = 30$ in., $b = 72$ in.
$A = \frac{1}{2} \times (30 + 72) \times 12$
$A = \frac{1}{2} \times (102 \times 12)$
$A = \frac{1}{2} \times 1224$
$A = 612$
The area is **612 square inches.**

Example B—Find the area of the trapezoid: $h = 4$ cm, $a = 2$ cm, $b = 9$ cm.
$A = \frac{1}{2} \times (2 + 9) \times 4$
$A = \frac{1}{2} \times (11 \times 4)$
$A = \frac{1}{2} \times 44$
$A = 22$
The area is **22 square centimeters.**

T322

14.7 Finding the Area of a Trapezoid

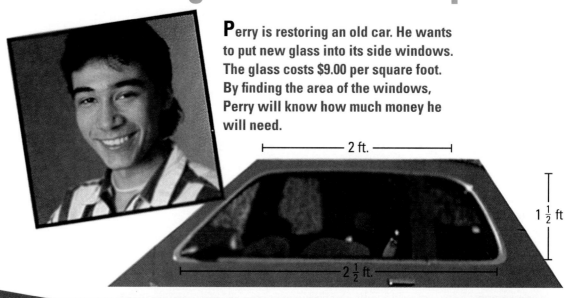

Perry is restoring an old car. He wants to put new glass into its side windows. The glass costs $9.00 per square foot. By finding the area of the windows, Perry will know how much money he will need.

Examples

To find the area of a trapezoid, use the formula.

trapezoid   a four-sided figure that has exactly one pair of parallel sides

$A = \frac{1}{2} \times (a + b) \times h,$
or $\frac{1}{2}(a + b)h$

$A =$ area, $h =$ height, $a =$ top base, $b =$ bottom base

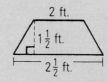

Find the area of the trapezoid.
$$A = \frac{1}{2} \times (2 + 2\frac{1}{2}) \times 1\frac{1}{2}$$
$$= \frac{1}{2} \times (4\frac{1}{2} \times 1\frac{1}{2})$$
$$= \frac{1}{2} \times 6\frac{3}{4}$$
$$= 3\frac{3}{8}$$

The area is **$3\frac{3}{8}$ square feet.**

▶ **Think and Discuss**

1. Solve. $\frac{1}{2} \times (31 + 47)$

2. Divide the trapezoid pictured to the right into 2 triangles. Can you think of another way to find its area?

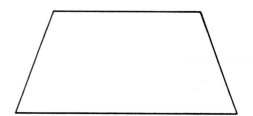

3. Refer to the introduction to this lesson. Estimate how much the glass costs for Perry's car.

4. Explain how the area of a trapezoid can be found using the average of its two bases.

5. How do you identify the bases of a trapezoid?

Exercises

Find the area of each trapezoid. (For more practice, see page 445.)

6.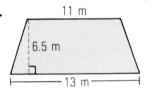

7.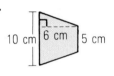

8.

9. $a = 1.6$ m
   $b = 2.8$ m
   $h = 1.4$ m

10. $a = 34$ in.
    $b = 28$ in.
    $h = 15$ in.

11. $a = 5$ cm
    $b = 12$ cm
    $h = 18$ cm

12.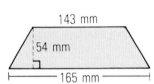

13.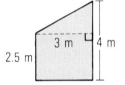

14.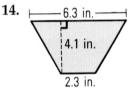

15. $a = 8$ in.
    $b = 19$ in.
    $h = 6$ in.

16. $a = 1.5$ m
    $b = 2.5$ m
    $h = 2.0$ m

17. $a = 3.0$ cm
    $b = 7.1$ cm
    $h = 4.2$ cm

▶ **Applications**

18. A trapezoid-shaped field measures 100 yards and 150 yards on its parallel sides and 200 yards across. What is the area of the field? **25,000 square yards**

19. One quart of paint covers 60 square feet. How many gallons should a painter buy to cover the wall shown here? **2 gallons**

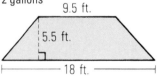

▶ **Review** (Lessons 6.1, 6.4, 6.6, 6.7)

Multiply or divide.

20. $4\frac{1}{2} \times 3\frac{5}{8}$ $16\frac{5}{16}$

21. $8\frac{5}{12} \div 7\frac{2}{3}$ $1\frac{9}{92}$

22. $\frac{1}{2} \times \frac{3}{8}$ $\frac{3}{16}$

23. $\frac{6}{3} \div \frac{2}{5}$ 5

Geometry: Perimeter and Area **323**

▶ **Think and Discuss Answers**

1. 39
2. A sample answer is to find the area of the 2 triangles and then add the areas together.
3. about $60.75
4. $A = \frac{1}{2} \times (a + b) \times h$ can be written as $A = \frac{a + b}{2} \times h$, where $\frac{a + b}{2}$ represents the average of the two bases. You can find the area of a trapezoid by multiplying its height by the average of its two bases.
5. They are the sides that are parallel.

Answers

6. 78 square meters
7. 45 square centimeters
8. 277.5 square feet
9. 3.08 square meters
10. 465 square inches
11. 153 square centimeters
12. 8316 square millimeters
13. 9.75 square meters
14. 17.63 square inches
15. 81 square inches
16. 4 square meters
17. 21.21 square centimeters

★ **Error Alert**

Errors may reveal that students are multiplying instead of adding the lengths of the bases.

Reinforcement

Extra Practice, page 445
EP/MR Worksheet 112, TRB, page 112

Challenge

Note to the Teacher: Draw the diagram shown below on the chalkboard.

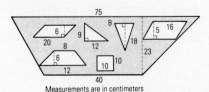

Measurements are in centimeters

Find the area of the shaded portion of the diagram. All measurements are centimeters. (836.5 square centimeters)

T323

Objective

• To find the area of a circle, given its radius or its diameter

Purpose

In this lesson you learn how to find the area of a circle. This knowledge can help you find the area of circular surfaces such as a round table top or a circular field.

Introducing the Lesson

Draw a circle on a large piece of paper and divide it into eight equal-sized pieces. Cut out the pieces and arrange them on another piece of paper as shown below. Draw a parallelogram around the pieces. Have students calculate the area of the parallelogram. Point out to students that the height of the parallelogram is the radius (r) of the circle. Since the base of the parallelogram is approximately $\pi \times r$ (half the circumference of the circle), the area of the parallelogram is approximately $\pi \times r \times r$.

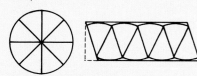

Alternative Examples

Example A—Find the area of the circle.
$r = 140$ ft.
$A = \pi \times r \times r$
$A \approx \frac{22}{7} \times 140 \times 140$
$A \approx \frac{22}{7} \times 19{,}600$
$A \approx \textbf{61,600 square feet}$

Example B—Find the area of the circle. Round to the nearest hundredth. $d = 0.4$ cm *First find the radius.*
$r = \frac{1}{2} \times d$
$r = \frac{1}{2} \times 0.4 = 0.2$
$A = \pi \times r$
$A \approx 3.14 \times 0.2 \times 0.2$
$A \approx 3.14 \times 0.04 = 0.1256$
$A \approx \textbf{0.13 square centimeters}$

14.8 Finding the Area of a Circle

Theora Baines is submitting a bid to paint the landing circle for the Centerville Hospital helicopter port. The diameter of the circle is 30 feet. Before she can figure out how much paint she will need, Theora must find the area of the circle.

Examples

To find the area of a circle, use the formula $A = \pi \times r \times r$.
$A = $ area, $r = $ radius
Use either 3.14 or $\frac{22}{7}$ for π.

A Find the area of the circle.

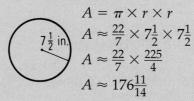

$A = \pi \times r \times r$
$A \approx \frac{22}{7} \times 7\frac{1}{2} \times 7\frac{1}{2}$
$A \approx \frac{22}{7} \times \frac{225}{4}$
$A \approx 176\frac{11}{14}$

$A \approx 176\frac{11}{14}$ **square inches**

B Find the area of the circle.

First find the radius. $r = \frac{1}{2} \times d$
$r = \frac{1}{2} \times 30 = 15$

$A = \pi \times r \times r$
$A \approx 3.14 \times 15 \times 15$
$A \approx 3.14 \times 225$
$A \approx 706.5$
$A \approx \textbf{706.5 square feet}$

▶ Think and Discuss

1. What is the area of a circle that has a radius of 10 inches?

2. What is the area of a circle that has a diameter of 14 meters?

3. If the radius of a circle is doubled, what happens to the area?

4. Refer to the introduction to this lesson. What is the area of the landing circle?

5. The circumference of a circle is 62.8 centimeters. Discuss ways to find its area. Then find it.

Exercises

Find the area. (See Example A.)

6. $r = 7$ m   **7.** $r = 12$ ft.   **8.** $r = 4.2$ cm   **9.** $r = 8\frac{1}{4}$ in.   **10.** $r = 5$ mi.

Find the area. Round answers to the nearest tenth.
(See Example B.)

11. $d = 13$ m   **12.** $d = 8$ mi.   **13.** $d = 42$ m   **14.** $d = 3$ km   **15.** $d = 5$ yd.

▶ **Mixed Practice** (For more practice, see page 446.)

Find the area. Round answers to the nearest tenth as needed.

16. $r = 3$ ft.   **17.** $r = 6.1$ m   **18.** $d = 36$ in.   **19.** $r = 10$ yd.   **20.** $r = 4\frac{1}{4}$ in.

21.
30 in.

22.
400 yd.

23.
$62\frac{1}{4}$ in.

24.
100 cm

25.
1 mi.

26.
15 in.

27.
9.5 mi.

28.
5.2 m

29.
7.3 mm

30.
2 ft.

▶ **Applications**

31. A radio station has a broadcast radius of 55 miles. How large is the area that the station serves?

32. The inside edge of a circular sidewalk is 20 feet from the center of its circle. The outside edge is 24 feet away. Find the area of the sidewalk.

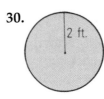
24 ft.
20 ft.

▶ **Review** (Lesson 3.9)

Simplify.

33. $3 \times 2 \times 7 + 15$ 57   **34.** $19 - 16 \div 4 \times 3$ 7   **35.** $6 \times 5 + 8 \times 8$ 94

▶ **Think and Discuss Answers**
  1. 314 square inches
  2. 153.86 square meters
  3. The area is increased four times.
  4. 706.5 square feet
  5. Dividing the circumference by π gives the diameter, which is 20 cm. One-half of the diameter gives the radius, so the radius is 10 cm. Hence, the area is 314 square centimeters.

Answers

  6. 153.86 or 154 square meters
  7. 452.16 square feet
  8. 55.3896 square centimeters
  9. 213.71625, or $213\frac{102}{112}$ square inches
  10. 78.5 square miles
  11. 132.7 square meters
  12. 50.2 square miles
  13. 1384.7 square meters
  14. 7.1 square kilometers
  15. 19.6 square yards
  16. 28.3 square feet
  17. 116.8 square meters
  18. 1017.4 square inches
  19. 314 square yards
  20. 56.7 square inches
  (continued on page T328)

★ **Error Alert**
Errors may indicate that students are doubling the radius instead of squaring it, or are using the diameter in the formula without first finding the radius.

Reinforcement
Extra Practice, page 446
EP/MR Worksheet 113, TRB, page 113

Project
Go to a gymnasium in your school or a park and measure the diameter of one of the circular areas painted on the floor. Compute the area of the circle. Include in your report a description of the location of the circle in the gymnasium, the sport in which it is used, and how many circles of the same area are present. (possible answer: the center circle in a basketball court has a diameter of 12 ft., a radius of 6 feet, and an area of about 113.0 sq. ft. There are three circles of the same area on the basketball court; the other two are the circles around the free-throw lines.)

Objective

• To apply geometry in analyzing diagrams

Purpose

This lesson helps you apply what you know about geometry to analyze and interpret diagrams such as floor plans and diagrams of plots of land.

Introducing the Lesson

Display a copy of an actual floor plan, architect's plan, or mechanical drawing in class. Elicit from students the kinds of information that are available from the drawing. (sample answers: dimensions, placement of installations or component parts) Point out that tradespeople use drawings for many different purposes, depending on the task they have to do. Explain to students that this lesson shows how to use their knowledge of geometry to help them interpret drawings.

14.9 Analyzing Diagrams

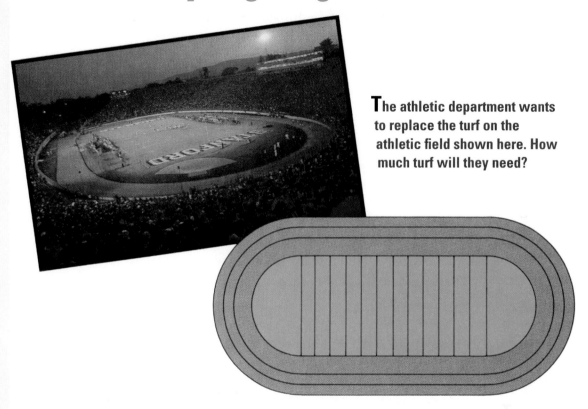

The athletic department wants to replace the turf on the athletic field shown here. How much turf will they need?

You can find the area of the entire field by adding the areas of each part. First, break the field into three parts: a rectangle and two semicircles.

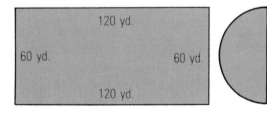

1. The two semicircles can be thought of as one circle, split into two pieces. What is the radius of the circle?
   30 yards

2. Find the area of the circle. Let $\pi = 3.14$. ≈ 2826 square yards

3. What is the area of the rectangle? 7200 square yards

4. What is the total area of the athletic field? ≈ 10,026 square yards

To solve area and perimeter problems based on diagrams, you may need to use several strategies, such as finding missing information and breaking the diagram into parts.

PROBLEM SOLVING

Here is the floor plan of a kitchen with parts cut out where built-in cabinets and appliances are located. Suppose you wanted to find the area needed for floor covering.

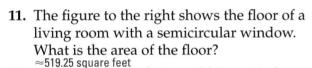

12 ft.   3 ft.

10 ft.

a

9 ft.

6 ft.

b

14 ft.

5. What is the total distance from the west (left) wall to the east (right) wall? 20 feet

6. What is the total distance from the north (top) wall to the south (bottom) wall? 12 feet

7. Find *a*. 8 feet

8. Find *b*. 2 feet

9. What is the amount of floor covering needed? 204 square feet

10. What is the area of the room's ceiling? 240 square feet

11. The figure to the right shows the floor of a living room with a semicircular window. What is the area of the floor?
≈519.25 square feet

12. At $0.30 a foot, what would it cost to buy molding to go around the entire room? ≈$29.31

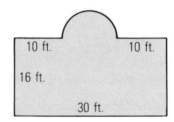

10 ft.   10 ft.

16 ft.

30 ft.

400 ft.

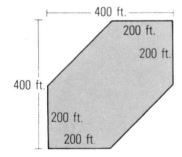

200 ft.

200 ft.

400 ft.

200 ft.

200 ft.

13. The figure to the left shows the dimensions of a plot of land. What is the total area of the plot of land?
120,000 square feet

14. If the land in Question 13 sells for $5000 an acre, about how much would this plot cost?
1 acre = 43,560 square feet
about $13,000 or $14,000

▶ **Review** (Lesson 11.5)

On a scale drawing, 1 inch = 12 feet. Find the following scale measurements.

15. $2\frac{1}{2}$ inches 30 feet

16. $\frac{3}{4}$ inch 9 feet

17. 1.25 inches 15 feet

★ **Error Alert**
Mistakes may occur if students use the incorrect formula or use the wrong number in a formula.

Reinforcement
EP/MR Worksheet 114, TRB, page 114

Challenge
Note to the Teacher: Draw the diagram shown below on the chalkboard.

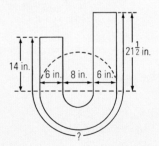

14 in. $21\frac{1}{2}$ in.

6 in. 8 in. 6 in.

?

Copy the diagram from the chalkboard on your paper. This drawing represents a piece of water pipe that must be replaced. The circle is drawn over the pipe to help you find the length of the outside circular portion of the pipe. Apply your knowledge of geometry to find the total length, to the nearest inch, of the curved line shown along the outside of the pipe. (67 inches)

Geometry: Perimeter and Area **327**

T327

Answers
1. regular
2. distance around
3. 54 inches
4. 28.6 centimeters
5. 15.12 meters
6. 32 feet 2 inches
7. 235.2 centimeters
8. 31.9 centimeters
9. $C = 25.12$ meters; $A = 50.24$ square meters
10. $C = 40.19$ centimeters; $A = 128.61$ square centimeters
11. $C = 81.64$ meters; $A = 530.66$ square meters
12. 35 square inches
13. 104.88 square meters
14. 77 square inches
15. 98 square centimeters

Answers

(continued from page T325)
21. 706.5 square inches
22. 125,600 square yards
23. 12,167.7 square inches
24. 7850 square centimeters
25. 3.1 square miles
26. 176.6 square inches
27. 283.4 square miles
28. 84.9 square miles
29. 167.3 square millimeters
30. 12.6 square feet
31. 9498.5 square feet
32. 552.64 square feet

Chapter 14 Review

REVIEW

Complete each statement. (Lesson 14.1)

1. All sides of a(n) ___■___ polygon have the same length.

2. Perimeter means ___■___ .

Find the perimeters of each polygon. (Lesson 14.2)

3.  9 in. 9 in. 9 in. 9 in. 9 in. 9 in.

4. Triangle with sides 9.3 cm, 8.5 cm, 10.8 cm

5. 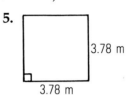 3.78 m 3.78 m

6. Rectangle with sides 6 ft. 5 in., and 9 ft. 8 in.

7. 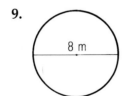 29.4 cm 29.4 cm 29.4 cm 29.4 cm 29.4 cm 29.4 cm 29.4 cm 29.4 cm

8. 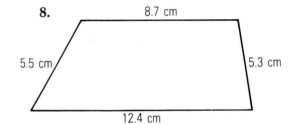 8.7 cm 5.5 cm 5.3 cm 12.4 cm

Find the circumference and area of each circle. (Lessons 14.4, 14.8)

9. 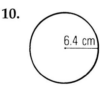 8 m

10. 6.4 cm

11. $r = 13$ m

Find the area of each figure. (Lessons 14.5, 14.6, 14.7)

12. 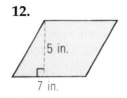 5 in. 7 in.

13. 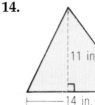 11.4 m 9.2 m

14. 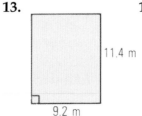 11 in. 14 in.

15. 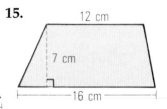 12 cm 7 cm 16 cm

Chapter 14 Test

Find the circumference and area of each circle. Round answers to the nearest hundredth.

1.

6.1 cm

2.

7 m

3.

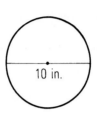

10 in.

Find the area of each figure.

4.

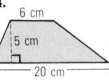

6 cm
5 cm
20 cm

5.

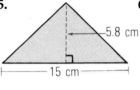

5.8 cm
15 cm

6.

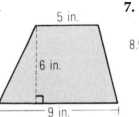

5 in.
6 in.
9 in.

7.

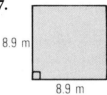

8.9 m
8.9 m

Complete each statement.

8. The formula for the ___ of a rectangle is $P = 2l + 2w$.

9. The distance around a circle is called the ___ .

10. The letter ___ represents the height in formulas for triangles, trapezoids, and parallelograms.

Find the perimeter of each polygon.

11.

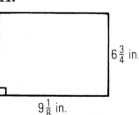

$6\frac{3}{4}$ in.
$9\frac{1}{8}$ in.

12.

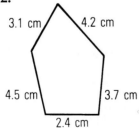

3.1 cm
4.2 cm
4.5 cm
3.7 cm
2.4 cm

13.

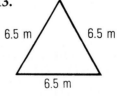

6.5 m
6.5 m
6.5 m

Answers
1. $C = 38.31$ cm; $A = 116.84$ square centimeters
2. $C = 21.98$ m; $A = 38.47$ square meters
3. $C = 31.4$ in.; $A = 78.5$ square inches
4. 65 square centimeters
5. 43.5 square centimeters
6. 42 square inches
7. 79.21 square meters
8. perimeter
9. circumference
10. h
11. $31\frac{3}{4}$ inches
12. 17.9 centimeters
13. 19.5 meters

Use surface area and volume to

• decide how much wrapping paper to buy.

• discover how much a box will hold.

• describe how much water a fish tank will hold.

• compare the capacity of two containers.

What are some other ways to use surface area and volume?

Geometry: Surface Area and Volume

A package designer designs functional and attractive packages.

- Package designers work for manufacturing or advertising companies.

- A package designer creates detailed blueprints of designs for packaging goods. A package designer should be creative, practical, and aware of the latest trends.

- This individual should be able to work with blueprints, maximize space, and minimize cost.

- To become a package designer, an individual usually completes a course of study in a college or an art school.

- Related careers include sales representatives, advertising writers, graphic designers, and marketing analysts and printers.

CAREER

PACKAGE DESIGNER

PORTFOLIO PROJECT: *Design a package.*

1. Choose a product that is sold in a package. Design a new package for your product that will help increase its sales.

2. Make a model of your package and a blueprint. Determine the surface area, volume, and cost of the package. *Show the math.*

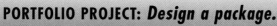

3. Change your package to increase the volume without increasing the total surface area. *Use the guess and check method and show the work.*

Students may want to survey the school with a few well-chosen questions about their proposed new package for an old item. Based on responses, their designs should address concerns and needs of those surveyed. All measurements are to be labeled at the blueprint stage. A mock-up of the new package is to be included. Students then change the dimensions of their package to increase the volume. The new volume can be figured on the bottom of the blueprint. Be sure students do not alter the total surface area. Encourage students to use the guess and check method to find the correct answer.

Assessment: The individual scoring rubric on page 161 of the Teacher's Resource Binder can be reproduced and used for assessment. Include the following information in the last two boxes. Students should have:
- created a package from a blueprint.
- accurately figured all the math, including the increased volume.

Objective

- To identify *faces*, *edges*, and vertices of *polyhedrons*.

Purpose

In the last chapter you studied 2-dimensional figures—rectangles, squares, parallelograms, triangles, trapezoids, and circles. In this lesson you learn about 3-dimensional figures such as cubes, cylinders, and cones.

Introducing the Lesson

Review finding the area of rectangles, squares, and triangles (Lessons 14.5, 14.6). Have volunteers give the formula for each figure and write it on the board.
(rectangle: $A = l \times w$
square: $A = s \times s$
triangle: $A = \frac{1}{2} \times b \times h$)

Alternative Strategies

Use a model of a 3-dimensional object. For example, using a gift box, have a student point to each vertex. Ask: How many vertices are there? (8) Have a student run his or her finger along each edge of the box. Ask: How many edges are there? (12) Now have a student move a flat hand across each face. Ask: How many faces are there? (6) Liken a vertex to a point, an edge to a line, and a face to a flat surface or polygon. Ask: What are you doing when you wrap a birthday present? (covering the surface area of the package) Ask: What are you doing when you pack a box? (filling its volume)

Answers

1. The bases of the cylinder and the cone are circles; the side of the cylinder is a rectangle; the base and faces of the prism are polygons.
2. Sample answers may include: cylinder—beverage can, roll of paper towels; prism—camping tent, office building; cone—ice cream cone, clown's hat.

15.1 Introduction to 3-Dimensional Figures

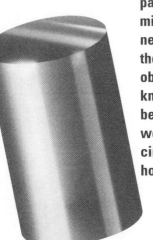

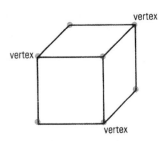

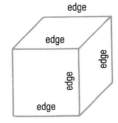

Look at the objects on this page. How would you determine the amount of paper needed to cover each object or the amount of water each object could hold? You already know a lot about this question because you know how to work with polygons and circles, how to measure, and how to multiply.

Figures like the ones above are called 3-dimensional figures. The 3 dimensions are length, width, and height.

1. Where do you see polygons and circles in the figures above?

2. Identify 2 objects that resemble each of the figures above.

▶ Express Yourself

Here are some terms that will help you in this chapter.

polyhedron — a 3-dimensional figure whose faces are polygons

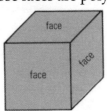

The polyhedrons shown above each have 6 **faces,** 12 **edges,** and 8 **vertices** (plural of vertex).

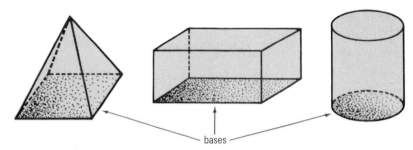

bases

surface area   the total area of the outside surface of a 3-dimensional figure

volume   a measure of the amount of space inside a 3-dimensional figure

cubic inches, cubic centimeters

units of volume

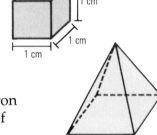
1 cm
1 cm
1 cm

▶ **Practice What You Know**

3. Look at the faces of the polyhedron shown to the right. What types of polygons are they?

4. Find the area of a rectangle 4 feet long and $3\frac{1}{4}$ feet wide. What formula did you use?   13 sq. ft.; $A = lw$

5. Find the area of a square with sides 5.6 centimeters long.
   31.36 square centimeters

6. Find the area of a triangle whose base is 18 inches and whose height is $10\frac{1}{2}$ inches. What formula did you use?   94.5 sq. in.; $A = \frac{1}{2}bh$

7. Use the following steps to draw a cube.

| a. Draw a square. | b. Draw another square the same size. | c. Connect the corners of each square. | d. Erase lines that would not be seen. |

          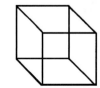   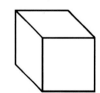

8. How many faces does a cube have? Edges? Vertices?
   6 faces; 12 edges; 8 vertices

9. Refer to the first polyhedron on this page. Find the number of faces, edges, and vertices it has.   5 faces; 8 edges; 5 vertices

Practice What You Know Answer

3. triangles and square

★ **Error Alert**
Mistakes may result when students use the wrong formula.

Teaching Aids
Patterns: Number cube, spinners, protractor
TA3, TRB, page 156
Pattern: Rectangular prism
TA4, TRB, page 157
Pattern: Pyramid
TA5, TRB, page 158
Pattern: Cylinder
TA6, TRB, page 159
Teaching suggestions precede the Teaching Aids worksheets.

Project
Identify ten objects in the classroom that can be represented by the 3-dimensional figures in this lesson. (sample answers: teacher's desk, book, wastebasket, piece of chalk, eraser) What kinds of polygons are the faces of each object? (circles, rectangles, squares) Find the measurements of an object of your choice in the classroom. Now determine the area of each face. (Answers depend on object selected.)

Objective

- To construct polyhedrons

Purpose

By making your own 3-dimensional figures, you can visualize the different kinds of polyhedrons, making it easier to determine the number of faces and the size and shape of each face.

Introducing the Lesson

Review the terms *polyhedron, face,* and *surface area* (Lesson 15.1). Pass around models of 3-dimensional figures. Use plastic or wooden models of polyhedrons as well as objects that can be found in the home—cereal box, small gift box, etc. Have students describe the faces of the models and the objects as geometric shapes.

15.2 Constructing Polyhedron Models

Model building is an enjoyable way to learn more about polyhedrons.

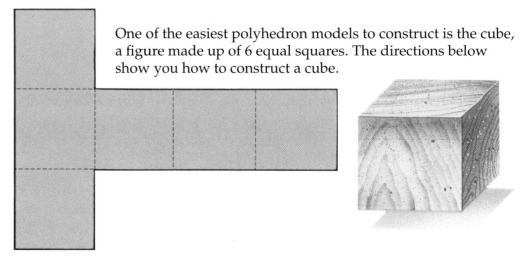

One of the easiest polyhedron models to construct is the cube, a figure made up of 6 equal squares. The directions below show you how to construct a cube.

Copy the figure above and cut out your drawing. Fold along dotted lines. Use tape to keep the edges together.

1. How many faces does a cube have? How many edges? How many vertices? 6 faces; 12 edges; 8 vertices

2. What shape is each face of a cube? Square

A T-shape is not the only shape you can use to construct a cube.

Copy and cut out each figure. Try to fold each into a cube. Which ones form a cube?

3. Forms cube   **4.** Forms cube   **5.** Does not form cube

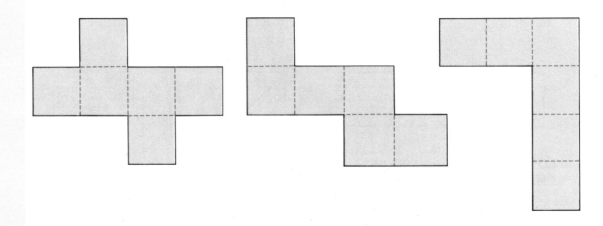

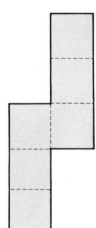

Work with 2 or 3 classmates.

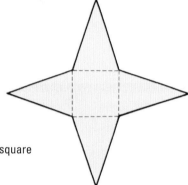

6. Form a cube from a drawing like the one shown at the left.

7. Make three drawings of your own that can be folded into cubes.
Drawings will vary.

8. Compare your drawings with those of your classmates. How many different drawings did your class come up with? Answers will vary.

A different polyhedron can be built using the figure at the right as a model. Before constructing the polyhedron, answer the following questions.

9. What 2-dimensional figure makes up the base? A square

10. What will the polyhedron look like? A pyramid

11. How many faces, edges, and vertices do you think the polyhedron will have? 5 faces; 8 edges; 5 vertices

12. Copy and cut out the figure above. Fold the figure along dotted lines. Use tape to join edges.

13. How many faces, edges, and vertices does your figure have?
5 faces; 8 edges; 5 vertices

▶ **Review** (Lesson 14.5)

Find the area of each figure.

14. Rectangle
$l = 4.6$ cm
$w = 3.3$ cm

15. Parallelogram
$b = 5\frac{1}{4}$ in.
$h = 2\frac{1}{2}$ in.

16. Square
$s = 9.8$ cm

17. Rectangle
$l = 6\frac{3}{8}$ in.
$w = 5\frac{1}{2}$ in.

18.

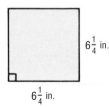

$6\frac{1}{4}$ in.

$6\frac{1}{4}$ in.

19.

12.4 cm

20.8 cm

20.

16.3 cm

19.5 cm

21.

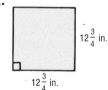

$12\frac{3}{4}$ in.

$12\frac{3}{4}$ in.

Answers

14. 15.18 square centimeters

15. $13\frac{1}{8}$ square inches

16. 96.04 square centimeters

17. $35\frac{1}{16}$ square inches

18. $39\frac{1}{16}$ square inches

19. 257.92 square centimeters

20. 317.85 square centimeters

21. $162\frac{9}{16}$ square inches

★ **Error Alert**

Errors may occur if students forget to count a vertex, or if they count a vertex more than once. The same applies to edges and faces.

Reinforcement

EP/MR Worksheet 115, TRB, page 115

Teaching Aids

Patterns: Number cube, spinners, protractor
TA 3, TRB, page 156
Teaching suggestions precede the Teaching Aids worksheets.

Pattern: Rectangular prism
TA 4, TRB, page 157
Teaching suggestions precede the Teaching Aids worksheets.

Pattern: Pyramid
TA 5, TRB, page 158
Teaching suggestions precede the Teaching Aids worksheets.

Project

Work in groups of three. Collect three boxes, one of which is a cube. Use your ruler to measure each edge to the nearest half inch. Make a chart for each box. Record the measurements, calculate the area of each face, and record the areas. What conclusions can you draw about the areas of the faces of each box? (sample answer: all boxes have three pairs of equal-area faces) Tape the chart to the box it belongs with so you can display your samples and data in the classroom.

Purpose

Knowing how to find surface area enables you to determine the amount of paint you must buy in order to paint a room or a house.

Introducing the Lesson

Review the definition of *surface area* (Lesson 15.1). (The total area of the outside surface of a 3-dimensional figure.) Ask: if you want to cover a book, what surfaces would you cover? (the 2 covers and the spine) Is this what is meant by surface area? Explain. (sample answer: no; you would not be covering all outside surfaces) When might you cover all outside surfaces? (sample answer: wrapping a book as a gift; making a cushion cover)

Alternative Examples

Example A—Find the surface area of a cube if $s = 12$ cm.
$A = 6(s \times s)$
Substitute 12 for s.
$A = 6(12 \times 12)$
Multiply.
$A = 6(144)$
$A = 864$
$A =$ **864 square centimeters**

Example B—Find the surface area of a rectangular prism if $h = 11$ in., $l = 13$ in., and $w = 8$ in.
$A = 2(lw) + 2(wh) + 2(lh)$
$A = 2(13 \times 8) + 2(8 \times 11) + 2(13 \times 11)$
$A = 208 + 176 + 286$
$A = 670$
$A =$ **670 square inches**

Meghan wants to make a terrarium like the one shown here. Which sheet of plexiglass will she need to buy? Meghan should find the surface area of the terrarium before making her decision.

Plexiglass Sale

36 in. X 48 in. X $\frac{1}{4}$ in. $19.50

21 in. X 15 in. X $\frac{1}{4}$ in. $14.30

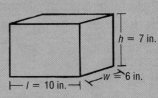

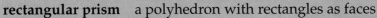

Examples

To find the surface area of a cube or a prism, add the areas of its faces.

cube   a polyhedron with squares as faces
$A = 6(s \times s)$
$A =$ surface area, $s =$ length of edge

$s = 9$ cm

rectangular prism   a polyhedron with rectangles as faces
$A = 2(lw) + 2(wh) + 2(lh)$
$A =$ surface area, $l =$ length,
$w =$ width, $h =$ height

Note: A prism is named for its base. There are other types of prisms, but we will study only rectangular prisms.

$h = 7$ in.
$l = 10$ in. $w = 6$ in.

A Find the surface area of the cube above.

$A = 6(s \times s)$
$A = 6(9 \times 9)$ Substitute 9 cm for s.
$A = 6(81)$ Multiply.
$A = 486$
$A =$ **486 square centimeters**

B Find the surface area of the prism above.

$A = 2(lw) + 2(wh) + 2(lh)$
$A = 2(10 \times 6) + 2(6 \times 7) + 2(10 \times 7)$
$A = 120 + 84 + 140$
$A = 344$
$A =$ **344 square inches**

▶ **Think and Discuss**

1. Find the surface area of a cube with edges 6 feet long.

2. What is the formula for the area of each face of a cube?

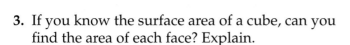

3. If you know the surface area of a cube, can you find the area of each face? Explain.

4. Refer to the introduction to this lesson. Which sheet of plexiglass should Meghan buy?

SKILLS

Exercises

Find the surface area of each cube. (See Example A.)

5. $s = 12$ cm   **6.** $s = 7\frac{1}{2}$ in.   **7.** $s = 2.6$ cm   **8.** $s = 6\frac{1}{4}$ in.

Find the surface area of each prism. (See Example B.)

9. $l = 15$ cm	**10.** $l = 18$ cm	**11.** $l = 4.1$ cm	**12.** $l = 11$ in.
$w = 20$ cm	$w = 12$ cm	$w = 6.2$ cm	$w = 6$ in.
$h = 8$ cm	$h = 20$ cm	$h = 8.8$ cm	$h = 7$ in.

▶ Mixed Practice (For more practice, see page 446.)

Find the surface area of each figure.

13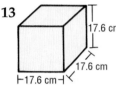
17.6 cm
17.6 cm
17.6 cm

14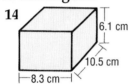
6.1 cm
10.5 cm
8.3 cm

15.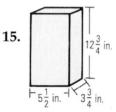
$12\frac{3}{4}$ in.
$5\frac{1}{2}$ in. $3\frac{3}{4}$ in.

16.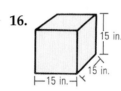
15 in.
15 in.
15 in.

17. Cube	**18.** Prism	**19.** Prism	**20.** Cube
$4\frac{1}{2}$-inch edges	$l = 9$ cm	$l = 3\frac{1}{2}$ in.	$s = 5.7$ cm
	$w = 7$ cm	$w = 6$ in.	
	$h = 3.15$ cm	$h = 8\frac{1}{4}$ in.	

▶ Applications

21. Each edge of Cube 1 is two inches long. Each edge of Cube 2 is twice as long. Is the surface area of Cube 2 twice that of Cube 1? Compute and show.
No; it is 4 times as large

22. A company sells thinner in cans like the one shown. How many square inches of metal are needed to make each can (excluding the cap and spout)? $251\frac{1}{2}$ sq. in.

$9\frac{1}{2}$ in.
4 in.
$6\frac{1}{2}$ in.

▶ Review (Lessons 14.4, 14.6, 14.8)

Find the area of each triangle. Find the circumference and area of each circle.

23. Triangle	**24.** Circle	**25.** Triangle	**26.** Circle
$b = 12$ in.	$r = 40$ cm	$b = 13$ in.	$d = 6$ m
$h = 18$ in.		$h = 7$ in.	

Purpose

To determine the amount of canvas needed to make a duffel bag with two circular faces or a tent that has triangular faces, you need to find surface area. this lesson shows you how to find surface areas of cylinders and pyramids.

Introducing the Lesson

Review counting faces of polyhedrons (Lesson 15.1) and finding surface area of cubes and prisms (Lesson 15.3). Ask: What is the formula for finding the area of triangles $(A = \frac{1}{2}bh)$; the area of circles? $(A = \pi \times r \times r)$ What is the formula for the circumference of a circle? $(C = \pi d,$ or $C = 2\pi r)$

Alternative Examples

Example A—Find the surface area of a square pyramid where $s = 15$ in. and $h = 12$ in.

$A = (s \times s) + 4(\frac{1}{2}sh)$

Substitute values for s and h.

$A = (15 \times 15) + 4(\frac{1}{2} \times 15 \times 12)$

$A = 225 + 360$ *Multiply.*

$A = 585$ *Simplify.*

$A =$ **585 square inches**

Example B—Find the surface area of a cylinder if $r = 5\frac{1}{4}$ cm and $h = 22$ cm.

Use $\frac{22}{7}$ for π.

$A = 2(\pi \times r \times r) + (C \times h)$

Substitute values for r and h.

Use $C = 2\pi r$.

$A \approx 2(\frac{22}{7} \times 5\frac{1}{4} \times 5\frac{1}{4})$
$\quad + (2 \times \frac{22}{7} \times 5\frac{1}{4} \times 22)$

Multiply.

$A \approx 173\frac{1}{4} + 726$

Simplify.

$A \approx 899\frac{1}{4}$

$A \approx 899\frac{1}{4}$ **square centimeters**

15.4 Finding the Surface Areas of Pyramids and Cylinders

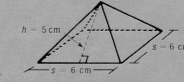

How much cardboard is used to make each of the mailing tubes shown here?

$h = 18$ in.

$d = 3\frac{1}{2}$ in.

Examples

To find the surface area of a pyramid, add the areas of its faces. To find the surface area of a cylinder, add the areas of the side and bases.

square pyramid   a polyhedron with a square base whose other faces are triangles. All the triangular faces meet at a vertex.

$A = (s \times s) + 4(\frac{1}{2}sh)$

$A =$ surface area, $s =$ side, $h =$ height

$h = 5$ cm

$s = 6$ cm

$s = 6$ cm

cylinder   a 3-dimensional figure with two bases that are equal circles

$A = 2(\pi \times r \times r) + (Ch)$

$A =$ surface area, $r =$ radius,

$C =$ circumference, $h =$ height

Use 3.14 or $\frac{22}{7}$ for π.

$r = 1\frac{3}{4}$ in.

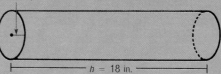

$h = 18$ in.

Note: A pyramid is named for its base. There are other types of pyramids, but we will study only square pyramids.

A Find the surface area of the pyramid above.

$A = (s \times s) + 4(\frac{1}{2}sh)$

$A = (6 \times 6) + 4(\frac{1}{2} \times 6 \times 5)$ Substitute values for s and h.

$A = 36 + 60 = 96$ Simplify.

$A =$ **96 square centimeters**

B Find the surface area of the cylinder above.

$A = 2(\pi \times r \times r) + (Ch)$ Use $C = 2\pi r$.

$A \approx 2(\frac{22}{7} \times \frac{7}{4} \times \frac{7}{4}) + (2 \times \frac{22}{7} \times \frac{7}{4} \times 18)$ Substitute values for r and h. Use $\frac{22}{7}$ for π.

$A \approx 19\frac{1}{4} + 198 = 217\frac{1}{4}$ Simplify.

$A \approx 217\frac{1}{4}$ **square inches.**

▶ Think and Discuss

1. Refer to the introduction to this lesson. How much cardboard was needed to make the first cylinder?

2. How many triangular faces does a square pyramid have? What is the formula for the area of each triangular face?

3. Explain where the formula $A = (s \times s) + 4(\frac{1}{2}sh)$ comes from.

4. A printed label covers all but the ends of a mailing tube. What shape is the label?

Exercises

Find the surface area of each pyramid. (See Example A.)

5. $s = 4$ in.	**6.** $s = 3$ cm	**7.** $s = 10$ in.	**8.** $s = 10.4$ cm
$h = 5$ in.	$h = 6$ cm	$h = 9$ in.	$h = 12.6$ cm

Find the surface area of each cylinder. (See Example B.)

9. $h = 5$ in.	**10.** $h = 15$ in.	**11.** $h = 25$ cm	**12.** $h = 17.8$ cm
$r = 5$ in.	$r = 10$ in.	$r = 7$ cm	$r = 6.3$ cm

▶ Mixed Practice (For more practice, see page 447.)

Find the surface area of each figure.

13. Cylinder	**14.** Pyramid	**15.** Cylinder	**16.** Pyramid
$h = 25$ in.	$s = 10$ cm	$r = 4$ in.	$h = 6.6$ cm
$r = 14$ in.	$h = 12$ cm	$h = 12\frac{1}{2}$ in.	$s = 4.2$ cm

▶ Applications

17. How many square feet of canvas are needed to make the tent shown here? 180 sq. ft.

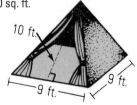

10 ft.
9 ft.
9 ft.

18. A can of tomatoes is 5 inches tall and 3 inches in diameter. How many square inches of paper (disregarding overlap) make up the label that covers the can? 47.1 sq. in.

▶ Review (Lesson 14.5)

Find the area of each figure.

19. Parallelogram	**20.** Rectangle	**21.** Rectangle	**22.** Parallelogram
$b = 3$ m	$l = 4.5$ cm	$l = 9\frac{1}{2}$ ft.	$b = 13$ cm
$h = 1.6$ m	$w = 2.8$ cm	$w = 7$ ft.	$h = 45$ cm

▶**Think and Discuss Answers**
1. $217\frac{1}{4}$ square inches
2. 4; $A = \frac{1}{2}bh$
3. The formula comes from the area of the base of a square pyramid plus the areas of four triangular faces.
4. rectangular

Answers

5. 56 square inches
6. 45 square centimeters
7. 280 square inches
8. 370.24 square centimeters
9. ≈314 square inches
10. ≈1570 square inches
(continued on page T347)

★ **Error Alert**

Errors may occur using the pyramid formula if students omit the fraction $\frac{1}{2}$ for the areas of the faces. Errors may occur using the cylinder formula if students confuse the values for the radius and diameter.

Reinforcement

Extra Practice, page 447
EP/MR Worksheet 117, TRB, page 117

Teaching Aids

Pattern: Pyramid
TA 5, TRB, page 158
Teaching suggestions precede the Teaching Aids worksheets.

Patterns: Cylinder and cone
TA 6, TRB, page 159
Teaching suggestions precede the Teaching Aids worksheets.

Challenge

Determine the surface area of a cylinder that has a radius of 14 inches and a height of 20 inches. (2992 sq. in.) Divide the measurements in half and find the new surface area. (748 sq. in.) Do the same for a square pyramid with 16-inch sides and a height of 12 inches. (640 sq. in.; 160 sq. in.) Describe how the surface area of the small cylinder compares with the surface area of the large cylinder. (It is one-fourth as great.) Is this true of the two pyramids? (yes)

15.5 Finding the Volumes of Cubes, Prisms, and Pyramids

Do you think the larger cube shown has twice as much space (volume) inside as the smaller cube? Three times as much? More? The answer might surprise you.

2 cm

4 cm

Examples

To find the volume of cubes, prisms, and pyramids, use the appropriate formula.

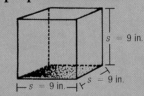

$s = 9$ in.

$s = 9$ in.

$V = s \times s \times s$
$V = $ volume,
$s = $ side

$h = 8$ cm

$w = 7$ cm

$l = 12$ cm

$V = Bh$
$V = $ volume, $h = $ height,
$B = $ area of base (lw)

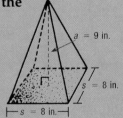

$a = 9$ in.

$s = 8$ in.

$s = 8$ in.

$V = \frac{1}{3}Ba$
$V = $ volume, $a = $ altitude,
$B = $ area of base ($s \times s$)

A Find the volume of the cube above.

$V = s \times s \times s$
$V = 9 \times 9 \times 9$
$V = 729$
$V = \textbf{729 cubic inches}$

B Find the volume of the prism above.

$V = Bh$
$V = lwh$
$V = 12 \times 7 \times 8$
$V = 672$
$V = \textbf{672 cubic centimeters}$

C Find the volume of the pyramid above.

$V = \frac{1}{3}Ba$
$V = \frac{1}{3} \times s \times s \times a$
$V = \frac{1}{3}(8 \times 8 \times 9)$
$V = 192$
$V = \textbf{192 cubic inches}$

▶ Think and Discuss

1. Refer to the introduction to this lesson. Find the volume of the two cubes. How many times bigger is the second cube?

2. Find the volume of a prism with $l = 6$ in., $w = 6$ in., and $h = 3$ in. Find the volume of a pyramid with the same dimensions.

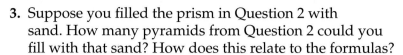

3. Suppose you filled the prism in Question 2 with sand. How many pyramids from Question 2 could you fill with that sand? How does this relate to the formulas?

4. What is the formula for the volume of a cube? What is the formula for the area of a square? How are they related?

SKILLS

Exercises

Find the volume of each cube. (See Example A.)

5. $s = 10$ cm
6. $s = 9$ in.
7. $s = 16$ cm
8. $s = 5.6$ cm

Find the volume of each prism. (See Example B.)

9. $l = 7$ m
$w = 15$ m
$h = 6$ m

10. $l = 8$ cm
$w = 4$ cm
$h = 2$ cm

11. $l = 10$ ft.
$w = 16$ ft.
$h = 19$ ft.

12. $l = \frac{1}{4}$ in.
$w = \frac{3}{4}$ in.
$h = \frac{5}{8}$ in.

Find the volume of each pyramid. (See Example C.)

13. $s = 6$ in.
$a = 5$ in.

14. $s = 18$ cm
$a = 9$ cm

15. $s = 12$ in.
$a = 6$ in.

16. $s = 5.2$ m
$a = 3$ m

▶ **Mixed Practice** (For more practice, see page 447.)

Find the volume of each figure.

17.
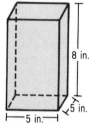
8 in.
5 in.
5 in.

18.
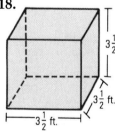
$3\frac{1}{2}$
$3\frac{1}{2}$ ft.
$3\frac{1}{2}$ ft.

19.
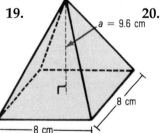
$a = 9.6$ cm
8 cm
8 cm

20.
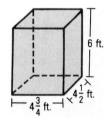
6 ft.
$4\frac{1}{2}$ ft.
$4\frac{3}{4}$ ft.

▶ **Applications**

21. The Great Pyramid of Egypt was originally 481 feet high. Its base was 756 feet on each side. Find the volume of the original pyramid. Use a calculator.
91,636,272 cu. ft.

22. A driveway is ninety-six feet long and twelve feet wide. It is paved with concrete six inches thick. At a cost of $3.50 per cubic foot, what did the concrete cost?
$2016

▶ **Review** (Lesson 11.2)

Tell whether each statement is a proportion. Use = or ≠ .

23. $\frac{1}{3} \blacksquare \frac{15}{45}$ =

24. $\frac{4}{70} \blacksquare \frac{12}{15}$ ≠

25. $\frac{12}{20} \blacksquare \frac{30}{50}$ =

26. $\frac{8}{9} \blacksquare \frac{72}{80}$ ≠

Geometry: Surface Area and Volume **341**

▶ **Think and Discuss Answers**

Answers
(see pages T348–T349)

★ **Error Alert**
Errors may indicate students are having problems with the formulas for finding the surface area and the volume of pyramids. They might confuse the altitude (*a*) of the pyramid with the slant height (*h*) of its triangular faces.

Reinforcement
Extra Practice, page 447
EP/MP Worksheet 118, TRB, page 118

Teaching Aids
Patterns: Number cube, spinners, protractor
TA 3, TRB, page 156
Teaching suggestions precede the Teaching Aids worksheets.

Pattern: Rectangular prism
TA 4, TRB, page 157
Teaching suggestions precede the Teaching Aids worksheets.

Pattern: Pyramid
TA 5, TRB, page 158
Teaching suggestions precede the Teaching Aids worksheets.

Challenge
Look at the chart below. The basic formulas for finding the volume of a prism and a pyramid are given. Notice how the formula is written for the volume of a square prism or cube. What do the parentheses enclose? (the formula for the area of the base) Follow this pattern to complete the chart for the formulas given.

PRISM	
Base	$V = Bh$
Square	$V = (s \times s) \times h$
Rectangular	$[V = (lw)h]$
Triangular	$[V = (\frac{1}{2}ba)h]$, where a is the altitude of the triangle.

PYRAMID	
Base	$B = \frac{1}{3}Ba$
Square	$[V = \frac{1}{3}(s \times s) \times a]$
Rectangular	$[V = \frac{1}{3}(lw)a]$
Triangular	$[V = \frac{1}{3}(\frac{1}{2}bh)a]$

15.6 Breaking a Problem into Parts

A pet store is holding a contest. A fish tank is filled with marbles. The person who gives the closest guess of how many marbles are in the tank wins a platypus named Mark.

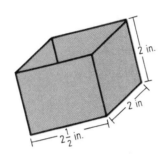

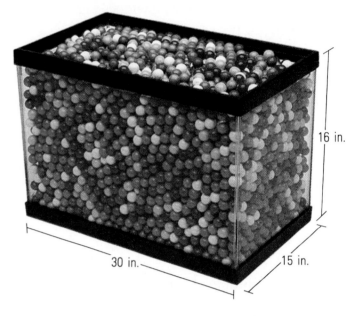

Sam and Brian took a very organized approach to solving this problem and solved the problem in two parts.

First Part   They took a smaller box, shown above, and they were able to fit 146 marbles in the smaller box.

Second Part   They determined the volume of the small box and the volume of the fish tank.

1. What is the volume of the small box in cubic inches?   10 cu. in.

2. What is the volume of the fish tank in cubic inches?   7200 cu. in.

3. About how many of the small boxes would fill the fish tank?
720 boxes

By putting the parts together, Sam and Brian estimated the number of marbles that would fit in the fish tank.

4. How did Sam and Brian use their answers from Part 1 to estimate the number of marbles in the fish tank?   Multiplied 720 by 146

5. How many marbles did they estimate would fit in the fish tank?   105,120 marbles

6. Did Sam and Brian's method give an exact answer or just a good guess? Explain.

The fish-tank problem was solved by breaking the problem into parts. The next problem shows other methods of breaking problems into parts.

The swimming pool in Stockton is shown here. Notice the irregular shape and sloping bottom of the pool. The village officials need to find out the volume of the pool to determine a water tax.

An official spoke to the man responsible for filling the pool each spring. He reported that the pump supplies water at 250 gallons per minute. It takes about 90 minutes to fill the pool.

7. Explain how you can estimate how many gallons of water the pool holds.

8. About how many gallons of water does the pool hold?
About 22,500 gal.

9. One gallon of water has a volume of 0.13 cubic feet. Estimate the volume of the pool. About 2925 cu. ft.

10. The village collects a 10-cent water tax for each cubic foot of water used in pools. What is the tax for the water used in this pool? About $292.50

Describe how you would break the following problems into parts to solve them.

11. Calculate the weight of 2000 nickels.

12. Find how much 500 pounds of pennies is worth.

13. Decide how many gallons of punch to have at a school dance.

14. Estimate how long it will take to drive 1000 miles.

15. Estimate how many gallons of gas a car would use in a year.

▶ **Review** (Lesson 3.8)

Write which operation you would use to solve each problem. Then solve.

16. A drawing of Laura's bedroom is shown at the right. How many square feet of carpeting does she need to buy? Multiplication; $99\frac{3}{4}$ sq. ft.

17. One type of carpet sells for $18.69 a square yard. Another type is on sale for one-third that price. How much does the sale carpet cost per square yard?
Multiplication or division; $6.23 sq. yd.

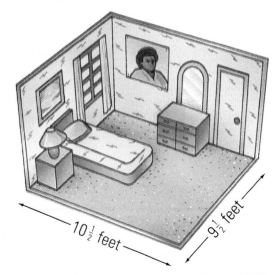

$10\frac{1}{2}$ feet

$9\frac{1}{2}$ feet

Geometry: Surface Area and Volume **343**

Answers
(continued)

7. You can estimate how much water the pool holds by multiplying 250 gallons of water per minute by the 90 minutes it takes to fill the pool.

11. sample answer: weigh 10 nickels and then multiply this number by 200

12. sample answer: find the value of one pound of pennies and multiply this number by 500

13. sample answer: estimate how many people a gallon will serve (for example, 25) and then divide the total number of people expected by this number

14. sample answer: estimate the time needed to drive 100 miles (for example, 2 hours) and multiply by 10

15. sample answer: estimate the number of gallons used in a week (for example, 15) and multiply by 52

★ **Error Alert**
Errors may occur in a two-part problem if students answer the first part but neglect to answer the second part.

Problem Solving
PS Worksheet 9, TRB, pages 195–196

Challenge
Picture an 8-inch cube with a square pyramid on top of it. The pyramid and cube have identical bases. The triangular height of the pyramid's faces is 5 inches. The altitude of the pyramid is 3 inches. Find the outside surface area of the solid that is formed. Then find the volume of the new solid. Write the formulas you use. You may need to adjust some of the formulas you have worked with. (answer: area of 5 sides of cube = $5(s \times s)$ = 320 sq. in; area of 4 triangular sides of pyramid = $4(\frac{1}{2}bh)$ = 80 sq. in.; total surface area = 400 sq. in; volume of cube = $s \times s \times s$ = 512 cu. in.; volume of pyramid = $\frac{1}{3}Ba$ = 64 cu. in.; total volume of solid = 576 cu. in.)

15.7 Finding the Volumes of Cylinders and Cones

Objective

- To find the volumes of cylinders and cones

Purpose

In this lesson you will learn the formulas for finding the volume of a cylinder and a cone. Determining which container holds more can be an important part of manufacturing.

Introducing the Lesson

Review the basic formulas for finding the volume of a prism and a pyramid (Lesson 15.5). Write the formulas on the chalkboard: prism: $V = Bh$; pyramid: $V = \frac{1}{3}Ba$. Ask: How does the volume of a pyramid compare with the volume of a prism having the same dimensions? (It is $\frac{1}{3}$ the volume.) Point out that the letter h refers to the altitude or height of the prism and the letter a represents the altitude of the pyramid.

Alternative Examples

Example A—Find the volume of a cylinder.
Use $\frac{22}{7}$ for π, $r = 6$ in., $h = 7$ in.
$V = Bh$
$V \approx (\frac{22}{7} \times 6 \times 6 \times 7)$
$V \approx$ **792 cubic inches**

Example B—Find the volume of the cone.
Use 3.14 for π, $r = 1.5$ ft., $a = 3$ ft.
$V = \frac{1}{3}Ba$
$V = \frac{1}{3} \times (3.14 \times 1.5 \times 1.5) \times 3$
$V \approx$ **7.065 cubic feet**

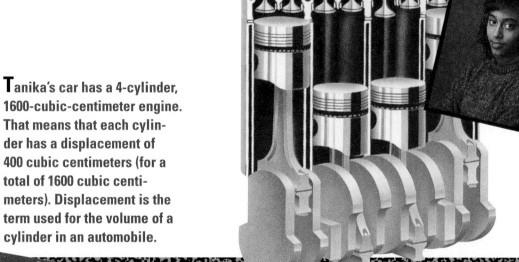

Tanika's car has a 4-cylinder, 1600-cubic-centimeter engine. That means that each cylinder has a displacement of 400 cubic centimeters (for a total of 1600 cubic centimeters). Displacement is the term used for the volume of a cylinder in an automobile.

Examples

To find the volumes of cylinders and cones, use the appropriate formula.

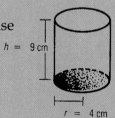

$V = Bh$
$V = $ volume
$B = $ area of the base
$\quad (\pi \times r \times r)$
$h = $ height

$h = 9$ cm
$r = 4$ cm

cone a 3-dimensional figure with a circular base connected to a vertex

$V = \frac{1}{3}Ba$
$B = \pi \times r \times r$
$a = $ altitude

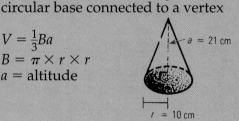

$a = 21$ cm
$r = 10$ cm

A Find the volume of the cylinder.

$V = Bh$
$V = \pi \times r \times r \times h$
$V \approx (3.14 \times 4 \times 4) \times 9$
$V \approx 50.24 \times 9$
$V \approx$ **452.16 cubic centimeters**

B Find the volume of the cone.

$V = \frac{1}{3} \times Ba$
$V = \frac{1}{3} \times \pi \times r \times r \times a$
$V \approx \frac{1}{3} \times (\frac{22}{7} \times 10 \times 10) \times 21$
$V \approx \frac{1}{3} \times \frac{2200}{7} \times 21$
$V \approx$ **2200 cubic centimeters**

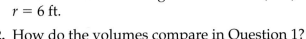

▶ Think and Discuss

1. Find the volume of a cylinder and the volume of a cone with the following dimensions. h (or a) = 8 ft. r = 6 ft.

2. How do the volumes compare in Question 1?

3. In talking about volume, someone said, "Cones are to cylinders as pyramids are to prisms." What do you think he was talking about? Discuss.

Exercises

Find the volume of each cylinder. (See Example A.)

4. $r = 10$ ft.
$h = 18$ ft.
≈5652 cubic feet

5. $h = 8$ in.
$r = 3$ in.
≈226.08 cubic inches

6. $r = 3$ cm
$h = 16$ cm
≈452.16 cubic centimeters

7. $h = 7.4$ m
$r = 6$ m
≈836.5 cubic meters

Find the volume of each cone. (See Example B.)

8. $r = 8$ ft.
$a = 21$ ft.
≈1406.72 or 1408 cubic feet

9. $a = 12$ cm
$d = 6$ cm
≈113.04 cubic centimeters

10. $r = 9$ in.
$a = 18$ in.
≈1526.04 cubic inches

11. $a = 16.8$ m
$d = 6.4$ m
≈180.06 cubic meters

▶ Mixed Practice (For more practice, see page 448.)

Find the volume of each figure.

12. Cone
$d = 6$ cm
$a = 9$ cm
≈84.78 cubic centimeters

13. Cylinder
$h = 18$ ft.
$r = 10$ ft.
≈5652 cubic feet

14. Cylinder
$r = 6$ cm
$h = 14$ cm
≈1582.56 or 1584 cubic centimeters

15. Cone
$a = 5.5$ m
$d = 3$ m
≈12.95 cubic meters

16. Cylinder
$h = 6$ cm
$r = 14$ cm
≈3692.64 or 3696 cubic centimeters

17. Cone
$d = 7$ in.
$a = 15$ in.
≈192.33 or $192\frac{1}{2}$ cubic inches

18. Cylinder
$r = 8\frac{3}{4}$ in.
$h = 16$ in.
≈$3846\frac{1}{2}$ or 3850 cubic inches

19. Cone
$r = 4\frac{1}{5}$ ft.
$a = 10$ ft.
≈184.63 or $184\frac{4}{5}$ cubic feet

▶ Applications

20. How much water can the drinking cup hold? Round your answer to the nearest cubic inch.
5 cu. in.
$\vdash\!-2\frac{1}{2}\text{ in.}\!-\!\dashv$
3 in.

21. Each cylinder in an 8-cylinder engine has a 3-inch diameter and covers 4 inches (height). Find the engine's total displacement (volume). Round your final answer to the nearest cubic inch.
226 cu. in.

▶ Review (Lesson 3.9)

Simplify.

22. $6(8 + 3) + 24$ 90

23. $9 + 20 \times 4 + 3 \times 3$ 98

24. $5 \times 9 - 8 \times 3$ 21

25. $15 - 6 \div 2 + 8 \times 5$ 52

26. $49 \div 7 + 8 \div 4$ 9

27. $9(6) - 3(5)$ 39

▶ Think and Discuss Answers

1. 904.32 cu. ft.; 301.44 cu. ft.

2. The volume of the cone is $\frac{1}{3}$ the volume of the cylinder.

3. A cone has a volume that is $\frac{1}{3}$ the volume of a cylinder with the same base and altitude and a pyramid has a volume that is $\frac{1}{3}$ the volume of a prism with the same base and altitude.

★ Error Alert

Mistakes may indicate that students are computing the areas of the bases using the diameter instead of the radius. Diameter measurements must be divided by two.

Reinforcement
Extra Practice, page 448
EP/MR Worksheet 119, TRB, page 119

Teaching Aids
Patterns: Cylinder and cone
TA 6, TRB, page 159
Teaching suggestions precede the Teaching Aids worksheets.

Project
Use tag board to make a cylinder and a cone of the same diameter and depth. Fill the cone with packing beads. How many times do you need to fill the cone to fill the cylinder? (about 3) Now measure the diameter and height of the cylinder as well as the diameter and altitude of the cone. Record the measurements to the nearest centimeter. Use the formulas to compute the volumes of the cylinder and the cone. (Answers depend on containers used.) How do the computed volumes compare? (sample answers: volume of the cone is about $\frac{1}{3}$ the volume of the cylinder; cylinder is about 3 times the volume of the cone).

Purpose

Finding the surface area and volume are practical skills. You could use the idea of surface area to decide how much paint to buy to cover the walls and ceiling of a room. You need to know about about volume to determine how much concrete is needed for foundations and sidewalks. This lesson gives you an idea of how surface area and volume are used in the building industry.

Introducing the Lesson

Review the formulas presented in this chapter (Lessons 15.3, 15.4, 15.5, 15.7). Discuss occupations in which volume and surface area are used. (sample answers: contractor; manufacturer; sculptor) Ask: What do you think an architect does? (Answers should include design buildings such as homes and offices.)

Alternative Strategy

Use pictures or models of several structures. Have students identify the various 3-dimensional solids they see. For example, an apartment building could be a rectangular solid, a silo could be a cylinder, a steeple could be a pyramid. Try to have some buildings that represent two or more distinct solids, such as a barn that is a triangular prism on top of a rectangular prism.

15.8 Geometry: A Career Application

Architects are among the many people involved in the planning and building of skyscrapers. They often need to compute surface areas and volumes. Let's look at some of the factors an architect considers while working on the plans for a skyscraper.

One of the concerns of an architect is to assure that the building has a solid and safe foundation. The dimensions of pillars (and their volume) are an important factor when estimating costs of a foundation.

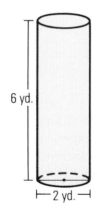

6 yd.

2 yd.

1. Find the number of cubic yards of concrete needed for each pillar shown. 18.84 cu. yd.
2. At $50 per cubic yard of concrete, how much would 28 pillars cost? $26.376

If the building is made of brick, an architect works with a bricklayer.

3. Determine the volume and surface area of the brick shown. $V = 67\frac{1}{2}$ cu. in.; $A = 112\frac{7}{8}$ sq. in.

4. One story of a building is 9 feet high and the bricks will be separated by $\frac{1}{2}$ inch of mortar. Determine how many rows of bricks are needed for one story. **39 rows**

$2\frac{1}{4}$ in.

$3\frac{3}{4}$ in.

8 in.

Another concern of architects is window space and location. Architects want to assure proper energy conservation.

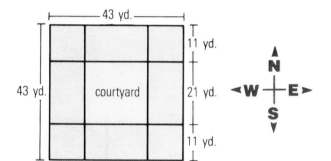

43 yd.

11 yd.

43 yd.   courtyard   21 yd.

11 yd.

11 yd. 21 yd. 11 yd.

N
W   E
S

5. A skyscraper is ten stories tall. Each story is 9 feet high. All outside walls are glass. Find the surface area of the glass walls for one story. What is the surface area of the glass walls for the entire skyscraper? **516 sq. yd.; 5160 sq. yd.**

6. If glass is $7.40 a square yard, what would one story of glass walls cost? **$3818.40**

7. The west, north, and east windows that do not face the courtyard need special glass for extra protection against the wind and extreme temperatures. How many square yards of this special glass must be ordered? **3870 sq. yd.**

A building must also be properly insulated.

8. Fiberglass insulation is going to be used for a wall 90 feet wide and 9 feet high. If a 75-square-foot roll of insulation sells for $17.94, how much will it cost to insulate the wall?
$193.75 or $197.34

▶ **Review** (Lesson 2.11)

Solve. Tell whether you used mental math, paper-and-pencil, or a calculator.

9. the cost of 5 dozen eggs at $0.79 a dozen **$3.95; paper-and-pencil**

10. the total number of legs on 25 dogs **100 legs; mental math**

11. the average miles per gallon of gasoline used if you traveled 257.8 miles on 7 gallons of gas $\approx$**36.8 mi. per gal.; calculator**

Answers
4. 96 square inches
5. 82 square meters
6. ≈326.56 square centimeters
7. 160 square centimeters
8. ≈628 square inches
9. 8.64 square centimeters
10. 960 square centimeters
11. 432 square centimeters
12. ≈837$\frac{1}{3}$ cubic centimeters
13. 280 cubic feet
14. 720 cubic inches
15. ≈552.64 cubic centimeters
16. 2420 cubic centimeters
17. ≈923.16 or 924 cubic inches
18. 37.44 cubic centimeters
19. ≈2486.88 cubic centimeters

▶ **Think and Discuss Answers**
(from page T341)
1. 8 cu. in., and 64 cu. in.; 8 times as large
2. 108 cu. in.; 36 cu. in.
3. 3; the volume of a pyramid is $\frac{1}{3}$ the volume of a prism with the same dimensions
4. $V \times s \times s \times s$; $A = s \times s$; multiplying the length of the edge of a cube by itself gives the area; multiplying the area by the length of the edge gives the volume
(continued on page T349)

Chapter 15 Review

REVIEW

Complete each statement. (Lessons 15.1, 15.2, 15.3, 15.4, 15.7)

1. A soda can is an example of a(n) ___. Cylinder

2. A cereal box is an example of a(n) ___. Prism

3. The ___ in Egypt are examples of 3-dimensional figures with a square bottom and triangular faces. pyramids

Find the surface area of each figure. (Lessons 15.3, 15.4)

4. Cube
   $s = 4$ in.

5. prism
   $l = 3$ m
   $w = 2$ m
   $h = 7$ m

6.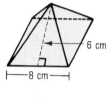

7.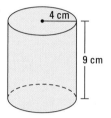

8. Cylinder
   $d = 10$ in.
   $h = 15$ in.

9.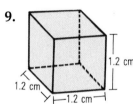

10. Pyramid
    $s = 20$ cm
    $h = 14$ cm

11.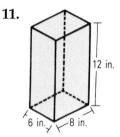

Find the volume of each figure. (Lessons 15.5, 15.7)

12.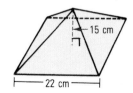

13. Prism
    $l = 8$ ft.
    $w = 5$ ft.
    $h = 7$ ft.

14. Pyramid
    $s = 12$ in.
    $a = 15$ in.

15.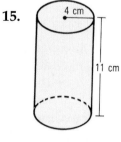

16.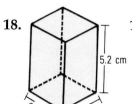

17. Cone
    $r = 7$ in.
    $a = 18$ in.

18.

19. Cylinder
    $h = 22$ cm
    $d = 12$ cm

Chapter 15 Test

Find the volume of each figure.

1. Cylinder
$r = 1.5$ m
$h = 4$ m

2. Cube
$s = 7$ in.

3.

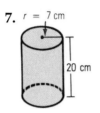
16 m
2 m
3 m

4.

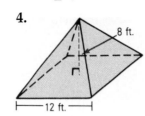
8 ft.
12 ft.

5.

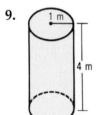
5.2 cm
5.2 cm
5.2 cm

6. Prism
$l = 12$ in.
$w = 10$ in.
$h = 16$ in.

7. $r = 7$ cm

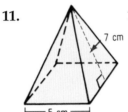
20 cm

8. Pyramid
$s = 40$ in.
$a = 52$ in.

Find the surface area of each figure.

9.

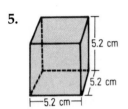
1 m
4 m

10. Cube
$s = 9$ in.

11.

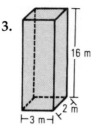
7 cm
5 cm

12. Prism
$l = 6$ cm
$w = 4$ cm
$h = 2$ cm

13.

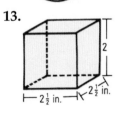
2
$2\frac{1}{2}$ in.
$2\frac{1}{2}$ in.

14. Cylinder
$h = 22$ cm
$r = 7$ cm

15.

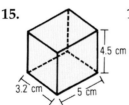
4.5 cm
3.2 cm
5 cm

16. Pyramid
$s = 10$ in.
$h = 12$ in.

Complete each statement.

17. A figure with 2 circular bases is called a(n) ___. Cylinder

18. A figure with 6 square faces is called a(n) ___. Cube

19. A figure with 4 triangular faces and 1 square base is called a(n) ___. Square pyramid

20. A figure with 6 rectangular faces is called a(n) ___. Rectangular prism

Career Focus Activity

Materials: journal, pen, prepared list of questions

Procedure: The career of being a recording engineer is an ideal opportunity for job shadowing. Students can actually follow a recording engineer or other related professional through a day's activities.

• Contact a local recording studio. Ask if one or two students may observe one recording engineer or other related professional during the day.

• Each student should bring a journal and a pen to record events, impressions, and experiences of the day. They can share a prepared list of questions to be asked. Partners can take turns asking questions.

• The journal is to be signed by the recording engineer or other related professional at the end of the visit.

• When students return, they should report on the experience for the class.

• A thank-you note to the host business should be written and sent by all who attended within three days of the visit.

Use expressions and sentences to describe

• the purchase of two products with the same price.

• the number of items in an unknown number of packages.

• weekly income for someone who earns a salary plus tips.

• the average of four test scores when the final test score is unknown.

What are some other ways to use expressions and sentences?

Pre-Algebra: Expressions and Sentences

A recording engineer records music and other sounds.

- Recording engineers work for record companies, bands, and musicians.

- A recording engineer should enjoy music and know how to choose equipment and its placement for quality sound production.

- A recording engineer monitors signal strengths and determines the percent of mixtures on different tracks of multitrack recorders.

- A recording engineer also computes elapsed and remaining times.

- To become a recording engineer, an individual can learn from other recording engineers.

- Related careers include musicians, producers, sound-effects specialists, songwriters, and studio operators.

CAREER

RECORDING ENGINEER

PORTFOLIO PROJECT: *Plan how to make a music tape.*

1. Choose five of your favorite songs.

2. Time and record the length of each song.

3. Describe how long a tape that includes each of the five songs would have to be. Write an algebraic expression for the math. *Show the math.*

About the Portfolio Project

Students may choose any pre-approved record album, tape, or CD they have presented to you. At home, they are to time five songs and record those times, then complete step 3. On the day students present their projects, they should be allowed to play some of the music to which they listened.

Assessment: The individual scoring rubric on page 161 of the Teacher's Resource Binder can be reproduced and used for assessment. Include the following information in the last two boxes. Students should have:
- listened to and recorded times for at least five songs.
- written an algebraic expression to express the math.

16.1 Introduction to Algebra

In the last two chapters, you used formulas like $C = 2\pi r$ and $A = lw$. These formulas are examples of the use of algebra in mathematics. Algebra takes words and sentences and replaces them with numbers and symbols. After that, you just apply the mathematics you already know.

▶ Express Yourself

Here are some of the terms used in algebra:

unknown or **variable** — any symbol, such as *b* or *n*, that may be replaced by a number or numbers

expression — a mathematical phrase, such as 6, $n + 2$, or $6b$

equation — a mathematical sentence stating that two expressions are equal, such as $6 = n + 2$

Choose one of the above words to complete each sentence.

1. The letter *b* found in $9b + 7$ is called a(n) _____ or a(n) _____.
   Unknown; variable
2. The phrase $b - 4$ is called a(n) _____. Expression
3. The sentence $14 + n = 6$ is called a(n) _____. Equation

▶ Practice What You Know

Throughout this book you have been answering questions based on situations that involve mathematics. Now you will ask mathematical questions based on information supplied. Take, for example, the statement "Sheila read a 485-page book in five days." A question might be "What was the average number of pages Sheila read each day?"

For each situation below, ask a mathematical question.

4. Patrick went out to lunch four times last week. The average price of the four lunches was $3.52.

5. Nora earns $75 a week. Her employer takes out $12.50 a week for taxes.

The Price

PROBLEM SOLVING

6. Tickets to a play cost $15 and $12. Miss Wu has $300 to take 24 students to the play.

7. The Morgans just sold their house for $184,000. When they bought the house, they paid $137,000.

8. Rob is a waiter. He earns $3.75 an hour and works 6 hours a day, 5 days a week. This week he made $175 in tips.

9. Marcus is making a costume for the school play. He needs $2\frac{1}{4}$ yards of velvet at $8.99 a yard and $1\frac{1}{2}$ yards of satin at $12.59 a yard.

10. You will need to use the words *increase* and *decrease* in this chapter. Use *increase* and *decrease* in a sentence. Write $m + 5$ in words, using *increase*. Write $m - 3$ in words, using *decrease*.

More than one mathematical operation may occur in an expression or equation, for example: $6 + 8 \times 2 = a$. To solve problems with more than one operation, recall the order of operations:

1. Do all operations within parentheses.
2. Do all multiplications and divisions from left to right.
3. Do all additions and subtractions from left to right.

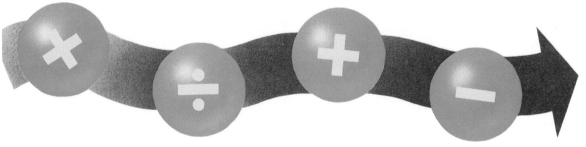

Simplify.

11. $3 + (6 \times 4)$ 27

12. $15 \div 3 + 2$ 7

13. $18 - 9 + 4$ 13

14. $18 \div (6 + 3)$ 2

15. $(5 + 4) + 6$ 15

16. $12 \times 2 + 15$ 39

17. $42 \div 3 + 4$ 18

18. $14 + 6 - 3$ 17

19. $4 \times (7 + 8) \div 2$ 30

20. three plus seven times eight 59

21. eighteen divided by six, plus three times four 15

Practice What You Know Answers (continued)

6. sample answer: How many tickets of each price can Miss Wu buy for her 24 students?

7. sample answer: How much of a profit did the Morgans make on their house?

8. sample answer: What were Rob's earnings for the entire week?

9. sample answer: How much must Marcus pay for the satin and velvet?

10. sample answer: I hope to increase my wages and decrease my expenses. Increase m by five. Decrease m by three.

★ **Error Alert**

Incorrect answers for Exercises 4–9 may reveal that students are not using the information supplied as a basis for their questions.

Challenge

Using the four operational symbols $+$, $-$, $\times$, $\div$, replace the boxes in the number sequence to create three mathematical expressions. You may use parentheses wherever you wish. Use the rules for the order of operations to simplify each expression.

5 ☐ 3 ☐ 2 ☐ 4 ☐ 1

[Sample answers include:

$(5 + 3) \div 2 - 4 \times 1 = 0$

$5 - (3 - 2) \div 4 + 1 = 5\frac{3}{4}$

$5 \times 3 - 2 \div (4 - 1) = 15\frac{2}{3}$

or $\frac{47}{3}$.]

16.2 Writing Expressions

"How did you do selling ceramics last weekend?" James asked Rochelle. Rochelle smiled and replied, "My best day was Saturday, when I made fifteen dollars less than three times what I made on Sunday." "Hold on," said James, annoyed. "I've got to write an algebraic expression to understand what that means!"

Objectives

- To write word phrases, with and without variables, as algebraic expressions
- To write algebraic expressions in words

Purpose

Translating words into algebraic expressions is the first step you can use to solve a problem like this: Fifteen less than 3 times some number is 30. What is the number?

Introducing the Lesson

Review the introduction to algebra (Lesson 16.1). Use the example: Determine whether the following are algebraic expressions or algebraic equations. If there is an unknown, what is it?—$24 \div 3$ (expression); $3 \times 5.75 = p$ (equation; p); $9z + 10$ (expression; z); $3 + z = 9$ (equation; z).

Alternative Examples

Example A—Write as an algebraic expression: fifty-one multiplied by three.
51×3

Example B—Write as an algebraic expression: nine plus some number. Let n be the variable.
$9 + n$ or $n + 9$

Example C—Write as an algebraic expression: twelve, plus five divided by a number. Let b be the variable.
$12 + \frac{5}{b}$ or $12 + (5 \div b)$

Example D—Write in words: $4n - 13$.
thirteen less than four times some number

▶ Think and Discuss Answers

1. 12×20
2. $3m - 15$, where m is the amount Rochelle made on Sunday
3. thirteen more than twelve times some number
4. x
5. $-$ or $<$, depending on the context

Examples

To write an algebraic expression, first choose a variable if needed. Then decide what operations are involved.

A Write as an algebraic expression: forty-nine divided by seven.

$49 \div 7$ or $\frac{49}{7}$

B Write as an algebraic expression: six less than some number. Let b be the variable.

some number $\rightarrow b - 6 \leftarrow$ six less

C Write as an algebraic expression: fifteen more than three times some number. Let n be the variable.

three times some number $\rightarrow 3n + 15 \leftarrow$ fifteen more

D Write in words: $2n + 12$.

Twelve more than twice some number

▶ Think and Discuss

1. Write as an algebraic expression: twelve times twenty.
2. Refer to the introduction to this lesson. Write the amount that Rochelle made on Saturday as an algebraic expression.
3. Write $12b + 13$ in words.
4. What mathematical symbol is used for the term *times*?
5. What mathematical symbol is used for the term *less than*?

Exercises

Write as an algebraic expression. (See Example A.)

6. fifty-six divided by eight $56 \div 8$ or $\frac{56}{8}$

7. seventy-two minus twelve $72 - 12$

8. twenty-nine times five 29×5

9. forty plus eighteen $40 + 18$

Write as an algebraic expression. (See Example B.)

10. seventeen minus some number $17 - n$

11. ninety-nine times some number $99n$

12. some number divided by six $\frac{n}{6}$

13. the sum of five and some number $5 + n$

Write as an algebraic expression. (See Example C.)

14. four times some number, plus five $4n + 5$

15. sixteen minus twice some number $16 - 2n$

16. forty-two divided by the product of three and some number $42 \div 3n$ or $\frac{42}{3n}$

17. five less than five times some number $5n - 5$

Write in words. (See Example D.)

18. $4 + 7b$

19. $m \div 3$

20. $17 - b$

21. $36a + 7$

22. $14t - 7$

▶ **Mixed Practice** (For more practice, see page 448.)

Write as an algebraic expression or in words.

23. thirty-six divided by three $36 \div 3$ or $\frac{36}{3}$

24. twelve times twelve 12×12

25. seven decreased by some number $7 - n$

26. the sum of two and some number $2 + n$

27. eleven times some number $11n$

28. $4y - 7$ 7 less than 4 times some number

▶ **Applications**

29. The New York Yankees have played in 33 World Series. They have won 22. Write the number of times they have lost as an algebraic expression. $33 - 22$

30. The coastline of Alaska is five hundred miles plus nine times the length of the California coastline. Let c equal the California coastline. Write the length of the Alaskan coast as an algebraic expression. $500 + 9c$

▶ **Review** (Lesson 5.2)

Rewrite as a whole number or mixed number.

31. $\frac{7}{7}$ 1

32. $\frac{21}{6}$ $3\frac{1}{2}$

33. $\frac{24}{4}$ 6

34. $\frac{29}{8}$ $3\frac{5}{8}$

35. $\frac{57}{9}$ $6\frac{1}{3}$

36. $\frac{24}{12}$ 2

37. $\frac{16}{4}$ 4

38. $\frac{10}{10}$ 1

39. $\frac{18}{6}$ 3

40. $\frac{60}{12}$ 5

41. $\frac{81}{9}$ 9

42. $\frac{41}{5}$ $8\frac{1}{5}$

Answers

Answers may vary for Exercises 18–22. Sample answers are given.

18. four more than seven times some number
19. some number divided by three
20. seventeen minus some number
21. thirty-six times some number, plus seven
22. seven less than fourteen times some number

★ **Error Alert**

Mistakes may reveal that students are not translating the algebraic expression from words to symbols correctly. For example, "ten less than some number" may be incorrectly written as $10 - n$ instead of $n - 10$.

Reinforcement

Extra Practice, page 448
EP/MR Worksheet 121, TRB, page 121

Challenge

Write the letter of the algebraic expression in the blank next to the expression in words that matches it.

1. Half of the boxes were opened.
2. Shere spent $6.
3. 3 names were added to the list.
4. Jim made 3 times as many and sold 12.
5. 12 people left at half-time, but 3 returned.
6. 3 less than expected showed up.
7. Double the amount.
8. Bridget is twice my age plus 12.
9. Divide the books into stacks of 10.
10. Add a $3 tip and divide the total by 12.

a. $3y - 12$ b. $k \div 10$
c. $m - 12 + 3$ d. $2b + 12$
e. $x - 6$ f. $c - 3$
g. $a + 3$ h. $(q + 3) \div 12$
i. $2z$ j. $\frac{1}{2}n$

(answers: 1. j; 2. e; 3. g; 4. a; 5. c; 6. f; 7. i; 8. d; 9. b; 10. h)

Objective

• To find the value of an expression when the value of the variable is given

Purpose

This lesson helps you to determine the value of expressions such as 8.50*n* when you know the value of *n*. For example, if you earn $8.50 per hour, you can determine your weekly wages when *n* equals the number of hours you work in a given week.

Introducing the Lesson

Review writing expressions (Lesson 16.2). Use the example: Write each of the following as an algebraic expression—twenty-five divided by some number ($25 \div x$); ten more than three times some number ($3x + 10$); twelve less than some number ($x - 12$); two less than five times some number ($5x - 2$).

Alternative Examples

Example A—Find the value of $c - 10$ when $c = 13$.
$$c - 10 = 13 - 10$$
$$c - 10 = \textbf{3}$$

Example B—Find the value of $25 - 7e$ when $e = 3$.
$$25 - 7e = 25 - (7 \times e)$$
$$25 - 7e = 25 - (7 \times 3)$$
$$25 - 7e = 25 - 21$$
$$25 - 7e = \textbf{4}$$

▶ Think and Discuss Answers

1. 30
2. 0
3. 9250 lire
4. no; a variable in the expression 2*p* can have any value, depending on the context

16.3 Finding the Value of an Expression

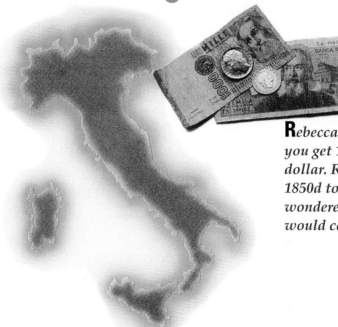

Rebecca's teacher said that in Italy you get 1850 lire for every American dollar. Rebecca wrote the expression 1850d to remember this. Rebecca wondered what a $5 movie ticket would cost in lire.

Examples

To find the value of an expression, first substitute the value given for the variable, and then compute.

A Find the value of $a + 6$ when $a = 20$.

$a + 6 = 20 + 6$ ← Substitute the value
$a + 6 = \textbf{26}$ of *a*.

B Find the value of $3d - 5$ when $d = 4$.

$3d - 5 = (3 \times d) - 5$
$3d - 5 = (3 \times 4) - 5$
$3d - 5 = 12 - 5$
$3d - 5 = \textbf{7}$

▶ Think and Discuss

1. Find the value of $5c$ when $c = 6$.

2. Find the value of $\frac{36}{e} - e$ when $e = 6$.

3. Refer to the introduction to this lesson. What would a $5 movie ticket cost in lire?

4. Are there any values *p* cannot have in the expression 2*p*? Explain.

Exercises

★ **Error Alert**
Incorrect answers may occur if students substitute the value for an unknown in the wrong place in the expression.

Find the value of each expression. (See Example A.)

5. $n + 9$ when $n = 7$ 16

6. $23 - m$ when $m = 9$ 14

7. $\frac{d}{7}$ when $d = 42$ 6

8. $15 + k$ when $k = 19$ 34

9. $17 - r$ when $r = 9$ 8

10. $\frac{16}{b}$ when $b = 2$ 8

Find the value of each expression. (See Example B.)

11. $12a - 6$ when $a = 11$ 126

12. $9d + 22$ when $d = 6$ 76

13. $4n - 7$ when $n = 5$ 13

14. $11h \div 4$ when $h = 12$ 33

15. $6b + 32$ when $b = 15$ 122

16. $\frac{17n}{5}$ when $n = 10$ 34

17. $18 + n - n$ when $n = 10$ 18

18. $\frac{21}{n} - n$ when $n = 3$ 4

▶ Mixed Practice (For more practice, see page 449.)

Find the value of each expression.

19. $\frac{f}{8}$ when $f = 16$ 2

20. $d + \frac{15}{d}$ when $d = 5$ 8

21. $32 - 2h$ when $h = 9$ 14

22. $6f - 9$ when $f = 4$ 15

23. $m + 4m$ when $m = 2$ 10

24. $a + 19$ when $a = 1$ 20

▶ Applications

25. Alice played in five more soccer games this month than last month. Write an algebraic expression to represent the number of games Alice played in this month. Find the value of the expression if Alice played in nine games last month. $s + 5$; 14

26. Al sells shoes. He earns $45 a day plus $3 for each pair he sells. On Monday he sold six pairs of shoes. Write an algebraic expression to represent his daily earnings. Then find its value for Monday.
$45 + 3p$; $63

▶ Review (Lesson 5.3)

Find 3 fractions equivalent to each fraction. Answers will vary.

27. $\frac{3}{4}$ $\frac{6}{8}, \frac{9}{12}, \frac{12}{16}$
28. $\frac{2}{3}$ $\frac{4}{6}, \frac{6}{9}, \frac{8}{12}$
29. $\frac{1}{2}$ $\frac{2}{4}, \frac{3}{6}, \frac{4}{8}$
30. $\frac{4}{5}$ $\frac{8}{10}, \frac{12}{15}, \frac{16}{20}$
31. $\frac{1}{12}$ $\frac{2}{24}, \frac{3}{36}, \frac{4}{48}$
32. $\frac{7}{10}$ $\frac{14}{20}, \frac{21}{30}, \frac{28}{40}$

Use division to find a fraction equivalent to each fraction.

33. $\frac{12}{15}$ $\frac{4}{5}$
34. $\frac{15}{30}$ $\frac{1}{2}$
35. $\frac{30}{45}$ $\frac{2}{3}$
36. $\frac{65}{100}$ $\frac{13}{20}$
37. $\frac{21}{28}$ $\frac{3}{4}$
38. $\frac{33}{36}$ $\frac{11}{12}$

Reinforcement
Extra Practice, page 449
EP/MR Worksheet 122, TRB, page 122

Challenge
Find the value of the expression
$a + 3b - c + \frac{d}{5}$ when $a = 3$, $b = 1$, $c = 5$, and $d = 10$. (answer: 3)

Objective

- To write sentences as equations

Purpose

An equation can summarize information in a brief form. For example, the new price of a coat is $1\frac{1}{2}$ times the old price. An equation for this statement would be $n = 1\frac{1}{2}p$ where n is the new price and p is the old price. If the old price is $50, the new price would be $n = 1\frac{1}{2}(50) = 75$, or $75.

Introducing the Lesson

Review writing expressions and finding the value of an expression (Lessons 16.2, 16.3). Use the example: Write each of the following as an algebraic expression with n as the unknown, and find the value of the expression when $n = 5$—The product of three and some number, minus thirteen, ($3n - 13 = 3(5) - 13 = 15 - 13 = 2$); thirty-two minus the product of five and some number, ($32 - 5n = 32 - 5(5) = 32 - 25 = 7$).

Alternative Examples

Example A—Write as an equation: some number plus eleven is twenty-three.
$n + 11 = 23$

Example B—Write as an equation: seventeen minus the product of three and some number is fifteen.
$17 - 3m = 15$

▶ Think and Discuss Answers

1. $n + 12 = 18$
2. $4n = 32$
3. $220 = 55t$; t represents the time in motion; however, other variables could also be used
4. An expression is one part of an equation; in an equation there are two expressions with an equal sign between them; expression: $n + 3$; equation $n + 3 = 60$.

16.4 Writing Equations

A complicated sentence like "The distance traveled by a moving object is equal to its speed multiplied by its time in motion" is easier to understand when it is written as the equation $d = rt$. You might use this equation to figure out how far you can go in 2 hours at 35 miles per hour: $d = 35 \times 2$. In this lesson you'll be writing your own equations.

▶ Examples

To write equations, first choose a letter for your variable. Then translate words into symbols.

A Write as an equation: Some number minus sixteen is forty-three.

$$e - 16 = 43$$

some number — minus sixteen — is forty-three

B Write as an equation: Nine plus the product of two and some number is fifty-nine.

$$9 + 2f = 59$$

nine plus — the product of two and some number — is fifty-nine

▶ Think and Discuss

1. Write as an equation: Some number plus twelve is eighteen.

2. Write as an equation: The product of four and some number is thirty-two.

3. Refer to the introduction to this lesson. If you were in a car traveling 55 miles per hour and you went 220 miles, what equation could you write to find how many hours you had traveled? What letter did you choose for your variable? Why?

4. What is the difference between an expression and an equation? Give an example of each.

Exercises

Write as an equation. (See Example A.)

5. Some number plus eight is thirteen. $n + 8 = 13$

6. Two times some number is fifteen. $2n = 15$

7. Twelve divided by some number is four. $\frac{12}{n} = 4$

8. The difference between some number and one is eight. $n - 1 = 8$

Write as an equation. (See Example B.)

9. Two times some number, minus one, is thirty-seven. $2n - 1 = 37$

10. Some number divided by five, plus nine, is sixteen. $\frac{n}{5} + 9 = 16$

11. Four times some number divided by two, plus two, is ten. $\frac{4n}{2} + 2 = 10$

12. The sum of eight and some number times three is eleven. $8 + 3n = 11$

13. Twelve divided by some number, plus two, is three. $\frac{12}{n} + 2 = 3$

▶ Mixed Practice (For more practice, see page 449.)

Write as an equation.

14. Some number divided by five is fifteen. $\frac{n}{5} = 15$

15. Three times some number, plus eight, is seventeen. $3n + 8 = 17$

16. Eight less than some number is zero. $n - 8 = 0$

17. Some number divided by two is twenty-eight. $\frac{n}{2} = 28$

▶ Applications

18. In 1980, the population of Washington, D.C., was 638,432, or 118,236 less than its population in 1970. Let p represent the population in 1970. Write an equation using p to describe the population in 1980.
$p - 118{,}236 = 638{,}432$

19. In 1998, a baseball player was awarded a salary of $1.85 million. That's $450,000 more than twice his 1997 salary. Let s represent his 1997 salary. Write an equation using s to describe his 1998 salary.
$2s + \$450{,}000 = \$1{,}850{,}000$

▶ Review (Lessons 1.9, 1.10, 1.11)

Add or subtract.

20. $679 + 847$
1526

21. $12.14 + 11.0$
23.14

22. $99.8 - 89.9$
9.9

23. $1381 - 1270$
111

24. $\begin{array}{r} 95.7 \\ -\ 50.83 \\ \hline 44.87 \end{array}$

25. $\begin{array}{r} 6874 \\ +\ 5199 \\ \hline 12{,}073 \end{array}$

26. $\begin{array}{r} 7.965 \\ +\ 6.037 \\ \hline 14.002 \end{array}$

27. $\begin{array}{r} 5000 \\ -\ 2857 \\ \hline 2143 \end{array}$

Reinforcement
Extra Practice, page 449
EP/MR Worksheet 123, TRB, page 123

Challenge
Write an as equation: Fifteen less than the product of eight and some number is three less than the quantity of that same number plus the quotient of eighteen and nine. (answer: $8n - 15 = (n + \frac{18}{9}) - 3$; the value of n is 2)

- To apply the Guess and Check strategy to solve algebraic equations

Purpose

This lesson helps you to find the solution of an equation using the Guess and Check strategy. For example, you can use the Guess and Check strategy to solve the equation $4x + 7 = 31$.

Introducing the Lesson

Review using Guess and Check to solve problems (Lesson 6.3). Also, review writing equations (Lesson 16.4). Use the example: Write each of the following an an equation—Three times some number, plus nine, is eighteen, $(3n + 9 = 18)$; five less than some number is eleven, $(n - 5 = 11)$; nine, plus some number divided by two, is six, $(9 + n \div 2 = 6)$.

Answers

2. Possible methods include: guessing; substituting numbers to try them; and solving them by adding, subtracting, multiplying, or dividing.

16.5 Using Guess and Check to Solve Equations

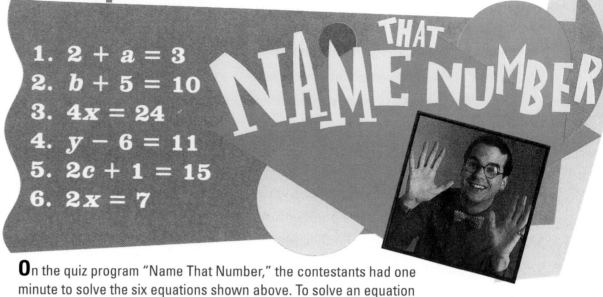

1. $2 + a = 3$
2. $b + 5 = 10$
3. $4x = 24$
4. $y - 6 = 11$
5. $2c + 1 = 15$
6. $2x = 7$

On the quiz program "Name That Number," the contestants had one minute to solve the six equations shown above. To solve an equation means to find a number that can replace the variable and make the statement true.

1. Give yourself one minute. Do as many problems as you can.

2. What methods did you use?

Now you will solve equations like the ones shown above using Guess and Check. For each problem, follow the steps in the chart.

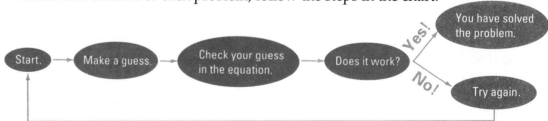

Solve the equation $c + 25 = 65$.

3. Guess 20 for c. Does 20 plus 25 equal 65? No

4. Should your second guess be greater or less than 20? Why?
   Greater because 45 is less than 65

5. Guess another number and substitute it for c. Does your guess solve the equation? Continue until you have solved the equation. Answers will vary.

6. What value of c solves the equation? $c = 40$

Exercises

Use Guess and Check to solve each equation.

7. $s + 25 = 51$ $s = 26$

8. $42 - c = 33$ $c = 9$

9. $v - 13 = 17$ $v = 30$

10. $32 + m = 99$ $m = 67$

11. $3y = 102$ $y = 34$

12. $5d = 65$ $d = 13$

13. $\frac{b}{10} = 10$ $b = 100$

14. $\frac{b}{9} = 10$ $b = 90$

15. $2d + 2 = 6$ $d = 2$

16. $5c - 1 = 99$ $c = 20$

17. $2a = 5$ $a = 2\frac{1}{2}$

18. $5 = \frac{25}{c}$ $c = 5$

19. $17 = t + 4$ $t = 13$

20. $22 = 44 - h$ $h = 22$

21. $3z - 1 = 29$ $z = 10$

22. $4 + c = 7$ $c = 3$

23. $\frac{99}{z} = 3$ $z = 33$

24. $7b + 1 = 50$ $b = 7$

For the final round of the quiz program, the contestants were asked to write the following problems as equations and then solve each equation. Do the same.

25. Two added to a number equals twenty-two. $2 + n = 22; n = 20$

26. Three times a number equals ninety-six. $3n = 96; n = 32$

27. If you take 5 away from a number, the result is 13.
$n - 5 = 13; n = 18$

28. If you divide a number by six, the result is one.
$n \div 6 = 1; n = 6$

29. If you multiply a number by 5 and then add 6 to the product, the result is 31. $5n + 6 = 31; n = 5$

30. If you multiply a number by 3 and then subtract 1 from the product, the result is 17.
$3n - 1 = 17; n = 6$

31. Seven subtracted from a number is equal to forty-one.
$n - 7 = 41; n = 48$

32. If you divide a number by 3 and then subtract 1 from the quotient, the result is 2. $\frac{n}{3} - 1 = 2; n = 9$

33. Now you have used Guess and Check to solve equations. Can you suggest any shortcuts to solve equations such as $2x = 16$ or $x + 8 = 36$? Explain.

▶ ## Review (Lesson 2.11)

Solve. Tell whether you used mental math, paper-and-pencil, or a calculator.

34. Four items cost $16.50 each and three items cost $5.85 each. There is a shipping charge of 5% of the total cost. Find the final cost of the order.
$87.73; pencil-and-paper or calculator

35. What is the change from $20 for 2 items at $3 each and 4 items at $1 each? $10; mental math

Objective

• To solve equations by using addition or subtraction

Purpose

You can use the Guess and Check strategy to solve equations. This lesson introduces you to methods that are usually faster than using the Guess and Check strategy.

Introducing the Lesson

Review writing equations (Lesson 16.4). Use the example: Solve the following equations by finding the value of the expression on the right-hand side of the equals sign—
$n = 11 - 5$, $(n = 6)$; $m = 16 + 3$, $(m = 19)$; $z = 5 + 10 - 1$, $(z = 14)$; $x = 6 - 5 + 9$, $(x = 10)$.

Alternative Examples

Example A—Solve. $z + 19 = 33$
$z + 19 = 33$
Subtract 19 from both sides.
$z + 19 - 19 = 33 - 19$
$z + 0 = 14$
$z = \mathbf{14}$
Substitute 14 for z in the original equation.
Check: $14 + 19 \stackrel{?}{=} 33$
$33 = 33$

Example B—Solve. $a - 16 = 25$
$a - 16 = 25$
Add 16 to both sides.
$a - 16 + 16 = 25 + 16$
$a + 0 = 41$
$a = \mathbf{41}$
Substitute 41 for a in the original equation.
Check: $41 - 16 \stackrel{?}{=} 25$
$25 = 25$

16.6 Solving Equations Using Addition or Subtraction

What number should be placed on the empty tray to balance the scale shown above? A balance scale is like an equation. If you add to or subtract from one side, you must do the same on the other side to keep both sides in balance.

Examples

To solve an equation using addition or subtraction, isolate the variable on one side.

A Solve. $m + 14 = 20$

$m + 14 = 20$
$m + 14 - 14 = 20 - 14$ Subtract 14 from both sides.
$m + 0 = 6$ $14 - 14 = 0$
$m = \mathbf{6}$
Check: $6 + 14 \stackrel{?}{=} 20$ Substitute 6 for m in the original equation.
$20 = 20$

B Solve. $p - 7 = 11$

$p - 7 = 11$
$p - 7 + 7 = 11 + 7$ Add 7 to both sides.
$p + 0 = 18$ Simplify.
$p = \mathbf{18}$
Check: $18 - 7 \stackrel{?}{=} 11$ Substitute 18 for p in the original equation.
$11 = 11$

▶ Think and Discuss

1. Solve. $a + 11 = 21$

2. Solve. $d - 4 = 13$

3. One student solved the equation $g - 4 = 8$ and got the answer $g = 4$. Show that this answer is incorrect. How do you think the error was made? Explain.

4. Is it easier to solve $n + 103 = 267$ by the method in this lesson or by Guess and Check? Explain.

Exercises

Solve. (See Example A.)

5. $n + 8 = 14$ $n = 6$ 6. $a + 15 = 24$ $a = 9$ 7. $d + 19 = 36$ $d = 17$

8. $b + 5 = 31$ $b = 26$ 9. $c + 12 = 19$ $c = 7$ 10. $f + 21 = 30$ $f = 9$

11. $a + 7 = 34$ $a = 27$ 12. $d + 25 = 26$ $d = 1$ 13. $n + 3 = 26$ $n = 23$

Solve. (See Example B.)

14. $p - 9 = 8$ $p = 17$ 15. $f - 12 = 3$ $f = 15$ 16. $b - 19 = 24$ $b = 43$

17. $n - 2 = 21$ $n = 23$ 18. $f - 27 = 48$ $f = 75$ 19. $c - 7 = 0$ $c = 7$

20. $d - 15 = 15$ $d = 30$ 21. $a - 18 = 8$ $a = 26$ 22. $n - 5 = 21$ $n = 26$

▶ **Mixed Practice** (For more practice, see page 450.)

Solve.

23. $b - 21 = 19$ $b = 40$ 24. $f + 9 = 11$ $f = 2$ 25. $d + 16 = 23$ $d = 7$

26. $f - 11 = 12$ $f = 23$ 27. $p + 11 = 12$ $p = 1$ 28. $c - 7 = 14$ $c = 21$

29. $n + 15 = 22$ $n = 7$ 30. $d - 8 = 29$ $d = 37$ 31. $f - 19 = 1$ $f = 20$

▶ **Applications**

32. After spending $9 for two movie tickets, Michael had $34 left. How much did he have before buying the tickets? Write an equation and then solve.
$n - \$9 = \$34; n = \$43$

33. The diameter of Jupiter is 80,773 miles greater than the diameter of the Earth. Use the information in the photo to determine the diameter of the Earth. Write an equation and then solve.
$e + 80,773 = 88,700; e = 7927$

88,700 miles

▶ **Review** (Lessons 2.4, 2.8, 3.5, 3.12)

Multiply or divide.

34. 49×72 3528   35. $459 \div 27$ 17   36. 5×0.49 2.45   37. $391.4 \div 4.12$ 95

38. $462 \div 17$ 27 R3   39. 98×44.5 4361   40. $682 \div 22$ 31   41. $1560 \div 24$ 65

42. 1240×60 74,400   43. $40.2 \div 8.04$ 5   44. 76.12×11 837.32   45. $60.8 \div 3.8$ 16

Objective

- To solve equations by using multiplication or division

Purpose

Being able to solve equations using multiplication and division allows you to solve an equation such as $\frac{x}{3} = 155$ in order to find what your total must be for 3 games to have a bowling average of 155.

Introducing the Lesson

Review writing equations (Lesson 16.4) and finding the value of an expression (Lesson 16.3). Use the examples: Solve the following equations by finding the values of the expressions on the right-hand side of the equals sign—$n = 5(2)$, $(n = 10)$; $x = 30 \div 6$, $(x = 5)$; $z = \frac{100}{25}$, $(z = 4)$; $p = 13(2) + 1$, $(p = 27)$.

Alternative Examples

Example A—Solve.　$6x = 102$
$6x = 102$
Divide both sides by 6.
$\frac{6x}{6} = \frac{102}{6}$
$x = \textbf{17}$
Substitute 17 for x in the original equation.
Check: $6 \times 17 \stackrel{?}{=} 102$
　　　　$102 = 102$

Example B—Solve.　$\frac{n}{4} = 19$
$\frac{n}{4} = 19$
Multiply both sides by 4.
$4 \times \frac{n}{4} = 4 \times 19$
　　$n = \textbf{76}$
Substitute 76 for n in the original equation.
Check: $\frac{76}{4} \stackrel{?}{=} 19$
　　　　$19 = 19$

16.7 Solving Equations Using Multiplication or Division

Tenesha works for a veterinary hospital. She is in charge of feeding the animals. One Great Dane named Soren gets 24 ounces of food each day. If Tenesha feeds Soren twice a day, how many ounces must she weigh out for each meal?

You could write an equation to describe this problem.

Examples

To solve equations using multiplication or division, isolate the variable on one side of the equation.

A Solve.　$2y = 24$

$2y = 24$
$\frac{2y}{2} = \frac{24}{2}$ 　　　　Divide both sides of the equation by 2.
$1y = 12$ 　　　　$\frac{2}{2} = 1$
$y = \textbf{12}$
Check: $2 \times 12 \stackrel{?}{=} 24$ 　　　Substitute 12 for y in the original equation.
　　　　$24 = 24$

B Solve.　$\frac{z}{3} = 13$

$\frac{z}{3} = 13$

$3 \times \frac{z}{3} = 3 \times 13$ 　　Multiply both sides of the equation by 3.
　　$1z = 39$ 　　　$\frac{3}{3} = 1$
　　　$z = \textbf{39}$
Check: $\frac{39}{3} \stackrel{?}{=} 13$ 　　　Substitute 39 for z in the original equation.
　　　　$13 = 13$

▶ Think and Discuss

1. Solve. $7t = 21$

2. Solve. $\dfrac{a}{9} = 5$

3. Refer to the introduction to this lesson. How much food should Tenesha feed Soren at each meal?

4. Can you tell, without solving them, whether the equations $5 \times 5y = 50$ and $25y = 50$ have different solutions? Explain.

Exercises

Solve. (See Example A.)

5. $6d = 42$ $d = 7$ 6. $9n = 81$ $n = 9$ 7. $5b = 55$ $b = 11$ 8. $16y = 64$ $y = 4$

9. $13r = 91$ $r = 7$ 10. $17m = 85$ $m = 5$ 11. $4h = 52$ $h = 13$ 12. $7t = 7$ $t = 1$

13. $15k = 90$ $k = 6$ 14. $22b = 88$ $b = 4$ 15. $13c = 169$ $c = 13$ 16. $25b = 2500$ $b = 100$

Solve. (See Example B.)

17. $\dfrac{s}{7} = 8$ $s = 56$ 18. $\dfrac{m}{16} = 7$ $m = 112$ 19. $\dfrac{n}{10} = 4$ $n = 40$ 20. $\dfrac{d}{3} = 17$ $d = 51$

21. $\dfrac{t}{5} = 5$ $t = 25$ 22. $\dfrac{d}{12} = 9$ $d = 108$ 23. $\dfrac{r}{8} = 11$ $r = 88$ 24. $\dfrac{s}{9} = 3$ $s = 27$

25. $\dfrac{k}{14} = 14$ $k = 196$ 26. $\dfrac{k}{7} = 21$ $k = 147$ 27. $\dfrac{y}{21} = 5$ $y = 105$ 28. $\dfrac{z}{15} = 4$ $z = 60$

▶ Mixed Practice (For more practice, see Page 450.)

Solve

29. $8k = 96$ $k = 12$ 30. $\dfrac{t}{4} = 17$ $t = 68$ 31. $\dfrac{y}{11} = 12$ $y = 132$ 32. $6d = 54$ $d = 9$

33. $13f = 78$ $f = 6$ 34. $\dfrac{v}{8} = 15$ $v = 120$ 35. $\dfrac{m}{17} = 5$ $m = 85$ 36. $7n = 84$ $n = 12$

37. $\dfrac{k}{25} = 4$ $k = 100$ 38. $9b = 81$ $b = 9$ 39. $\dfrac{w}{6} = 18$ $w = 108$ 40. $18c = 144$ $c = 8$

▶ Applications

41. James prints T-shirts. He earns $6 an hour. How many hours must he work to earn $72? Write an equation and solve.
$\$6n = \$72$; $n = 12$

42. Al bowled three games. His average score was 167. What was his total for the three games? Write an equation and solve.
$\dfrac{n}{3} = 167$; 501

▶ Review (Lessons 6.1, 6.2, 6.4)

Multiply. Write the answers in lowest terms.

43. $\dfrac{3}{8} \times \dfrac{3}{4}$ $\dfrac{9}{32}$ 44. $7 \times 5\dfrac{1}{7}$ 36   45. $4\dfrac{1}{2} \times \dfrac{2}{15}$ $\dfrac{3}{5}$ 46. $1\dfrac{1}{3} \times 1\dfrac{7}{8}$ $2\dfrac{1}{2}$ 47. $\dfrac{7}{15} \times 5$ $2\dfrac{1}{3}$

Pre-Algebra: Expressions and Sentences **365**

▶ **Think and Discuss Answers**
1. $t = 3$
2. $a = 45$
3. 12 ounces
4. They would have the same answers, since $5 \times 5y = 25y$.

★ **Error Alert**
Incorrect answers may occur if students do not multiply or divide by the same number on both sides of the equation.

Reinforcement
Extra Practice, page 450
EP/MR Worksheet 126, TRB, page 126

Challenge
Dean must have a total of $564 to attend a teen summer retreat. Of this amount, he must pay $\dfrac{3}{4}$; the remaining $\dfrac{1}{4}$ is being paid by a benefactor. He found a job that pays $4.25 per hour after payroll deductions. How many hours must he work to earn the amount necessary? Write an equation and then solve. (answer: $4.25n = \dfrac{3}{4}(564)$ $n \approx$ 99.5; he must work about 100 hours)

Objective

• To solve equations using addition or subtraction and multiplication or division

Purpose

Being able to solve two-step equations allows you to solve more difficult problems, such as determining how many hours you worked if you are paid $9 per hour, your deductions were $32, and you received $112.

Introducing the Lesson

Review solving equations using addition and subtraction, multiplication and division (Lessons 16.6, 16.7). Use the example: Solve the following equations—$m + 15 = 110$, ($m = 95$); $x - 33 = 94$, ($x = 127$); $5y = 1015$, ($y = 203$); $\frac{z}{15} = 47$, ($z = 705$).

Alternative Examples

Example A—Solve. $8d - 7 = 25$
$8d - 7 = 25$
$8d - 7 + 7 = 25 + 7$ *Add 7 to*
       $8d = 32$ *both sides.*
$\frac{8d}{8} = \frac{32}{8}$ *Divide both*
$1d = 4$ *sides by 8.*
   $d = \mathbf{4}$
Substitute 4 for d.
Check: $(8 \times 4) - 7 \overset{?}{=} 25$
       $32 - 7 \overset{?}{=} 25$
           $25 = 25$

Example B—Solve. $\frac{e}{3} + 19 = 25$
$\frac{e}{3} + 19 = 25$
Subtract 19 from both sides.
$\frac{e}{3} + 19 - 19 = 25 - 19$
       $\frac{e}{3} = 6$
Multiply both sides by 3.
$3 \times \frac{e}{3} = 3 \times 6$
   $1e = 18$
    $e = \mathbf{18}$
Substitute 18 for e.
Check: $\frac{18}{3} + 19 \overset{?}{=} 25$
     $6 + 19 \overset{?}{=} 25$
        $25 = 25$

Max was saving up to buy a new pair of hockey skates. Then disaster struck. In one day he had to spend half his savings on new shoes for track and pay back $25 he borrowed from his sister. That left him only $15.

To find out how much Max had saved, you can solve an equation.

Examples

To solve 2-step equations, first add or subtract. Then multiply or divide.

A Solve. $5r + 6 = 41$

         $5r + 6 = 41$
$5r + 6 - 6 = 41 - 6$ Subtract 6 from both sides.
           $5r = 35$
         $\frac{5r}{5} = \frac{35}{5}$ Divide both sides by 5.
          $1r = 7$
           $r = 7$
Check: $(5 \times 7) + 6 \overset{?}{=} 41$ Substitute 7 for *r*.
           $35 + 6 \overset{?}{=} 41$
              $41 = 41$

B Solve. $\frac{q}{2} - 25 = 15$

        $\frac{q}{2} - 25 = 15$
$\frac{q}{2} - 25 + 25 = 15 + 25$ Add 25 to both sides.
          $\frac{q}{2} = 40$
     $2 \times \frac{q}{2} = 2 \times 40$ Multiply both sides by 2.
         $1q = 80$
          $q = \mathbf{80}$
Check: $\frac{80}{2} - 5 \overset{?}{=} 35$ Substitute 80 for *q*.
         $40 - 5 \overset{?}{=} 35$
           $35 = 35$

▶ Think and Discuss

1. Solve. $7p + 6 = 55$

2. Solve. $\frac{c}{10} - 5 = 5$

3. Refer to the introduction to this lesson. How much money had Max saved before his disaster?

Exercises

Solve. (See Example A.)

4. $4t - 9 = 15$
$t = 6$

5. $7y + 8 = 36$
$y = 4$

6. $12b + 3 = 39$
$b = 3$

7. $9f - 12 = 51$
$f = 7$

8. $15k - 9 = 66$
$k = 5$

9. $3n + 15 = 21$
$n = 2$

10. $4a - 10 = 38$
$a = 12$

11. $7q + 4 = 60$
$q = 8$

Solve. (See Example B.)

12. $\frac{m}{8} + 5 = 7$
$m = 16$

13. $\frac{r}{10} - 13 = 6$
$r = 190$

14. $\frac{s}{7} - 24 = 1$
$s = 175$

15. $\frac{b}{17} + 16 = 18$
$b = 34$

16. $\frac{a}{5} + 19 = 20$
$a = 5$

17. $\frac{d}{16} - 5 = 11$
$d = 256$

18. $\frac{z}{6} + 12 = 15$
$z = 18$

19. $\frac{c}{12} - 5 = 0$
$c = 60$

▶ Mixed Practice (For more practice, see page 451.)

Solve.

20. $8r + 3 = 67$ $r = 8$

21. $\frac{h}{9} - 7 = 4$ $h = 99$

22. $13y - 5 = 73$ $y = 6$

23. $14k - 21 = 21$ $k = 3$

24. $\frac{f}{24} + 3 = 15$ $f = 288$

25. $\frac{t}{11} - 11 = 11$ $t = 242$

▶ Applications

26. Margaret brought her dogs to work one day. Altogether 38 feet walked into the building. How many dogs does Margaret have? Write an equation and then solve. $4f + 2 = 38; f = 9$

27. Roger rented a car for one day from pro-Auto Rentals. His bill came to $72. Use the table below to find out how many miles Roger traveled. Write an equation and solve it.

Days	$ per Day	$ per Mile
1	24.00	0.08
2 – 4	20.00	0.075
5+	18.50	0.07

$24 + 0.08m = 72; m = 600$

▶ Review (Lesson 1.5)

Compare. Use > , < , or = .

28. 659 ▓ 699 $<$

29. 897 ▓ 978 $<$

30. 1279 ▓ 1257 $>$

31. 1956 ▓ 1758 $>$

▶ Think and Discuss Answers

1. $p = 7$
2. $c = 100$
3. $80

★ Error Alert

Incorrect answers may occur if students do not do the same things to both sides of an equation.

Reinforcement

Extra Practice, page 451
EP/MR Worksheet 127, TRB, page 127

Challenge

Dan had extensive orthodontic repair work done on the braces on his teeth. The orthodontist determined that $25 per band must be paid in addition to a fee of $35 for each appointment necessary to complete the repair work. Dan was responsible for the repair work on some of the bands plus one appointment fee. His parents paid for the repair work on the rest of the bands plus the remaining appointment fees. Four appointments were necessary. Dan paid $110 and his parents paid $255. How many bands were repaired altogether? Write an equation to determine how many bands Dan paid for and another equation to determine how many bands his parents paid for. Determine the total number of bands repaired. (answer: Suppose b stands for the number of bands.

Dan: $25b + 35 = 110$
$b = 3$
Parents: $25b + 3(35) = 255$
$b = 6$
The total number of bands is $3 + 6$, so 9 bands were repaired.)

Vocabulary and Writing Practice
VW Worksheet 16, TRB, page 152

Calculator Activities
CA Worksheet 16, TRB, page 177

Enrichment
E Worksheet 16, TRB, pages 229–230

Real Life Application
RL Worksheet 16, TRB, pages 263–264

Answers

7. five more than the product of eighteen and some number
8. twenty-five minus some number
9. eight more than four times some number
10. eighteen times some number
11. forty-two minus the product of two and some number

Chapter 16 Review

REVIEW

Complete each statement. (Lesson 16.1)

1. The letter d found in the ▆ 24d is called a(n) ▆ .
Expression; variable or unknown

2. $5y - 14 = 36$ is called a(n) ▆ . Equation

Write as an algebraic expression. (Lesson 16.2)

3. five plus some number $5 + n$

4. some number minus twenty $n - 20$

5. the product of five and four 5×4

6. eighteen divided by some number $\frac{18}{n}$

Write in words. (Lesson 16.2)

7. $5 + 18x$ 8. $25 - b$ 9. $4y + 8$ 10. $18c$ 11. $42 - 2q$

Find the value of each expression. (Lesson 16.3)

12. $15 + m$ when $m = 15$ 30

13. $8c - 20$ when $c = 4$ 12

14. $\frac{15b}{3}$ when $b = 12$ 60

Write as an equation. (Lesson 16.4)

15. The quotient of some number and nine is ten. $\frac{n}{9} = 10$

16. The difference of some number and twenty is seventy-seven. $n - 20 = 77$

Solve. (Lesson 16.6)

17. $d - 8 = 32$
$d = 40$

18. $25 + a = 72$
$a = 47$

19. $a + 33 = 90$
$a = 57$

20. $y - 56 = 19$
$y = 75$

21. $e + 12 = 56$
$e = 44$

22. $f - 11 = 39$
$f = 50$

23. $h - 30 = 21$
$h = 51$

24. $i + 29 = 42$
$i = 13$

Solve. (Lesson 16.7)

25. $4c = 88$
$c = 22$

26. $\frac{b}{3} = 17$
$b = 51$

27. $12e = 72$
$e = 6$

28. $\frac{m}{9} = 13$
$m = 117$

29. $12a = 108$
$a = 9$

30. $\frac{m}{30} = 120$
$m = 3600$

31. $\frac{n}{9} = 81$
$n = 729$

32. $25b = 125$
$b = 5$

Solve. (Lesson 16.8)

33. $5a - 11 = 114$ $a = 25$

34. $\frac{r}{2} + 34 = 84$ $r = 100$

35. $15c + 18 = 108$ $c = 6$

36. $\frac{n}{10} - 36 = 27$ $n = 630$

37. $12a + 21 = 81$ $a = 5$

38. $\frac{d}{5} - 7 = 8$ $d = 75$

39. $\frac{w}{3} + 92 = 305$ $w = 639$

40. $44b - 68 = 416$ $b = 11$

41. $10b + 12 = 82$ $b = 7$

Chapter 16 Test

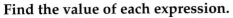

TEST

Find the value of each expression.

1. $14n$ when $n = 8$ 112

2. $\frac{125}{b}$ when $b = 25$ 5

3. $22n - 5$ when $n = 3$ 61

4. $b - 42$ when $b = 70$ 28

5. $\frac{b}{3}$ when $b = 18$ 6

Solve.

6. $3b + 15 = 39$ $b = 8$

7. $a + 62 = 109$ $a = 47$

8. $40n - 123 = 77$ $n = 5$

9. $\frac{108}{m} = 108$ $m = 1$

10. $t - 58 = 83$ $t = 141$

11. $18 + 2b = 106$ $b = 44$

Write as an algebraic expression.

12. some number times fifteen $15n$

13. sixteen less than some number $n - 16$

14. thirty-three plus some number $33 + n$

15. the quotient of forty and four $40 \div 4$

Write as an equation.

16. fifteen more than some number is seventy. $n + 15 = 70$

17. Five less than some number divided by eight is five. $\frac{n}{8} - 5 = 5$

18. The product of some number and fourteen is one hundred eighty-two $14n = 182$

Write in words.

19. $\frac{14}{y} + 13$

20. $12r - 3$

21. $\frac{370}{b} - 4$

22. $2z + 15$

Chapter Tests
Short Answer, Forms A and B, TRB,
   pages 327–328, 329–330
Multiple Choice, Forms A and B, TRB,
   pages 395–396, 397–398

Teaching Aids
Answer sheet
TA 8, TRB, page 161a
Teaching suggestions precede the
   Teaching Aids worksheets.

Answers
19. fourteen divided by some number, plus thirteen
20. twelve times some number, minus three
21. three hundred seventy divided by some number, minus four
22. two times some number, plus fifteen

Career Focus Activity

Materials: pencils, paper

Procedure: Organize students into four groups. Students arrange to have a computer programmer speak to the class.
- The first group writes an invitation to a computer programmer to visit the classroom.
- The second group compiles a list of questions to ask the individual about the job, activities the job entails, level of difficulty, required education, rewards of the job, how math skills are utilized, etc.
- During the visit, members of the third group ask the questions and record responses.
- Members of the fourth group compose a thank-you note to be sent within three days of the visit.
- All students evaluate the experience.

TEACHER NOTE: If computers are not available, have students complete the project using paper and pencil and a calculator.

Use integers and equations to

- describe temperature.
- describe gains and losses during a football game.
- determine a team's average score in five games played.
- identify a route using a coordinate graph or map.

What are some other ways to use integers and equations?

Pre-Algebra: Integers and Equations

A *computer programmer* writes instructions for computers to follow.

- Computer programmers work for small businesses, large corporations, and software companies.

- A computer programmer needs to be creative, must be able to think in a very logical way, and work well under pressure.

- A computer programmer writes instructions that enable a computer to perform mathematical calculations and other operations.

- To become a computer programmer, an individual completes a course of study in a college or vocational school.

- Related careers include software writers, computer graphics designers, computer operators, computer service representatives, computer engineers, and computer manufacturers.

CAREER

COMPUTER PROGRAMMER

PORTFOLIO PROJECT: *Use a computer program to prepare a math test.*

1. Use a computer to write a 10-item test using integers.

2. Prepare an answer key for your test, and check your answers. You can use the computer's calculator or a hand-held one. *Show the math.*

3. Exchange on-screen tests with a friend. Take each other's test. *Show the math.*

Objective

- To use the terms *integer, positive integer, negative integer,* and *opposite integer*

Purpose

This lesson helps you understand the relationship between whole numbers and negative integers. You need to use negative integers to record temperatures below zero. Negative integers are also useful in solving many other kinds of problems.

Introducing the Lesson

Review addition and subtraction of whole numbers (Lessons 1.9, 1.10, 1.11). Ask students to give examples of opposites that are used to identify temperature readings (above zero, below zero); elevations (above sea level, below sea level); banking transactions (deposits, withdrawals). Explain that this lesson deals with numbers that express these opposite actions and values.

17.1 Introduction to Integers

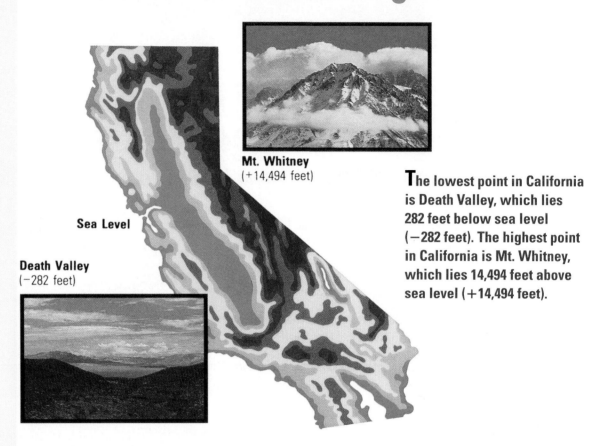

Mt. Whitney
(+14,494 feet)

Sea Level

Death Valley
(−282 feet)

The lowest point in California is Death Valley, which lies 282 feet below sea level (−282 feet). The highest point in California is Mt. Whitney, which lies 14,494 feet above sea level (+14,494 feet).

You have already met whole numbers like 6 and 28. On a number line, we can picture the whole numbers and their opposites. The opposites of 6 and 28 are −6 and −28. Together the whole numbers and their opposites are the **integers.**

► Express Yourself

Here are some terms that will help you in this chapter.

positive integer a whole number greater than zero. Positive integers can be shown with a positive sign (+) and are to the right of zero on a number line.

negative integer   an integer less than zero.

Negative integers have a negative sign (−) and are to the left of zero on a number line.

opposite integers   two integers with different signs that are equally distant from zero on a number line.

1. Describe two other ways you have heard the terms *positive,* *negative,* and *opposite* used.

2. What are the opposite integers for 14,494 and −282?

3. Refer to the introduction to this lesson. Find the difference in elevation between the top of Mt. Whitney and the lowest point in Death Valley.

PROBLEM SOLVING

▶ Practice What You Know

Add.

4. 49 + 28
77

5. 63 + 12
75

6. 15 + 1500
1515

7. 325 + 4562
4887

8. 238 + 671
909

9. 5553 + 228
5781

10. 3857 + 2246
6103

11. 9089 + 2378
11,467

12. 37 + 26
63

13. 444 + 93
537

14. 3286 + 992
4278

15. 701 + 52
753

Subtract.

16. 12 − 6 6

17. 33 − 16 17

18. 45 − 9 36

19. 89 − 81 8

20. 875 − 87 788

21. 349 − 32 317

22. 4562 − 3729 833

23. 2600 − 34 2566

24. 812 − 379
433

25. 64 − 32
32

26. 2709 − 84
2625

27. 965 − 868
97

Write an equation and solve.

28. What is the distance between the highest point in Florida and the highest point in Wyoming?

29. The difference between the highest point in New York and the highest point in another state is 4538 feet. What is the height of the highest point of the other state? What is the other state?

30. The highest point in one state is 7514 feet higher than the highest point in Illinois. Identify the state.

State	Highest Point
Florida	345 ft.
Illinois	1235 ft.
Mississippi	806 ft.
New York	5344 ft.
South Dakota	7242 ft.
Texas	8749 ft.
Wyoming	13,804 ft.

Express Yourself Answers

1. Sample answers may include: *positive* self-image; *positive* that you are going to do something; *negative* attitude; *negative* self-esteem; *opposite* or across from someone; *opposite* opinion.

2. −14,494; 282

3. 14,776 ft.

Practice What You Know Answers

28. 13,804 − 345 = *n*; 13,459 ft.

29. 5344 − 4538 = *n*; 806 ft.; Mississippi

30. 1235 + 7514 = *n*; 8749 ft.; Texas

★ Error Alert

Incorrect answers may indicate that students are not lining up columns correctly when they add and subtract.

Puzzle

Fill in each missing number of this magic square. The sum of each row, column, and 5-number diagonal is the same.

(17)	4	(18)	24	15
13	(23)	27	10	(5)
(3)	9	19	(21)	26
25	14	(12)	7	(20)
20	(28)	2	16	12

Objective

• To add integers

Purpose

This lesson introduces adding integers. If you know the temperature was −3° and that it went up 7°, you can add −3 and 7 to find the new temperature.

Introducing the Lesson

Write the following positive and negative numbers on the chalkboard to indicate the daily change in the Dow Jones average for the stock market: −4, +13, +2, −11, +8. Ask: How would you find the total number of points the market is up or down for the week? (Add the integers.)

Alternative Examples

Example A—Add. +2 + +2
Begin at 0. Move 2 units to the right. Then move 2 more units to the right.
+2 + +2 = **+4**

Example B—Add. −9 + −1
Begin at 0. Move 9 units to the left. Now move 1 more unit to the left.
−9 + −1 = **−10**

Example C—Add. +9 + −10
Begin at 0. Move 9 units to the right. Then move 10 units to the left.
+9 + −10 = **−1**

Alternative Strategies

Explain: If signs are the same, add the numbers without their signs and put their common sign on the answer. If signs are different, remove their signs and subtract the smaller number from the larger. Then put the sign of the number that is farther from zero on the answer.

17.2 Adding Integers

First Down! Jim throws a 5-yard forward pass to Juan. Juan runs 4 yards. Total gain is 9 yards.

Second Down! Bill is tackled 3 yards behind the line of scrimmage and he fumbles the ball. The ball rolls back 5 yards before his teammate falls on it. Total loss is 8 yards.

Third Down! Jim completes a 10-yard forward pass to Bob. Bob is forced back 2 yards. Total gain is 8 yards.

Adding integers can help you keep up with the total yards gained or lost in a football game.

Examples

To add integers, you can use a number line. Find zero on the number line. Then move to the right to add a positive (+) number or to the left to add a negative (−) number.

A Add. +5 + +4   Begin at 0. Move 5 units to the right. Then move 4 more units to the right. +5 + +4 = +9

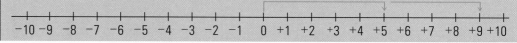

B Add. −3 + −5   Begin at 0. Move 3 units to the left. Then move five more units to the left. −3 + −5 = −8

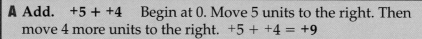

C Add. +10 + −2   Begin at 0. Move 10 units to the right. Then move 2 units to the left. +10 + −2 = +8

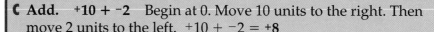

Think and Discuss

1. If you are adding a negative number, do you move to the left or to the right?

2. Which number is farther from zero, -25 or $+19$?

3. Refer to the introduction to this lesson. What is the total loss or gain in the series of three downs?

4. Without adding, decide if $-27 + {}^+14$ is positive. Explain.

▶ Think and Discuss Answers
1. left
2. -25
3. 9-yard gain
4. The sum is negative because -27 is farther from zero than $+14$.

★ Error Alert
Errors may occur when students ignore the signs of integers.

Exercises

Add. (See Example A.)

5. $^+4 + {}^+4$ $_{+8}$ 6. $^+1 + {}^+5$ $_{+6}$ 7. $^+5 + {}^+8$ $_{+13}$ 8. $^+6 + 0$ $_{+6}$ 9. $^+8 + {}^+7$ $_{+15}$

10. $^+3 + {}^+4$ $_{+7}$ 11. $^+7 + {}^+2$ $_{+9}$ 12. $^+2 + {}^+3$ $_{+5}$ 13. $^+5 + {}^+3$ $_{+8}$ 14. $^+9 + {}^+8$ $_{+17}$

Add. (See Example B.)

15. $-2 + {}^-2$ $_{-4}$ 16. $-5 + {}^-5$ $_{-10}$ 17. $-8 + 0$ $_{-8}$ 18. $-4 + {}^-3$ $_{-7}$ 19. $-7 + {}^-5$ $_{-12}$

20. $-5 + {}^-2$ $_{-7}$ 21. $-1 + {}^-4$ $_{-5}$ 22. $-3 + {}^-3$ $_{-6}$ 23. $-3 + {}^-6$ $_{-9}$ 24. $-9 + {}^-7$ $_{-16}$

Add. (See Example C.)

25. $-7 + {}^+8$ $_{+1}$ 26. $^+4 + {}^-9$ $_{-5}$ 27. $-2 + {}^+1$ $_{-1}$ 28. $^+8 + {}^-4$ $_{+4}$ 29. $-5 + {}^+9$ $_{+4}$

30. $^+6 + {}^-9$ $_{-3}$ 31. $-7 + {}^+3$ $_{-4}$ 32. $^+6 + {}^-9$ $_{-3}$ 33. $-5 + {}^+6$ $_{+1}$ 34. $^+8 + {}^-3$ $_{+5}$

▶ Mixed Practice (For more practice, see page 451.)

Add.

35. $-5 + {}^-1$ $_{-6}$ 36. $-9 + {}^+7$ $_{-2}$ 37. $^+8 + {}^-9$ $_{-1}$ 38. $^+4 + {}^+2$ $_{+6}$ 39. $-7 + {}^-4$ $_{-11}$

40. $^+9 + {}^-9$ $_0$ 41. $-7 + {}^-2$ $_{-9}$ 42. $-4 + {}^+7$ $_{+3}$ 43. $^+6 + {}^-8$ $_{-2}$ 44. $^+8 + {}^-5$ $_{+3}$

▶ Applications

45. The Bears lost thirteen yards on first down and twelve yards on second down. A pass was caught for a twenty-yard gain. What was the total gain or loss for the three downs? Loss of 5 yards

46. Maria had $26 in her checking account. She wrote checks for $13 and $15. How much money does Maria need to deposit to make sure her checks can be cashed? $2

Reinforcement
Extra Practice, page 451
EP/MR Worksheet 128, TRB, page 128

Project
Use the business section of your daily newspaper. Record the changes in the Dow Jones industrial average for five consecutive days. Express each as a positive or negative number. Does the Dow Jones show a net gain or loss? (Answer will depend on current data.)

▶ Review (Lesson 11.3)

Solve each proportion.

47. $\dfrac{6}{9} = \dfrac{\blacksquare}{180}$

$\blacksquare = 120$

48. $\dfrac{\blacksquare}{7} = \dfrac{25}{35}$

$\blacksquare = 5$

49. $\dfrac{10}{12} = \dfrac{30}{\blacksquare}$

$\blacksquare = 36$

50. $\dfrac{18}{\blacksquare} = \dfrac{12}{96}$

$\blacksquare = 144$

Purpose

You can use subtraction anytime you need to determine the amount of change between two numbers. For example, you can subtract to find the change in elevation from the base of a ski hill to the top and the change in temperature when readings go from above zero to below zero.

Introducing the Lesson

Review adding integers (Lesson 17.2). Use the examples: +2 + +7 = (+9); −2 + −7 = (−9); +2 + −7 = (−5); −2 + +7 = (+5). Ask students if they have ever counted lines on a thermometer to determine the change in temperature. Suppose a thermometer showed 8° F below 0 at 8 A.M. and 3° F above 0 at noon. Ask: Did the temperature rise or drop? (rise) Use a thermometer or vertical number line to find the change in temperature. Tell students to start at −8 and count the number of units to +3. What does this tell you about the temperature? (11° rise)

Alternative Examples

Example A—Subtract. +8 − −9
+8 − −9 = +8 + +9   *Add the*
+8 − −9 = +17   *opposite*
+8 − −9 = **+17**   *of −9.*

Example B—Subtract. +5 − +13
Use a number line. Begin at 0. Move 5 units to the right. Then move 13 units to the left.
+5 − +13 = **−8.**

Example C—Subtract. −4 − −10
Use a number line. Begin at 0. Move 4 units to the left. Then move 10 units to the right.
−4 − −10 = **+6.**

17.3 Subtracting Integers

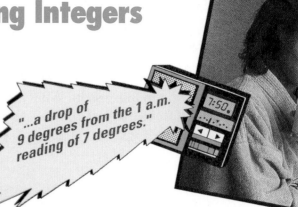

Catherine usually listens to the radio in the morning to find out what the weather is like. This morning, she caught the tail end of the weather report. All she heard was . . . .

"...a drop of 9 degrees from the 1 a.m. reading of 7 degrees."

Catherine could subtract to find the temperature.

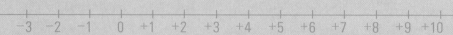

Examples

To subtract an integer, you can add its opposite.

A Subtract.   +5 − −3

+5 − −3 = 5 + +3   Add the opposite of −3.
+5 − −3 = **+8**

B Subtract.   +7 − +9

Use a number line. Begin at 0. Move 7 units to the right. Then move 9 units to the left.

+7 − +9 = **−2**

C Subtract. −6 − −4

−6 − −4 = −6 + +4
Use a number line. Begin at 0. Move 6 units to the left. Then move 4 units to the right.

−6 − −4 = **−2**

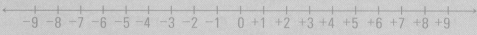

▶ **Think and Discuss**

1. What is the opposite of +1? Of −1?

2. Refer to the introduction to this lesson. What was the temperature?

3. Subtract. $^-9 - {}^+4$

4. Complete the table below.

Working on a number line, you move:

to the right	to add a positive integer.
▓	to add a negative integer.
▓	to subtract a positive integer.
▓	to subtract a negative integer.

Exercises

Subtract. (See Example A.)

5. $^+3 - {}^-2$ $_{+5}$ 6. $^+5 - {}^-6$ $_{+11}$ 7. $^+4 - {}^-3$ $_{+7}$ 8. $^+7 - {}^-9$ $_{+16}$ 9. $^+5 - {}^-4$ $_{+9}$

10. $0 - {}^-1$ $_{+1}$ 11. $^+8 - {}^-8$ $_{+16}$ 12. $^+3 - 0$ $_{+3}$ 13. $^+6 - {}^-1$ $_{+7}$ 14. $^+7 - {}^-8$ $_{+15}$

Subtract. (See Example B.)

15. $^+1 - {}^+4$ $_{-3}$ 16. $^+5 - {}^+3$ $_{+2}$ 17. $^+2 - {}^+7$ $_{-5}$ 18. $^+8 - {}^+3$ $_{+5}$ 19. $^+9 - {}^+2$ $_{+7}$

20. $^+9 - {}^+9$ $_{0}$ 21. $0 - {}^+2$ $_{-2}$ 22. $^+7 - {}^+5$ $_{+2}$ 23. $^+2 - {}^+8$ $_{-6}$ 24. $^+6 - {}^+4$ $_{+2}$

Subtract. (See Example C.)

25. $^-6 - {}^-2$ $_{-4}$ 26. $^-8 - {}^-9$ $_{+1}$ 27. $^-5 - {}^-6$ $_{+1}$ 28. $^-1 - {}^-4$ $_{+3}$ 29. $^-3 - {}^-7$ $_{+4}$

30. $^-9 - {}^-4$ $_{-5}$ 31. $^-1 - {}^-1$ $_{0}$ 32. $^-2 - {}^-6$ $_{+4}$ 33. $^-3 - {}^-4$ $_{+1}$ 34. $^-9 - {}^-6$ $_{-3}$

► **Mixed Practice** (For more practice, see page 452.)

Subtract.

35. $^-5 - {}^-11$ $_{+6}$ 36. $^-6 - {}^-3$ $_{-3}$ 37. $^+6 - {}^+9$ $_{-3}$ 38. $^-11 - {}^+4$ $_{-15}$

39. $^+15 - {}^-9$ $_{+24}$ 40. $^-7 - {}^+11$ $_{-18}$ 41. $^-2 - {}^+1$ $_{-3}$ 42. $^+9 - {}^+11$ $_{-2}$

43. $^+4 - {}^+12$ $_{-8}$ 44. $^-3 - {}^-12$ $_{+9}$ 45. $^+6 - {}^+10$ $_{-4}$ 46. $0 - {}^+4$ $_{-4}$

47. $^-12 - {}^+3$ $_{-15}$ 48. $^-12 - {}^-8$ $_{-4}$ 49. $^+7 - {}^+3$ $_{+4}$ 50. $^-9 - {}^+9$ $_{-18}$

► **Applications**

51. The temperature is 72° F inside and $^-12°$ F outside. What is the difference in temperatures? 84°F

52. How much warmer is it in Boston than it is in Portland? 18°

Boston   Portland

► **Review** (Lesson 12.7)

Find each number.

53. 60% of 1570 942   54. $7\frac{1}{2}$ of 500 37.5   55. 475% of 80 380

17.4 Mapping and Coordinate Graphing

Jerome received a letter and a map from his cousin, Diane. "I'm looking forward to seeing you in Philadelphia during the holidays," Diane wrote. "Here's a map of central Philadelphia. Let me know where you want to go."

Jerome can use coordinate graphing to explain to Diane the locations of the places on the map he'd like to visit.

You have worked with number lines and have made line graphs. The grid on the right was made by drawing a horizontal number line and a vertical number line. The point where the two lines meet is called the **origin**. The origin is labeled with a zero. The grid is divided into four sections. You can name any point on the grid by using a pair of numbers called an **ordered pair**. Find the ordered pair (3, ⁻2). The first number tells how far to move to the right or to the left on the horizontal number line. The second number tells how far to move up or down on the vertical number line.

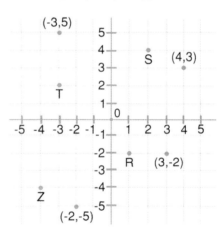

▶ Think and Discuss

1. Starting at the origin, what direction would you move on a horizontal number line for a negative number?

2. Starting at the origin, what direction would you move on a vertical number line for a negative number?

3. Write ordered pairs for the points S, T, R, and Z.

Look at the map of central Philadelphia below. You can use a grid to help you locate places on the map.

4. What street is on the horizontal number line? Arch Street

5. What street is on the vertical number line? 10th Street

6. Using the grid, how would you express the location of the corner of 11th Street and Cherry Street? (−1, 1)

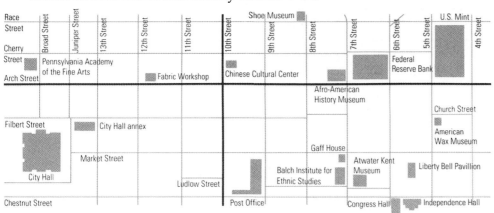

Exercises
(For more practice, see page 452.)

Use the map to find the streets at these ordered pairs.

7. (−2, 0)
   12th & Arch

8. (1, −2)
   9th & Market

9. (−1, 2)
   11th & Race

10. (−3, −3)
    13th & Chestnut

Use the map to find the landmarks at these ordered pairs.

11. (3, 0)
    Afro-American History Museum

12. (4, −3)
    Congress Hall

13. (5, 2)
    U.S. Mint

▶ Applications

14. Diane and Jerome want to visit the Gaff House and the Shoe Museum. Write ordered pairs and name the streets that cross at each location. (3, −2); 7th & Market; (2, 2); 8th & Race

15. Draw a grid on a sheet of paper. Label your school at the origin. Plot the locations and write ordered pairs for landmarks near your school. Answers will vary.

▶ Review (Lesson 12.3)

Write as a percent.

16. $\frac{3}{5}$ 60%

17. $\frac{1}{2}$ 50%

18. $\frac{10}{10}$ 100%

19. $\frac{1}{10}$ 10%

20. $\frac{5}{6}$ $83\frac{1}{3}$%

21. $\frac{1}{5}$ 20%

22. $\frac{3}{8}$ $37\frac{1}{2}$%

23. $\frac{13}{16}$ $81\frac{1}{4}$%

★ **Error Alert**
Incorrect answers may indicate that students are moving the wrong direction on the grid for one or both coordinates or that they are making all moves from the origin.

Reinforcement
Extra Practice, page 452
EP/MR Worksheet 130, TRB, page 130

Teaching Aids
Quarter-inch grid
TA 7, TRB, page 160
Teaching suggestions precede the Teaching Aids worksheets.

Challenge
The ordered pairs (2, 5), (3, 6), and (4, 7) name points on the same line. To find the equation of that line, determine how the coordinates for each ordered pair are related. Look at the first pair. Ask yourself what must be done to the first number, called x, to get the second number, called y. If this works for the other two pairs, you can write the equation of the line. Make a list as follows:

(x, y)
(2, 5)   2 + 3 = 5
(3, 6)   3 + 3 = 6
(4, 7)   4 + 3 = 7

Since each y is obtained by adding 3 to the corresponding x-value, the equation of the line is $y = x + 3$.

Find the equation for the following sets of ordered pairs.
1. (2, 1), (4, 2), (6, 3)   ($y = x/2$)
2. (4, 7), (6, 11), (7, 13)   ($y = 2x − 1$)

Objective

- To multiply integers

17.5 Multiplying Integers

What does it mean to say, "My telephone number is not unlisted"? What does it mean to say, "My telephone bill is not unpaid"? In ordinary language, having the word *not* followed by a word beginning with the prefix *un-* can be like multiplying two negative integers.

Examples

To multiply two integers, multiply as with whole numbers. If the signs are the same, the product is positive. If the signs are different, the product is negative.

A Multiply. $+8 \times +9$
Same signs:
positive product

$+8 \times +9 = +\mathbf{72}$

B Multiply. -4×-7
Same signs:
positive product

$-4 \times -7 = +\mathbf{28}$

C Multiply. $-7 \times +3$
Different signs:
negative product

$-7 \times +3 = -\mathbf{21}$

▶ Think and Discuss

1. Is the product of two negative numbers negative?

2. Multiply. $-9 \times +5$

3. What is the product of zero and any integer?

4. Does "not unfriendly" mean friendly? Explain.

5. If you multiply seven negative integers together, will the product be positive or negative?

6. Explain how the use of *not* followed by *un-* in ordinary language can be like multiplication of two negative integers.

Exercises

Multiply. (See Example A.)

7. +5 × +4 +20   **8.** +7 × +7 +49   **9.** +10 × +1 +10   **10.** +4 × +20 +80

11. −7 × +8 +56   **12.** +7 × +11 +77   **13.** +6 × +12 +72   **14.** +14 × +7 +98

15. +5 × +40 +200   **16.** +9 × +16 +144   **17.** +8 × +30 +240   **18.** +15 × +4 +60

Multiply. (See Example B.)

19. −6 × −3 +18   **20.** −3 × −6 +18   **21.** −9 × −11 +99   **22.** −8 × −4 +32   **23.** −7 × −4 +28

24. −4 × −12 +48   **25.** −2 × −24 +48   **26.** −7 × −8 +56   **27.** −9 × −9 +81   **28.** −11 × −7 +77

Multiply. (See Example C.)

29. −6 × +4 −24   **30.** −1 × +10 −10   **31.** +2 × −12 −24   **32.** +5 × −20 −100

33. −7 × +9 −63   **34.** −5 × +6 −30   **35.** +7 × −12 −84   **36.** +8 × −11 −88

▶ Mixed Practice (For more practice, see page 453.)

Multiply.

37. −3 × −5 +15   **38.** +9 × −1 −9   **39.** +9 × +1 +9   **40.** −5 × −10 +50   **41.** −7 × −15 +105

42. −4 × +4 −16   **43.** +8 × +10 +80   **44.** −7 × −6 +42   **45.** −9 × +10 −90   **46.** −12 × +5 −60

47. +5 × +5 +25   **48.** −1 × −7 +7   **49.** +8 × −7 −56   **50.** +6 × +6 +36   **51.** −20 × −4 +80

▶ Applications

52. At 6 p.m. the temperature was 0° C. In the next three hours it dropped 3° each hour. What was the temperature at 9 p.m.? −9° C

53. A stock lost four points each day for four days. Then for two days it gained a point each day. Write the total change as an integer.
−14 points

6 Day Results						
	M	**T**	**W**	**T**	**F**	**M**
PrgKn	−4	−4	−4	−4	+1	+1

▶ Review (Lesson 12.9)

Find each number.

54. 225% of what number is 81?
36

55. 16% of what number is 8?
50

56. 95% of what number is 285?
300

57. 4% of what number is 13.12?
328

58. 700% of what amount is $35,000?
$5000

59. 48% of what number is 5.76?
12

▶ Think and Discuss Answers

1. no
2. −45
3. 0
4. no, a person who is not unfriendly could be either friendly or neutral
5. negative
6. The *not* and *un-* sometimes "cancel" each other out. For example, "not un-listed" means "listed." In this case, a double negative makes a positive. This is similar to the fact that the product of two negative integers is positive.

★ Error Alert

Incorrect answers may indicate that students are confusing the rules for multiplying integers with the rules for adding integers: they may show the product of two negative integers to be negative.

Reinforcement

Extra Practice, page 453
EP/MR Worksheet 131, TRB, page 131

Challenge

Square each of the following numbers: 0, 2, −2, 7, −7, 112, −112. What conclusions can you draw about squares? (All squares are positive or 0 because of the multiplication rules for integers.)

Objective

- To divide integers

Purpose

Finding averages may require dividing a negative integer by a positive integer. This might happen, for example, if you wanted to find the average temperature for several very cold days. This lesson shows how to divide integers.

Introducing the Lesson

Review division of whole numbers (Lessons 3.2, 3.5, 3.6) and multiplication of integers (Lesson 17.5). Use the examples:
$+7 \times +9 (+63); +7 \times -9 (-63);$
$-7 \times +9 (-63); -7 \times -9 (+63).$

Alternative Examples

Example A—Divide. $+132 \div +12$
Same signs: positive quotient
$+132 \div +12 = \textbf{+11}$

Example B—Divide. $-100 \div -4$
Same signs: positive quotient
$-100 \div -4 = \textbf{+25}$

Example C—Divide. $+75 \div -15$
Different signs: negative quotient
$+75 \div -15 = \textbf{-5}$

17.6 Dividing Integers

David, a railroad employee in Chicago, charts winter temperatures. When the temperature drops below freezing, David starts heaters so that the railroad switches do not freeze up. For four days in January, Chicago temperatures were $-22°$ F, $-15°$ F, $-18°$ F, and $-13°$ F. The sum of these temperatures is $-68°$ F. What is the average temperature for those four days?

The rules for determining signs when dividing integers are exactly the same as the rules for determining signs when multiplying integers.

Examples

To divide integers, divide as with whole numbers. If the signs are the same, the quotient is positive. If the signs are different, the quotient is negative.

A Divide. $+36 \div +4$

Same signs:
positive quotient
$+36 \div +4 = +9$

B Divide. $-56 \div -7$

Same signs:
positive quotient
$-56 \div -7 = +8$

C Divide. $-68 \div +4$

Different signs:
negative quotient
$-68 \div +4 = -17$

▶ Think and Discuss

1. Divide. $-48 \div -6$

2. Divide. $-64 \div +8$

3. Does a negative integer divided by a positive integer give a positive or negative quotient?

4. Does a positive integer divided by a negative integer give a positive or negative quotient?

5. What is the quotient of any integer divided by one?

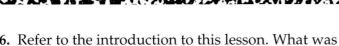

6. Refer to the introduction to this lesson. What was the average temperature for the four days?

7. If you divide two negative integers, and then divide that quotient by a negative integer, will the final quotient be positive or negative?

Exercises

Divide. (See Example A.)

8. +81 ÷ +9
+9
9. +25 ÷ +5
+5
10. +8 ÷ +8
+1
11. +45 ÷ +9
+5
12. +21 ÷ +7
+3

13. +56 ÷ +8
+7
14. +10 ÷ +1
+10
15. +48 ÷ +4
+12
16. +63 ÷ +7
+9
17. +72 ÷ 9
+8

Divide. (See Example B.)

18. −90 ÷ −9
+10
19. −54 ÷ −6
+9
20. −36 ÷ −3
+12
21. −12 ÷ −6
+2
22. −80 ÷ −8
+10

23. −7 ÷ −7
+1
24. −72 ÷ −8
+9
25. −22 ÷ −2
+11
26. −45 ÷ −9
+5
27. −63 ÷ −7
+9

Divide. (See Example C.)

28. +16 ÷ −4
−4
29. −20 ÷ +4
−5
30. +25 ÷ −5
−5
31. +36 ÷ −9
−4
32. −49 ÷ +7
−7

33. −50 ÷ +5
−10
34. +56 ÷ −8
−7
35. −81 ÷ +9
−9
36. +72 ÷ −8
−9
37. −63 ÷ +9
−7

▶ Mixed Practice (For more practice, see page 453.)

Divide.

38. −60 ÷ −6
+10
39. −10 ÷ +2
−5
40. −24 ÷ +8
−3
41. +72 ÷ +3
+24
42. −64 ÷ −8
+8

43. +15 ÷ −5
−3
44. +9 ÷ −1
−9
45. +13 ÷ +1
+13
46. −18 ÷ +6
−3
47. −42 ÷ −7
+6

48. +27 ÷ −3
−9
49. −56 ÷ −4
+14
50. +48 ÷ +6
+8
51. −12 ÷ +1
−12
52. +64 ÷ −4
−16

▶ Applications

53. The per-gallon cost of heating oil rose from $1.57 to $1.75 in two months. What was the average monthly change in the price per gallon? $0.09

54. The low in Bismarck, North Dakota, was −10 degrees Fahrenheit one day. The next day the low was −12. Find the average low temperature for these two days.
−11° F

▶ Review (Lesson 16.6)

Solve and check each equation.

55. $a - 12 = 74$
$a = 86$
56. $21 + w = 98$
$w = 77$
57. $x + 3.6 = 8$
$x = 4.4$
58. $n - 47 = 9$
$n = 56$

59. $b - 53 = 29$
$b = 82$
60. $c - 80 = 142$
$c = 222$
61. $78 + r = 123$
$r = 45$
62. $s + 16 = 43$
$s = 27$

▶ Think and Discuss Answers

1. +8
2. −8
3. negative quotient
4. negative quotient
5. the integer
6. −17° F
7. negative

★ Error Alert

Incorrect answers may indicate that students are confusing the rules for dividing integers with the rules for adding integers: they may show the quotient of two negative integers to be negative.

Reinforcement

Extra Practice, page 453
EP/MR Worksheet 132, TRB, page 132

Puzzle

Multiply or divide as indicated by the symbol in the triangle to find the missing integers in these puzzles. Perform horizontal computations from left to right and vertical computations from top to bottom. Do not multiply or divide diagonally. Use the answer in the lower-right box to check your math. It must work for both the row and column it is in.

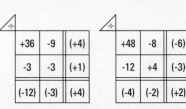

×		
+4	+6	(+24)
-3	-2	(+6)
(-12)	(-12)	(+144)

×		
+2	-7	(-14)
-5	+4	(-20)
(-10)	(-28)	(+280)

÷		
+36	-9	(+4)
-3	-3	(+1)
(-12)	(-3)	(+4)

÷		
+48	-8	(-6)
-12	+4	(-3)
(-4)	(-2)	(+2)

17.7 Solving Addition and Subtraction Equations Involving Integers

"I'm thinking of a number," Mr. Marvin told his class. "When you subtract −6 from it, you get −4. Can you guess what my number is?"

One way to find the number is to set up and solve an equation.

Examples

To solve an equation, isolate the variable on one side.

A Solve. $c + -5 = +4$

$$c + -5 = +4$$
$$c + -5 - -5 = +4 - -5 \quad \text{Subtract −5 from both sides.}$$
$$c + 0 = +4 - -5 \quad -5 + +5 = 0$$
$$c = +9$$
Check: $+9 + -5 \stackrel{?}{=} +4$ \quad Substitute 9 for *c* in the original equation.
$$+4 = +4$$

B Solve. $b - -6 = -4$

$$b - -6 = -4$$
$$b - -6 + -6 = -4 + -6 \quad \text{Add −6 to both sides.}$$
$$b + 0 = -4 + -6 \quad +6 + -6 = 0$$
$$b = -10$$
Check: $-10 - -6 \stackrel{?}{=} -4$ \quad Substitute −10 for *b* in the original equation.
$$-10 + +6 \stackrel{?}{=} -4$$
$$-4 = -4$$

Think and Discuss

1. Solve. $a + {}^-5 = {}^-8$

2. Solve. $b - {}^-12 = {}^+24$

3. Refer to the introduction to this lesson. What was Mr. Marvin's number?

4. Use an equation to solve "12 more than an integer is ${}^-8$."

5. Use an equation to solve "An integer decreased by 18 is ${}^-20$."

6. Try to solve these equations mentally.

$x + {}^-3 = {}^+5$ $\quad y + {}^+4 = {}^-1$ $\quad z - {}^-2 = {}^+1$ $\quad w - {}^+5 = {}^-1$

SKILLS

▶ Think and Discuss Answers
1. $a = {}^-3$
2. $b = {}^+12$
3. ${}^-10$
4. $a + 12 = {}^-8; a = {}^-20$
5. $a - 18 = {}^-20; a = {}^-2$
6. $x = {}^+8; y = {}^-5; z = {}^-1; w = {}^+4$

★ Error Alert

Incorrect answers may indicate that students are not adding or subtracting the correct integer on both sides.

Exercises

Solve. (See Example A.) Check your answers.

7. $x + {}^+3 = {}^-1$
$x = {}^-4$

8. $y + {}^+5 = {}^+2$
$y = {}^-3$

9. $z + {}^+2 = {}^+1$
$z = {}^-1$

10. $a + {}^+5 = {}^-5$
$a = {}^-10$

11. $e + {}^-6 = {}^+10$
$e = {}^+16$

12. $j + {}^-1 = {}^-1$
$j = 0$

13. $b + {}^-4 = {}^+12$
$b = {}^+16$

14. $m + {}^-8 = {}^-6$
$m = {}^+2$

Solve. (See Example B.) Check your answers.

15. $x - {}^-2 = {}^-3$
$x = {}^-5$

16. $y - {}^-4 = {}^+2$
$y = {}^-2$

17. $z - {}^-4 = {}^-8$
$z = {}^-12$

10. $a - {}^-6 = {}^+2$
$a = {}^-4$

19. $a - {}^-1 = {}^+1$
$a = 0$

20. $b - {}^-1 = {}^-1$
$b = {}^-2$

21. $c - {}^+5 = 0$
$c = {}^+5$

22. $d - {}^+4 = {}^-3$
$d = {}^+1$

▶ Mixed Practice (For more practice, see page 454.)

Solve.

23. $e - {}^-2 = {}^+2$
$e = 0$

24. $f + {}^+5 = {}^-7$
$f = {}^-12$

25. $g + {}^-9 = {}^-10$
$g = {}^-1$

26. $h - {}^+6 = {}^+5$
$h = {}^+11$

27. $i + {}^-7 = {}^-4$
$i = {}^+3$

28. $j - {}^-4 = {}^-2$
$j = {}^-6$

29. $k + {}^+1 = {}^+1$
$k = 0$

30. $l + {}^+9 = {}^-4$
$l = {}^-13$

31. $m - {}^-10 = 0$
$m = {}^-10$

32. $n + {}^+8 = {}^+6$
$n = {}^-2$

33. $p + {}^-3 = {}^-1$
$p = {}^+2$

34. $g - {}^+1 = {}^-10$
$g = {}^-9$

35. $r - {}^-6 = {}^+2$
$r = {}^-4$

36. $s + {}^-5 = {}^+5$
$s = {}^+10$

37. $v + {}^+9 = {}^+12$
$v = {}^+3$

38. $w + {}^-8 = {}^-14$
$w = {}^-6$

▶ Applications

39. The temperature fell twelve degrees to three degrees below zero. How cold was it before? Set up an equation and solve.
$n - 12 = {}^-3; n = {}^+9$

40. When you add this number to ${}^-32$, the sum is ${}^-18$. Find the number using an equation.
$n + {}^-32 = {}^-18; n = {}^+14$

▶ Review (Lesson 16.7)

Solve and check each equation.

41. $\frac{n}{8} = 14$ $\quad n = 112$

42. $\frac{x}{3} = 55$ $\quad x = 165$

43. $11s = 132$ $\quad s = 12$

44. $7t = 266$ $\quad t = 38$

Reinforcement

Extra Practice, page 454
EP/MR Worksheet 133, TRB, page 133

Challenge

Use the rules for solving equations to solve inequalities. Use the example:

$$d - {}^+5 > {}^-11$$
$$d - {}^+5 > {}^-11$$
$$d - {}^+5 + {}^+5 > {}^-11 + {}^+5$$
$$d > {}^-6$$

To check this answer, pick any value for d that is greater than ${}^-6$. For example,

If $d = {}^-2$, then ${}^-2 - {}^+5 \overset{?}{>} {}^-11$
$$\qquad {}^-7 > {}^-11$$

If $d = {}^+4$, then ${}^+4 - {}^+5 \overset{?}{>} {}^-11$
$$\qquad {}^-1 > {}^-11$$

Solve the following inequalities. Check each answer using at least two integers that satisfy your solution.

1. $y - 6 < {}^-8$ $\qquad (y < {}^-2)$
2. ${}^-3 + p > {}^-7$ $\qquad (p > {}^-4)$
3. $f - 2 > {}^+6$ $\qquad (f > {}^+8)$

Objective

• To solve equations with integers by using multiplication or division

Purpose

Solving equations with integers uses what you have learned about integers, equations, and inverse operations. In this lesson you solve multiplication and division equations involving integers. This procedure can help you solve word problems.

Introducing the Lesson

Review the rules for multiplying and dividing integers (Lessons 17.5, 17.6). Multiplication and division of integers follow the same rule—like signs give a positive answer and unlike signs yield a negative answer. Review multiplication and division as inverse operations. Use the examples: $+7 \times +3 = +21$, $+21 \div +3 = +7$; $-4 \times +8 = -32$, $-32 \div +8 = -4$. Review solving equations using multiplication or division (Lesson 16.7). Use the examples: $3x = 42$ ($x = 14$); $\frac{x}{9} = 24$ ($x = 216$).

Note: Golf scores can be given two ways: as the total number of strokes or as the number of strokes above or below par for the course. In the introduction on the student page, Monica is referring to a score below par as a negative number.

Alternative Examples

Example A—Solve. $-4k = +20$
$-4k = +20$
Divide both sides of equation by −4.
$\frac{-4k}{-4} = \frac{+20}{-4}$
$+1k = \frac{+20}{-4}$
$k = -5$
Check: *Substitute −5 for k in the original equation.*
$-4 \times -5 \stackrel{?}{=} +20$
$+20 = +20$

17.8 Solving Multiplication and Division Equations Involving Integers

Monica, a student in Mr. Marvin's class, raised her hand. "I played nine holes of golf and I scored below par. My score multiplied by negative 8 equals 16. Can you figure out my golf score?"

Mr. Marvin smiled. "For this problem I must solve an equation."

Examples

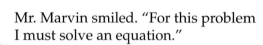

To solve an equation, isolate the variable on one side.

A Solve. $-8a = +16$

$$-8a = +16$$
$$\frac{-8a}{-8} = \frac{+16}{-8} \qquad \text{Divide both sides of the equation by } -8$$
$$+1a = \frac{+16}{-8} \qquad \frac{-8}{-8} = +1$$
$$a = -2$$
Check: $-8 \times -2 \stackrel{?}{=} +16 \qquad$ Substitute -2 for a in the original equation.
$$+16 = +16$$

B Solve. $\frac{b}{+6} = -7$

$$\frac{b}{+6} = -7$$
$$+6 \times \frac{b}{+6} = +6 \times -7 \qquad \text{Multiply both sides of the equation by } +6.$$
$$+1b = +6 \times -7 \qquad \frac{+6}{+6} = +1$$
$$b = -42$$
Check: $\frac{-42}{+6} \stackrel{?}{=} -7 \qquad$ Substitute -42 for b in the original equation.
$$-7 = -7$$

▶ Think and Discuss

1. Solve and then show the check. $-2k = -8$

2. Refer to the introduction to this lesson. What was Monica's score?

3. Try to solve these equations mentally.

$$-2k = -8 \qquad \frac{h}{+3} = +5 \qquad +4l = -12 \qquad \frac{m}{-4} = +3$$

4. Why do you multiply both sides of the equation $\frac{t}{+8} = +16$ by 8 to solve it?

Exercises ▶

Solve. (See Example A.)

5. $-3p = +9$
$p = -3$

6. $-2m = +10$
$m = -5$

7. $-1n = 0$
$n = 0$

8. $+5q = -5$
$q = -1$

Solve. (See Example B.)

9. $\frac{p}{+2} = -4$
$p = -8$

10. $\frac{m}{+6} = +3$
$m = +18$

11. $\frac{n}{+6} = -3$
$n = -18$

12. $\frac{q}{-5} = -6$
$q = +30$

▶ Mixed Practice (For more practice, see page 454.)

Solve

13. $\frac{p}{-1} = -1$
$p = +1$

14. $-5m = +15$
$m = -3$

15. $+2n = 0$
$n = 0$

16. $\frac{q}{-4} = +20$
$q = -80$

17. $\frac{a}{+3} = -3$
$a = -9$

18. $\frac{b}{-7} = +2$
$b = -14$

19. $+5c = -5$
$c = -1$

20. $-1d = -4$
$d = +4$

21. $\frac{e}{+3} = -5$
$e = -15$

22. $-5f = +20$
$f = -4$

23. $+9q = -18$
$q = -2$

24. $+2h = +2$
$h = +1$

▶ Applications

25. Monica played 3 rounds of golf. In all, she was 9 below par. What was her average score?
3 below par

26. Alicia and Thomas sell homemade pastries. Every month they divide their profits equally. In June each got $457.50. What was their total profit? $\frac{x}{2} = \$457.50$; $x = \$915.00$

▶ Review (Lesson 16.8)

Solve and check each equation.

27. $3a + 7 = 31$
$a = 8$

28. $\frac{y}{9} - 13 = 7$
$y = 180$

29. $16b - 48 = 192$
$b = 15$

Pre-Algebra: Integers and Equations **387**

Alternative Examples (continued)

Example B—Solve. $\frac{w}{+7} = -8$

$\frac{w}{+7} = -8$

Multiply both sides of equation by +7.

$+7 \times \frac{w}{+7} = +7 \times -8$

$+1w = +7 \times -8$

$w = \mathbf{-56}$

Check: *Substitute −56 for w in the original equation.*

$\frac{-56}{+7} \stackrel{?}{=} -8$

$-8 = -8$

▶ Think and Discuss Answers
(see page T394)

★ Error Alert
Incorrect answers may indicate that students need to review multiplication or division of integers.

Reinforcement
Extra Practice, page 454
EP/MR Worksheet 134, TRB, page 134

Challenge
Solve the following equations. Arrange your answers in order from least to greatest. Use the corresponding letters to find out what Bonnie said at the end of the speed skating competition.

N = 222 + 79	(301)
U = 518 ÷ 37	(14)
R = 3 × (49 − 7)	(126)
B = $5^2 + 3^3$	(52)
N = (8 − 5) − ($\frac{12}{4}$)	(0)
E = (11 − 4 + 6) × 9	(117)
M = 18 + 44 − (7 × 3)	(41)
O = (−12)(−24)	(288)
A = ($\frac{54}{-6}$) + −8	(−17)
E = −132 − −446	(314)
I = $\frac{(-15 \times 14 \times -6)}{-35}$	(−36)
M = (−7 − +8) ÷ 5	(−3)

(answer: −36, −17, −3, 0, 14, 41, 52, 117, 126, 288, 301, 314, I/ AM/ NUMBER/ ONE)

Objective

- To solve Fermi problems

Purpose

When all the facts needed for a problem are not readily available, you can use the methods of this lesson to make a reasonable estimate instead of a wild guess.

Introducing the Lesson

Review estimation (Lessons 1.12, 2.6, 3.4) and planning to solve a problem (Lesson 2.5).

Answers

1. Any reasonable estimate is acceptable.
2. 60 seconds
3. Answers may range from 1 to 4 words.

17.9 Solving Fermi Problems

Every year, in January, the President of the United States speaks to the Congress. The speech is called the State of the Union Address and is broadcast on television. The President usually speaks for about 45 minutes.

1. Estimate how many words the President says in this speech.

Did you have to guess in Question 1? Guessing is one way to estimate a quantity, but sometimes it is very difficult to make a reasonable guess. In this lesson, you will learn ways to improve your estimates as you learn about Fermi problems.

In a **Fermi problem**, you are asked a question and expected to give a reasonable estimate as your answer. To form your estimate, you are only allowed to use everyday facts you already know, as well as your common sense. The problem of the President's speech can be treated as a Fermi problem.

▶ **Activity**

Working with 2 or 3 classmates. Try to solve the problem about the President's speech. The answers to the following questions use everyday facts and common sense. They will help you estimate the number of words the President spoke. In Fermi problems, you can estimate and round any of the numbers you use.

2. How many seconds are in a minute?

3. Discuss how many words the President might say each second. Decide on an estimate.

Enrico Fermi, physicist, (1901–1954)

4. About how many words would the President say in 1 minute?

5. About how many words would the President say in 45 minutes?

Notice how the questions above allow you to organize the solution to the problem. You can sometimes make a reasonable estimate to solve a problem by breaking it down into smaller problems.

6. What was your group's solution to the problem? Compare it with the solution of another group. Compare the methods used by the two groups to solve the problem.

Now you are ready to solve some Fermi problems on your own.

Exercises

For each problem below, give a reasonable estimate. In addition, outline the steps by which you reached your estimate.

7. How many times do you inhale in the course of a day?

8. How many inflated balloons could you fit in your classroom?

9. How many teenagers live in the United States?

10. How many foul balls are hit into the stands during a major-league baseball season?

11. How many dentists are there in California?

▶ **Review** (Lessons 16.4, 16.6, 16.7, 16.8)

Write as an equation. Then solve.

12. Two times twelve equals some number. $2 \times 12 = n$; $n = 24$

13. Some number divided by 13 is 4. $n \div 13 = 4$; $n = 52$

14. Seven minus three is some number. $7 - 3 = n$; $n = 4$

15. Twenty times some number is sixty. $20 \times n = 60$; $n = 3$

16. The difference between nine and three is some number.
$9 - 3 = n$; $n = 6$

17. Eighteen plus two is some number. $18 + 2 = n$; $n = 20$

18. Ten plus two times two is some number. $10 + 2 \times 2 = n$; $n = 14$

19. One plus one times some number is six. $1 + 1 \times n = 6$; $n = 5$

20. Some number times three minus twelve is thirty.
$n \times 3 - 12 = 30$; $n = 14$

Objective

• To solve equations with integers by using addition or subtraction and then multiplication or division

Purpose

This lesson shows you how to use the correct operations in the proper order to solve equations with two operations involving integers. This skill can help you use equations to solve interesting problems.

Introducing the Lesson

Review the order of operations (Lesson 3.9), operations with integers (Lessons 17.2, 17.3, 17.5, 17.6), and using inverse operations to solve two-step equations (Lesson 16.8). Use the examples: $5x + 9 = 44$ ($x = 7$); $11y - 8 = 25$ ($y = 3$).

Alternative Examples

Example A—Solve. $4n - +8 = -16$
$4n - +8 = -16$
Add +8 to both sides.
$4n - +8 + +8 = -16 + +8$
$\qquad 4n = -8$
Divide both sides by 4.
$\frac{4n}{4} = \frac{-8}{4}$
$n = \mathbf{-2}$
Check: *Substitute −2 for n.*
$4(-2) - +8 \stackrel{?}{=} -16$
$\quad -8 + -8 \stackrel{?}{=} -16$
$\qquad -16 = -16$

Example B—Solve. $\frac{y}{+2} + +7 = -14$
$\frac{y}{+2} + +7 = -14$
Subtract +7 from both sides.
$\frac{y}{+2} + +7 - +7 = -14 - +7$
$\qquad \frac{y}{+2} = -21$
Multiply both sides by +2.
$+2 \times \frac{y}{+2} = +2 \times -21$
$\qquad y = \mathbf{-42}$
Check: *Substitute −42 for y.*
$\frac{-42}{+2} + +7 \stackrel{?}{=} -14$
$\quad -21 + +7 \stackrel{?}{=} -14$
$\qquad -14 = -14$

17.10 Solving 2-Step Equations Involving Integers

Three girls started making birdhouses. Each contributed the same amount of money to buy supplies. The first week they sold 1 birdhouse for $9 but had a total loss of $15. How much did each contribute?

Examples

To solve two-step equations involving negative numbers, first add or subtract. Then multiply or divide.

A Solve. $3a + 9 = -15$

$$3a + 9 - 9 = -15 - 9 \qquad \text{Subtract 9 from both sides}$$
$$3a = -24$$
$$\frac{3a}{3} = \frac{-24}{3} \qquad \text{Divide both sides by 3.}$$
$$a = -8$$

Check: $3 \times -8 + 9 \stackrel{?}{=} -15$ Substitute −8 for *a*.
$\qquad -24 + 9 \stackrel{?}{=} -15$
$\qquad\qquad -15 = -15$

B Solve. $\frac{a}{+3} - +9 = -36$

$$\frac{a}{+3} - +9 + +9 = -36 + +9 \qquad \text{Add +9 to both sides.}$$
$$\frac{a}{+3} = -27$$
$$+3 \times \frac{a}{+3} = +3 \times -27 \qquad \text{Multiply both sides by +3.}$$
$$a = -81$$

Check: $\frac{-81}{+3} - +9 \stackrel{?}{=} -36$ Substitute −81 for *a*.
$\qquad -27 - +9 \stackrel{?}{=} -36$
$\qquad\qquad -36 = -36$

▶ Think and Discuss

1. Describe how you would solve $-2m + -3 = +3$.

2. What steps would you use to solve $\frac{t}{+2} - +2 = -3$? Solve.

3. Refer to the introduction to this lesson. How much did the three girls each pay for supplies in their first week of business?

4. Solve $+6x + (-3) = +9$ by subtracting before dividing. Then try to solve the equation by dividing before subtracting. Which method is easier? Are both correct?

▶ Think and Discuss Answers

1. Subtract -3 from both sides. Divide both sides by -2.

2. Add $+2$ to both sides. Multiply both sides by $+2$. $t = -2$.

3. $8

4. $x = +2$; subtracting before dividing is easier; both are correct; if you divide first, you must divide $+6x$ <u>and</u> -3 as well as $+9$ by $+6$

Exercises

Solve. (See Example A.)

5. $+2k + -3 = +5$
$k = +4$

6. $-3m + +1 = +10$
$m = -3$

7. $+6n - -4 = -8$
$n = -2$

Solve. (See Example B.)

8. $\frac{k}{+2} + -6 = -1$
$k = +10$

9. $\frac{p}{-4} - -2 = +5$
$p = -12$

10. $\frac{q}{-3} + +4 = +2$
$q = +6$

▶ Mixed Practice (For more practice, see page 455.)

Solve.

11. $\frac{k}{1} + -5 = +2$
$k = -7$

12. $+2m + -3 = +13$
$m = +8$

13. $-5n - -5 = -10$
$n = +3$

14. $+3p - +1 = -1$
$p = 0$

15. $\frac{r}{+4} + -4 = +4$
$r = +32$

16. $\frac{q}{-3} + +4 = -2$
$q = +18$

17. $-1w + +6 = +2$
$w = +4$

18. $\frac{h}{+3} - -5 = -3$
$h = -24$

19. $+6j - +5 = +13$
$j = +3$

▶ Applications

20. A business earned $1795 and had expenses of $262. How much did each of three partners receive if they divided the profits evenly? $511

21. Refer to the introduction to this lesson. One month, the three girls purchased $63 worth of supplies. They had a profit of $45. How many $9 birdhouses did they sell that month? 12 birdhouses

▶ Review (Lesson 3.9)

Simplify.

22. $8 \times 6 + 9 \times 6$ 102

23. $11 - 64 \div 8 + 2$ 5

24. $27 + 5 \times 8 \div 10$ 31

25. $4 \times 4 \times 4 + 36$ 100

26. $9 + (2 \times 5 \times 3)$ 39

27. $11 \times (5 + 7)$ 132

Reinforcement

Extra Practice, page 455
EP/MR Worksheet 136, TRB, page 136

Challenge

You may, from time to time, come across shortcuts for computation. To multiply a number by 5, add one zero and then divide by 2. For example, $195 \times 5 = 1950 \div 2 = 975$. To multiply by 50, add two zeros and then divide by 2. Do these rules work for negative numbers? Give an example of each to support your answer. (yes; sample examples: $-87 \times 5 = -870 \div 2 = -435$; $-29 \times 50 = -2900 \div 2 = -1450$)

Can you find a similar method for multiplying by 25? (Yes) What is it? (Add two zeros and then divide by 4) Why does it work? (Adding two zeros and then dividing by 4 is the same as multiplying by 100, and then dividing by 4, which is the same as multiplying by 25.) Give two examples of this, using a positive integer and a negative integer. (sample answers: $+17 \times 25 = +1700 \div 4 = +425$; $-3 \times 25 = -300 \div 4 = -75$)

Purpose

Formulas are equations that can be used to solve word problems containing the same information as the formula. For example, $A = l \times w$ would be used to solve word problems involving the area of a rectangle, its length, and its width. In this lesson, you learn to substitute data in formulas and solve problems.

Introducing the Lesson

Remind students that they have already learned a number of formulas in this book. Review any of the following: unit pricing (Lesson 11.4); finding simple probability (Lesson 13.2); computing odds (Lesson 13.3); finding perimeters of polygons (Lesson 14.2); finding the areas of rectangles, and parallelograms (Lesson 14.5); finding the areas of triangles, trapezoids, and circles (Lessons 14.6, 14.7, 14.8); finding surface areas (Lessons 15.3, 15.4); finding volumes (Lessons 15.5, 15.7). Ask students for examples of other formulas. (sample answers: changing Fahrenheit to Celsius, $\frac{5}{9} \times (F - 32) = C$; finding distance, $D = RT$; finding work done, $W = RT$; finding interest earned, $I = PRT$)

17.11 Using a Formula

Formulas are often used in sports. For example, to find a team's winning percentage you would use the formula:

$$\text{Winning Percentage (Pct.)} = \frac{\text{Number of wins}}{\text{Number of wins} + \text{number of losses}}$$

Look at the chart below.

Southwest Division				
Team	W	L	Pct	GB
Jackson	8	2	0.800	
Pelham	7	3	0.700	?
Kingsbridge	6	4	0.600	?
Polk	3	7	0.300	?
Flyport	1	9	0.100	?

1. How many games has Pelham High School won? How many games have they lost? How many games have they played? 7 games; 3 games; 10 games
2. Find the winning percentage for Pelham's team. Substitute information from the chart into the formula above. 0.700

Fans often want to know how far a team is from first place. In newspapers this is listed as GB, which stands for Games Behind. To find how many games behind the first-place team your team is, you can use the formula:

$$GB = \frac{(\text{wins} - \text{losses for first place team}) - (\text{wins} - \text{losses for your team})}{2}$$

For the Polk team,

$$GB = \frac{(8 - 2) - (3 - 7)}{2} = \frac{6 - (-4)}{2} = \frac{10}{2} = 5 \text{ games behind Jackson}$$

3. How many games behind Jackson is the Kingsbridge team? 2 games
4. How many games behind Jackson is the Flyport team? 7 games
5. How many games behind Jackson is the Pelham team? 1 game
6. How many games behind Jackson is Jackson? 0 games
7. Which of the four questions above were solved by using negative integers? Question 4

Shown below are the National League standings on June 28, 1999. Copy the table and complete the Pct and GB columns.

Eastern Division

	Team	W	L	Pct	GB	
	Atlanta	46	29	.613	0	
8.	New York	42	33	.560	▓	4
9.	Philadelphia	39	34	▓	6	.534
10.	Montreal	28	43	.394	▓	16

Central Division

	Team	W	L	Pct	GB	
	Cincinnati	41	31	.569	0	
11.	Houston	42	32	▓	0	.568
12.	Pittsburgh	37	39	▓	4.5	.507
13.	Chicago	36	36	.500	▓	5
14.	St. Louis	37	38	.493	▓	5.5

Western Division

	Team	W	L	Pct	GB	
	Arizona	43	33	.566	0	
15.	San Francisco	41	35	▓	2	.539
16.	Colorado	34	37	▓	6.5	.470
17.	San Diego	34	38	.466	▓	7.5

To find a pitcher's earned-run average (ERA), use the formula:

$$\text{ERA} = \frac{\text{Number of earned runs allowed} \times 9}{\text{Number of innings pitched}}$$

Copy the chart below and complete the ERA column. Round to the nearest hundredth.

	Year	Pitcher	Team	Innings Pitched	Earned Runs	ERA	
18.	1984	Alejando Pena	Los Angeles	199	55	▓	2.49
19.	1988	Joe Margrane	St. Louis	165	40	▓	2.18
20.	1992	Bill Swift	San Francisco	164	38	▓	2.08
21.	1988	Greg Maddux	Atlanta	251	62	▓	2.22

▶ Review (Lesson 8.9)

Copy and complete the table.

	Starting Time	Finishing Time	Elapsed Time	
22.	6:50 a.m.	1:45 p.m.	▓▓▓	6 hours, 55 minutes
23.	8:15 p.m.	▓▓▓	10 hours, 52 minutes	7:07 a.m.
24.	▓▓▓	7:40 a.m.	8 hours, 30 minutes	11:10 p.m.

★ Error Alert

Incorrect answers may indicate that students are not using the correct order of operations.

Problem Solving

PS Worksheet 10, TRB, pages 197–198

Challenge

Polygons can be divided into triangles by drawing diagonals, or lines, from one vertex to every other vertex. For each triangle, the sum of the three angles is 180 degrees. Look at the table; observe the pattern for the first three polygons. Use this information to complete the chart. First determine how many triangles will be formed by the diagonals. Then determine the total number of degrees in the triangles that the diagonals form.

Polygon	Number of Sides	Number of Triangles	Number of Degrees
Triangle	3	1	180
Quadrilateral	4	2	360
Pentagon	5	3	540
Hexagon	6	(4)	(720)
Octagon	8	(6)	(1080)
Decagon	10	(8)	(1440)

▶ **Think and Discuss Answers**
(from page T387)

1.
$$-2 \times k = -8$$
$$\frac{(-2 \times k)}{-2} = \frac{-8}{-2}$$
$$+1k = \frac{-8}{-2}$$
$$k = +4$$
Check: $-2 \times +4 \stackrel{?}{=} -8$
$$-8 = -8$$

2. -2, or 2 below par
3. $k = +4$; $h = +15$; $l = -3$; $m = -12$
4. because you want to get t all by itself on the left side of the equation

◢ **Answers**

(continued from page T389)
9. Accept any reasonable estimate. Steps may include estimating the fraction of the people in the United States who are teenagers and multiplying by an estimate of the population of the United States.
10. Accept any reasonable estimate. Steps may include estimating the number of foul balls per inning, per game, the number of games played per season, and so on.
11. Accept any reasonable estimate. Steps may include estimating the number of people one dentist sees in a year, the population of California, the number of times people in California see a dentist in a year, and so on.

Chapter 17 Review

REVIEW

Write true or false. (Lesson 17.1)

1. Negative numbers are located to the right of zero on a number line. False

2. The numbers 6 and 0 are opposite integers. False

3. The sum of an integer and its opposite is zero. True

Add. (Lesson 17.2)

4. $-3 + {}^+7$ +4
5. $-8 + -12$ −20
6. $+6 + {}^+16$ +22
7. $+9 + -15$ −6

8. $-13 + -5$ −18
9. $-4 + {}^+16$ +12
10. $+17 + {}^+2$ +19
11. $+1 + -1$ 0

Subtract. (Lesson 17.3)

12. $-7 - {}^+8$ −15
13. $+14 - {}^+7$ +7
14. $+11 - -8$ +19
15. $-9 - -1$ −8

16. $-20 - {}^+10$ −30
17. $+15 - {}^+5$ +10
18. $-16 - {}^+8$ −24
19. $-30 - -40$ +10

Multiply. (Lesson 17.5)

20. -3×-9 +27
21. $+9 \times -8$ −72
22. $+6 \times {}^+11$ +66
23. $-10 \times {}^+5$ −50

24. $-4 \times {}^+15$ −60
25. -2×-13 +26
26. $+12 \times -3$ −36
27. $+7 \times {}^+7$ +49

Divide. (Lesson 17.6)

28. $-64 \div {}^+8$ −8
29. $+54 \div {}^+6$ +9
30. $-28 \div -4$ +7
31. $+40 \div -8$ −5

32. $+35 \div {}^+5$ +7
33. $+56 \div -7$ −8
34. $-45 \div -15$ +3
35. $-40 \div {}^+10$ −4

Solve and check each equation. (Lessons 17.7, 17.8)

36. $b + {}^+5 = -4$ $b = -9$
37. $a - -6 = -12$ $a = -18$
38. $x - {}^+3 = +17$ $x = +20$

39. $e + -5 = +25$ $e = +30$
40. $\frac{m}{-6} = +6$ $m = -36$
41. $n \times {}^+8 = -32$ $n = -4$

42. $-5 \times r = +45$ $r = -9$
43. $\frac{z}{+9} = -9$ $z = -81$
44. $x - {}^+12 = -8$ $x = +4$

Solve and check each equation. (Lesson 17.10)

45. $-6n + (-8) = -56$
$n = +8$

46. $\frac{q}{-2} - {}^+10 = -25$
$q = +30$

47. $\frac{r}{+4} - -21 = +12$
$r = -36$

Chapter 17 Test

Multiply or divide.

1. $-5 \times +11$ — -55

2. $-93 \div -3$ — $+31$

3. $+85 \div -5$ — -17

4. $+16 \times -4$ — -64

5. $+48 \div +12$ — $+4$

6. $-77 \div +11$ — -7

7. -14×-3 — $+42$

8. $+22 \times +4$ — $+88$

9. $-32 \div -4$ — $+8$

10. $-8 \times +71$ — -568

11. -27×-18 — $+486$

12. $-63 \div +9$ — -7

13. $+19 \times -32$ — -608

14. $-11 \div -1$ — $+11$

15. $+90 \div +5$ — $+18$

Solve and check each equation.

16. $\frac{p}{-8} = -14$
$p = 112$

17. $+3m - +9 = +30$
$m = 13$

18. $c + -35 = -10$
$c = +25$

19. $\frac{w}{20} + -4 = +4$
$w = +160$

20. $y - -17 = -17$
$y = -34$

21. $a + +29 = +70$
$a = +41$

22. $\frac{r}{3} = -22$
$r = -66$

23. $-5b - -50 = +200$
$b = -30$

24. $12d = -144$
$d = -12$

25. $e - +45 = +15$
$e = +60$

26. $2s + -16 = -54$
$s = -19$

27. $\frac{c}{-18} = +6$
$c = -108$

28. $f - -18 = -27$
-45

29. $\frac{12}{z} = -2$
-6

30. $7x + +3 = -18$
-3

Complete each statement.

31. On a number line, negative numbers are to the ▊ of zero and positive numbers are to the ▊ of zero.
Left; right

32. When you multiply two negative numbers, the product is ▊. Positive

33. When you add two negative numbers, the sum is ▊.
Negative

Add or subtract.

34. $+4 - -4$ — $+8$

35. $-16 + -16$ — -32

36. $-8 - +21$ — -29

37. $+17 + -7$ — $+10$

38. $+13 + +14$ — $+27$

39. $+25 - +25$ — 0

40. $-55 - -45$ — -10

41. $-24 + +48$ — $+24$

42. $-86 + +31$ — -55

43. $-86 - -47$ — -39

44. $+307 + -112$ — $+195$

45. $-99 + -27$ — -126

Chapter Tests
Short Answer, Forms A and B, TRB, pages
331–332, 333–334
Multiple Choice, Forms A and B, TRB, pages
399–400, 401–402

Teaching Aids
Answer sheet
TA 8, TRB, page 161a
Teaching suggestions precede the
Teaching Aids worksheets.

Cumulative Test Chapters 1–17

▶ **Choose the letter that shows the correct answer.**

1. $3n = 36$
- **a.** $n = 18$
- **b.** $n = 12$
- **c.** $n = 9$
- **d.** not given

2. $50t + 8 = 13$
- **a.** $t = 5$
- **b.** $t = 25$
- **c.** $t = 11$
- **d.** not given

3. $^-9 - {}^-6 = $ ▩
- **a.** $^-15$
- **b.** $^+3$
- **c.** $^-3$
- **d.** not given

4. $n + n \times 7 = $ ▩
when $n = 6$
- **a.** 48
- **b.** 84
- **c.** 49
- **d.** not given

▶ **Find the area of each figure.**

5. circle
$r = 8$ in.
- **a.** 50.24 sq. in.
- **b.** 50.24 in.
- **c.** 200.96 sq. in.
- **d.** not given

6. parallelogram
$b = 5$ in.
$h = 9$ in.
- **a.** 14 sq. in.
- **b.** 28 in.
- **c.** 45 sq. in.
- **d.** not given

7. triangle
$b = 10$ ft.
$h = 15$ ft.
- **a.** 150 ft.
- **b.** 150 sq. ft.
- **c.** 75 ft.
- **d.** not given

8. square
$s = 12$ ft.
- **a.** 48 sq. ft.
- **b.** 144 sq. ft.
- **c.** 16 sq. ft.
- **d.** not given

▶ **Choose the letter that shows the correct answer.**

9. 2 c. = ▩ fl. oz.
- **a.** 32
- **b.** 12
- **c.** 8
- **d.** not given

10. $4\frac{1}{3}$ yd. = ▩ in.
- **a.** 13
- **b.** 42
- **c.** 52
- **d.** not given

11. 12 oz. = ▩ lb.
- **a.** $\frac{3}{4}$
- **b.** $1\frac{1}{2}$
- **c.** $\frac{2}{3}$
- **d.** not given

▶ **Write each of the following as a mathematical expression or equation.**

12. the product of thirty and five
- **a.** $\frac{5}{30}$
- **b.** $\frac{30}{5}$
- **c.** 30×5
- **d.** not given

13. 8 increased by 9 times some number
- **a.** $8 + 9 + n$
- **b.** $8 + 9n$
- **c.** $8 \times 9 \times n$
- **d.** not given

14. Eighty less than some number is fifty-four.
- **a.** $80 - n = 54$
- **b.** $n - 80 = 54$
- **c.** $80 - 54 = n$
- **d.** not given

Compute

15. -8×-7
- **a.** -56
- **(b.)** $+56$
- **c.** $+54$
- **d.** not given

16. $-54 \div +9$
- **(a.)** -6
- **b.** $+6$
- **c.** -7
- **d.** not given

17. $+25 \div -5$
- **a.** $+5$
- **(b.)** -5
- **c.** -1
- **d.** not given

18. $-4 + -5$
- **a.** $+20$
- **b.** $+9$
- **(c.)** -9
- **d.** not given

Solve.

19. Jose bought a camera on sale for 25% off. He paid $86.25. What was the original price?
- **a.** $65.19
- **(b.)** $115
- **c.** $111.25
- **d.** not given

20. Ticket sales for a concert were 550 tickets at $6.25 each. How much money was raised by ticket sales?
- **(a.)** $3437.50
- **b.** $343,750
- **c.** $343.75
- **d.** not given

21. The temperatures for the week were: $66°$, $37°$, $47°$, $45°$, $51°$, $39°$, and $37°$. What was the average temperature?
- **a.** $41°$
- **b.** $54°$
- **(c.)** $46°$
- **d.** not given

22. Paul hiked $8\frac{1}{2}$ miles the first day and $7\frac{3}{4}$ miles the second day. How far did he hike in two days?
- **a.** $15\frac{1}{4}$ mi.
- **(b.)** $16\frac{1}{4}$ mi.
- **c.** $16\frac{1}{2}$ mi.
- **d.** not given

Choose the best estimate.

23. 89×32
- **a.** ≈ 2400
- **(b.)** ≈ 2700
- **c.** ≈ 3600
- **d.** not given

24. $9.06 - 4.158$
- **(a.)** ≈ 5
- **b.** ≈ 3
- **c.** ≈ 6
- **d.** not given

25. $5,567 \div 70$
- **a.** ≈ 70
- **(b.)** ≈ 80
- **c.** ≈ 800
- **d.** not given

26. $3\frac{7}{8} + 9\frac{1}{12}$
- **a.** ≈ 12
- **(b.)** ≈ 13
- **c.** ≈ 14
- **d.** not given

Compute.

27. $8 \times \$9.39$
- **a.** $72.12
- **b.** $75.04
- **c.** $74.42
- **(d.)** not given

28. $5 - 0.057$
- **a.** $75.04
- **b.** $3943
- **(c.)** 4.943
- **d.** not given

29. $91 \div 0.13$
- **(a.)** 700
- **b.** 70
- **c.** 7
- **d.** not given

30. $15 + 4.8 + 7.96$
- **a.** 859
- **b.** 26.66
- **(c.)** 27.76
- **d.** not given

Open-Ended Questions

44. Scoring Rubric

4 explanation gives clear description of how to divide the polygon two different ways to find the area; computation is correct.

3 explanation shows an understanding of how to find the area one way; computation is correct.

2 explanation show a limited understanding of how to divide the figure, but knows the formula for area.

1 shows little or no understanding of how to solve the problem.

45. Scoring Rubric

4 gives clear explanation of why the prism will be about one-half full (volume of cylinder is 640 cm3, cube is 1331 cm3 and prism is 13503); applies all formulas correctly.

3 explanation shows some understanding of how to find volume and how full the prism will be; finds some of the volumes of the containers.

2 explanation shows limited understanding of volume; only one formula is applied correctly.

1 shows little or no understanding of how to solve the problem or apply formulas.

▶ **Choose the letter that shows the correct answer.**

31. 5650 is 113% of what number?
  a. 5000
  b. 50,000
  c. 500
  d. not given

32. $\frac{1}{2}$% of 300 is
  a. 15
  b. 150
  c. 1.5
  d. not given

33. 80% of 570 is
  a. 456
  b. 45.6
  c. 45,600
  d. not given

▶ **Solve.**

34. Jane works 6 hours on Saturdays. She earns $6.45 an hour. How much will she have earned after four Saturdays?
  a. $0.40
  b. $116.10
  c. $154.80
  d. not given

35. Sam jogs 3 miles a day during the week and 4 miles a day on Saturdays and Sundays. How far does he jog in a week?
  a. 100 miles
  b. 19 miles
  c. 20 miles
  d. not given

▶ **Complete each statement. Choose the more reasonable measure.**

36. A college basketball player is 2 ___ tall.   cm   m

37. A rock has a mass of 8 ___.   mg   kg

38. Soda is sold in 2- ___ bottles.   mL   L

39. The temperature on a hot summer day in Dallas might be 42 ___.   degrees Celsius   degrees Fahrenheit

40. An airmail letter weighs about $\frac{1}{2}$ ___.   oz.   lb.

41. A small carton of whipping cream contains 8 ___.   fl. oz.   c.

▶ **Solve.**

42. Jose earns $7.12 an hour. He works from 5 to 9 on Mondays and Wednesdays and from 11 to 4 on Saturdays. How much does he earn in a week?
  a. $92.56
  b. $91.44
  c. $158.64
  d. not given

43. Which is a better buy, $3.98 for 64 oz. of laundry soap or $2.19 for 32 oz.?
  a. 32. oz. for $2.19
  b. 64 oz. for $3.98
  c. They are equal.
  d. not given

► **Answer the following open-ended questions. Show your work on a separate sheet of paper.**

44. Find the area of this polygon two different ways. Explain each way. Show your work. Skills used—using formulas to find the area of rectangles, analyzing diagrams

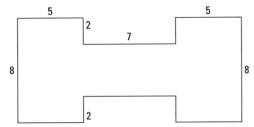

45. Danny is pouring water from the cylinder, which is full, into the cube. If any water is left over, he will pour it into the rectangular prism. About how much of the prism will be filled? Explain your answer. Skills used—using formulas to find the volumes of cubes, prisms, and cylinders, solving problems by breaking them into parts

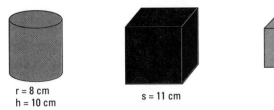

r = 8 cm
h = 10 cm

s = 11 cm

l = 15 cm
w = 10 cm
h = 9 cm

Read this problem. Then look at the equation that solves the problem.

46. Gina sells tickets to ride the giant roller coaster. The amusement park closed at 11:00 A.M. due to thunderstorms. Gina had sold 45 tickets in the morning. When it started to rain, 15 people returned their tickets for refunds. How many people actually rode? Skills used—writing and solving algebraic equations using addition and subtraction

$$n = 45 - 15$$
$$n = 30$$

Here is another equation. Write your own word problem that can be solved by using this equation. Then, solve the equation. Show your work.

$$n = 2(8) + 7$$

47. Using graph paper, plot these points on a coordinate graph.

A(3,2)
B(3,7)
C(7,6)

Connect each point to make a triangle. Multiply each coordinate by −1 and plot the new points. Connect these points to form a second triangle. What is the different about the triangles? the same? Explain how multiplication with integers made the difference. Show your work. Skills used—locating ordered pairs on a grid, multiplying integers, comparing points on a grid

Open-Ended Questions
46. Scoring Rubric
4 student-generated problem is clear and makes sense; can be solved by using the equation, which is solved correctly (23).
3 only part of the problem the student writes is related to the equation; solves equation correctly.
2 student's problem barely relates to the equation, probably because the meaning of the parentheses was not understood; solution reflects this misunderstanding.
1 shows little or no understanding of how the equation relates to a problem.

47. Scoring Rubric
4 coordinate graph shows correctly plotted triangles, both in the positive and negative; comparison is clear and complete; explanation of the product of a positive and a negative number is clear and complete .
3 coordinate graph shows positive coordinates accurately, but some computation involving multiplication with a negative number is incorrect, which interferes with the comparison; explanation of the product of a positive and a negative number is vague.
2 coordinate graph shows an effort to plot the coordinates; some are correct, but others are not, which alters the shape of the triangle, making comparison impossible; explanation of the product of a positive and a negative number is incorrect or missing.
1 student work shows little or no understanding of graphing ordered pairs in four quadrants, nor of multiplying a positive number by a negative number.

T400

Extra Practice

▶ Lesson 1.1

Find the place value of the 4 in each number.

1. 4387 — Thousands
2. 46,322 — Ten thousands
3. 809,497 — Hundreds
4. 461,003 — Hundred thousands
5. 24,028,099 — Millions

Write each number in words.

6. 9047
7. 81,502
8. 435,007
9. 600,536
10. 9,054,013
11. 755
12. 40,123
13. 109,066
14. 515,000
15. 3,330,001

Write the standard numeral.

16. 2 million, 75 thousand, 621
17. 73 million, 4 thousand, 25
18. 30 thousand, 700
19. 100 thousand, 42
20. 83 thousand, 427
21. 92 million, 761 thousand, 8
22. 6 billion, 122 thousand, 705
23. 2 thousand 19
24. 11 thousand, 900
25. 35 million, 54 thousand
26. 8 billion, 35 million, 67
27. 9 billion, 241
28. 627 million, 78 thousand, 5
29. 94 million, 375 thousand, 302

▶ Lesson 1.2

Find the place value of the 7 in each number.

1. 9.278 — Hundredths
2. 2.6457 — Ten thousandths
3. 4.752 — Tenths
4. 7.902 — Ones
5. 0.0672 — Thousandths

Write each decimal in words.

6. 4.91
7. 3.898
8. 1.0059
9. 0.066
10. 8.123
11. 9.7
12. 2.005
13. 12.17
14. 5.024
15. 3.6

Write the decimal.

16. eight and six hundredths
17. one and twelve hundredths
18. three and forty-two thousandths
19. ten and nine tenths
20. 54 hundredths
21. 78 and 91 thousandths
22. two thousandths
23. 14 and 503 thousandths
24. 338 thousandths
25. 100 and 7 hundredths
26. five and sixty-four thousandths
27. eighty-one and seven tenths
28. 3 thousand 607 and 14 ten thousandths
29. six hundred two and seventy-six thousandths

▶ Lesson 1.5

Compare. Use >, <, or = .

1. 4567 ▨ 921   >
2. 56,423 ▨ 65,423   <
3. 978,504 ▨ 987,504   <
4. 7291 ▨ 7219   >
5. 3,052,769 ▨ 4,052,869   <
6. 71,434 ▨ 71,432   >
7. 8919 ▨ 9818   <
8. 190,655 ▨ 190,566   >
9. 9762 ▨ 10,439   <
10. 36,461 ▨ 46,461   <
11. 8,003,758 ▨ 803,785   >
12. 520,388 ▨ 520,386   >
13. 89,052 ▨ 98,025   <
14. 776,321 ▨ 775,321   >
15. 144,648 ▨ 144,486   >

Order from greatest to least.

16. 3467   3476   3477   3466
17. 75,965   7695   75,956   796
18. 50,531   50,513   50,135
19. 17,749   16,750   16,748
20. 429,672   429,267   429,726
21. 5,896,420   5,896,428   589,542
22. 2,078,399   2,068,993   4,079,393
23. 4,503,255   405,955   450,255
24. 8964   894   8846   9864
25. 69,304   690,304   69,403

26. Which is higher, Mt. Everest at 29,028 feet above sea level, or Mt. McKinley, at 20,322 feet? Mt. Everest

27. Which river is shorter, the Yangtze in China (3437 miles) or the Yenisey in the USSR (3442 miles)? the Yangtze

▶ Lesson 1.6

Compare. Use >, <, or = .

1. 5.8 ▨ 9.1   <
2. 99.05 ▨ 99.50   <
3. 3.83 ▨ 3.23   >
4. 2.08 ▨ 2.0800   =
5. 4.897 ▨ 4.987   <
6. 5.3094 ▨ 5.3086   >
7. 7.452 ▨ 4.725   >
8. 9.1 ▨ 8.999   >
9. 8.700 ▨ 8.7   =
10. 5.62 ▨ 5.629   <
11. 30.7 ▨ 3.077   >
12. 4.53 ▨ 4.518   >
13. 0.02 ▨ 0.0020   >
14. 2.49 ▨ 2.398   >
15. 0.6 ▨ 6.0   <

Order from least to greatest.

16. 3.9   3.891   3.7665   3.92
17. 0.051   0.0015   0.0515   0.01
18. 4.23   4.32   4.33   4.22
19. 7.58   7.8   7.5   7.588
20. 9.1   8.7   7.9   9.9
21. 0.11   1.19   0.19   0.91
22. 5.5   4.56   6.55   4.6
23. 13.0   13.72   13.726   13.7
24. 2.04   2.004   2.4   2.404
25. 0.83   0.8139   0.81   0.819

26. Which is shorter, a race track that is 29.095 miles, or one that is 28.9 miles? 28.9 miles

27. Which route is longer, one that is 124.89 kilometers, or one that is 118.9 kilometers? 124.89 km

Extra Practice **401**

Extra Practice Answers
Lesson 1.5
16. 3477 > 3476 > 3467 > 3466
17. 75,965 > 75,956 > 7695 > 796
18. 50,531 > 50,513 > 50,135
19. 17,749 > 16,750 > 16,748
20. 429,726 > 429,672 > 429,267
21. 5,896,428 > 5,896,420 > 589,542
22. 4,079,393 > 2,078,399 > 2,068,993
23. 4,503,255 > 450,255 > 405,955
24. 9864 > 8964 > 8846 > 894
25. 690,304 > 69,403 > 69,304

Extra Practice Answers
Lesson 1.6
16. 3.7665 < 3.891 < 3.9 < 3.92
17. 0.0015 < 0.01 < 0.051 < 0.0515
18. 4.22 < 4.23 < 4.32 < 4.33
19. 7.5 < 7.58 < 7.588 < 7.8
20. 7.9 < 8.7 < 9.1 < 9.9
21. 0.11 < 0.19 < 0.91 < 1.19
22. 4.56 < 4.6 < 5.5 < 6.55
23. 13.0 < 13.7 < 13.72 < 13.726
24. 2.004 < 2.04 < 2.4 < 2.404
25. 0.81 < 0.8139 < 0.819 < 0.83

Lesson 1.7

Lesson 1.7

1. 40	**2.** 600
3. 8130	**4.** 19,660
5. 780,550	**6.** 7890
7. 35,650	**8.** 44,210
9. 500,480	**10.** 115,000
11. 80	**12.** 910
13. 2580	**14.** 58,410
15. 9,964,020	
16. 94,300	
17. 408,800	
18. 55,800	
19. 476,300	
20. 99,500	
21. 600	**22.** 1000
23. 7400	**24.** 67,600
25. 932,200	**26.** 800
27. 51,300	**28.** 29,000
29. 44,700	**30.** 3,062,500
31. 3000	**32.** 45,000
33. 68,000	**34.** 98,000
35. 506,000	**36.** 8000
37. 717,000	**38.** 20,000
39. 377,000	**40.** 239,000

Lesson 1.7

Round to the nearest ten.

1. 39 **2.** 604 **3.** 8125 **4.** 19,663 **5.** 780,552

6. 7893 **7.** 35,647 **8.** 44,211 **9.** 500,478 **10.** 114,996

11. 84 **12.** 912 **13.** 2575 **14.** 58,409 **15.** 9,964,017

Round to the nearest hundred.

16. 94,283 **17.** 408,834 **18.** 55,751 **19.** 476,272 **20.** 99,499

21. 588 **22.** 953 **23.** 7425 **24.** 67,638 **25.** 932,171

26. 818 **27.** 51,339 **28.** 28,966 **29.** 44,742 **30.** 3,062,523

Round to the nearest thousand.

31. 2699 **32.** 44,735 **33.** 67,511 **34.** 98,463 **35.** 505,949

36. 8188 **37.** 717,351 **38.** 19,802 **39.** 376,590 **40.** 239,412

Round 89,415 to the nearest

41. ten. **42.** ten thousand. **43.** thousand. **44.** hundred.
89,420   90,000   89,000   89,400

Round $44,572 to the nearest

45. thousand dollars. **46.** hundred dollars. **47.** ten dollars.
$45,000 $44,600 $44,570

Lesson 1.8

Round to the nearest whole number or dollar.

1. 7.2 7 **2.** 3.088 3 **3.** 5.501 6 **4.** $19.63 $20 **5.** 0.445 0

6. 9.83 10 **7.** $5.15 $5 **8.** $39.49 $39 **9.** 1.711 2 **10.** $2.75 $3

11. $114.89 $115 **12.** 34.5 35 **13.** 8.55 9 **14.** 805.19 805 **15.** $75.38 $75

Round to the nearest tenth or ten cents.

16. $5.86 $5.90 **17.** 6.945 6.9 **18.** 4.193 4.2 **19.** 11.025 11.0 **20.** $3.61 $3.60

21. 1.39 1.4 **22.** $0.75 $0.80 **23.** 0.052 0.1 **24.** $43.23 $43.20 **25.** 2.66 2.7

26. 73.982 74.0 **27.** 115.536 115.5 **28.** 99.949 99.9 **29.** 8.291 8.3 **30.** 23.45 23.5

Round to the nearest hundredth.

31. 3.672 3.67 **32.** 0.325 0.33 **33.** 9.9992 10.00 **34.** 6.004 6.00 **35.** 5.0773 5.08

36. 2.816 2.82 **37.** 4.0537 4.05 **38.** 7.194 7.19 **39.** 18.0054 18.01 **40.** 8.982 8.98

Round 7.2853 to the nearest

41. tenth. **42.** thousandth. **43.** whole number. **44.** hundredth.
7.3   7.285   7   7.29

Round $64.947 to the nearest

45. 10 dollars. **46.** dollar. **47.** 10 cents. **48.** 100 dollars.
$60 $65 $64.90 $100

▶ Lesson 1.9

Add.

1. 23 + 89 112	**2.** 0.654 + 0.875 1.529	**3.** 926 + 877 1803	**4.** 4.57 + 9.65 14.22	**5.** 8093 + 5867 13,960
6. 97,635 + 62,179 159,814	**7.** 9.352 + 9.967 19.319	**8.** 5677 + 5488 11,165	**9.** 35,608 + 89,543 125,151	**10.** 46.727 + 93.847 140.574
11. 5675 + 8493 14,168	**12.** 77,563 + 95,431 172,994	**13.** 3.9 + 6.5 10.4	**14.** 9.86 + 4.57 14.43	**15.** 7637 + 899 8536
16. 6.905 + 4.865 11.770	**17.** 47.56 + 38.75 86.31	**18.** 5.5087 + 7.8952 13.4039	**19.** 13,805 + 978 14,783	**20.** 15.079 + 7.951 23.030

21. 44 + 73 + 92   209
22. 403 + 6795 + 9758   16,956
23. 7.9 + 8.3 + 3.9   20.1
24. 5.6 + 8.84 + 7.96   22.4
25. 4.067 + 5 + 9.9   18.967
26. 0.38 + 0.006 + 7   7.386
27. 4.823 + 1.2295   6.0525
28. 0.765 + 0.84 + 3   4.605
29. 6743 + 0.9685   6743.9685
30. 75,403 + 9865   85,268
31. 77,925 + 95,357   173,282
32. 0.57 + 34 + 8.6   43.17
33. 66 + 87 + 29 + 58   240
34. 928 + 594 + 877   2399
35. 2.36 + 1.84 + 7   11.2
36. 5624 + 19,408   25,032
37. 0.07 + 7.77 + 77.07   84.91
38. 8 + 5.6 + 4.13   17.73

▶ Lesson 1.10

Subtract.

1. 276 − 198 78	**2.** 5.24 − 2.67 2.57	**3.** 8365 − 4676 3689	**4.** 9.631 − 6.387 3.244	**5.** 45,728 − 18,819 26,909
6. 4.16 − 1.85 2.31	**7.** 9.5 − 5.8 3.7	**8.** 8.43 − 6.87 1.56	**9.** 6.561 − 1.785 4.776	**10.** 7632 − 3986 3646
11. 19.2348 − 13.8769 5.3579	**12.** 9.24 − 7.45 1.79	**13.** 81,423 − 9,654 71,769	**14.** 9789 − 6435 3354	**15.** 7.6 − 4.4 3.2
16. 3.91 − 1.45 2.46	**17.** 33,824 − 29,956 3868	**18.** 5.6 − 3.9 1.7	**19.** 99.72 − 7.89 91.83	**20.** 4321 − 892 3429

21. 9.25 − 6.75 2.5
22. 4359 − 2467 1892
23. 6.14 − 2.22 3.92
24. 45,962 − 8973 36,989
25. 63,248 − 41,459 21,789
26. 3.4 − 2.5 0.9
27. 54.762 − 38.883 15.879
28. 15.61 − 7.85 7.76
29. 9472 − 684 8788
30. 7.6 − 5.9 1.7
31. 3255 − 699 2556
32. 427 − 99 328
33. 8.1 − 4.7 3.4
34. 452.8 − 339.9 112.9
35. 8271 − 575 7696
36. 9.78 − 3.06 6.72
37. 14.36 − 8.27 6.09
38. 2467 − 895 1572

▶ **Lesson 1.11**

Subtract.

1. 502
  − 389
  113

2. 4005
  − 1728
  2277

3. 8072
  − 7388
  684

4. 60,307
  − 22,548
  37,759

5. 70,043
  − 49,165
  20,878

6. 1.09
  − 0.16
  0.93

7. 8.0
  − 2.6
  5.4

8. 7.05
  − 6.2
  0.85

9. 2.002
  − 0.74
  1.262

10. 6.0306
  − 3.5617
  2.4689

11. 10.8052
  − 5.9678
  4.8374

12. 14
  − 6.75
  7.25

13. 407
  − 205
  202

14. 28.09
  − 8.36
  19.73

15. 2.2
  − 1.689
  0.511

16. 450.2
  − 68.04
  382.16

17. 80,060
  − 33,457
  46,603

18. 10
  − 8.5
  1.5

19. 4065
  − 1873
  2192

20. 1.075
  − 0.889
  0.186

21. 9007 − 5328 3679

22. 60,904 − 25,867 35,037

23. 90,530 − 44,682 45,848

24. 9 − 5.8 3.2

25. $34.07 − $13.75 $20.32

26. 0.4001 − 0.1976 0.2025

27. $900 − $145.89 $754.11

28. 16 − 4.783 11.217

29. $5000 − $2618 $2382

30. 7064 − 895 6169

31. 3.9 − 0.8675 3.0325

32. 46 − 9.35 36.65

33. How much greater is the distance between the Earth and the sun (93,210,000 miles) than the distance between the Earth and the moon (238,906 miles)?
92,971,094 miles

34. How much longer is the Nile River in Africa (4145 miles) than the Amazon River in South America (4006 miles)?
139 miles

▶ **Lesson 1.12**

Estimate the sum or difference.

1. 566
  + 714
  ≈1300 or ≈1280

2. 974
  − 396
  ≈600 or ≈570

3. 814
  + 852
  ≈1700 or ≈1660

4. 898
  − 607
  ≈290 or ≈300

5. 165
  + 672
  ≈900 or ≈840

6. 935
  − 212
  ≈700 or ≈730

7. 9.45
  − 5.78
  ≈3

8. 5.241
  + 8.765
  ≈14

9. 73.85
  − 15.92
  ≈58 or ≈50

10. 7.637
  + 7.927
  ≈16

11. 93.37
  − 42.57
  ≈50

12. 6.49
  + 4.53
  ≈11

13. 3089
  + 4455
  ≈7000 or ≈7600

14. 8376
  + 7903
  ≈16,000 or ≈16,400

15. 8500
  − 1298
  ≈8000 or ≈7200

16. 9833
  − 3645
  ≈6000 or ≈6200

17. 6741
  + 7499
  ≈14,000 or ≈14,200

18. 7457
  − 3809
  ≈3000 or ≈3700

19. $7.95
  + 4.26
  ≈$12.00

20. $4.07
  − 1.59
  ≈$2.00

21. 8.67
  + 9.18
  ≈18

22. 36.992
  − 27.873
  ≈9 or ≈10

23. 73.506
  + 68.747
  ≈143 or ≈140

24. 9.639
  − 8.75
  ≈1

25. 17,726
  − 9,254
  ≈9000 or ≈8400

26. 33,465
  + 21,599
  ≈55,000 or ≈50,000

27. 987
  − 76
  ≈910 or ≈900

28. $45.66
  − 16.25
  ≈$30

29. 439
  565
  + 64
  ≈1100 or ≈1070

30. $3.74
  8.89
  + 2.31
  ≈$15

▶ **Lesson 2.2**

Multiply.

1. 9862
× 5
49,310

2. 63
× 8
504

3. 777
× 4
3108

4. 369
× 9
3321

5. 3878
× 6
23,268

6. 534
× 7
3738

7. 2976
× 5
14,880

8. 95
× 3
285

9. 4895
× 9
44,055

10. 6048
× 8
48,384

11. 37
× 4
148

12. 307
× 7
2149

13. 5814
× 2
11,628

14. 88
× 9
792

15. 7009
× 0
0

16. 919
× 6
5514

17. 1954
× 3
5862

18. 69
× 9
621

19. 4075
× 8
32,600

20. 566
× 7
3962

21. 942 × 8
7536

22. 68 × 7
476

23. 535 × 4
2140

24. 999 × 9
8991

25. 4386 × 6
26,316

26. 97 × 3
291

27. 442 × 8
3536

28. 7000 × 5
35,000

29. 63 × 2
126

30. 7096 × 7
49,672

31. One box contains 356 pencils. How many pencils are in 9 boxes? 3204 pencils

32. One package contains 575 pins. How many pins are in 7 boxes? 4025 pins

▶ **Lesson 2.3**

Multiply mentally.

1. 50 × 300

2. 7000 × 700

3. 15 × 400

4. 9 × 4000

5. 70 × 60

6. 100 × 50

7. 32 × 10

8. 800 × 800

9. 1000 × 78

10. 20 × 500

11. 80 × 60

12. 10 × 996

13. 900 × 3000

14. 500 × 900

15. 600 × 500

16. 43 × 1000

17. 10 × 6589

18. 800 × 50

19. 100 × 9700

20. 400 × 400

21. 1000 × 27

22. 9 × 90,000

23. 700 × 90

24. 70 × 80

25. 100 × 84

26. 30 × 400

27. 8000 × 200

28. 763 × 1000

29. 56,432 × 10

30. 2000 × 50

31. 400 × 800

32. 4000 × 400

33. A truck carries 576 cartons. Another truck carries 100 times that many. How many does the second truck carry?
57,600 cartons

34. There are 50 envelopes in a box and there are 9 boxes. How many envelopes are there in all?
450 envelopes

35. A page of stamps contains 100 stamps. How many stamps are there on 75 pages?
7500 stamps

36. Terri drove 98 miles. Kim drove 10 times as far. How far did Kim drive?
980 miles

Extra Practice Answers

Lesson 2.3

1. 15,000
2. 4,900,000
3. 6000
4. 36,000
5. 4200
6. 5000
7. 320
8. 640,000
9. 78,000
10. 10,000
11. 4800
12. 9960
13. 2,700,000
14. 450,000
15. 300,000
16. 43,000
17. 65,890
18. 40,000
19. 970,000
20. 160,000
21. 27,000
22. 810,000
23. 630,000
24. 5600
25. 8400
26. 12,000
27. 1,600,000
28. 763,000
29. 564,320
30. 100,000
31. 320,000
32. 1,600,000

▶ Lesson 2.4

Multiply.

1. 81 $\times$ 62 = 5022	**2.** 75 $\times$ 93 = 6975	**3.** 54 $\times$ 84 = 4536	**4.** 237 $\times$ 29 = 6873	**5.** 856 $\times$ 91 = 77,896
6. 525 $\times$ 407 = 213,675	**7.** 306 $\times$ 505 = 154,530	**8.** 186 $\times$ 890 = 165,540	**9.** 771 $\times$ 573 = 441,783	**10.** 8029 $\times$ 609 = 4,889,661
11. 90 $\times$ 84 = 7560	**12.** 603 $\times$ 72 = 43,416	**13.** 5007 $\times$ 15 = 75,105	**14.** 791 $\times$ 40 = 31,640	**15.** 33 $\times$ 88 = 2904
16. 520 $\times$ 42 = 21,840	**17.** 178 $\times$ 81 = 14,418	**18.** 6000 $\times$ 46 = 276,000	**19.** 53 $\times$ 13 = 689	**20.** 805 $\times$ 409 = 329,245

21. 23×418 = 9614 **22.** 639×107 = 68,373 **23.** 75×905 = 67,875 **24.** 92×981 = 90,252 **25.** 41×552 = 22,632

26. 60×346 = 20,760 **27.** 500×649 = 324,500 **28.** 88×94 = 8272 **29.** 207×117 = 24,219 **30.** 81×235 = 19,035

31. A box contains 5250 cards. How many cards are in 18 boxes? 94,500 cards

32. An airplane seats 338 passengers. If every seat is taken, how many people fly in 410 trips? 138,580 people

▶ Lesson 2.6

Estimate each product.

1. 45 $\times$ 56 $\approx$3000	**2.** 83 $\times$ 91 $\approx$7200	**3.** 76 $\times$ 3 $\approx$240	**4.** 97 $\times$ 3 $\approx$300	**5.** 62 $\times$ 74 $\approx$4200
6. 185 $\times$ 43 $\approx$8000	**7.** 450 $\times$ 8 $\approx$4000	**8.** 917 $\times$ 66 $\approx$63,000	**9.** 872 $\times$ 49 $\approx$45,000	**10.** 833 $\times$ 6 $\approx$4800
11. 49 $\times$ 6 $\approx$300	**12.** 72 $\times$ 6 $\approx$420	**13.** 93 $\times$ 9 $\approx$810	**14.** 329 $\times$ 43 $\approx$12,000	**15.** 816 $\times$ 32 $\approx$24,000
16. 390 $\times$ 74 $\approx$28,000	**17.** 17 $\times$ 29 $\approx$600	**18.** 86 $\times$ 92 $\approx$8100	**19.** 72 $\times$ 9 $\approx$630	**20.** 38 $\times$ 7 $\approx$280

21. Carl saves $89 a month. About how much will he save in 18 months? $\approx$$1800

22. JoJo earns $167 a week during the summer. About how much can she earn in 11 weeks? $\approx$$1700 or $\approx$$2000

23. There are 65 classes at King High School. Each class has about 27 students. About how many students are in the school? $\approx$2100 students

24. There are 894 packages of paper in each carton. About how many packages are there in 511 cartons? $\approx$450,000 packages

Lesson 2.7

Multiply.

1. $\begin{array}{r} 98 \\ \times\ 4.1 \\ \hline 401.8 \end{array}$

2. $\begin{array}{r} 462 \\ \times\ 0.5 \\ \hline 231 \end{array}$

3. $\begin{array}{r} 707 \\ \times\ 9.2 \\ \hline 6504.4 \end{array}$

4. $\begin{array}{r} \$5.39 \\ \times\ 7 \\ \hline \$37.73 \end{array}$

5. $\begin{array}{r} \$26.98 \\ \times\ 3 \\ \hline \$80.94 \end{array}$

6. $\begin{array}{r} 8 \\ \times\ 0.4 \\ \hline 3.2 \end{array}$

7. $\begin{array}{r} 12.6 \\ \times\ 2 \\ \hline 25.2 \end{array}$

8. $\begin{array}{r} \$19.54 \\ \times\ 8 \\ \hline \$156.32 \end{array}$

9. $\begin{array}{r} 2 \\ \times\ 0.259 \\ \hline 0.518 \end{array}$

10. $\begin{array}{r} 2.873 \\ \times\ 5 \\ \hline 14.365 \end{array}$

11. $\begin{array}{r} 2.75 \\ \times\ 7 \\ \hline 19.25 \end{array}$

12. $\begin{array}{r} 903 \\ \times\ 0.06 \\ \hline 54.18 \end{array}$

13. $\begin{array}{r} \$8.49 \\ \times\ 17 \\ \hline \$144.33 \end{array}$

14. $\begin{array}{r} 68 \\ \times\ 4.9 \\ \hline 333.2 \end{array}$

15. $\begin{array}{r} 5.5 \\ \times\ 82 \\ \hline 451 \end{array}$

16. 3 × $55.75 $167.25
17. 1.14 × 9 10.26
18. 6 × 4.3 25.8
19. 0.209 × 7 1.463

20. 21 × $4.06 $85.26
21. 8.5 × 35 297.5
22. 99 × $1.19 $117.81
23. 7 × 3.691 25.837

24. 0.026 × 6 0.156
25. 54 × 9.03 487.62
26. 5.5 × 317 1743.5
27. $8.23 × 4 $32.92

28. 7 × 0.008 0.056
29. 452 × 3.3 1491.6
30. 2 × $89.06 $178.12
31. 0.095 × 4 0.38

32. 16 × $0.78 $12.48
33. 5 × 52.4 262
34. 4.367 × 3 13.101
35. $19.95 × 6 $119.70

Lesson 2.8

Multiply.

1. 76.5 × 100
2. 1000 × 4.5
3. 40 × 0.007
4. 0.08 × 1000

5. 10 × 0.532
6. 1.46 × 50
7. 8.9 × 700
8. 100 × 6.789

9. 72.09 × 100
10. 0.06 × 10
11. 4.9 × 1000
12. 60 × 5.5

13. 800 × $0.50
14. 1000 × $42.75
15. $99.99 × 100
16. 300 × 8.6

17. 0.326 × 100
18. 77.9 × 40
19. $0.62 × 900
20. 1000 × 3.91

21. $0.07 × 1000
22. 100 × 8.906
23. 400 × $0.40
24. 800 × 3.9

25. Yahna wants to buy 250 balloons at $0.03 each. What is the total cost? **$7.50**

26. Colored paper costs $0.08. How much will 1000 sheets cost? **$80**

27. A box of paper clips contains 100 clips. Each box cost $0.79. How much will 10 boxes cost? **$7.90**

28. Fabric is on sale for $6.99 a yard. Kim buys 20 yards. How much does she have to pay? **$139.80**

29. Henry's old car costs him $0.24 a mile to operate. How much does it cost Henry to drive 1000 miles? **$240**

30. Aluminum for recycling is bought for $0.38 a pound. How much money can you make if you sell 100 pounds? **$38**

► **Lesson 2.10**

Multiply.

1.	9.3 × 2.1 ‾‾‾‾ 19.53	**2.**	0.006 × 0.05 ‾‾‾‾ 0.0003	**3.**	1.8 × 0.9 ‾‾‾ 1.62	**4.**	7.02 × 1.95 ‾‾‾‾ 13.6890	**5.**	0.88 × 7.69 ‾‾‾‾ 6.7672
6.	5.55 × 4.4 ‾‾‾‾ 24.42	**7.**	0.091 × 6.7 ‾‾‾‾ 0.6097	**8.**	25.3 × 1.9 ‾‾‾‾ 48.07	**9.**	32.79 × 0.06 ‾‾‾‾ 1.9674	**10.**	4.4 × 2.9 ‾‾‾ 12.76
11.	8.005 × 0.4 ‾‾‾‾ 3.202	**12.**	0.381 × 1.07 ‾‾‾‾ 0.40767	**13.**	0.7 × 0.9 ‾‾‾ 0.63	**14.**	7.0 × 0.9 ‾‾‾ 6.3	**15.**	7.007 × 9.09 ‾‾‾‾ 63.69363
16.	7.0 × 9.0 ‾‾‾ 63	**17.**	9.07 × 4.009 ‾‾‾‾ 36.36163	**18.**	8.5 × 0.072 ‾‾‾‾ 0.612	**19.**	4.17 × 0.07 ‾‾‾‾ 0.2919	**20.**	2.4 × 8.2 ‾‾‾ 19.68
21.	0.905 × 2.06 ‾‾‾‾ 1.8643	**22.**	3.8 × 0.8 ‾‾‾ 3.04	**23.**	67.13 × 0.08 ‾‾‾‾ 5.3704	**24.**	1.46 × 0.56 ‾‾‾‾ 0.8176	**25.**	5.75 × 1.25 ‾‾‾‾ 7.1875

26. 9.3 × 2.1   19.53

27. 0.25 × 5.7   1.425

28. 8.8 × 0.8   7.04

29. 2.305 × 9.7   22.3585

30. 0.6 × 73.9   44.34

31. 1.14 × 2.36   2.6904

32. 8.2 × 0.5   4.1

33. 3.92 × 0.178   0.69776

34. Joel needs a piece of wood that is 2.5 times as long as a pole 1.9 meters long. How long a piece does he need? 4.75 m

35. Jenny makes $6.78 an hour. How much does she make if she works 6.5 hours? $44.07

► **Lesson 3.2**

Divide.

1. 6)594 99

2. 9)3082 342 R4

3. 8)978 122 R2

4. 3)5343 1781

5. 5)8985 1797

6. 2)145 72 R1

7. 4)652 163

8. 7)2349 335 R4

9. 6)4186 697 R4

10. 3)936 312

11. 9)4572 508

12. 5)623 124 R3

13. 8)632 79

14. 2)12,810 6405

15. 6)872 145 R2

16. 4)32,200 8050

17. 7)1295 185

18. 3)2763 921

19. 5)10,700 2140

20. 8)904 113

21. 98 ÷ 4 24 R2

22. 86 ÷ 2 43

23. 400 ÷ 8 50

24. 3192 ÷ 6 532

25. 3065 ÷ 9 340 R5

26. 609 ÷ 5 121 R4

27. 976 ÷ 7 139 R3

28. 8864 ÷ 2 4432

29. 99 ÷ 3 33

30. 2832 ÷ 4 708

31. 565 ÷ 6 94 R1

32. 7123 ÷ 8 890 R3

33. Derrick uses 2 washers for each nut and bolt he uses. How many nuts and bolts can he tighten if he has 503 washers? 251 nuts and bolts

34. Jonita is making packages of cards. Each package contains 8 cards. How many packages can she make with 456 cards? 57 packages

Lesson 3.3

Divide.

1. $6.89 \div 100$
   0.0689

2. $0.9 \div 1000$
   0.0009

3. $4752 \div 10$
   475.2

4. $0.56 \div 100$
   0.0056

5. $58,932 \div 1000$
   58.932

6. $751 \div 10$
   75.1

7. $123,495 \div 100$
   1234.95

8. $9000 \div 30$
   300

9. $400 \div 200$
   2

10. $0.16 \div 100$
    0.0016

11. $8000 \div 500$
    16

12. $7.698 \div 100$
    0.07698

13. $63,000 \div 90$
    700

14. $456,322 \div 10$
    45,632.2

15. $4900 \div 70$
    70

16. $25,500 \div 10$
    2550

17. $320,000 \div 80$
    4000

18. $7835 \div 1000$
    7.835

19. $3.6 \div 1000$
    0.0036

20. $56,000 \div 800$
    70

21. $450 \div 90$
    5

22. $3600 \div 600$
    6

23. $9.83 \div 100$
    0.0983

24. $0.075 \div 100$
    0.00075

25. $20,000 \div 500$
    40

26. $1800 \div 90$
    20

27. $5.4 \div 10$
    0.54

28. $54,000 \div 60$
    900

29. For the school dance, Lamar bought 3500 tickets in rolls of 50 each. How many rolls did he buy? 70 rolls

30. It is Cary's job to unload the boxes of books. There are 850 books. How many stacks of ten books can he make? 85 stacks

Lesson 3.4

Estimate.

1. $199 \div 19$

2. $732 \div 8$

3. $3456 \div 97$

4. $689 \div 32$

5. $60,438 \div 525$

6. $470 \div 77$

7. $399 \div 5$

8. $9875 \div 249$

9. $624 \div 7$

10. $7936 \div 38$

11. $9119 \div 29$

12. $32,228 \div 436$

13. $15,987 \div 387$

14. $808 \div 9$

15. $356 \div 41$

16. $839 \div 778$

17. $425 \div 58$

18. $2811 \div 92$

19. $742 \div 13$

20. $6399 \div 78$

21. $277 \div 18$

22. $6219 \div 329$

23. $555 \div 7$

24. $3978 \div 83$

25. $62,649 \div 888$

26. $448 \div 52$

27. $7234 \div 86$

28. $604 \div 35$

29. On a trip the Jimenez family drove 2389 miles at an average speed of 55 miles per hour. Estimate the number of driving hours it took. 40 hours

30. On a map each centimeter represents 46 kilometers. The distance between two cities is 987 kilometers. About how many centimeters would that be on the map? about 20 centimeters

Extra Practice Answers
Lesson 3.4

1. ≈ 10
2. ≈ 73
3. ≈ 35
4. ≈ 23
5. ≈ 120
6. ≈ 6
7. ≈ 80
8. ≈ 40 or ≈ 50
9. ≈ 62
10. ≈ 200
11. ≈ 300
12. ≈ 80
13. ≈ 40
14. ≈ 80
15. ≈ 9
16. ≈ 1
17. ≈ 7
18. ≈ 28 or ≈ 30
19. ≈ 70 or ≈ 74
20. ≈ 80
21. ≈ 14 or ≈ 15
22. ≈ 20
23. ≈ 60 or ≈ 80
24. ≈ 50
25. ≈ 70 or ≈ 60
26. ≈ 9
27. ≈ 70 or ≈ 80
28. ≈ 15

▶ **Lesson 3.5**

Divide.

1. $80\overline{)567}$
7 R7

2. $11\overline{)9744}$
885 R9

3. $60\overline{)960}$
16

4. $25\overline{)925}$
37

5. $31\overline{)378}$
12 R6

6. $58\overline{)600}$
10 R20

7. $20\overline{)6423}$
321 R3

8. $99\overline{)431}$
4 R35

9. $40\overline{)620}$
15 R20

10. $12\overline{)840}$
70

11. $66\overline{)6666}$
101

12. $75\overline{)1500}$
20

13. $30\overline{)8492}$
283 R2

14. $70\overline{)635}$
9 R5

15. $50\overline{)9533}$
190 R33

16. $24\overline{)1680}$
70

17. $14\overline{)1190}$
85

18. $90\overline{)873}$
9 R63

19. $20\overline{)660}$
33

20. $81\overline{)794}$
9 R65

21. $412 \div 39$ 10 R22

22. $3105 \div 69$ 45

23. $1080 \div 72$ 15

24. $250 \div 40$ 6 R10

25. $1050 \div 25$ 42

26. $1960 \div 70$ 28

27. $794 \div 60$ 13 R14

28. $3060 \div 30$ 102

29. $2250 \div 18$ 125

30. $5000 \div 42$ 119 R2

31. $998 \div 20$ 49 R18

32. $4850 \div 37$ 131 R3

33. Marbles are packaged with 35 marbles per package. How many packages can be made from 3360 marbles?
96 packages

34. Tracy collects quarters. How many quarters are in 78 dollars?
312 quarters

▶ **Lesson 3.6**

Divide.

1. $125\overline{)3875}$
31

2. $903\overline{)17,157}$
19

3. $600\overline{)31,598}$
52 R398

4. $805\overline{)4830}$
6

5. $550\overline{)12,660}$
23 R10

6. $799\overline{)15,980}$
20

7. $186\overline{)959}$
5 R29

8. $400\overline{)21,742}$
54 R142

9. $491\overline{)17,185}$
35

10. $310\overline{)9300}$
30

11. $212\overline{)1698}$
8 R2

12. $890\overline{)44,500}$
50

12. $700\overline{)28,855}$
41 R155

14. $298\overline{)3278}$
11

15. $103\overline{)721}$
7

16. $500\overline{)8590}$
17 R90

17. $86,945 \div 900$
96 R545

18. $6494 \div 191$
34

19. $7555 \div 150$
50 R55

20. $72,912 \div 300$
243 R12

21. Rubber bands are boxed in groups of 500. How many full boxes can be made from 25,125 rubber bands? 50 boxes

22. Tickets are sold in lots of 800. How many full lots are needed for a crowd of 53,629? 67 full lots

23. Prize money of $1,625,000 is divided evenly among 125 winners. How much money does each winner receive? $13,000

24. Colored paper comes in packages of 250 sheets. How many packages can be made from 60,000 sheets? 240 packages

Lesson 3.9

Simplify.

1. $4 \times (2 + 3)$ 20
2. $18 - 2 \times 3 + 4$ 16
3. $(4 \times 6) - (5 \times 2)$ 14
4. $(72 \div 8) \times 3$ 27
5. $2 \times 2 + (64 \div 8)$ 12
6. $20 \div 4 + 6 \times 6$ 41
7. $9 \times 2 + 6 - 20$ 4
8. $50 - (5 \times 5) - 1$ 24
9. $3 \times 8 + (24 \div 8)$ 27
10. $5 + (5 \times 5) - 5$ 25
11. $(5 + 5) \times 5 - 5$ 45
12. $5 - 5 + 5 \times 5$ 25
13. $19 - (16 - 8) \times 2$ 3
14. $54 \div 6 \times 8 + 3$ 75
15. $90 \div 9 + 80 \div 8$ 20
16. $14 - 4 \times (0 \times 9)$ 14
17. $2 \times 2 \times 5 \div (5 + 5)$ 2
18. $(24 + 36) \div 12$ 5
19. $32 \div 4 + 6 \times 5$ 38
20. $3 + 2 \times 5 - 7$ 6
21. $29 - 7 \times 3 + 4$ 12
22. $8 \times 7 + 15 \div 3$ 61
23. $3 \times 3 \times 3 - 14$ 13
24. $0 \times (12 \div 6 + 3)$ 0
25. $80 - 2 \times 2 \times 5$ 60
26. $9 \div 9 \times 9 - 9$ 0
27. $42 \div 6 + (4 - 2)$ 9
28. $(60 - 30) \div 5 + 4$ 10
29. $44 - 28 \div 4 \times 2$ 30
30. $12 + 35 \div 5 - 9$ 10

Lesson 3.10

Divide.

1. $16 \overline{)0.48}$ 0.03
2. $7 \overline{)2.10}$ 0.3
3. $25 \overline{)52.5}$ 2.1
4. $35 \overline{)0.315}$ 0.009
5. $8 \overline{)167.2}$ 20.9
6. $42 \overline{)37.8}$ 0.9
7. $5 \overline{)\$45.95}$ $9.19
8. $11 \overline{)0.814}$ 0.074
9. $3 \overline{)6.9}$ 2.3
10. $66 \overline{)12.54}$ 0.19
11. $9 \overline{)0.081}$ 0.009
12. $93 \overline{)6.51}$ 0.07
13. $4 \overline{)0.96}$ 0.24
14. $2 \overline{)21.8}$ 10.9
15. $15 \overline{)141.0}$ 9.4
16. $8 \overline{)\$56.32}$ $7.04
17. $51 \overline{)0.663}$ 0.013
18. $7 \overline{)0.049}$ 0.007
19. $36 \overline{)14.4}$ 0.4
20. $21 \overline{)134.4}$ 6.4
21. $109.2 \div 6$ 18.2
22. $0.748 \div 44$ 0.017
23. $98.1 \div 3$ 32.7
24. $0.207 \div 23$ 0.009
25. $0.0056 \div 7$ 0.0008
26. $10.50 \div 5$ 2.1
27. $0.666 \div 18$ 0.037
28. $294.5 \div 95$ 3.1
29. $0.0054 \div 2$ 0.0027
30. $\$74.22 \div 3$ $24.74
31. $0.008 \div 2$ 0.004
32. $1.891 \div 31$ 0.061

33. Five friends had dinner out together. The bill was $48.25. What was each person's equal share of the bill? $9.65

34. Twelve relay runners each ran an equal lap of a 57.6 mile race. How many miles did each person run? 4.8 miles

▶ Lesson 3.11

Divide. Round the quotient to the nearest tenth or nearest cent.

1. $46\overline{)89}$ 1.9
2. $13\overline{)5.8}$ 0.4
3. $5\overline{)62.7}$ 12.5
4. $3\overline{)74}$ 24.7
5. $19\overline{)557}$ 29.3

6. $4\overline{)\$34.91}$ $8.73
7. $7\overline{)88}$ 12.6
8. $4\overline{)3.21}$ 0.8
9. $11\overline{)\$56.24}$ $5.11
10. $3\overline{)\$97.63}$ $32.54

11. $25\overline{)86}$ 3.4
12. $18\overline{)488}$ 27.1
13. $34\overline{)\$560}$ $16.47
14. $21\overline{)8.7}$ 0.4
15. $3\overline{)368}$ 122.7

16. $74\overline{)\$90}$ $1.22
17. $49\overline{)39}$ 0.8
18. $8\overline{)700}$ 87.5
19. $5\overline{)0.813}$ 0.2
20. $5\overline{)\$15.72}$ $3.14

21. $\$9.89 \div 2$ $4.95
22. $3 \div 16$ 0.2
23. $4.59 \div 4$ 1.1
24. $892 \div 22$ 40.5

25. $\$89.17 \div 5$ $17.83
26. $777 \div 4$ 194.3
27. $9.41 \div 6$ 1.6
28. $\$7.79 \div 8$ $0.97

29. $38.6 \div 12$ 3.2
30. $\$46.45 \div 3$ $15.48
31. $73 \div 4$ 18.3
32. $4.96 \div 5$ 1.0

33. Seven girls chipped in together to buy a large bag of cosmetics on sale for $33.57. How much did each girl have to contribute? $4.80

34. On the class trip to Washington, 45 people ride in each bus. If 837 people have signed up for the trip, how many buses are needed? 19 buses

▶ Lesson 3.12

Divide. Round to the nearest tenth, if needed.

1. $1.7\overline{)16.83}$ 9.9
2. $1.11\overline{)6.549}$ 5.9
3. $0.02\overline{)8.36}$ 418
4. $0.5\overline{)1.265}$ 2.5

5. $4.5\overline{)9.0}$ 2
6. $1.3\overline{)16.9}$ 13
7. $0.4\overline{)0.324}$ 0.8
8. $0.08\overline{)0.3568}$ 4.5

9. $0.19\overline{)1.52}$ 8
10. $7.8\overline{)47.58}$ 6.1
11. $0.03\overline{)90.6}$ 3020
12. $0.25\overline{)1.975}$ 7.9

13. $6.4\overline{)569.6}$ 89
14. $0.6\overline{)0.738}$ 1.2
15. $1.2\overline{)66.48}$ 55.4
16. $0.81\overline{)38.07}$ 47

17. $0.01\overline{)453.8}$ 45,380
18. $4.3\overline{)4.128}$ 1.0
19. $22.2\overline{)1.554}$ 0.07
20. $0.7\overline{)26.67}$ 38.1

21. $61.1 \div 6.5$ 94.
22. $2.925 \div 0.75$ 3.9
23. $17.69 \div 2.9$ 6.1
24. $98.65 \div 0.005$ 19,730

25. $0.872 \div 0.2$ 4.4
26. $157.5 \div 3.5$ 45
27. $79.2 \div 1.8$ 44
28. $388.6 \div 0.58$ 670

29. $12.5 \div 0.5$ 25
30. $8.136 \div 4.52$ 1.8
31. $8.1 \div 6.75$ 1.2
32. $36.96 \div 0.06$ 616

33. Hilary runs 10.75 miles every five days. How far does she run each day? 2.15 miles per day

34. Henry has $33.75 in quarters. How many quarters does he have? 135 quarters

► **Lesson 3.13**

Divide. Round to the nearest tenth, if needed.

1. $0.08)\overline{64}$ 800
2. $1.5)\overline{6}$ 4
3. $8.2)\overline{41}$ 5
4. $0.45)\overline{3}$ 6.7
5. $2.4)\overline{12}$ 5

6. $1.05)\overline{84}$ 80
7. $0.03)\overline{9}$ 300
8. $2.5)\overline{5}$ 2
9. $1.5)\overline{555}$ 370
10. $0.12)\overline{48}$ 400

11. $0.7)\overline{147}$ 210
12. $6.3)\overline{315}$ 50
13. $0.01)\overline{8}$ 800
14. $4.57)\overline{914}$ 200
15. $0.75)\overline{2}$ 2.7

16. $0.6)\overline{18}$ 30
17. $0.85)\overline{255}$ 300
18. $9.1)\overline{8190}$ 900
19. $0.5)\overline{9}$ 18
20. $3.3)\overline{528}$ 160

21. $45 \div 0.2$ 225
22. $16 \div 8.35$ 1.9
23. $9 \div 0.06$ 150
24. $90 \div 0.4$ 225

25. $112 \div 2.8$ 40
26. $12 \div 2.36$ 5.1
27. $843 \div 2.81$ 300
28. $1356 \div 4.52$ 300

29. $15,536 \div 15.5$ 1002.3
30. $74,856 \div 9.02$ 8298.9
31. $400 \div 78.9$ 5.1

32. Pete drove 182 miles in his car. He used 6.5 gallons of gas. How many miles did he average per gallon of gas? 28 miles per gallon

33. The distance between two cities on a map is 540 kilometers. On a map this measures 4.5 centimeters. How many kilometers does each centimeter represent on the map? 120 kilometers

► **Lesson 4.2**

Convert each measure.

1. 73 m to mm
2. 9.9 km to cm
3. 256 mm to cm
4. 4.6 cm to m
5. 8732 m to km
6. 19.8 m to cm
7. 65.4 cm to mm
8. 0.328 km to m
9. 7243 mm to m
10. 16 m to km
11. 508 cm to mm
12. 1.89 m to mm
13. 9 cm to mm
14. 9087 mm to m
15. 5 km to cm
16. 5280 m to km
17. 0.85 m to cm
18. 5136 mm to m
19. 181 cm to km
20. 1.9 mm to cm
21. 2.4 km to cm
22. 680 m to km
23. 3737 mm to m
24. 85.4 m to cm
25. 29 cm to mm
26. 6 km to cm
27. 739 m to mm
28. 4526 cm to km
29. 97.4 cm to mm
30. 0.997 m to km
31. 164 mm to cm
32. 1000 mm to m
33. 39.5 km to cm
34. 8762 cm to mm
35. 8.05 mm to m
36. 5.51 km to m
37. 709 cm to km
38. 113 cm to m
39. 5.67 mm to cm

Extra Practice Answers
Lesson 4.2
1. 73,000 mm
2. 990,000 cm
3. 25.6 cm
4. 0.046 m
5. 8.732 km
6. 1980 cm
7. 654 mm
8. 328 m
9. 7.243 m
10. 0.016 km
11. 5080 mm
12. 1890 mm
13. 90 mm
14. 9.087 m
15. 500,000 cm
16. 5.28 km
17. 85 cm
18. 5.136 m
19. 0.00181 km
20. 0.19 cm
21. 240,000 cm
22. 0.68 km
23. 3.737 m
24. 8540 cm
25. 290 mm
26. 600,000 cm
27. 739,000 mm
28. 0.04526 km
29. 974 mm
30. 0.000997 km
31. 16.4 cm
32. 1 m
33. 3,950,000 cm
34. 87,620 mm
35. 0.00805 m
36. 5510 m
37. 0.00709 km
38. 1.13 m
39. 0.567 cm

▶ Lesson 4.3

Measure the length of each of the following to the nearest centimeter and the nearest millimeter. Answers will vary

1. your math book
2. your thumb
3. an earring
4. your pencil
5. a piece of hair
6. a carrot
7. an eraser
8. a belt
9. a shoestring
10. an envelope
11. a stapler
12. a calculator

Complete each statement. Choose the more reasonable measure.

13. A light switch is about 11 ___ long.   m   (cm)

14. A chair is about 1 ___ tall.   mm   (m)

15. A paper clip is about 3 ___ long.   mm   (cm)

16. A one-foot ruler has about 300 ___ on it.   cm   (mm)

17. A refrigerator is about 2 ___ tall.   cm   (m)

18. A box of cereal is about 26 ___ tall.   m   (cm)

19. A hockey stick is about 1.5 ___ long.   mm   (m)

▶ Lesson 4.5

Convert each measure.

1. 0.97 mg to g
   0.00097 g
2. 0.17 mg to g
   0.00017 g
3. 899 g to kg
   0.899 kg
4. 3 mg to g
   0.003 g
5. 250 g to mg
   250,000 mg
6. 75 g to kg
   0.075 kg
7. 190 mg to g
   0.19 g
8. 60.8 kg to mg
   60,800,000 mg
9. 8.98 g to kg
   0.00898 kg
10. 56 g to kg
    0.056 kg
11. 117.4 kg to g
    117,400 g
12. 0.25 mg to g
    0.00025 g
13. 400 mg to g
    0.4 g
14. 50.4 g to mg
    50,400 mg
15. 4.75 kg to g
    4750 g

Complete each statement. Choose the more reasonable measure.

16. The mass of an apple is about 250 ___ .   (g)   kg

17. The mass of a personal computer is about 18 ___ .   g   (kg)

18. The mass of a car is about 2 ___ .   kg   (T)

19. The mass of a dust particle is measured in ___ .   g   (mg)

20. The mass of a dime is about 2 ___ .   (g)   mg

21. The mass of a dollar bill is about 1 ___ .   (g)   mg

22. The mass of a large stone statue is about 3 ___ .   (T)   mg

▶ Lesson 4.6

Convert each measure.

1. 6.5 L to mL 6500 mL
2. 887 mL to L 0.887 L
3. 40 L to mL 40,000 mL
4. 99 mL to L 0.099 L
5. 2.5 L to mL 2500 mL
6. 7.85 L to mL 7850 mL
7. 4.7 L to mL 4700 mL
8. 15 L to mL 15,000 mL
9. 4.25 mL to L 0.00425 L
10. 400 mL to L 0.4 L
11. 37 L to mL 37,000 mL
12. 0.98 L to mL 980 mL
13. 4.18 L to mL 4180 mL
14. 20.88 mL to L 0.02088 L
15. 100.6 mL to L 0.1006 L

Complete each statement. Choose the more reasonable measure.

16. Harvey bought 30 _____ of gas for his car.   mL (L)

17. A graduated cylinder contains 100 _____ of liquid. (mL) L

18. The chef added 4 _____ of anise flavoring to the cookie dough. (mL) L

19. The decorator bought 75 _____ of paint for the new building.   mL (L)

20. Each hiker carried a _____ of water in her canteen.   mL (L)

21. Joan bought a 1 _____ container of orange juice.   mL (L)

22. He gave her 50 _____ of perfume for her birthday. (mL) L

23. A large bottle of soy sauce contains 592 _____ . (mL) L

▶ Lesson 5.2 Answers may vary. Suggested answers are given.

Find 3 fractions equivalent to each fraction.

1. $\frac{3}{4}$
2. $\frac{11}{12}$
3. $\frac{7}{9}$
4. $\frac{12}{8}$
5. $\frac{2}{5}$
6. $\frac{3}{16}$
7. $\frac{4}{15}$
8. $\frac{10}{9}$
9. $\frac{3}{8}$
10. $\frac{5}{2}$
11. $\frac{5}{16}$
12. $\frac{9}{10}$

Find a fraction equivalent to each fraction.

13. $\frac{5}{10}$ $\frac{1}{2}$
14. $\frac{15}{25}$ $\frac{3}{5}$
15. $\frac{6}{9}$ $\frac{2}{3}$
16. $\frac{8}{12}$ $\frac{2}{3}$
17. $\frac{3}{12}$ $\frac{1}{4}$
18. $\frac{21}{30}$ $\frac{7}{10}$

19. $\frac{15}{45}$ $\frac{3}{9}$ or $\frac{1}{3}$
20. $\frac{20}{32}$ $\frac{10}{16}$ or $\frac{5}{8}$
21. $\frac{20}{60}$ $\frac{1}{3}$
22. $\frac{15}{20}$ $\frac{3}{4}$
23. $\frac{18}{15}$ $\frac{6}{5}$
24. $\frac{56}{64}$ $\frac{7}{8}$

25. $\frac{3}{9}$ $\frac{1}{3}$
26. $\frac{18}{36}$ $\frac{1}{2}$
27. $\frac{25}{40}$ $\frac{5}{8}$
28. $\frac{9}{27}$ $\frac{1}{3}$
29. $\frac{40}{30}$ $\frac{4}{3}$
30. $\frac{9}{15}$ $\frac{3}{5}$

31. $\frac{20}{50}$ $\frac{2}{5}$
32. $\frac{24}{18}$ $\frac{4}{3}$
33. $\frac{30}{100}$ $\frac{3}{10}$
34. $\frac{6}{24}$ $\frac{1}{4}$
35. $\frac{5}{30}$ $\frac{1}{6}$
36. $\frac{15}{50}$ $\frac{3}{10}$

37. $\frac{12}{9}$ $\frac{4}{3}$
38. $\frac{15}{30}$ $\frac{1}{2}$
39. $\frac{18}{10}$ $\frac{9}{5}$
40. $\frac{25}{30}$ $\frac{5}{6}$
41. $\frac{21}{24}$ $\frac{7}{8}$
42. $\frac{2}{16}$ $\frac{1}{8}$

43. $\frac{16}{14}$ $\frac{8}{7}$
44. $\frac{10}{16}$ $\frac{5}{8}$
45. $\frac{6}{10}$ $\frac{3}{5}$
46. $\frac{9}{18}$ $\frac{1}{2}$
47. $\frac{45}{25}$ $\frac{9}{5}$
48. $\frac{9}{6}$ $\frac{3}{2}$

Extra Practice Answers

Lesson 5.2

1. $\frac{6}{8}, \frac{9}{12}, \frac{12}{16}$, etc.
2. $\frac{22}{24}, \frac{33}{36}, \frac{44}{48}$, etc.
3. $\frac{14}{18}, \frac{21}{27}, \frac{28}{36}$, etc.
4. $\frac{3}{2}, \frac{6}{4}, \frac{24}{16}$, etc.
5. $\frac{4}{10}, \frac{6}{15}, \frac{8}{20}$, etc.
6. $\frac{6}{32}, \frac{9}{48}, \frac{12}{64}$, etc.
7. $\frac{8}{30}, \frac{12}{45}, \frac{16}{60}$, etc.
8. $\frac{20}{18}, \frac{30}{27}, \frac{40}{36}$, etc.
9. $\frac{6}{16}, \frac{9}{24}, \frac{12}{32}$, etc.
10. $\frac{10}{4}, \frac{15}{6}, \frac{20}{8}$, etc.
11. $\frac{10}{32}, \frac{15}{48}, \frac{20}{64}$, etc.
12. $\frac{18}{20}, \frac{27}{30}, \frac{36}{40}$, etc.

▶ Lesson 5.3

Write each improper fraction as a whole or mixed number.

1. $\frac{9}{8}$ $1\frac{1}{8}$
2. $\frac{13}{2}$ $6\frac{1}{2}$
3. $\frac{5}{5}$ 1
4. $\frac{61}{8}$ $7\frac{5}{8}$
5. $\frac{4}{4}$ 1
6. $\frac{23}{4}$ $5\frac{3}{4}$

7. $\frac{57}{8}$ $7\frac{1}{8}$
8. $\frac{21}{12}$ $1\frac{9}{12}$ or $1\frac{3}{4}$
9. $\frac{19}{8}$ $2\frac{3}{8}$
10. $\frac{3}{3}$ 1
11. $\frac{17}{10}$ $1\frac{7}{10}$
12. $\frac{15}{6}$ $2\frac{3}{6}$ or $2\frac{1}{2}$

13. $\frac{10}{10}$ 1
14. $\frac{15}{4}$ $3\frac{3}{4}$
15. $\frac{18}{6}$ 3
16. $\frac{12}{5}$ $2\frac{2}{5}$
17. $\frac{82}{9}$ $9\frac{1}{9}$
18. $\frac{30}{5}$ 6

19. $\frac{9}{9}$ 1
20. $\frac{16}{2}$ 8
21. $\frac{11}{3}$ $3\frac{2}{3}$
22. $\frac{20}{4}$ 5
23. $\frac{19}{19}$ 1
24. $\frac{22}{3}$ $7\frac{1}{3}$

Write each mixed or whole number as an improper fraction.

25. $4\frac{1}{6}$
26. 8
27. 6
28. $8\frac{1}{9}$
29. $6\frac{7}{10}$
30. $25\frac{3}{4}$

31. $2\frac{7}{9}$
32. $4\frac{2}{3}$
33. $3\frac{5}{6}$
34. 22
35. $3\frac{3}{8}$
36. $10\frac{7}{9}$

37. 12
38. $5\frac{2}{9}$
39. $3\frac{5}{12}$
40. $5\frac{9}{10}$
41. $2\frac{5}{6}$
42. $6\frac{1}{6}$

43. $2\frac{1}{4}$
44. 20
45. $4\frac{2}{5}$
46. $1\frac{3}{16}$
47. 15
48. $2\frac{8}{9}$

▶ Lesson 5.4

Compare. Use $<$, $>$, or $=$.

1. $\frac{5}{8}$ ▨ $\frac{2}{3}$ $<$
2. $\frac{1}{2}$ ▨ $\frac{10}{20}$ $=$
3. $\frac{9}{10}$ ▨ $\frac{7}{10}$ $>$
4. $\frac{1}{8}$ ▨ $\frac{1}{5}$ $<$

5. $\frac{2}{3}$ ▨ $\frac{10}{15}$ $=$
6. $\frac{3}{10}$ ▨ $\frac{2}{5}$ $<$
7. $2\frac{1}{2}$ ▨ $\frac{3}{2}$ $>$
8. $3\frac{3}{4}$ ▨ $2\frac{3}{4}$ $>$

9. $\frac{1}{3}$ ▨ $\frac{5}{6}$ $<$
10. $\frac{7}{8}$ ▨ $\frac{14}{16}$ $=$
11. $9\frac{2}{9}$ ▨ $5\frac{7}{9}$ $>$
12. $\frac{3}{16}$ ▨ $\frac{11}{16}$ $<$

13. $\frac{4}{9}$ ▨ $\frac{1}{9}$ $>$
14. $3\frac{1}{3}$ ▨ $3\frac{7}{10}$ $<$
15. $\frac{15}{4}$ ▨ $\frac{15}{16}$ $>$
16. $\frac{8}{8}$ ▨ $\frac{3}{3}$ $=$

17. $2\frac{1}{6}$ ▨ $2\frac{1}{5}$ $<$
18. $\frac{16}{8}$ ▨ $\frac{10}{20}$ $>$
19. $\frac{4}{5}$ ▨ $\frac{7}{10}$ $>$
20. $\frac{5}{20}$ ▨ $\frac{1}{4}$ $=$

21. $\frac{15}{25}$ ▨ $\frac{2}{5}$ $>$
22. $\frac{7}{12}$ ▨ $\frac{5}{12}$ $>$
23. $\frac{5}{8}$ ▨ $1\frac{3}{8}$ $<$
24. $\frac{14}{20}$ ▨ $\frac{9}{10}$ $<$

25. $3\frac{6}{9}$ ▨ $3\frac{1}{3}$ $>$
26. $\frac{7}{8}$ ▨ $\frac{3}{8}$ $>$
27. $6\frac{1}{6}$ ▨ $6\frac{5}{6}$ $<$
28. $4\frac{1}{2}$ ▨ $3\frac{7}{9}$ $>$

29. $\frac{7}{16}$ ▨ $\frac{15}{16}$ $<$
30. $\frac{5}{5}$ ▨ $\frac{9}{9}$ $=$
31. $\frac{25}{3}$ ▨ $8\frac{1}{3}$ $=$
32. $\frac{5}{6}$ ▨ $\frac{4}{5}$ $>$

33. 4 ▨ $\frac{16}{4}$ $=$
34. $2\frac{1}{8}$ ▨ $2\frac{1}{6}$ $<$
35. $1\frac{4}{5}$ ▨ $\frac{9}{6}$ $>$
36. $\frac{11}{12}$ ▨ $\frac{9}{8}$ $<$

37. $2\frac{3}{4}$ ▨ $\frac{11}{3}$ $<$
38. $7\frac{2}{3}$ ▨ $9\frac{2}{3}$ $<$
39. $\frac{15}{5}$ ▨ 3 $=$
40. $\frac{3}{4}$ ▨ $\frac{9}{12}$ $=$

► **Lesson 5.5**

List the factors.

1. 9	**2.** 21	**3.** 30	**4.** 25	**5.** 7	**6.** 24
7. 19	**8.** 5	**9.** 45	**10.** 50	**11.** 28	**12.** 11

Find the GCF of each pair of numbers.

13. 3 6 3	**14.** 10 25 5	**15.** 8 24 8	**16.** 45 10 5	**17.** 9 30 3
18. 15 5 5	**19.** 40 60 20	**20.** 7 21 7	**21.** 5 4 1	**22.** 13 39 13
23. 8 16 8	**24.** 8 18 2	**25.** 18 6 6	**26.** 21 28 7	**27.** 50 30 10
28. 14 7 7	**29.** 17 2 1	**30.** 55 11 11	**31.** 10 26 2	**32.** 42 14 14
33. 5 30 5	**34.** 8 9 1	**35.** 18 15 3	**36.** 20 19 1	**37.** 12 9 3
38. 32 64 32	**39.** 24 60 12	**40.** 49 63 7	**41.** 25 100 25	**42.** 19 29 1
43. 30 45 15	**44.** 34 17 17	**45.** 12 15 3	**46.** 35 85 5	**47.** 29 43 1

► **Lesson 5.6**

Write in lowest terms.

1. $\frac{10}{15}$ $\frac{2}{3}$	**2.** $\frac{30}{40}$ $\frac{3}{4}$	**3.** $\frac{25}{125}$ $\frac{1}{5}$	**4.** $\frac{50}{75}$ $\frac{2}{3}$	**5.** $\frac{18}{22}$ $\frac{9}{11}$	**6.** $\frac{35}{45}$ $\frac{7}{9}$
7. $\frac{25}{30}$ $\frac{5}{6}$	**8.** $\frac{6}{36}$ $\frac{1}{6}$	**9.** $\frac{10}{50}$ $\frac{1}{5}$	**10.** $\frac{55}{10}$ $\frac{11}{2}$	**11.** $\frac{9}{30}$ $\frac{3}{10}$	**12.** $\frac{9}{24}$ $\frac{3}{8}$
13. $\frac{15}{12}$ $\frac{5}{4}$	**14.** $\frac{9}{6}$ $\frac{3}{2}$	**15.** $\frac{6}{8}$ $\frac{3}{4}$	**16.** $\frac{10}{4}$ $\frac{5}{2}$	**17.** $\frac{12}{9}$ $\frac{4}{3}$	**18.** $\frac{5}{15}$ $\frac{1}{3}$
19. $\frac{12}{48}$ $\frac{1}{4}$	**20.** $\frac{35}{25}$ $\frac{7}{5}$	**21.** $\frac{25}{75}$ $\frac{1}{3}$	**22.** $\frac{14}{16}$ $\frac{7}{8}$	**23.** $\frac{20}{45}$ $\frac{4}{9}$	**24.** $\frac{14}{12}$ $\frac{7}{6}$
25. $\frac{14}{4}$ $\frac{7}{2}$	**26.** $\frac{20}{30}$ $\frac{2}{3}$	**27.** $\frac{32}{36}$ $\frac{8}{9}$	**28.** $\frac{13}{26}$ $\frac{1}{2}$	**29.** $\frac{50}{6}$ $\frac{25}{3}$	**30.** $\frac{16}{24}$ $\frac{2}{3}$
31. $\frac{36}{30}$ $\frac{6}{5}$	**32.** $\frac{14}{21}$ $\frac{2}{3}$	**33.** $\frac{8}{48}$ $\frac{1}{6}$	**34.** $\frac{6}{48}$ $\frac{1}{8}$	**35.** $\frac{20}{25}$ $\frac{4}{5}$	**36.** $\frac{40}{36}$ $\frac{10}{9}$

List the factors and write in lowest terms.

37. $\frac{4}{9}$	**38.** $\frac{13}{15}$	**39.** $\frac{7}{8}$	**40.** $\frac{11}{25}$	**41.** $\frac{5}{28}$	**42.** $\frac{3}{16}$
43. $\frac{15}{19}$	**44.** $\frac{5}{12}$	**45.** $\frac{3}{40}$	**46.** $\frac{16}{25}$	**47.** $\frac{9}{8}$	**48.** $\frac{14}{17}$
49. $\frac{30}{11}$	**50.** $\frac{7}{24}$	**51.** $\frac{9}{4}$	**52.** $\frac{6}{5}$	**53.** $\frac{27}{35}$	**54.** $\frac{15}{32}$

Extra Practice Answers
Lesson 5.5

1. 1, 3, 9
2. 1, 3, 7, 21
3. 1, 2, 3, 5, 6, 10, 15, 30
4. 1, 5, 25
5. 1, 7
6. 1, 2, 3, 4, 6, 8, 12, 24
7. 1, 19
8. 1, 5
9. 1, 3, 5, 9, 15, 45
10. 1, 2, 5, 10, 25, 50
11. 1, 2, 4, 7, 14, 28
12. 1, 11

Extra Practice Answers
Lesson 5.6

37. 4: 1, 2, 4; 9: 1, 3, 9; $\frac{4}{9}$
38. 13: 1, 13; 15: 1, 3, 5, 15; $\frac{13}{15}$
39. 7: 1, 7; 8: 1, 2, 4, 8; $\frac{7}{8}$
40. 11: 1, 11; 25: 1, 5, 25; $\frac{11}{25}$
41. 5: 1, 5; 28: 1, 2, 4, 7, 14, 28; $\frac{5}{28}$
42. 3: 1, 3; 16: 1, 2, 4, 8, 16; $\frac{3}{16}$
43. 15: 1, 3, 5, 15; 19: 1, 19; $\frac{15}{19}$
44. 5: 1, 5; 12: 1, 2, 3, 4, 6, 12; $\frac{5}{12}$
45. 3: 1, 3; 40: 1, 2, 4, 5, 8, 10, 20, 40; $\frac{3}{40}$
46. 16: 1, 2, 4, 8, 16; 25: 1, 5, 25: $\frac{16}{25}$
47. 9: 1, 3, 9; 8: 1, 2, 4, 8; $\frac{9}{8}$
48. 14: 1, 2, 7, 14; 17: 1, 17; $\frac{14}{17}$
49. 30: 1, 2, 3, 5, 6, 10, 15, 30; 11: 1, 11; $\frac{30}{11}$
50. 7: 1, 7; 24: 1, 2, 3, 4, 6, 8, 12, 24; $\frac{7}{24}$
51. 9: 1, 3, 9; 4: 1, 2, 4; $\frac{9}{4}$
52. 6: 1, 2, 3, 6; 5: 1, 5; $\frac{6}{5}$
53. 27: 1, 3, 9, 27; 35: 1, 5, 7, 35; $\frac{27}{35}$
54. 15: 1, 3, 5, 15; 32: 1, 2, 4, 8, 16, 32; $\frac{15}{32}$

▶ Lesson 5.7

Convert each fraction to a decimal and each decimal to a fraction.

1. $\frac{13}{15}$ 0.8$\overline{6}$
2. 0.6 $\frac{3}{5}$
3. 0.035 $\frac{7}{200}$
4. $\frac{13}{20}$ 0.65
5. $\frac{4}{9}$ 0.$\overline{4}$
6. 0.04 $\frac{1}{25}$

7. $\frac{2}{15}$ 0.1$\overline{3}$
8. $\frac{21}{100}$ 0.21
9. $\frac{1}{6}$ 0.1$\overline{6}$
10. $\frac{1}{30}$ 0.0$\overline{3}$
11. 0.8 $\frac{4}{5}$
12. 0.08 $\frac{2}{25}$

13. $\frac{3}{8}$ 0.375
14. $\frac{19}{20}$ 0.95
15. 0.85 $\frac{17}{20}$
16. 0.1 $\frac{1}{10}$
17. $\frac{6}{11}$ 0.$\overline{54}$
18. $\frac{1}{5}$ 0.2

19. $\frac{5}{8}$ 0.625
20. $\frac{1}{8}$ 0.125
21. 0.875 $\frac{7}{8}$
22. 0.98 $\frac{49}{50}$
23. 0.255 $\frac{51}{200}$
24. 0.148 $\frac{37}{250}$

25. 0.011 $\frac{11}{1000}$
26. 0.002 $\frac{1}{500}$
27. $\frac{3}{11}$ 0.$\overline{27}$
28. $\frac{5}{16}$ 0.3125
29. 0.2 $\frac{1}{5}$
30. $\frac{5}{9}$ 0.$\overline{5}$

31. $\frac{10}{11}$ 0.$\overline{90}$
32. $\frac{5}{12}$ 0.41$\overline{6}$
33. 0.76 $\frac{19}{25}$
34. 0.041 $\frac{41}{1000}$
35. 0.199 $\frac{199}{1000}$
36. $\frac{2}{9}$ 0.$\overline{2}$

37. 0.4 $\frac{2}{5}$
38. 0.007 $\frac{7}{1000}$
39. $\frac{7}{15}$ 0.4$\overline{6}$
40. $\frac{1}{16}$ 0.0625
41. 0.097 $\frac{97}{1000}$
42. $\frac{1}{12}$ 0.83$\overline{}$

43. 0.03 $\frac{3}{100}$
44. $\frac{1}{9}$ 0.$\overline{1}$
45. 0.3 $\frac{3}{10}$
46. $\frac{11}{12}$ 0.91$\overline{6}$
47. 0.33 $\frac{33}{100}$
48. 0.44 $\frac{11}{25}$

49. $\frac{11}{15}$ 0.7$\overline{3}$
50. $\frac{13}{50}$ 0.26
51. 0.009 $\frac{9}{1000}$
52. 0.28 $\frac{7}{25}$
53. $\frac{14}{15}$ 0.9$\overline{3}$
54. 0.999 $\frac{999}{1000}$

▶ Lesson 6.1

Multiply. Write the answers in lowest terms.

1. $5 \times \frac{2}{3}$ 3$\frac{1}{3}$
2. $\frac{2}{3} \times \frac{2}{3}$ $\frac{4}{9}$
3. $\frac{5}{6} \times \frac{1}{8}$ $\frac{5}{48}$
4. $2 \times \frac{7}{8}$ 1$\frac{3}{4}$

5. $11 \times \frac{2}{9}$ 2$\frac{4}{9}$
6. $\frac{1}{6} \times \frac{3}{4}$ $\frac{1}{8}$
7. $\frac{2}{5} \times \frac{3}{4}$ $\frac{3}{10}$
8. $8 \times \frac{5}{6}$ 6$\frac{2}{3}$

9. $\frac{1}{8} \times \frac{1}{9}$ $\frac{1}{72}$
10. $4 \times \frac{5}{12}$ 1$\frac{2}{3}$
11. $12 \times \frac{1}{5}$ 2$\frac{2}{5}$
12. $\frac{4}{5} \times \frac{4}{9}$ $\frac{16}{45}$

13. $\frac{1}{16} \times \frac{1}{2}$ $\frac{1}{32}$
14. $7 \times \frac{4}{7}$ 4
15. $\frac{3}{8} \times \frac{2}{3}$ $\frac{1}{4}$
16. $\frac{5}{6} \times \frac{2}{3}$ $\frac{5}{9}$

17. $3 \times \frac{1}{9}$ $\frac{1}{3}$
18. $\frac{3}{5} \times \frac{3}{8}$ $\frac{9}{40}$
19. $\frac{3}{4} \times \frac{1}{5}$ $\frac{3}{20}$
20. $6 \times \frac{7}{8}$ 5$\frac{1}{4}$

21. $\frac{1}{8} \times \frac{5}{9}$ $\frac{5}{72}$
22. $\frac{3}{16} \times \frac{1}{4}$ $\frac{3}{64}$
23. $\frac{7}{9} \times \frac{2}{3}$ $\frac{14}{27}$
24. $2 \times \frac{4}{5}$ 1$\frac{3}{5}$

25. $3 \times \frac{5}{8}$ 1$\frac{7}{8}$
26. $\frac{2}{3} \times \frac{5}{12}$ $\frac{5}{18}$
27. $\frac{3}{4} \times \frac{1}{8}$ $\frac{3}{32}$
28. $13 \times \frac{1}{4}$ 3$\frac{1}{4}$

29. $\frac{7}{12} \times \frac{1}{10}$ $\frac{7}{120}$
30. $\frac{3}{10} \times \frac{1}{5}$ $\frac{3}{50}$
31. $10 \times \frac{7}{9}$ 7$\frac{7}{9}$
32. $\frac{1}{9} \times \frac{2}{5}$ $\frac{2}{45}$

33. A rice salad recipe uses 3 cups of rice and serves 12 people. How much rice would you use if you made $\frac{1}{2}$ the recipe? 1$\frac{1}{2}$ cups

34. Sam is a terrific basketball player. He makes $\frac{2}{3}$ of all the baskets he attempts. How many baskets does he make if he attempts 36 shots? 24 baskets

Lesson 6.2

Multiply. Write the answers in lowest terms.

1. $\frac{7}{8} \times \frac{6}{9}$ $\frac{7}{12}$

2. $\frac{5}{8} \times \frac{3}{10}$ $\frac{3}{16}$

3. $\frac{4}{5} \times \frac{1}{6}$ $\frac{2}{15}$

4. $\frac{9}{10} \times \frac{5}{12}$ $\frac{3}{8}$

5. $\frac{6}{10} \times \frac{7}{14}$ $\frac{3}{10}$

6. $\frac{1}{8} \times \frac{4}{5}$ $\frac{1}{10}$

7. $\frac{2}{9} \times \frac{3}{16}$ $\frac{1}{24}$

8. $\frac{1}{6} \times \frac{3}{8}$ $\frac{1}{16}$

9. $\frac{7}{10} \times \frac{5}{12}$ $\frac{7}{24}$

10. $\frac{5}{9} \times \frac{3}{5}$ $\frac{1}{3}$

11. $\frac{1}{12} \times \frac{9}{16}$ $\frac{3}{64}$

12. $\frac{11}{16} \times \frac{8}{9}$ $\frac{11}{18}$

13. $\frac{5}{6} \times \frac{1}{5}$ $\frac{1}{6}$

14. $\frac{4}{9} \times \frac{1}{2}$ $\frac{2}{9}$

15. $\frac{5}{16} \times \frac{4}{5}$ $\frac{1}{4}$

16. $\frac{2}{3} \times \frac{9}{16}$ $\frac{3}{8}$

17. $\frac{1}{12} \times \frac{4}{9}$ $\frac{1}{27}$

18. $\frac{3}{5} \times \frac{15}{16}$ $\frac{9}{16}$

19. $\frac{1}{4} \times \frac{4}{9}$ $\frac{1}{9}$

20. $\frac{5}{6} \times \frac{3}{10}$ $\frac{1}{4}$

21. $\frac{11}{12} \times \frac{4}{5}$ $\frac{11}{15}$

22. $\frac{5}{16} \times \frac{2}{5}$ $\frac{1}{8}$

23. $\frac{5}{8} \times \frac{9}{10}$ $\frac{9}{16}$

24. $\frac{4}{5} \times \frac{7}{16}$ $\frac{7}{20}$

25. $\frac{6}{8} \times \frac{3}{12}$ $\frac{3}{16}$

26. $\frac{14}{16} \times \frac{8}{28}$ $\frac{1}{4}$

27. $\frac{5}{7} \times \frac{35}{45}$ $\frac{5}{9}$

28. $\frac{10}{15} \times \frac{20}{50}$ $\frac{4}{15}$

29. Pablo sold $\frac{4}{5}$ of the tickets to the school carnival. Students bought $\frac{5}{8}$ of the tickets he sold. What fraction of the tickets were bought by students? $\frac{1}{2}$ of the tickets

30. Half of the students at North High School work on Saturdays. Two-fifths of those who work also play on a school team. What fraction of the students work and play on a team? $\frac{1}{5}$ of the students

Lesson 6.4

Multiply. Write the answers in lowest terms.

1. $2\frac{2}{9} \times 1\frac{4}{5}$ 4

2. $9\frac{1}{2} \times \frac{1}{8}$ $1\frac{3}{16}$

3. $6 \times 2\frac{3}{10}$ $13\frac{4}{5}$

4. $4\frac{1}{8} \times 2\frac{2}{3}$ 11

5. $1\frac{15}{16} \times 8$ $15\frac{1}{2}$

6. $2\frac{5}{8} \times 1\frac{1}{5}$ $3\frac{3}{20}$

7. $\frac{7}{12} \times 3\frac{3}{4}$ $2\frac{3}{16}$

8. $5\frac{1}{3} \times \frac{7}{8}$ $4\frac{2}{3}$

9. $1\frac{1}{10} \times \frac{14}{15}$ $1\frac{2}{75}$

10. $3\frac{1}{9} \times 1\frac{3}{4}$ $5\frac{4}{9}$

11. $8\frac{5}{8} \times 1\frac{1}{3}$ $11\frac{1}{2}$

12. $\frac{9}{16} \times 2\frac{3}{4}$ $1\frac{35}{64}$

13. $5\frac{5}{6} \times 3$ $17\frac{1}{2}$

14. $5 \times 4\frac{9}{10}$ $24\frac{1}{2}$

15. $\frac{4}{5} \times 7\frac{2}{9}$ $5\frac{7}{9}$

16. $\frac{11}{12} \times 3\frac{3}{10}$ $3\frac{1}{40}$

17. $1\frac{1}{16} \times 3\frac{1}{5}$ $3\frac{2}{5}$

18. $3\frac{5}{9} \times \frac{3}{8}$ $1\frac{1}{3}$

19. $6\frac{2}{9} \times 1\frac{4}{5}$ $11\frac{1}{5}$

20. $1\frac{1}{3} \times \frac{3}{16}$ $\frac{1}{4}$

21. $4\frac{1}{2} \times \frac{2}{9}$ 1

22. $3\frac{3}{5} \times 1\frac{2}{3}$ 6

23. $2\frac{1}{6} \times 2$ $4\frac{1}{3}$

24. $\frac{2}{5} \times 2\frac{1}{12}$ $\frac{5}{6}$

25. $5\frac{1}{3} \times 2\frac{7}{16}$ 13

26. $4\frac{3}{4} \times 3\frac{1}{5}$ $15\frac{1}{5}$

27. $10\frac{2}{3} \times 1\frac{1}{2}$ 16

28. $14 \times 1\frac{3}{8}$ $19\frac{1}{4}$

29. A pizza recipe uses $1\frac{2}{3}$ cups of sliced mushrooms. How many cups do you need for 8 pizzas? $13\frac{1}{3}$ cups

30. Kiri uses $2\frac{1}{2}$ yards of ribbon for each yard of fabric. How much ribbon does she need for $4\frac{2}{3}$ yards of fabric? $11\frac{2}{3}$ yards

▶ Lesson 6.6

Find the reciprocal.

1. $\frac{3}{4}$ $\frac{4}{3}$

2. 7 $\frac{1}{7}$

3. 30 $\frac{1}{30}$

4. $\frac{7}{8}$ $\frac{8}{7}$

5. $\frac{4}{9}$ $\frac{9}{4}$

6. $\frac{13}{15}$ $\frac{15}{13}$

7. $\frac{5}{12}$ $\frac{12}{5}$

8. 19 $\frac{1}{19}$

9. $\frac{7}{10}$ $\frac{10}{7}$

10. 3 $\frac{1}{3}$

11. $\frac{4}{5}$ $\frac{5}{4}$

12. 8 $\frac{1}{8}$

Divide.

13. $\frac{1}{3} \div \frac{4}{9}$ $\frac{3}{4}$

14. $\frac{15}{16} \div 5$ $\frac{3}{16}$

15. $\frac{11}{12} \div \frac{3}{4}$ $1\frac{2}{9}$

16. $\frac{5}{6} \div 9$ $\frac{5}{54}$

17. $\frac{3}{8} \div \frac{3}{4}$ $\frac{1}{2}$

18. $\frac{9}{10} \div \frac{7}{8}$ $1\frac{1}{35}$

19. $\frac{3}{4} \div 6$ $\frac{1}{8}$

20. $\frac{13}{16} \div 4$ $\frac{13}{64}$

21. $\frac{2}{9} \div \frac{5}{6}$ $\frac{4}{15}$

22. $\frac{1}{3} \div 15$ $\frac{1}{45}$

23. $\frac{14}{15} \div \frac{3}{5}$ $1\frac{5}{9}$

24. $\frac{9}{16} \div 9$ $\frac{1}{16}$

25. $\frac{5}{16} \div \frac{5}{9}$ $\frac{9}{16}$

26. $\frac{11}{12} \div 3$ $\frac{11}{36}$

27. $\frac{7}{8} \div \frac{3}{4}$ $1\frac{1}{6}$

28. $\frac{7}{10} \div \frac{7}{9}$ $\frac{9}{10}$

29. $\frac{4}{5} \div 10$ $\frac{2}{25}$

30. $\frac{3}{10} \div 6$ $\frac{1}{20}$

31. $\frac{3}{16} \div \frac{3}{5}$ $\frac{5}{16}$

32. $\frac{4}{5} \div \frac{1}{16}$ $12\frac{4}{5}$

33. Ben wants to divide a 9-foot board into pieces $\frac{3}{4}$ of a foot long. How many pieces will there be? **12 pieces**

34. A piece of wire is $\frac{11}{12}$ of a yard in length. Paul needs wire pieces $\frac{1}{3}$ of a yard in length. How many pieces of wire can be cut from the wire? **2 pieces with $\frac{3}{4}$ yard left over**

▶ Lesson 6.7

Divide. Write the answers in lowest terms.

1. $1\frac{2}{3} \div 4\frac{1}{2}$ $\frac{10}{27}$

2. $\frac{3}{8} \div 1\frac{1}{6}$ $\frac{9}{28}$

3. $6\frac{5}{6} \div \frac{5}{6}$ $8\frac{1}{5}$

4. $\frac{3}{16} \div 5\frac{1}{8}$ $\frac{3}{82}$

5. $2\frac{3}{4} \div \frac{4}{5}$ $3\frac{7}{16}$

6. $\frac{9}{10} \div 1\frac{1}{2}$ $\frac{3}{5}$

7. $3\frac{3}{5} \div 3\frac{3}{5}$ 1

8. $4\frac{2}{9} \div 1\frac{7}{12}$ $2\frac{2}{3}$

9. $2\frac{1}{16} \div 1\frac{5}{6}$ $1\frac{1}{8}$

10. $3\frac{5}{9} \div 2$ $1\frac{7}{9}$

11. $11\frac{1}{4} \div \frac{3}{16}$ 60

12. $\frac{5}{6} \div 3\frac{1}{9}$ $\frac{15}{56}$

13. $7\frac{1}{2} \div \frac{3}{5}$ $12\frac{1}{2}$

14. $1\frac{3}{8} \div 3\frac{2}{3}$ $\frac{3}{8}$

15. $\frac{4}{5} \div 2\frac{1}{2}$ $\frac{8}{25}$

16. $\frac{5}{12} \div 2\frac{1}{4}$ $\frac{5}{27}$

17. $5\frac{5}{6} \div 2\frac{11}{12}$ 2

18. $\frac{2}{3} \div 1\frac{1}{3}$ $\frac{1}{2}$

19. $1\frac{1}{4} \div \frac{5}{16}$ 4

20. $2\frac{1}{8} \div \frac{3}{4}$ $2\frac{5}{6}$

21. $3\frac{7}{8} \div \frac{7}{8}$ $4\frac{3}{7}$

22. $1\frac{9}{16} \div 2\frac{5}{8}$ $\frac{25}{42}$

23. $\frac{7}{15} \div 1\frac{1}{9}$ $\frac{21}{50}$

24. $\frac{15}{16} \div 3\frac{3}{4}$ $\frac{1}{4}$

25. $\frac{11}{20} \div 5\frac{1}{2}$ $\frac{1}{10}$

26. $6\frac{1}{9} \div 1\frac{3}{8}$ $4\frac{4}{9}$

27. $\frac{7}{8} \div 5\frac{3}{5}$ $\frac{5}{32}$

28. $9\frac{7}{9} \div 1\frac{5}{6}$ $5\frac{1}{3}$

29. A desk phone is $4\frac{3}{4}$ inches wide. How may phones can fit on a desk that is $30\frac{1}{2}$ inches wide? **6 phones**

30. A rope is $16\frac{1}{2}$ feet long. How many pieces $\frac{3}{4}$ of a foot long can be cut from the rope? **22 pieces**

▶ **Lesson 7.1**

Add or subtract. Write the answers in lowest terms.

1. $\dfrac{5}{8} - \dfrac{1}{8}$ $\dfrac{1}{2}$

2. $\dfrac{11}{16} + \dfrac{9}{16}$ $1\dfrac{1}{4}$

3. $\dfrac{5}{6} - \dfrac{1}{6}$ $\dfrac{2}{3}$

4. $\dfrac{7}{9} + \dfrac{5}{9}$ $1\dfrac{1}{3}$

5. $\dfrac{7}{8} - \dfrac{1}{8}$ $\dfrac{3}{4}$

6. $\dfrac{9}{10} - \dfrac{4}{10}$ $\dfrac{1}{2}$

7. $\dfrac{1}{2} + \dfrac{1}{2} + \dfrac{1}{2}$ $1\dfrac{1}{2}$

8. $\dfrac{8}{9} + \dfrac{5}{9} + \dfrac{2}{9}$ $1\dfrac{2}{3}$

9. $\dfrac{11}{12} + \dfrac{5}{12} + \dfrac{7}{12}$ $1\dfrac{11}{12}$

10. $\dfrac{5}{16} + \dfrac{9}{16} + \dfrac{15}{16}$ $1\dfrac{13}{16}$

11. $\dfrac{4}{5} + \dfrac{2}{5} + \dfrac{3}{5}$ $1\dfrac{4}{5}$

12. $\dfrac{2}{3} + \dfrac{1}{3} + \dfrac{2}{3}$ $1\dfrac{2}{3}$

13. $\dfrac{15}{16} - \dfrac{9}{16}$ $\dfrac{3}{8}$

14. $\dfrac{5}{12} - \dfrac{1}{12}$ $\dfrac{1}{3}$

15. $\dfrac{14}{15} - \dfrac{8}{15}$ $\dfrac{2}{5}$

16. $\dfrac{4}{9} + \dfrac{5}{9}$ 1

17. $\dfrac{7}{12} - \dfrac{5}{12}$ $\dfrac{1}{6}$

18. $\dfrac{7}{9} + \dfrac{8}{9}$ $1\dfrac{2}{3}$

19. $\dfrac{5}{9} - \dfrac{4}{9}$ $\dfrac{1}{9}$

20. $\dfrac{11}{12} + \dfrac{5}{12}$ $1\dfrac{1}{3}$

21. $\dfrac{9}{16} - \dfrac{1}{16}$ $\dfrac{1}{2}$

22. $\dfrac{3}{10} - \dfrac{1}{10}$ $\dfrac{1}{5}$

23. $\dfrac{3}{4} + \dfrac{1}{4}$ 1

24. $\dfrac{7}{8} + \dfrac{3}{8}$ $1\dfrac{1}{4}$

25. $\dfrac{11}{15} - \dfrac{8}{15}$ $\dfrac{1}{5}$

26. $\dfrac{13}{16} - \dfrac{7}{16}$ $\dfrac{3}{8}$

27. Juan swam $\dfrac{11}{16}$ of a mile. Maria swam $\dfrac{9}{16}$ of a mile. Who swam the shorter distance? How much shorter? Maria; $\dfrac{1}{8}$ mile

28. Kim lives $\dfrac{7}{10}$ of a mile east of the school. Carla lives $\dfrac{7}{10}$ of a mile west of the school. How far is it from Kim's house to Carla's house? $1\dfrac{2}{5}$ miles

▶ **Lesson 7.2**

List the first five multiples.

1. 9   9, 18, 27, 36, 45
2. 14   14, 28, 42, 56, 70
3. 24   24, 48, 72, 96, 120
4. 40   40, 80, 120, 160, 200
5. 16   16, 32, 48, 64, 80
6. 36   36, 72, 108, 144, 180

Find the LCD.

7. $\dfrac{2}{15}$ $\dfrac{11}{12}$ 60

8. $\dfrac{1}{2}$ $\dfrac{3}{4}$ $\dfrac{5}{6}$ 12

9. $\dfrac{3}{8}$ $\dfrac{4}{5}$ 40

10. $\dfrac{3}{10}$ $\dfrac{4}{5}$ 10

11. $\dfrac{2}{3}$ $\dfrac{7}{8}$ 24

12. $\dfrac{3}{4}$ $\dfrac{5}{8}$ $\dfrac{1}{2}$ 8

13. $\dfrac{2}{5}$ $\dfrac{2}{3}$ 15

14. $\dfrac{1}{4}$ $\dfrac{2}{5}$ $\dfrac{7}{10}$ 20

15. $\dfrac{9}{16}$ $\dfrac{1}{2}$ $\dfrac{7}{8}$ 16

16. $\dfrac{3}{4}$ $\dfrac{5}{12}$ 12

17. $\dfrac{4}{5}$ $\dfrac{5}{9}$ 45

18. $\dfrac{1}{3}$ $\dfrac{5}{6}$ 6

19. $\dfrac{1}{8}$ $\dfrac{5}{12}$ 24

20. $\dfrac{5}{6}$ $\dfrac{4}{5}$ 30

21. $\dfrac{1}{3}$ $\dfrac{1}{4}$ 12

22. $\dfrac{1}{6}$ $\dfrac{7}{8}$ 24

23. $\dfrac{7}{15}$ $\dfrac{2}{3}$ 15

24. $\dfrac{7}{8}$ $\dfrac{2}{9}$ 72

25. $\dfrac{5}{8}$ $\dfrac{4}{9}$ $\dfrac{1}{2}$ 72

26. $\dfrac{3}{10}$ $\dfrac{1}{15}$ 30

27. $\dfrac{5}{6}$ $\dfrac{2}{3}$ $\dfrac{1}{2}$ 6

28. $\dfrac{4}{5}$ $\dfrac{9}{10}$ $\dfrac{8}{15}$ 30

29. $\dfrac{1}{12}$ $\dfrac{5}{9}$ $\dfrac{1}{6}$ 36

30. $\dfrac{1}{3}$ $\dfrac{7}{9}$ 9

31. $\dfrac{7}{10}$ $\dfrac{1}{2}$ 10

32. $\dfrac{3}{5}$ $\dfrac{1}{10}$ $\dfrac{1}{8}$ 40

33. $\dfrac{1}{6}$ $\dfrac{5}{9}$ 18

34. $\dfrac{1}{2}$ $\dfrac{5}{12}$ $\dfrac{2}{9}$ 36

▶ Lesson 7.3

Add. Write the answers in lowest terms.

1. $\frac{2}{3}$ $+\frac{1}{9}$ $\frac{7}{9}$

2. $\frac{7}{8}$ $+\frac{3}{4}$ $1\frac{5}{8}$

3. $\frac{4}{5}$ $+\frac{3}{4}$ $1\frac{11}{20}$

4. $\frac{5}{16}$ $+\frac{1}{8}$ $\frac{7}{16}$

5. $\frac{1}{3}$ $+\frac{1}{8}$ $\frac{11}{24}$

6. $\frac{7}{10}$ $+\frac{1}{5}$ $\frac{9}{10}$

7. $\frac{5}{6}$ $+\frac{1}{4}$ $1\frac{1}{12}$

8. $\frac{2}{9}$ $+\frac{1}{3}$ $\frac{5}{9}$

9. $\frac{1}{4}$ $+\frac{9}{16}$ $\frac{13}{16}$

10. $\frac{5}{8}$ $+\frac{1}{5}$ $\frac{33}{40}$

11. $\frac{1}{2}$ $+\frac{9}{10}$ $1\frac{2}{5}$

12. $\frac{5}{12}$ $+\frac{5}{6}$ $1\frac{1}{4}$

13. $\frac{3}{4}$ $+\frac{1}{6}$ $\frac{11}{12}$

14. $\frac{7}{8}$ $+\frac{3}{16}$ $1\frac{1}{16}$

15. $\frac{2}{3}$ $+\frac{3}{10}$ $\frac{29}{30}$

16. $\frac{3}{8}$ $+\frac{11}{12}$ $1\frac{7}{24}$

17. $\frac{11}{16}$ $+\frac{1}{2}$ $1\frac{3}{16}$

18. $\frac{4}{5}$ $+\frac{7}{10}$ $1\frac{1}{2}$

19. $\frac{2}{3}+\frac{4}{9}$ $1\frac{1}{9}$

20. $\frac{7}{16}+\frac{1}{4}$ $\frac{11}{16}$

21. $\frac{1}{10}+\frac{1}{6}$ $\frac{4}{15}$

22. $\frac{5}{12}+\frac{1}{4}$ $\frac{2}{3}$

23. $\frac{1}{6}+\frac{1}{3}+\frac{3}{4}$ $1\frac{1}{4}$

24. $\frac{1}{2}+\frac{5}{6}+\frac{4}{9}$ $1\frac{7}{9}$

25. $\frac{7}{8}+\frac{2}{3}+\frac{1}{6}$ $1\frac{17}{24}$

26. $\frac{3}{4}+\frac{1}{2}+\frac{4}{5}$ $2\frac{1}{20}$

27. Sandra picked $\frac{1}{3}$ of the apples on one day and $\frac{3}{8}$ of the apples the next day. What fraction of the apples did she pick in all? $\frac{17}{24}$

28. Greg sprinted $\frac{1}{4}$ of a mile on Tuesday, $\frac{1}{5}$ of a mile on Wednesday, and $\frac{1}{8}$ of a mile on Thursday. How far did he sprint altogether? $\frac{23}{40}$ of a mile

▶ Lesson 7.4

Add. Write the answers in lowest terms.

1. $1\frac{3}{8}$ $+2\frac{1}{2}$ $3\frac{7}{8}$

2. $10\frac{1}{8}$ $+6\frac{7}{8}$ 17

3. $5\frac{3}{8}$ $+2\frac{2}{5}$ $7\frac{31}{40}$

4. $3\frac{9}{16}$ $+2\frac{11}{16}$ $6\frac{1}{4}$

5. $8\frac{2}{3}$ $+4\frac{2}{3}$ $13\frac{1}{3}$

6. $1\frac{9}{10}$ $+3\frac{4}{5}$ $5\frac{7}{10}$

7. $4\frac{1}{8}$ $+3\frac{3}{16}$ $7\frac{5}{16}$

8. $1\frac{5}{8}$ $+2\frac{7}{8}$ $4\frac{1}{2}$

9. $5\frac{7}{9}$ $+4\frac{7}{9}$ $10\frac{5}{9}$

10. $6\frac{1}{2}$ $+4\frac{3}{4}$ $11\frac{1}{4}$

11. $3\frac{1}{6}+2\frac{4}{9}$ $5\frac{11}{18}$

12. $1\frac{3}{4}+4\frac{2}{5}$ $6\frac{3}{20}$

13. $8\frac{1}{9}+7\frac{5}{12}$ $15\frac{19}{36}$

14. $9\frac{7}{15}+3\frac{2}{15}$ $12\frac{3}{5}$

15. $6\frac{2}{3}+1\frac{8}{9}$ $8\frac{5}{9}$

16. $1\frac{1}{12}+1\frac{1}{6}$ $2\frac{1}{4}$

17. $4\frac{7}{8}+9\frac{3}{10}$ $14\frac{7}{40}$

18. $5\frac{2}{9}+3\frac{7}{9}$ 9

19. $1\frac{5}{6}+4\frac{5}{6}$ $6\frac{2}{3}$

20. $3\frac{9}{10}+3\frac{5}{6}$ $7\frac{11}{15}$

21. $4\frac{4}{15}+8\frac{1}{15}$ $12\frac{1}{3}$

22. $7\frac{1}{2}+6\frac{1}{2}$ 14

23. Jo has $3\frac{3}{16}$ yards of silk. Ina has $4\frac{3}{4}$ yards of silk. How much silk do they have in all? $7\frac{15}{16}$ yards

24. Terry rode his bike $9\frac{7}{10}$ miles. Jim rode his bike $8\frac{2}{3}$ miles. How far did the boys ride in all? $18\frac{11}{30}$ miles

Subtract. Write the answers in lowest terms.

1. $\dfrac{5}{8}$
   $-\dfrac{1}{3}$ $\dfrac{7}{24}$

2. $\dfrac{3}{4}$
   $-\dfrac{1}{16}$ $\dfrac{11}{16}$

3. $\dfrac{7}{10}$
   $-\dfrac{2}{5}$ $\dfrac{3}{10}$

4. $\dfrac{11}{12}$
   $-\dfrac{1}{6}$ $\dfrac{3}{4}$

5. $\dfrac{7}{8}$
   $-\dfrac{1}{4}$ $\dfrac{5}{8}$

6. $\dfrac{3}{4}$
   $-\dfrac{1}{5}$ $\dfrac{11}{20}$

7. $\dfrac{8}{9}$
   $-\dfrac{1}{3}$ $\dfrac{5}{9}$

8. $\dfrac{1}{2}$
   $-\dfrac{3}{16}$ $\dfrac{5}{16}$

9. $\dfrac{9}{10}$
   $-\dfrac{3}{4}$ $\dfrac{3}{20}$

10. $\dfrac{5}{8}$
    $-\dfrac{1}{12}$ $\dfrac{13}{24}$

11. $\dfrac{3}{4}$
    $-\dfrac{1}{6}$ $\dfrac{7}{12}$

12. $\dfrac{7}{12}$
    $-\dfrac{1}{3}$ $\dfrac{1}{4}$

13. $\dfrac{5}{6} - \dfrac{2}{3}$ $\dfrac{1}{6}$

14. $\dfrac{7}{10} - \dfrac{2}{3}$ $\dfrac{1}{30}$

15. $\dfrac{5}{9} - \dfrac{1}{6}$ $\dfrac{7}{18}$

16. $\dfrac{1}{2} - \dfrac{1}{10}$ $\dfrac{2}{5}$

17. $\dfrac{3}{5} - \dfrac{1}{3}$ $\dfrac{4}{15}$

18. $\dfrac{3}{4} - \dfrac{2}{5}$ $\dfrac{7}{20}$

19. $\dfrac{5}{6} - \dfrac{3}{8}$ $\dfrac{11}{24}$

20. $\dfrac{11}{12} - \dfrac{7}{8}$ $\dfrac{1}{24}$

21. $\dfrac{9}{10} - \dfrac{1}{3}$ $\dfrac{17}{30}$

22. $\dfrac{15}{16} - \dfrac{3}{4}$ $\dfrac{3}{16}$

23. $\dfrac{3}{8} - \dfrac{1}{5}$ $\dfrac{7}{40}$

24. $\dfrac{8}{9} - \dfrac{1}{6}$ $\dfrac{13}{18}$

25. $\dfrac{4}{5} - \dfrac{1}{8}$ $\dfrac{27}{40}$

26. $\dfrac{7}{12} - \dfrac{1}{5}$ $\dfrac{23}{60}$

27. $\dfrac{5}{6} - \dfrac{4}{15}$ $\dfrac{17}{30}$

28. Gabe finished $\dfrac{7}{10}$ of his job. Jim finished $\dfrac{3}{4}$ of his job. Who completed more of his job? By what fraction? Jim; $\dfrac{1}{20}$

29. Zoe collected $\dfrac{7}{12}$ of the junior class fund. Nicole collected $\dfrac{3}{8}$ of the fund. Who collected more? By what fraction? Zoe; $\dfrac{5}{24}$

Rename each whole number.

1. $8 = 7\dfrac{\blacksquare}{20}$ 20

2. $4 = 3\dfrac{\blacksquare}{2}$ 2

3. $20 = 19\dfrac{\blacksquare}{16}$ 16

4. $9 = 8\dfrac{\blacksquare}{5}$ 5

Subtract. Write the answers in lowest terms.

5. 9
   $-2\dfrac{1}{6}$ $6\dfrac{5}{6}$

6. 4
   $-3\dfrac{1}{2}$ $\dfrac{1}{2}$

7. 15
   $-6\dfrac{1}{3}$ $8\dfrac{2}{3}$

8. 7
   $-1\dfrac{1}{10}$ $5\dfrac{9}{10}$

9. 3
   $-1\dfrac{3}{5}$ $1\dfrac{2}{5}$

10. $6 - 3\dfrac{5}{12}$ $2\dfrac{7}{12}$

11. $20 - 5\dfrac{1}{4}$ $14\dfrac{3}{4}$

12. $8 - 2\dfrac{2}{5}$ $5\dfrac{3}{5}$

13. $5 - 2\dfrac{7}{8}$ $2\dfrac{1}{8}$

14. $25 - 5\dfrac{9}{10}$ $19\dfrac{1}{10}$

15. $12 - 4\dfrac{5}{16}$ $7\dfrac{11}{16}$

16. $12 - 9\dfrac{2}{9}$ $2\dfrac{7}{9}$

17. $40 - 25\dfrac{7}{20}$ $14\dfrac{13}{20}$

18. $66 - 23\dfrac{1}{2}$ $42\dfrac{1}{2}$

19. $39 - 13\dfrac{4}{9}$ $25\dfrac{5}{9}$

20. $50 - 25\dfrac{1}{8}$ $24\dfrac{7}{8}$

21. $38 - 11\dfrac{8}{9}$ $26\dfrac{1}{9}$

22. Meagan hiked 9 miles on the first day and $7\dfrac{1}{10}$ miles on the second day. How much farther did she hike the first day? $1\dfrac{9}{10}$ miles

23. Dave worked $3\dfrac{2}{3}$ hours Friday and 8 hours Saturday. How much longer did he work on Saturday? $4\dfrac{1}{3}$ hours

▶ **Lesson 7.9**

Rename each mixed number.

1. $6\frac{1}{2} = 5\frac{\blacksquare}{2}$ 3

2. $4\frac{3}{4} = 3\frac{\blacksquare}{4}$ 7

3. $2\frac{5}{8} = 1\frac{\blacksquare}{8}$ 13

4. $8\frac{9}{10} = 7\frac{\blacksquare}{10}$ 19

Subtract. Write the answers in lowest terms.

5. $\begin{array}{r} 3\frac{1}{4} \\ -1\frac{3}{4} \end{array}$ $1\frac{1}{2}$

6. $\begin{array}{r} 8\frac{7}{8} \\ -2\frac{1}{6} \end{array}$ $6\frac{17}{24}$

7. $\begin{array}{r} 5\frac{11}{12} \\ -3\frac{1}{6} \end{array}$ $2\frac{3}{4}$

8. $\begin{array}{r} 6\frac{1}{9} \\ -2\frac{1}{8} \end{array}$ $3\frac{71}{72}$

9. $\begin{array}{r} 9\frac{5}{9} \\ -1\frac{1}{3} \end{array}$ $8\frac{2}{9}$

10. $\begin{array}{r} 7\frac{2}{15} \\ -3\frac{4}{15} \end{array}$ $3\frac{13}{15}$

11. $\begin{array}{r} 6\frac{11}{16} \\ -4\frac{3}{16} \end{array}$ $2\frac{1}{2}$

12. $\begin{array}{r} 10\frac{1}{8} \\ -6\frac{5}{8} \end{array}$ $3\frac{1}{2}$

13. $\begin{array}{r} 12\frac{1}{4} \\ -6\frac{1}{3} \end{array}$ $5\frac{11}{12}$

14. $\begin{array}{r} 15\frac{4}{5} \\ -5\frac{3}{5} \end{array}$ $10\frac{1}{5}$

15. $11\frac{1}{10} - 3\frac{4}{5}$ $7\frac{3}{10}$

16. $9\frac{7}{12} - 4\frac{1}{12}$ $5\frac{1}{2}$

17. $8\frac{1}{6} - 4\frac{1}{3}$ $3\frac{5}{6}$

18. $4\frac{1}{4} - 1\frac{1}{2}$ $2\frac{3}{4}$

19. $17\frac{8}{9} - 9\frac{4}{9}$ $8\frac{4}{9}$

20. $20\frac{3}{5} - 4\frac{2}{5}$ $16\frac{1}{5}$

21. $13\frac{5}{12} - 6\frac{11}{12}$ $6\frac{1}{2}$

22. $16\frac{7}{8} - 2\frac{1}{16}$ $14\frac{13}{16}$

23. $18\frac{5}{6} - 9\frac{1}{4}$ $9\frac{7}{12}$

24. $24\frac{3}{10} - 14\frac{3}{5}$ $9\frac{7}{10}$

25. $15\frac{5}{12} - 8\frac{1}{12}$ $7\frac{1}{3}$

26. $7\frac{2}{3} - 5\frac{1}{2}$ $2\frac{1}{6}$

27. $12\frac{5}{9} - 6\frac{7}{9}$ $5\frac{7}{9}$

28. $14\frac{9}{10} - 6\frac{1}{10}$ $8\frac{4}{5}$

29. $19\frac{3}{4} - 17\frac{7}{8}$ $1\frac{7}{8}$

30. $21\frac{11}{12} - 8\frac{3}{8}$ $13\frac{13}{24}$

31. Reg skated $6\frac{3}{4}$ miles. Rich skated $7\frac{5}{6}$ miles. How much farther did Rich skate?
$1\frac{1}{12}$ miles

32. Claire watched the Superbowl for $1\frac{5}{12}$ hours. Jed watched it for $2\frac{1}{12}$ hours. What was the difference in their viewing time?
$\frac{2}{3}$ hour

▶ **Lesson 7.10**

Estimate to the nearest whole number and to the nearest $\frac{1}{2}$.

1. $4\frac{5}{8} + 3\frac{3}{8}$ 8; 8

2. $12\frac{9}{10} - 5\frac{3}{4}$ 7; 7

3. $5\frac{5}{6} + 4\frac{4}{9}$ 10; $10\frac{1}{2}$

4. $7\frac{1}{9} - 4\frac{1}{6}$ 3; 3

5. $3\frac{7}{16} - 2\frac{1}{3}$ 1; 1

6. $9\frac{5}{15} - 3\frac{9}{16}$ 5; 6

7. $4\frac{1}{4} + 7\frac{5}{8}$ 12; 12

8. $3\frac{5}{12} + 2\frac{8}{9}$ 6; $6\frac{1}{2}$

9. $1\frac{5}{9} + 2\frac{2}{3}$ 5; 4

10. $7\frac{1}{3} - 5\frac{2}{5}$ 2; 2

11. $6\frac{2}{9} - 1\frac{5}{9}$ 4; $4\frac{1}{2}$

12. $4\frac{3}{4} + 4\frac{7}{8}$ 10; 10

13. $3\frac{1}{5} - 1\frac{4}{5}$ 1; 1

14. $5\frac{7}{16} + 1\frac{1}{8}$ 7; $6\frac{1}{2}$

15. $7\frac{5}{6} - 2\frac{2}{3}$ 5; $5\frac{1}{2}$

16. $5\frac{3}{5} + 6\frac{11}{12}$ 13; $12\frac{1}{2}$

17. $2\frac{1}{9} + 2\frac{8}{9}$ 5; 5

18. $8\frac{1}{4} - 2\frac{5}{8}$ 5; 6

19. $3\frac{2}{3} - 1\frac{7}{12}$ 2; 2

20. $7\frac{7}{9} + 8\frac{9}{16}$ 17; $16\frac{1}{2}$

21. Karl bought $3\frac{7}{8}$ pounds of peanuts and $2\frac{1}{3}$ pounds of walnuts. About how many pounds of nuts did he buy?
6 pounds; $6\frac{1}{2}$ pounds

22. Sandi bought $6\frac{1}{2}$ pounds of apples and $4\frac{3}{4}$ pounds of bananas. About how many pounds of fruit did she buy?
12 pounds; $11\frac{1}{2}$ pounds

Lesson 8.2

Convert each measure.

1. 489 ft. to yd.
2. 132 in. to ft.
3. 2 mi. to ft.
4. 5280 ft. to mi.
5. 7 mi. to ft.
6. 99 ft. to yd.
7. 216 in. to yd.
8. 3520 yd. to mi.
9. 48 ft. to yd.
10. 168 in. to ft.
11. 440 ft. to yd.
12. 8 yd. to in.
13. 732 in. to ft.
14. 3 mi. to ft.
15. 72 in. to ft.
16. 4 mi. to ft.
17. 663 yd. to ft.
18. 36 in. to yd.
19. 11 mi. to yd.
20. 133 yd. to ft.
21. 576 ft. to yd.
22. 77 yd. to ft.
23. 204 in. to ft.
24. 15 yd. to in.
25. 168 yd. to in.
26. 12 mi. to ft.
27. 648 in. to yd.
28. 456 ft. to yd.
29. 918 yd. to ft.
30. 31,680 ft. to mi.
31. 156 in. to ft.
32. 3 mi. to yd.
33. 14,080 yd. to mi.

Lesson 8.3

Measure each item to the nearest inch, $\frac{1}{2}$ inch, and $\frac{1}{4}$ inch.

1. _____ 4 in.; $3\frac{1}{2}$ in.; $3\frac{3}{4}$ in.

2. _____ 4 in.; 4 in.; $4\frac{1}{4}$ in.

3. _____

4. _____ 2 in.; $2\frac{1}{2}$ in.; $2\frac{1}{4}$ in.

   5 in.; 5 in.; 5 in.

5. the length of a calculator
6. the length of your shoe Answers will vary for 5–10.
7. the length of your pencil
8. the length of an envelope
9. the length of a cassette tape
10. the width of a book

Complete each statement. Choose the more reasonable measure.

11. A horse has legs about ▦ long. (3 ft.) 15 in.
12. A rabbit has ears about ▦ long. (4 in.) 2 ft.
13. The length of a whistle is about ▦. 6 ft. (2.5 in.)
14. Socks are about ▦ long. (12 in.) 4 ft.
15. The height of a quart bottle of milk is about ▦. 3 ft. (10 in.)
16. The distance between Milwaukee and Chicago is about ▦. 90,000 ft. (90 mi.)

Lesson 8.2

1. 163 yd.
2. 11 ft.
3. 10,560 ft.
4. 1 mi.
5. 36,960 ft.
6. 33 yd.
7. 6 yd.
8. 2 mi.
9. 16 yd.
10. 14 ft.
11. $146\frac{2}{3}$ yd.
12. 288 in.
13. 61 ft.
14. 15,840 ft.
15. 6 ft.
16. 21,120 ft.
17. 1989 ft.
18. 1 yd.
19. 19,360 yd.
20. 399 ft.
21. 192 yd.
22. 231 ft.
23. 17 ft.
24. 540 in.
25. 6048 in.
26. 63,360 ft.
27. 18 yd.
28. 152 yd.
29. 2754 ft.
30. 6 mi.
31. 13 ft.
32. 5280 yd.
33. 8 mi.

► **Lesson 8.4**

Convert each measure.

1. 490 oz. to lb.
30.625 lb.
2. 17 lb. to oz.
272 oz.
3. 5 T. to lb.
10,000 lb.

4. 8 lb. 5 oz. to oz.
133 oz.
5. 19,000 lb. to T.
9.5 T.
6. 336 oz. to lb.
21 lb.

7. 4 lb. 7 oz. to oz.
71 oz.
8. 55 lb. to oz.
880 oz.
9. 23 T. to lb.
46,000 lb.

10. 91 oz. to lb.
5 lb. 11 oz.
11. 25 lb. to oz.
400 oz.
12. 44,000 lb. to T.
22 T.

13. 788 oz. to lb.
49 lb. 4 oz.
14. 18 oz. to lb.
1 lb. 2 oz.
15. 297 oz. to lb.
18 lb. 9 oz.

16. 100 lb. to oz.
1600 oz.
17. 200 oz. to lb.
12.5 lb.
18. 923 oz. to lb.
57 lb. 11 oz.

19. 16 lb. to oz.
256 oz.
20. 44 oz. to lb.
2.75 lb.
21. 8 T. to lb.
16,000 lb.

22. 31,000 lb. to T.
15.5 T.
23. 81 lb. to oz.
1296 oz.
24. 800 oz. to lb.
50 lb.

Complete each statement. Choose the more reasonable measure.

25. A postcard weighs about $\frac{1}{2}$ ___ . (oz.) lb.

26. A full-grown dog weighs about 75 ___ . (lb.) T.

27. A truck weighs about 3 ___ . lb. (T.)

28. A baby elephant weighs about 300 ___ . (lb.) T.

► **Lesson 8.6**

Convert each measure.

1. 12 qt. to gal.
3 gal.
2. 43 c. to qt.
10 qt. 3 c.
3. 56 pt. to qt.
28 qt.

4. 60 fl. oz. to c.
7 c. 4 fl. oz.
5. 18 gal. to pt.
144 pt.
6. 21 qt. to c.
84 c.

7. 9 c. to fl. oz.
72 fl. oz.
8. 66 pt. to gal.
8 gal. 1 qt.
9. 16 gal. to qt.
64 qt.

10. 72 c. to pt.
36 pt.
11. 114 qt. to gal.
28 gal. 2 qt.
12. 100 pt. to c.
200 c.

13. 15 qt. to c.
60 c.
14. 88 fl. oz. to c.
11 c.
15. 72 c. to qt.
18 qt.

16. 46 gal. to qt.
184 qt.
17. 35 c. to fl. oz.
280 fl. oz.
18. 26 pt. to qt.
13 qt.

19. 27 gal. to pt.
216 pt.
20. 155 c. to qt.
38 qt. 3 c.
21. 18 qt. to pt.
36 pt.

22. 68 fl. oz. to c.
8 c. 4 fl. oz.
23. 97 qt. to gal.
24 gal. 1 qt.
24. 25 c. to qt.
6 qt. 1 c.

Complete each statement. Choose the more reasonable measure.

25. A small bottle of cough medicine contains 4 ___ . (fl. oz.) qt.

26. The cake recipe uses 2 ___ of milk. (c.) gal.

27. The bottle of shampoo contains 15 ___ . (fl. oz.) c.

28. Sam bought 3 ___ of paint. fl. oz. (gal.)

▶ **Lesson 8.7**

Add or subtract.

1.   19 lb. 11 oz.
    + 7 lb. 13 oz.
    ―――――――
     27 lb. 8 oz.

2.   4 yd. 1 ft. 8 in.
    + 5 yd. 2 ft. 9 in.
    ――――――――――
     10 yd. 1 ft. 5 in.

3.   7 gal. 1 qt.
    ― 3 gal. 3 qt.
    ――――――――
     3 gal. 2 qt.

4.   15 yd. 2 ft. 2 in.
    ― 12 yd. 2 ft. 7 in.
    ――――――――――
     2 yd. 2 ft. 7 in.

5.   6 gal. 3 qt.
    + 2 gal. 2 qt.
    ――――――――
     9 gal. 1 qt.

6.   15 T.   100 lb.
    ― 9 T. 1,200 lb.
    ―――――――――
     5 T. 900 lb

7.   18 min. 45 sec.
    + 32 min. 55 sec.
    ――――――――――
     51 min. 40 sec.

8.   6 yd. 2 ft. 10 in.
    + 8 yd. 2 ft. 11 in.
    ――――――――――
     15 yd. 2 ft. 9 in.

9.   16 lb. 14 oz.
    + 13 lb. 15 oz.
    ――――――――
     30 lb. 13 oz.

10.   100 lb. 10 oz.
    ― 75 lb. 14 oz.
    ――――――――
     24 lb. 12 oz.

11.   9 min.
    ― 2 min. 32 sec.
    ――――――――
     6 min. 28 sec.

12.   4 T. 1,772 lb.
    + 1 T.   968 lb.
    ――――――――
     6 T. 740 lb.

13.   6 hr. 17 min.
    ― 3 hr. 25 min.
    ――――――――
     2 hr. 52 min.

14.   5 hr. 33 min.
    + 3 hr. 48 min.
    ――――――――
     9 hr. 21 min.

15.   34 lb.
    ― 29 lb. 7 oz.
    ――――――――
     4 lb. 9 oz.

16.   10 yd. 2 ft. 10 in.
    + 15 yd. 2 ft.
    ――――――――――
     26 yd. 1 ft. 10 in.

17.   10 gal. 1 qt.
    + 7 gal. 3 qt.
    ――――――――
     18 gal.

18.   88 lb. 8 oz.
    + 55 lb. 8 oz.
    ――――――――
     144 lb.

▶ **Lesson 8.8**

Use the thermometer to determine each temperature.
Answers may vary. Suggested answers are given.

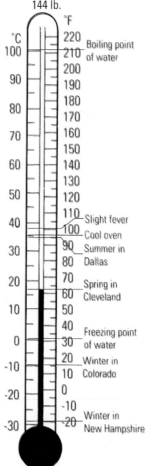

1. a spring day in Cleveland in degrees Fahrenheit 62°

2. a very cold winter day in Colorado in degrees Celsius −10°

3. a very cold winter day in New Hampshire in degrees Fahrenheit −20°

4. a very hot summer day in Dallas in degrees Celsius 34°

5. a person with a slight fever in degrees Fahrenheit 100°

6. a person with a slight fever in degrees Celsius 38°

7. a point just above when water turns to ice in degrees Fahrenheit 33°

8. a point just below when water turns to ice in degrees Celsius −1°

9. a point just below when water boils in degrees Celsius 99°

10. a point just above when water boils in degrees Fahrenheit 213°

11. a cool oven, set to let bread rise in degrees Celsius 35°

Extra Practice **427**

▶ Lesson 8.10

Determine the total hours worked each week. Determine the gross earnings.

1. First week
Sunday: 1–5
Tuesday: 5–9
Thursday: 5–9
Saturday: 12–5
Hourly rate: $6.75
17 hours; $114.75

2. Second week
Monday: 4–6
Tuesday: 4–6
Thursday: 4–6
Friday: 4–9
Hourly rate: $7.25
11 hours; $79.75

3. Third week
Tuesday: 6–9
Friday: 5–9
Saturday: 10–2
Sunday 2–5
Hourly rate: $6.13
14 hours; $85.32

4. Fourth week
Sunday: 12–5
Wednesday: 4–8
Friday: 4–9
Saturday: 9–12
Hourly rate: $6.81
17 hours; $115.77

5. Fifth week
Monday: 4–7
Tuesday: 5–8
Wednesday: 4–7
Thursday: 5–8
Hourly rate: $7.85
12 hours; $94.20

6. Sixth week
Monday: 6–10
Wednesday: 7–9
Thursday: 7–9
Friday: 6–10
Hourly rate: $6.95
12 hours; $83.40

▶ Lesson 9.2

Use the graph below to answer each question.

1. Which class is the most popular?
Low-impact aerobics

2. Which class is the least popular?
Beginning ballet

3. Which class has about twice as many students as Chinese cooking?
Low-impact aerobics

4. Which two classes have about the same number of students?
Beginning ballet and calligraphy

5. Which class has about $\frac{1}{3}$ as many students as Chinese cooking?
Upholstery

6. Estimate the total number of students.
About 190 or 200 students

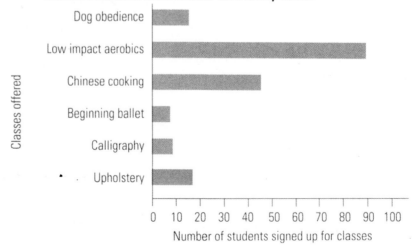

Classes Offered at the Riverside Community Center

► Lesson 9.3

Use the graph on the right to answer the following questions.

1. Twice as many boys as girls prefer to watch which sport?
Football

2. More girls than boys prefer to watch which sports?
Tennis, Basketball, Bowling, and Baseball

3. Which sport do both boys and girls like least to watch?
Golf

4. About $\frac{2}{3}$ as many boys as girls prefer to watch which sport?
Tennis

5. About $\frac{1}{3}$ as many boys as girls prefer to watch which sport?
Bowling

6. What three sports do most students prefer to watch?
Football, Basketball, and Baseball

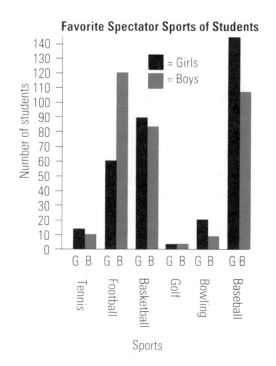

► Lesson 9.4

1. Construct a bar graph from the table below. Describe the results.
Student descriptions will vary.

1999 Sales for Mona's Pet Palace

Type of Animal	Number Sold
Dogs	50
Cats	80
Birds	42
Rodents	170
Reptiles	17

2. Construct a bar graph from the table below. Describe the results.
Student descriptions will vary.

Caloric Content of Foods

Type of Food	Number of Calories per Serving
Egg	80
8-oz. yogurt with fruit	240
$\frac{2}{3}$ c. of rice	120
$\frac{1}{8}$ of a cherry pie	310
Orange	75
3-oz. candy bar with nuts	450

Extra Practice Answers
Lesson 9.4

1. A sample bar graph is shown below:

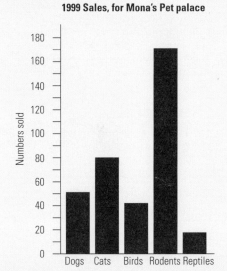

2. A sample bar graph is shown below:

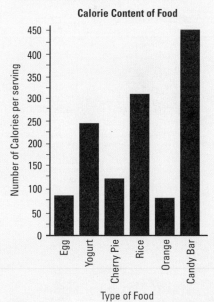

1. A sample line graph is shown below.

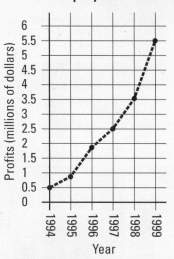

Profits for Success - Bright Company 1994–1999

2. A sample line graph is shown below.

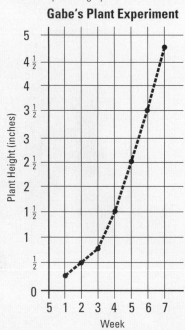

Gabe's Plant Experiment

▶ Lesson 9.5

Use the graph on the right to answer the following questions.

1. What was the price of a first-class stamp in 1978? 15¢

2. In what year did the first-class stamp double the 1952 cost? 1968

3. What was the shortest time between stamp price increases? 1 year (1974–1975)

4. What was the largest jump in first-class stamp prices? 5¢

5. Which price of stamp was used for the longest period of time? 3¢

6. What is the price of a first-class stamp today? 33¢ (as of 1/99); answer subject to change

▶ Lesson 9.6

1. Construct a line graph from the table below. Describe the results. Student descriptions will vary.

Profits for Success-Bright Company from 1994 – 1999

Year	Profits (in millions of dollars)
1994	0.5
1995	0.9
1996	1.8
1997	2.5
1998	3.6
1999	5.5

2. Construct a line graph from the table below. Describe the results. Student descriptions will vary.

Gabe's Plant Experiment

After Week:	Height of Plant in Inches
#1	$\frac{1}{4}$ in.
#2	$\frac{1}{2}$ in.
#3	$\frac{3}{4}$ in.
#4	$1\frac{1}{2}$ in.
#5	$2\frac{1}{2}$ in.
#6	$3\frac{1}{2}$ in.
#7	$4\frac{3}{4}$ in.

Cost of Sending a First Class Letter, 1952–1999

Prices of first class stamps in cents — Years of Increase

Lesson 9.7

Use the graph on the right to answer the following questions.

1. About how many television sets are there in Brazil?
   About 300 per 1000 people

2. Which country has about half the number of sets as the U.S.? Great Britain

3. About how many sets are there in Italy? About 500 per 1000 people

4. Which two countries have about the same number of sets?
   Soviet Union and Italy

5. Use the table below to construct a pictograph. Use one coin to represent $50.

Number of Television Sets in Some Countries

United States ⬜⬜⬜⬜⬜⬜⬜⬜⬜
Russia ⬜⬜▯
China ⬜
Japan ⬜⬜▯
Italy ⬜⬜▯
Great Britain ⬜⬜⬜▯
Brazil ⬜▯

⬜ = 200 television sets for each 1000 people.

Amounts Earned in the Freshman Class Candy Sale by Homerooms

Homeroom	Dollars Earned
206	$175
213	$65
301	$250
309	$105
310	$385

Lesson 9.8

Use the graph on the right to answer the following questions.

1. What type of music do most students prefer? Rock

2. What type of music is the second choice among students? Country

3. What 2 types of music are preferred by about the same number of students? Jazz and Folk

4. What type of music is chosen by the fewest number of students? Classical

5. What 3 types together make up about $\frac{1}{4}$ of the graph? Classical, Jazz, and Folk

Music Survey of Students at Kimberly High School

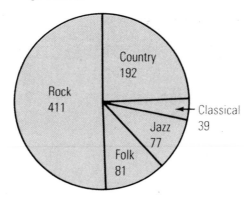

Rock 411
Country 192
Classical 39
Jazz 77
Folk 81

Extra Practice Answers

Lesson 10.2

Sample frequency tables are shown below.

Cost of Blank VCR Tapes	Frequency
$6	3
$5	1
$4	3
$3	4
$2	2

Number of Gymnasts	Frequency
10	1
9	2
8	0
7	0
6	2
5	3
4	1
3	7
2	3
1	5

▶ Lesson 10.2

Make a frequency table for each set of data below. Use your table to answer the questions at the right.

Cost of blank VCR tapes

$3	$2	$5	$4	$6
$3	$3	$4	$4	$6
$2	$3	$6		

Number of gymnasts from individual schools taking part in the statement

2	1	1	9	6	1
3	5	3	9	5	10
6	2	3	1	1	3
4	5	3	3	3	2

1. How much does the most expensive tape cost? $6

2. What is the most common cost for a tape? $3

3. What is the difference in cost between the least and the most expensive tape? $4

4. How many schools participated in the state gymnastics meet? 24

5. How many schools entered only one gymnast in the meet? 5

6. How many schools entered 7 or 8 gymnasts in the meet? None

7. How many schools entered 5 or more gymnasts in the meet? 8

▶ Lesson 10.3

Find the range, the mode, and the median.

1. 5   6   4.5   5.5   5.5
   1.5; 5.5; 5.5
2. 9   6.5   5.5   8.5   7.5
   3.5; none; 7.5
3. 18,933   24,635   33,941   32,627
   15,008; none; 28,631
4. 26,225   28,317   27,934   37,878
   2092; none; 27,906
5. 65   78   85   78   85   91
   26; 78, 85; 81.5
6. 79   83   83   79   89   83
   10; 83; 83
7. 13.2   8.9   7.9   12.4
   5.3; none; 10.65
8. 6.8   8.6   8.7   6.8   7.4
   1.9; 6.8, 7.4
9. $1285 $4360 $945 $2850
   $3415; none; $2067.50
10. $3650 $725 $1495 $3650
    $2925; $3650; $2572.50
11. 380   425   650   535   425   619
    270; 425; 480
12. 978   1237   1205   999   1327
    349; none; 1205
13. 400   385   400   376   400   385
    24; 400; 392.5
14. 265   310   275   275   266   305
    45; 275, 275
15. 22.3   18.9   17.5   18.1   11.8
    10.5; none; 18.1
16. $9.89 $5.65 $4.25 $4.25 $13.41
    $9.16; $4.25; $5.65
17. $77 $61 $98 $101 $98 $98
    $40; $98; $98
18. 99   94   96   96   94   99   94   94
    5; 94; 95
19. 12   13   14   14   12   12   13
    2; 12; 13
20. $6 $5 $9 $6 $5 $9 $5 $5
    $4; $5; $5.50

▶ **Lesson 10.4**

Find the mean.

1. $2.50 $4 $1.25 $5.75 $4.75
   $3.65
2. $6.50 $4.75 $3.75 $5.50 $4.25
   $4.95
3. 65   61   80   94   78   79   86   82
   78.125
4. 71   76   82   88   91   93   77
   82.571
5. 11   17   8   19   21   3   6   5   4
   10.4
6. 18   18   26   12   18   20   22   13
   18.375
7. $0.98 $1.82 $0.58 $0.44 $1.26
   $1.02
8. $0.51 $0.69 $1.55 $2.55 $1.10
   $1.28
9. 128   191   204   255   341   363
   247
10. 385   250   95   118   192   99   98
    176.714
11. 9   3   4   0   12   11   2   15   13   8
    7.7
12. 1   0   1   7   22   6   0   5   18   3
    6.3
13. $2.85 $3.90 $1.75 $1.20 $2.35
    $2.41
14. $5.95   41.85 $0.95 $4.30 $4.85
    $3.58
15. 2550   3175   2100   1900   3725   2890   2760
    2728.571
16. $1525 $1675 $1950 $2950 $1400 $2400 $1700
    $1942.86
17. $20,500 $45,900 $35,400 $68,700 $44,500 $35,400
    $41,733.33
18. 12,385   21,344   22,895   26,890   26,789   16,542
    21,140.833

▶ **Lesson 10.6**

Use the information in each table to construct a histogram.

1. Freshman students at Main High School with summer jobs.

Hours worked per week	0–4	5–8	9–12	13–16	17–20	21–24	25–28	29–36	36+
Number of students	6	12	45	62	35	37	16	15	9

Divide the number of hours into four categories: 0–12, 13–24, 35–36, 36+.

2. Snowblower sales at Harvey's Hardware Store

Month	Jan.	Feb.	Mar.	Apr.	May	June	July	Aug.	Sep.	Oct.	Nov.	Dec.
Number of Snowblowers	35	26	15	8	0	0	5	15	9	18	42	53

Divide the year into 2-month periods.

Extra Practice Answers
Lesson 10.6

1. A sample histogram is shown below.

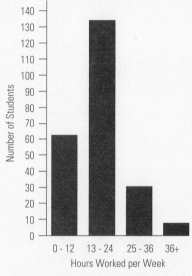

Freshmen Students at Main High School with Summer Jobs

2. A sample histogram is shown below.

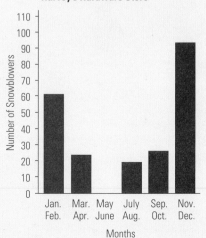

Snowblower Sales at Harvey's Hardware Store

▶ **Lesson 11.1**

Write each ratio in 3 different ways.

1. 6 puppies to 4 kittens
6 to 4; $\frac{6}{4}$; 6 : 4

2. 4 computers for 10 people
4 to 10; $\frac{4}{10}$; 4 : 10

3. 8 gloves for 4 hands
8 to 4; $\frac{8}{4}$; 8 : 4

4. $12.95 for 3 posters
$12.95 to 3; $\frac{\$12.95}{3}$; $12.95 : 3

5. $10 for 4 tickets
$10 to 4; $\frac{\$10}{4}$; $10 : 4

6. 6 goals in 2 games
6 to 2; $\frac{6}{2}$; 6 : 2

7. 2 runs for 13 times at bat
2 to 13; $\frac{2}{13}$; 2 : 13

8. $21.50 for 2 pairs of shoes
$21.50 to 2; $\frac{\$21.50}{2}$; $21.50 : 2

9. 1 cake with 14 candles
1 to 14; $\frac{1}{14}$; 1 : 14

10. 3 phones for 9 lines
3 to 9; $\frac{3}{9}$; 3 : 9

11. 30 tests for 30 students
30 to 30; $\frac{30}{30}$; 30 : 30

12. 1 calendar for 365 days
1 to 365; $\frac{1}{365}$; 1 : 365

Find 3 ratios equivalent to each ratio. Answers may vary.

13. 2 cages for 5 snakes $\frac{4}{10}, \frac{6}{15}, \frac{8}{20}$

14. 4 tokens for 6 boys $\frac{8}{12}, \frac{12}{18}, \frac{16}{24}$

15. 8 radios for 1 plug $\frac{16}{2}, \frac{24}{3}, \frac{32}{4}$

16. 14 maps for 2 globes $\frac{7}{1}, \frac{21}{3}, \frac{28}{4}$

17. 8 flowers for 32 leaves $\frac{16}{64}, \frac{24}{96}, \frac{32}{128}$

18. 3 mountains for 120 hikers $\frac{6}{240}, \frac{9}{360}, \frac{12}{480}$

19. 8 laces for 9 skates $\frac{16}{18}, \frac{24}{27}, \frac{32}{36}$

20. 1 train for 256 people $\frac{2}{512}, \frac{3}{768}, \frac{4}{1024}$

21. 10 buses for 320 riders $\frac{20}{640}, \frac{30}{960}, \frac{40}{1280}$

22. 6 dogs for 12 leashes $\frac{12}{24}, \frac{18}{36}, \frac{24}{48}$

▶ **Lesson 11.2**

Tell whether each statement is a proportion. Use = or ≠ .

1. $\frac{24}{1}$ ___ $\frac{96}{4}$ =

2. $\frac{16}{2}$ ___ $\frac{80}{5}$ ≠

3. $\frac{3}{1}$ ___ $\frac{9}{3}$ =

4. $\frac{12}{1}$ ___ $\frac{2}{24}$ ≠

5. $\frac{30}{1}$ ___ $\frac{300}{10}$ =

6. $\frac{364}{7}$ ___ $\frac{52}{2}$ ≠

7. $\frac{2}{1}$ ___ $\frac{4}{8}$ ≠

8. $\frac{32}{8}$ ___ $\frac{8}{2}$ =

9. $\frac{20}{6}$ ___ $\frac{50}{10}$ ≠

10. $\frac{5}{2}$ ___ $\frac{15}{4}$ ≠

11. $\frac{192}{3}$ ___ $\frac{64}{1}$ =

12. $\frac{1}{7}$ ___ $\frac{3}{24}$ ≠

13. $\frac{6}{16}$ ___ $\frac{12}{32}$ =

14. $\frac{30}{5}$ ___ $\frac{6}{1}$ =

15. $\frac{13}{169}$ ___ $\frac{12}{144}$ ≠

16. $\frac{17}{20}$ ___ $\frac{40}{34}$ ≠

17. $\frac{34}{40}$ ___ $\frac{17}{20}$ =

18. $\frac{88}{22}$ ___ $\frac{5}{4}$ ≠

19. $\frac{5}{10}$ ___ $\frac{10}{50}$ ≠

20. $\frac{24}{8}$ ___ $\frac{48}{16}$ =

21. $\frac{8}{9}$ ___ $\frac{64}{81}$ ≠

22. $\frac{9}{4}$ ___ $\frac{18}{8}$ =

23. $\frac{50}{45}$ ___ $\frac{10}{9}$ =

24. $\frac{6}{36}$ ___ $\frac{12}{48}$ ≠

25. $\frac{9}{1}$ ___ $\frac{2}{18}$ ≠

26. $\frac{3}{4}$ ___ $\frac{75}{100}$ =

27. $\frac{10}{6}$ ___ $\frac{30}{18}$ =

28. $\frac{12}{48}$ ___ $\frac{5}{10}$ ≠

29. $\frac{17}{3}$ ___ $\frac{51}{9}$ =

30. $\frac{24}{9}$ ___ $\frac{36}{12}$ ≠

31. $\frac{8}{7}$ ___ $\frac{56}{64}$ ≠

32. $\frac{33}{11}$ ___ $\frac{66}{22}$ =

33. $\frac{12}{4}$ ___ $\frac{6}{2}$ =

34. $\frac{81}{9}$ ___ $\frac{49}{7}$ ≠

35. $\frac{5}{3}$ ___ $\frac{15}{9}$ =

36. $\frac{8}{9}$ ___ $\frac{16}{19}$ ≠

37. $\frac{11}{2}$ ___ $\frac{24}{3}$ ≠

38. $\frac{20}{30}$ ___ $\frac{3}{2}$ ≠

39. $\frac{55}{5}$ ___ $\frac{88}{8}$ =

40. $\frac{12}{7}$ ___ $\frac{24}{14}$ =

▶ Lesson 11.3

Solve each proportion.

1. $\frac{8}{6} = \frac{\blacksquare}{60}$ 80
2. $\frac{4}{\blacksquare} = \frac{12}{36}$ 12
3. $\frac{3}{\blacksquare} = \frac{39}{169}$ 13
4. $\frac{22}{11} = \frac{\blacksquare}{49}$ 98

5. $\frac{3}{5} = \frac{\blacksquare}{25}$ 15
6. $\frac{125}{5} = \frac{625}{\blacksquare}$ 25
7. $\frac{\blacksquare}{9} = \frac{6}{18}$ 3
8. $\frac{14}{\blacksquare} = \frac{21}{15}$ 10

9. $\frac{\blacksquare}{3} = \frac{150}{225}$ 2
10. $\frac{24}{32} = \frac{\blacksquare}{4}$ 3
11. $\frac{91}{7} = \frac{65}{\blacksquare}$ 5
12. $\frac{200}{350} = \frac{\blacksquare}{70}$ 40

13. $\frac{4}{2} = \frac{16}{\blacksquare}$ 8
14. $\frac{9}{10} = \frac{9}{\blacksquare}$ 10
15. $\frac{\blacksquare}{39} = \frac{4}{52}$ 3
16. $\frac{6}{1} = \frac{\blacksquare}{300}$ 1800

17. $\frac{\blacksquare}{1} = \frac{378}{14}$ 27
18. $\frac{8}{20} = \frac{30}{\blacksquare}$ 75
19. $\frac{\blacksquare}{7} = \frac{18}{42}$ 3
20. $\frac{16}{\blacksquare} = \frac{17}{17}$ 16

21. $\frac{8}{14} = \frac{\blacksquare}{35}$ 20
22. $\frac{\blacksquare}{20} = \frac{15}{12}$ 25
23. $\frac{40}{\blacksquare} = \frac{90}{63}$ 28
24. $\frac{18}{5} = \frac{36}{\blacksquare}$ 10

25. $\frac{\blacksquare}{5} = \frac{104}{20}$ 26
26. $\frac{19}{\blacksquare} = \frac{57}{6}$ 2
27. $\frac{28}{42} = \frac{\blacksquare}{39}$ 26
28. $\frac{30}{18} = \frac{\blacksquare}{30}$ 50

29. $\frac{24}{8} = \frac{\blacksquare}{4}$ 12
30. $\frac{\blacksquare}{9} = \frac{6}{54}$ 1
31. $\frac{21}{\blacksquare} = \frac{49}{14}$ 6
32. $\frac{58}{29} = \frac{\blacksquare}{54}$ 108

33. $\frac{90}{\blacksquare} = \frac{10}{3}$ 27
34. $\frac{\blacksquare}{3} = \frac{64}{12}$ 16
35. $\frac{10}{\blacksquare} = \frac{50}{5}$ 1
36. $\frac{75}{2} = \frac{\blacksquare}{6}$ 225

37. $\frac{11}{8} = \frac{22}{\blacksquare}$ 16
38. $\frac{9}{\blacksquare} = \frac{27}{3}$ 1
39. $\frac{65}{\blacksquare} = \frac{13}{1}$ 5
40. $\frac{34}{17} = \frac{\blacksquare}{1}$ 2

▶ Lesson 11.4

Find the unit price.

1. $0.98 for 11 oz. of salad dressing $0.09
2. $1.69 for 4 doughnuts $0.42
3. $1.98 for 2.5 lb. of asparagus $0.79
4. $0.45 for 1.5 lb. of bananas $0.30
5. $15.65 for 3 apple pies $5.22
6. $9.78 for 4 pairs of socks $2.45
7. $5.15 for 4 rolls of tape $1.29
8. $17.66 for 5 rolls of film $3.53
9. $8.75 for 2 notebooks $4.38
10. $11.89 for 10 gallons of gas $1.19

Find the better buy.

11. ($4.46 for 5 lb. of oranges) or $2.71 for 3 lb. of oranges
12. $6.59 for $\frac{1}{2}$ lb. of nuts or ($13.08 for a lb. of nuts)
13. ($1.10 for 9 oz. of soy sauce) or $1.97 for 15 oz. of soy sauce
14. $1.76 for 3 lb. of potatoes or ($2.88 for 5 lb. of potatoes)
15. ($3.87 for a gallon of juice) or $0.99 for a quart of juice

Find the actual length for each scale length given.

1. 5 in.   scale: 1 in. = 25 mi.
125 mi.

2. 20.4 in.   scale: 1 in. = 15 yd.
306 yd.

3. 9.5 in.   scale: 1 in. = 15 mi.
142.5 mi.

4. $2\frac{7}{8}$ in.   scale: $\frac{1}{8}$ in. = 30 mi.
690 mi.

5. 4.6 in.   scale: 1 in. = 1.5 yd.
6.9 yd.

6. $3\frac{3}{4}$ in.   scale: $\frac{1}{4}$ in. = 10 mi.
150 mi.

7. $\frac{1}{4}$ in.   scale: $2\frac{1}{2}$ in. = 10 mi.
1 mi.

8. 3 in.   scale: 5 in. = 7.5 yd.
4.5 yd.

9. $1\frac{5}{8}$ in.   scale: $\frac{1}{4}$ in. = 40 mi.
260 mi.

10. 5.7 in.   scale: 5 in. = 50 ft.
57 ft.

Find the scale length for each actual length given.

11. 15.5 yd.   scale: 1 in. = 2 yd.
7.75 in.

12. 30 yd.   scale: 1 in. = 5 yd.
6 in.

13. 76 ft.   scale: $\frac{1}{2}$ in. = 2 ft.
19 in.

14. 550 yd.   scale: 0.5 in. = 50 yd.
5.5 in.

15. 225 mi.   scale: 1 in. = 50 mi.
$4\frac{1}{2}$ in.

16. 880 mi.   scale: 1 in. = 20 mi.
44 in.

17. 475 mi.   scale: 2 in. = 100 mi.
$9\frac{1}{2}$ in.

18. 10 yd.   scale: $\frac{1}{4}$ in. = 1 yd.
$2\frac{1}{2}$ in.

19. 32 mi.   scale: 5 in. = 160 mi.
1 in.

20. 1350 mi.   scale: 3 in. = 450 mi.
9 in.

▶ **Lesson 11.7**

Each pair of polygons is similar. Find the length of the unknown sides.

1.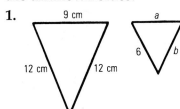

2.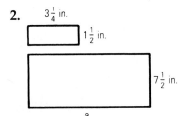

3.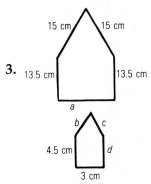

4.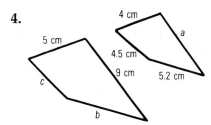

5.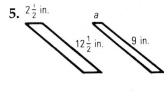

6.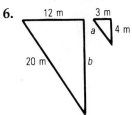

7.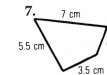

8.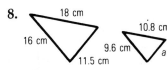

▶ Lesson 12.2

Write each decimal as a percent.

1. 0.1 — 10%
2. 0.86 — 86%
3. 0.33 — 33%
4. 0.175 — 17.5%
5. 0.858 — 85.8%
6. $0.66\overline{6}$ — $66\frac{2}{3}\%$
7. 0.97 — 97%
8. 0.206 — 20.6%
9. 0.41 — 41%
10. 0.06 — 6%
11. 0.29 — 29%
12. 0.8925 — 89.25%
13. 0.7 — 70%
14. 0.0225 — $2\frac{1}{4}\%$
15. 0.674 — 67.4%
16. 0.625 — 62.5%
17. 0.8 — 80%
18. 0.773 — $77\frac{1}{3}\%$
19. 0.09 — 9%
20. 0.11 — 11%
21. 0.028 — 2.8%
22. 0.59 — 59%
23. 0.035 — 3.5%
24. $0.55\overline{5}$ — $55\frac{1}{2}\%$
25. 0.084 — 8.4%
26. 0.48 — 48%
27. 0.915 — 91.5%
28. 0.30 — 30%
29. 0.73 — 73%
30. 0.059 — 5.9%

Write each percent as a decimal.

31. 69% — 0.69
32. 3% — 0.03
33. 19% — 0.19
34. 14.5% — 0.145
35. 40% — 0.4
36. $87\frac{1}{2}\%$ — 0.875
37. $8\frac{1}{2}\%$ — 0.085
38. 95% — 0.95
39. 11.8% — 0.118
40. 29% — 0.29
41. $13\frac{1}{2}\%$ — 0.135
42. $6\frac{1}{4}\%$ — 0.0625
43. 85% — 0.85
44. 6% — 0.06
45. $23\frac{3}{4}\%$ — 0.2375
46. 81% — 0.81
47. 65% — 0.65
48. $16\frac{2}{3}\%$ — $0.16\overline{6}$
49. $42\frac{1}{2}\%$ — 0.425
50. 21.4% — 0.214
51. 38.4% — 0.384
52. 76% — 0.76
53. $5\frac{1}{2}\%$ — 0.055
54. 22.6% — 0.226
55. $1\frac{1}{2}\%$ — 0.015
56. 2% — 0.02
57. 12% — 0.12
58. 43% — 0.43
59. 7.2% — 0.072
60. $83\frac{1}{3}\%$ — $0.833\overline{3}$

▶ Lesson 12.3

Write as a percent.

left column

1. $\frac{1}{10}$ — 10%
2. $\frac{16}{20}$ — 80%
3. $\frac{18}{27}$ — $66\frac{2}{3}\%$
4. $\frac{9}{24}$ — $37\frac{1}{2}\%$
5. $\frac{9}{20}$ — 45%
6. $\frac{1}{12}$ — $8\frac{1}{3}\%$
7. $\frac{25}{50}$ — 50%
8. $\frac{50}{60}$ — $83\frac{1}{3}\%$
9. $\frac{11}{12}$ — $91\frac{2}{3}\%$
10. $\frac{8}{8}$ — 100%
11. $\frac{9}{10}$ — 90%
12. $\frac{11}{25}$ — 44%
13. $\frac{2}{25}$ — 8%
14. $\frac{35}{45}$ — 77.8%
15. $\frac{12}{20}$ — 60%
16. $\frac{3}{12}$ — 25%
17. $\frac{15}{60}$ — 25%
18. $\frac{1}{6}$ — $16\frac{2}{3}\%$
19. $\frac{7}{12}$ — $58\frac{1}{3}\%$
20. $\frac{13}{20}$ — 65%
21. $\frac{13}{50}$ — 26%
22. $\frac{16}{25}$ — 64%
23. $\frac{13}{16}$ — $81\frac{1}{4}\%$
24. $\frac{6}{18}$ — $33\frac{1}{3}\%$
25. $\frac{1}{20}$ — 5%
26. $\frac{7}{25}$ — 28%
27. $\frac{2}{16}$ — 12.5%
28. $\frac{18}{30}$ — 60%
29. $\frac{25}{75}$ — $33\frac{1}{3}\%$
30. $\frac{5}{12}$ — $41\frac{2}{3}\%$
31. $\frac{39}{50}$ — 78%
32. $\frac{4}{5}$ — 80%
33. $\frac{17}{20}$ — 85%
34. $\frac{6}{8}$ — 75%
35. $\frac{1}{50}$ — 2%
36. $\frac{10}{10}$ — 100%

37. Susan made 33 out of 50 free throw attempts. What was her free throw percentage? 66%

38. Yolanda made 12 out of 15 free throw attempts. What was her free throw percentage? 80%

39. Paul made 8 out of 40 baskets during the last game. What was his shooting percentage? 20%

40. Jan made 28 out of 32 baskets during the same game. What was his shooting percentage? $87\frac{1}{2}\%$

▶ **Lesson 12.4**

Write as a fraction in lowest terms.

1. 60% $\frac{3}{5}$　　2. $8\frac{1}{3}$% $\frac{1}{12}$　　3. 2% $\frac{1}{50}$　　4. 93.75% $\frac{15}{16}$　5. 19% $\frac{19}{100}$　6. $91\frac{2}{3}$% $\frac{11}{12}$

7. $13\frac{1}{2}$% $\frac{27}{200}$　8. 6% $\frac{3}{50}$　　9. 74% $\frac{37}{50}$　10. 6.8% $\frac{17}{250}$　11. 3% $\frac{3}{100}$　12. 8% $\frac{2}{25}$

13. 80% $\frac{4}{5}$　　14. 29% $\frac{29}{100}$　15. 35% $\frac{7}{20}$　16. 50% $\frac{1}{2}$　　17. 44% $\frac{11}{25}$　18. $6\frac{2}{3}$% $\frac{1}{15}$

19. 7% $\frac{7}{100}$　20. $88\frac{1}{2}$% $\frac{177}{200}$ 21. $56\frac{1}{4}$% $\frac{9}{16}$　22. 10.5% $\frac{21}{200}$ 23. 68% $\frac{17}{25}$　24. 96% $\frac{24}{25}$

25. $35\frac{1}{4}$% $\frac{141}{400}$ 26. $87\frac{1}{2}$% $\frac{7}{8}$　27. 9% $\frac{9}{100}$　28. 70% $\frac{7}{10}$　29. $12\frac{1}{2}$% $\frac{1}{8}$　30. 15% $\frac{3}{20}$

31. In the mountains it snowed 78% of the days last year. What fraction is that? $\frac{39}{50}$

32. Last winter the sun was out 64% of the time. What fraction is that? $\frac{16}{25}$

33. It rained 25% of the time last summer. What fraction is that? $\frac{1}{4}$

34. In New York City, 10 percent of the temperatures were above 95 degrees last summer. What fraction is that? $\frac{1}{10}$

▶ **Lesson 12.6**

Write each fraction or decimal as a percent.

1. 8 800%　　2. $\frac{3}{800}$ 0.375%　3. $1\frac{3}{4}$ 175%　4. $\frac{9}{5}$ 180%　5. $\frac{2}{250}$ 0.8%　6. 2.2 220%

7. $6\frac{1}{2}$ 650%　8. 11 1100%　9. $\frac{6}{1000}$ 0.6%　10. $5\frac{2}{3}$ $566\frac{2}{3}$%　11. $\frac{45}{15}$ 300%　12. $5\frac{9}{10}$ 590%

13. 2.25 225%　14. $\frac{35}{7}$ 500%　15. 10.25 1025%　16. 4.4 440%　17. $\frac{7}{800}$ 0.875%　18. $\frac{5}{1000}$ 0.5%

19. 1.8 180%　20. 4.6 460%　21. 7.5 750%　22. $\frac{5}{800}$ 0.625%　23. $\frac{14}{7}$ 200%　24. $\frac{5}{600}$ $0.83\frac{1}{3}$%

25. 19 1900%　26. $\frac{10}{3}$ $333\frac{1}{3}$%　27. 12.5 1250%　28. $\frac{2}{1000}$ 0.2%　29. 9.75 975%　30. $\frac{2}{500}$ 0.4%

Write each percent as a fraction and as a decimal.

31. $\frac{7}{10}$%　　32. 525%　　33. $\frac{1}{20}$%　　34. $\frac{1}{3}$%　　35. $\frac{7}{8}$%　　36. $\frac{4}{5}$%

37. $\frac{1}{12}$%　　38. $\frac{7}{20}$%　　39. $\frac{1}{8}$%　　40. $\frac{2}{5}$%　　41. $\frac{3}{10}$%　　42. $\frac{2}{3}$%

43. $887\frac{1}{2}$%　44. $\frac{19}{20}$%　45. $166\frac{2}{3}$%　46. $\frac{1}{10}$%　　47. $\frac{1}{16}$%　　48. $\frac{1}{5}$%

Extra Practice Answers

Lesson 12.6

31. $\frac{7}{1000}$; 0.007

32. $5\frac{1}{4}$; 5.25

33. $\frac{1}{2000}$; 0.0005

34. $\frac{1}{300}$; $0.0033\frac{1}{3}$

35. $\frac{7}{800}$; 0.00875

36. $\frac{1}{125}$; 0.008

37. $\frac{1}{1200}$; $0.0008\frac{1}{3}$

38. $\frac{7}{2000}$; 0.0035

39. $\frac{1}{800}$; 0.00125

40. $\frac{1}{250}$; 0.004

41. $\frac{3}{1000}$; 0.003

42. $\frac{1}{150}$; $0.0066\frac{2}{3}$

43. $8\frac{7}{8}$; 8.875

44. $\frac{19}{2000}$; 0.0095

45. $1\frac{2}{3}$; $1.66\frac{2}{3}$

46. $\frac{1}{1000}$; 0.001

47. $\frac{1}{1600}$; 0.000625

48. $\frac{1}{500}$; 0.002

Find each number.

1. 40% of $32
$12.80

2. 15% of 2600
390

3. 300% of $250
$750

4. $66\frac{2}{3}$% of 1800
1200

5. 50% of 9
4.5

6. $33\frac{1}{3}$% of 66
22

7. 10% of 4321
432.1

8. 75% of 984
738

9. 64% of 8764
5608.96

10. 8% of 1790
143.2

11. 12% of $26,800
$3216

12. 9.5% of 784
74.48

13. 35% of $90
$31.50

14. 24% of 650
156

15. 300% of 430
1290

16. 63% of 78,500
49,455

17. 4% of 7890
315.6

18. 80% of $6400
$5120

19. $\frac{1}{4}$% of 240
0.6

20. 150% of 96
144

21. 0.5% of 40
0.2

22. 90% of $9840
$8856

23. 8% of $49
$3.92

24. 100% of 659
659

25. 50% of 964
482

26. 99% of 1700
1683

27. 12% of 992
119.04

28. 82% of 3750
3075

29. 136% of 225
306

30. 95% of 500
475

31. 37.5% of 96
36

32. 0.8% of 55
0.44

33. In a recent poll, 19% of the 400 people questioned said they preferred winter to summer. How many people was that?
76 people

34. In another poll, $\frac{1}{2}$% of 1000 people said they liked rainy days better than sunny days. How many people was that?
5 people

▶ **Lesson 12.8**

Find each percent.

1. 38 is what percent of 950? 4%

2. What percent of 88 is 528? 600%

3. 285 is what percent of 475? 60%

4. 322 is what percent of 2300? 14%

5. 616 is what percent of 1400? 44%

6. 0.28 is what percent of 35? $\frac{4}{5}$%

7. 33 is what percent of 264? 12.5%

8. 16 is what percent of 800? 2%

9. 1110 is what percent of 1200? 92.5%

10. What percent of 900 is 666? 74%

11. What percent of 5 is $\frac{1}{2}$? 10%

12. 504 is what percent of 56? 900%

13. 84 is what percent of 400? 21%

14. What percent of 80 is 0.4? $\frac{1}{2}$%

15. 57 is what percent of 152? 37.5%

16. 2.5 is what percent of 125? 2%

17. What percent of $10,000 is $750? 7.5%

18. 4.38 is what percent of 4.38? 100%

19. 150 is what percent of 60? 250%

20. 3466 is what percent of 13,864? 25%

21. Last year Company A made $30,000 in profits. This year the profits were $129,000. What percent of $30,000 is $129,000? 430%

22. Of the 900 people who work for the city, 702 of them received pay raises this year. What percent received pay raises? 78%

Extra Practice Answers

Lesson 13.5

(continued from page T442)

5. Outcomes:
h, h, h, h; h, h, h, t;
h, h, t, h; h, h, t, t;
h, t, h, h; h, t, h, t;
h, t, t, h; h, t, t, t;
t, h, h, h; t, h, h, t;
t, h, t, h; t, h, t, t;
t, t, h, h; t, t, h, t;
t, t, t, h; t, t, t, t

The probability is $\frac{6}{16}$ or $\frac{3}{8}$.

6. Outcomes:
1, 1; 1, 2; 1, 3; 1, 4;
1, 5; 1, 6; 2, 1; 2, 2;
2, 3; 2, 4; 2, 5; 2, 6;
3, 1; 3, 2; 3, 3; 3, 4;
3, 5; 3, 6; 4, 1; 4, 2;
4, 3; 4, 4; 4, 5; 4, 6;
5, 1; 5, 2; 5, 3; 5, 4;
5, 5; 5, 6; 6, 1; 6, 2;
6, 3; 6, 4; 6, 5; 6, 6

The probability is $\frac{2}{36}$ or $\frac{1}{18}$.

(continued on page T440)

▶ Lesson 12.9

Find the number.

1. 25% of what number is 69?
276

2. 2895 is 50% of what number?
5790

3. 100% of what number is 9.8?
9.8

4. 99% of what number is $19,800?
$20,000

5. 49% of what number is 3332?
6800

6. 24 is 80% of what number?
30

7. $695 is 8% of what number?
$8687.50

8. 300% of what number is 12?
4

9. 50 is 40% of what number?
125

10. 6 is 20% of what number?
30

11. 0.6% of what number is 3?
500

12. 87.5% of what number is 301?
344

13. $\frac{1}{2}$% of what number is 0.9?
180

14. $49.80 is 83% of what number?
$60

15. 45 is 5% of what number?
900

16. 396 is 90% of what number?
440

17. 18% of what number is $720?
$4000

18. 750% of what number is 7350?
980

19. $\frac{1}{4}$% of what number is 2.2?
880

20. $108 is 400% of what number?
$27

21. Seventy percent, or 266 students in the freshman class, eat fresh fruit for breakfast. How many students are there in the freshman class? 380 students

22. Thirty students, or 2.5% of the student body, are on the gymnastics team. How many students are there in all? 1200 students

▶ Lesson 12.10

Find the percent of change.

1. $25 to $30
20% increase

2. $150 to $75
50% decrease

3. 16 to 18
12.5% increase

4. 10 to 45
350% increase

5. 27 to 36
$33\frac{1}{3}$% increase

6. 144 to 168
$16\frac{2}{3}$% increase

7. $33 to $22
$33\frac{1}{3}$% decrease

8. $800 to $560
30% decrease

9. 8 to 10
25% increase

10. 75 to 45
40% decrease

11. $88 to $176
100% increase

12. $475 to $427.50
10% decrease

13. 21 to 105
400% increase

14. $9.90 to $6.93
30% decrease

15. 45,000 to 50,000
$11\frac{1}{9}$% increase

16. $36,000 to $20,160
44% decrease

17. $15.50 to $3.10
80% decrease

18. 300 to 500
$66\frac{2}{3}$% increase

19. 12 to 84
600% increase

20. 635 to 508
20% decrease

21. 10 to 11
10% increase

22. $700 to $1400
100% increase

23. 169 to 152.1
10% decrease

24. 80 to 24
70% decrease

25. $150 to $60
60% decrease

26. 4 to 36
800% increase

27. $45 to $42.75
5% decrease

28. The original cost of a computer was $1200. The price was lowered to $960. What was the percent of change? 20% decrease

29. A modem for a computer cost $125. The price was lowered to $115. What was the percent of change? 8% decrease

► # Lesson 13.2

One marble is drawn from a sack without looking. There are 5 blue marbles, 2 yellow marbles, and 3 white marbles. Find the probability of drawing the following.

1. a blue marble $\frac{5}{10}$ or $\frac{1}{2}$

2. a yellow marble $\frac{2}{10}$ or $\frac{1}{5}$

3. a blue or white marble $\frac{8}{10}$ or $\frac{4}{5}$

4. a blue or yellow marble $\frac{7}{10}$

A currency exchange sold the following license plates one day: MTH 458, MTH 459, MTH 460, MTH 461, MTH 462, 123 456, 123 457, and 123 458. You bought a license plate that day from the place and had no choice of plates. Find the probability that you received a license plate with the following.

5. an M $\frac{5}{8}$

6. numbers only $\frac{3}{8}$

7. a 6 $\frac{4}{5}$ or $\frac{1}{2}$

8. a T and a 5 $\frac{2}{8}$ or $\frac{1}{4}$

9. a 4 $\frac{8}{8}$ or $\frac{1}{1}$

10. a 4 and a 9 $\frac{1}{8}$

11. 2, 4, and 6 $\frac{2}{8}$ or $\frac{1}{4}$

12. an A $\frac{0}{8}$

► # Lesson 13.3

Before a skating contest 12 skaters drew numbers to determine the performance order. Find the following odds.

1. of skating first $\frac{1}{11}$

2. against skating last $\frac{11}{1}$

3. of skating in the first 6 $\frac{1}{1}$

4. of skating first or second $\frac{1}{5}$

5. against skating in the last 5 $\frac{7}{5}$

6. of skating in the first 10 $\frac{5}{1}$

The 26 company mailboxes were lettered A to Z and were assigned in no particular order. Find the following odds.

7. of getting the letter Q $\frac{1}{25}$

8. against getting the letter A $\frac{25}{1}$

9. against getting a vowel (A, E, I, O, or U) $\frac{21}{5}$

10. of getting a vowel (A, E, I, O, or U) $\frac{5}{21}$

11. of getting a letter in the first half of the alphabet $\frac{1}{1}$

12. against getting one of the first 10 letters $\frac{8}{5}$

Lesson 13.5

Tree diagrams are not shown.
1. Outcomes:
cheese pizza, thin crust;
cheese pizza, deep-dish crust;
sausage pizza, thin crust;
sausage pizza, deep-dish crust;
mushroom pizza, thin crust;
mushroom pizza, deep-dish crust;
combination pizza, thin crust;
combination pizza, deep-dish crust
2. Outcomes:
4-ounce juice, 4-ounce cola,
4-ounce milk, 4-ounce lemonade,
8-ounce juice, 8-ounce cola,
8-ounce milk, 8-ounce lemonade,
12-ounce juice, 12-ounce cola,
12-ounce milk, 12-ounce lemonade
3. Outcomes:
soccer and Spanish club,
soccer and pep band,
soccer and student council,
football and Spanish club,
football and pep band,
football and student council,
wrestling and Spanish club,
wrestling and pep band,
wrestling and student council,
baseball and Spanish club,
baseball and pep band,
baseball and student council,
track and Spanish club,
track and pep band,
track and student council
4. Outcomes:
h, h, 1; h, h, 2; h, h, 3;
h, h, 4; h, h, 5; h, h, 6;
h, t, 1; h, t, 2; h, t, 3;
h, t, 4; h, t, 5; h, t, 6;
t, h, 1; t, h, 2; t, h, 3;
t, h, 4; t, h, 5; t, h, 6;
t, t, 1; t, t, 2; t, t, 3;
t, t, 4; t, t, 5; t, t, 6

The probability is $\frac{1}{24}$.

(continued on page T439)

▶ **Lesson 13.5**

Draw a tree diagram listing all possible outcomes for each of the following.

1. making a cheese pizza, sausage pizza, mushroom pizza, or combination pizza with a thin crust or a deep-dish crust

2. choosing a 4-ounce, 8-ounce, or 12-ounce container of juice, soda, milk, or lemonade

3. choosing one sport from soccer, football, wrestling, baseball, and track and one club from Spanish club, pep band, and student council

Draw a tree diagram. Then find the probability of the underlined event. The order is not important.

4. a coin is tossed twice and a number cube is rolled; _2 heads and a 5_

5. a coin is tossed 4 times; _2 heads and 2 tails_

6. a number cube is rolled twice; _a 1 and a 2_

7. a number cube is rolled 3 times; _three 6s_

▶ **Lesson 13.6**

Find the number of possible outcomes. What is the probability that a computer would randomly select each of the underlined prizes?

1. vacations in Atlanta, Omaha, Detroit, Sacramento, or Buffalo staying at a hotel, motel, condominium, or resort; _resort in Atlanta_ 20 outcomes; $\frac{1}{20}$

2. $100, $500, $1000, or $5000 and a visit to the White House, the Grand Canyon, the Empire State Building, San Diego Zoo, the Statue of Liberty, or St. Louis Arch; _$500 and a trip to the White House_ 24 outcomes; $\frac{1}{24}$

3. tickets to 4 different concerts, 3 different plays, or 5 different sporting events and dinner at one of 10 different restaurants including La Diner; _a concert followed by dinner at La Diner_ 120 outcomes; $\frac{4}{120}$ or $\frac{1}{30}$

▶ **Lesson 14.2**

Find the perimeter of each polygon.

1.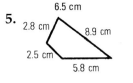
8.5 cm   8.5 cm
6.5 cm

2.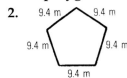
9.4 m   9.4 m
9.4 m   9.4 m
9.4 m

3.
$3\frac{1}{2}$ in.
$2\frac{3}{4}$ in.

4.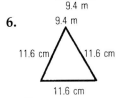
12 m
12 m

5.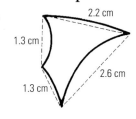
2.8 cm   8.9 cm
2.5 cm
5.8 cm

6.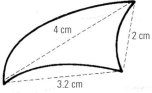
9.4 m
11.6 cm   11.6 cm
11.6 cm

7.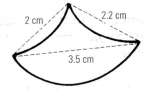
6.7 m
7.4 m

8.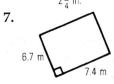
$1\frac{1}{2}$ in.
11 in.

9. Rectangle
$l = 12.7$ cm
$w = 2.9$ cm

10. Rectangle
$l = 6.2$ cm
$w = 3.9$ cm

11. Rectangle
$l = 5\frac{1}{2}$ ft.
$w = 8\frac{1}{2}$ ft.

12. Rectangle
$l = 9\frac{1}{2}$ in.
$w = 6\frac{3}{4}$ in.

13. 14.8 m   14.8 m   14.8 m   14.8 m

14. 9.2 cm   8.7 cm   6.3 cm

15. 7 in.   7 in.   7 in.   5 in.   5 in.

16. 12 ft.   13 ft.   8 ft.   9 ft.

▶ **Lesson 14.3**

Estimate the perimeter of each figure.

1.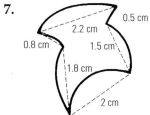
2.2 cm
1.3 cm
2.6 cm
1.3 cm

2.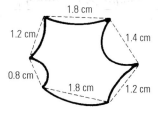
4 cm
2 cm
3.2 cm

3.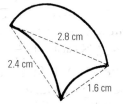
2 cm   2.2 cm
3.5 cm

4.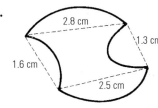
2.8 cm
1.3 cm
1.6 cm
2.5 cm

5.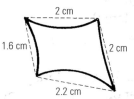
2 cm
1.6 cm   2 cm
2.2 cm

6.
2.8 cm
2.4 cm
1.6 cm

7.
0.5 cm
2.2 cm
0.8 cm   1.5 cm
1.8 cm
2 cm

8.
1.8 cm
1.2 cm   1.4 cm
0.8 cm
1.8 cm   1.2 cm

9.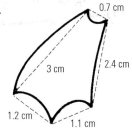
0.7 cm
3 cm   2.4 cm
1.2 cm   1.1 cm

▶ Lesson 14.4

Find each circumference.

1. $r = 0.9$ m
   ≈5.7 m
2. $d = 7$ cm
   ≈21.98 or 22 cm
3. $d = 100$ ft.
   ≈314 ft.
4. $r = 3.2$ cm
   ≈20.1 cm
5. $d = 15$ mm
   ≈47.1 mm
6. $r = 4.4$ m
   ≈27.6 m
7. $r = 1.7$ cm
   ≈10.7 cm
8. $d = 0.5$ m
   ≈1.6 m
9. $r = 16$ m
   ≈100.5 m
10. $r = 13$ cm
    ≈81.6 cm
11. $d = 20.2$ m
    ≈63.4 m
12. $d = 40$ ft.
    ≈125.6 ft.
13. $d = 3.6$ cm
    ≈11.3 cm
14. $r = 19$ m
    ≈119.3 m
15. $r = 16.5$ cm
    ≈103.6 cm
16. $d = 17$ m
    ≈53.4 m
17. $r = 0.3$ m
    ≈1.9 m
18. $d = 20$ cm
    ≈62.8 cm
19. $d = 5.1$ m
    ≈16.0 m
20. $r = 150$ ft.
    ≈942 ft.
21. $d = 1.1$ m
    ≈3.5 m
22. $r = 32$ mm
    ≈200.96 mm
23. $d = 11$ cm
    ≈34.54 cm
24. $r = 25$ in.
    ≈157 in.
25. $r = 55$ ft.
    ≈345.4 ft.
26. $d = 80$ mm
    ≈251.2 mm
27. $d = 260$ ft.
    ≈816.4 ft.
28. $r = 22$ cm
    ≈138.16 cm
29. $d = 0.2$ m
    ≈0.6 m
30. $d = 1.4$ cm
    ≈4.4 cm
31. $r = 5.7$ cm
    ≈35.8 cm
32. $r = 43$ m
    ≈270.04 m

▶ Lesson 14.5

Find the area of each parallelogram or rectangle.

1.
2.6 cm
2.6 cm

2.
6.5 m
7.5 m

3.
8 ft.
3 ft.

4.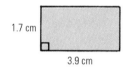
1.7 cm
3.9 cm

5.
3.5 m
8.2 m

6.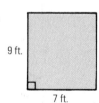
16 ft.
12 ft.

7.
5.6 cm
5.6 cm

8.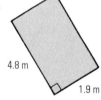
4.8 m
1.9 m

9.
$2\frac{3}{4}$ in.
3 in.

10.
14.5 m
14.5 m

11.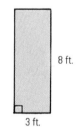
9 ft.
7 ft.

12.
5 cm
12 cm

13.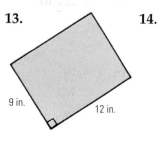
9 in.
12 in.

14.
15 ft.
5 ft.

15.
13.6 cm
13.6 cm

16.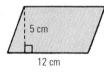
1.3 m
3.8 m

Extra Practice Answers
Lesson 14.5

1. 6.76 square centimeters
2. 48.75 square meters
3. 24 square feet
4. 6.63 square centimeters
5. 28.7 square meters
6. 192 square feet
7. 31.36 square centimeters
8. 9.12 square meters
9. $8\frac{1}{4}$ square inches
10. 210.25 square meters
11. 63 square feet
12. 60 square centimeters
13. 108 square inches
14. 75 square feet
15. 184.96 square centimeters
16. 4.94 square meters

▶ **Lesson 14.6**

Find the area of each triangle.

1.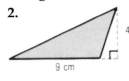
3 in.
4 in.

2.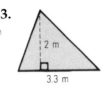
4 cm
9 cm

3.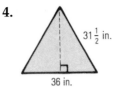
2 m
3.3 m

4.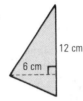
$31\frac{1}{2}$ in.
36 in.

5.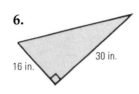
12 cm
10 cm

6.
16 in.
30 in.

7.
12 cm
6 cm

8.
6 ft.
1 ft.

9. $b = 9$ ft.
$h = 8$ ft.

10. $b = 25$ ft.
$h = 5\frac{1}{2}$ ft.

11. $b = 12$ cm
$h = 20$ cm

12. $b = 3.5$ m
$h = 15$ m

13. $b = 1.8$ m
$h = 7$ m

14. $b = 55$ in.
$h = 12$ in.

15. $b = 11.2$ cm
$h = 4.3$ cm

16. $b = 66$ mm
$h = 24$ mm

17. $b = 18$ m
$h = 20$ m

18. $b = 8\frac{1}{4}$ ft.
$h = 12\frac{2}{3}$ ft.

19. $b = 2.8$ m
$h = 3.2$ m

20. $b = 20$ cm
$h = 15$ cm

▶ **Lesson 14.7**

Find the area of each trapezoid.

1.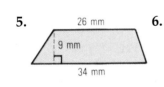
13 in.
8 in.
21 in.

2.
4.5 cm
3.0 cm
2.5 cm

3.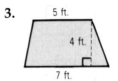
5 ft.
4 ft.
7 ft.

4.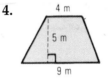
4 m
5 m
9 m

5.
26 mm
9 mm
34 mm

6.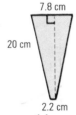
7.8 cm
20 cm
2.2 cm

7.
3.1 m
4 m
5.2 m

8.
17.7 cm
8 cm
8.9 cm

9. $a = 1.6$ m
$b = 8.6$ m
$h = 2$m

10. $a = 4$ in.
$b = 6$ in.
$h = 11$ in.

11. $a = 2.4$ cm
$b = 1.6$ cm
$h = 0.7$ cm

12. $a = 10\frac{1}{2}$ in.
$b = 15\frac{1}{2}$ in.
$h = 25$ in.

13. $a = 13$ in.
$b = 7$ in.
$h = 30$ in.

14. $a = 31$ in.
$b = 9\frac{1}{8}$ in.
$h = 8$ in.

15. $a = 9.7$ cm
$b = 15.1$ cm
$h = 5$ m

16. $a = 18\frac{3}{4}$ in.
$b = 19\frac{1}{4}$ in.
$h = 16$ in.

▶ **Lesson 14.8**

Find the area. Round answers to the nearest tenth as needed.

1. 2 m
2. 200 ft.
3. 1.3 cm
4. 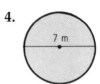 7 m

5. 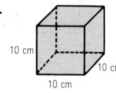 60 ft.
6. 14 ft.
7. 9 m
8. 42 cm

9. $r = 60$ ft.
10. $d = 4.8$ cm
11. $d = 80$ ft.
12. $r = 22$ in.

13. $d = 18.4$ cm
14. $r = 1.8$ m
15. $d = 42$ mm
16. $r = 80$ in.

17. $r = 19$ cm
18. $d = 150$ ft.
19. $d = 65$ m
20. $r = 17$ cm

21. $r = 6.2$ m
22. $d = 9.4$ m
23. $r = 0.3$ m
24. $d = 3.3$ cm

25. $d = 600$ ft.
26. $d = 75$ mm
27. $r = 99$ cm
28. $r = 430$ ft.

▶ **Lesson 15.3**

Find the surface area of each figure.

1. 10 cm, 10 cm, 10 cm
2. 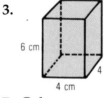 0.5 m, 0.8 m, 0.4 m
3. 6 cm, 4 cm, 4 cm
4. 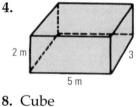 2 m, 3 m, 5 m

5. Prism
   $l = 12$ in.
   $w = 8$ in.
   $h = 4$ in.
6. Cube
   $s = 3.3$ m
7. Cube
   $s = 8.1$ cm
8. Cube
   $s = 3\frac{3}{4}$ ft.

9. Prism
   $l = 4$ in.
   $w = 3$ in.
   $h = 6$ in.
10. Cube
    $s = 9.8$ m
11. Cube
    $s = 13$ cm
12. Prism
    $l = 6.7$ cm
    $w = 4.1$ cm
    $h = 2.3$ cm

13. Prism
    $l = 3$ ft.
    $w = 1\frac{1}{2}$ ft.
    $h = 5\frac{1}{2}$ ft.
14. Cube
    $s = 25$ in.
15. Prism
    $l = 9$ in.
    $w = 7$ in.
    $h = 6$ in.
16. Cube
    $s = 12.2$ cm

Lesson 15.4

Find the surface area of each figure.

1.
10 in.
4 in.

2.
3 m
6 m

3.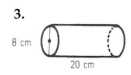
8 cm
20 cm

4.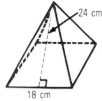
24 cm
18 cm

5. Cylinder
$h = 7$ cm
$r = 3$ cm

6. Pyramid
$s = 3$ m
$h = 6.5$ m

7. Cylinder
$h = 12$ m
$d = 10$ m

8. Cylinder
$h = 21$ m
$r = 8$ m

9. Cylinder
$h = 10$ ft
$d = 20$ ft.

10. Pyramid
$s = 8$ ft.
$h = 6$ ft.

11. Cylinder
$h = 9$ m
$r = 10$ m

12. Cylinder
$h = 4$ cm
$r = 4$ cm

13. Pyramid
$s = 6$ in.
$h = 5$ in.

14. Cylinder
$h = 11$ m
$r = 30$ m

15. Pyramid
$s = 11.5$ cm
$h = 9$ cm

16. Cylinder
$h = 6$ m
$d = 4$ m

Lesson 15.5

Find the volume of each figure.

1.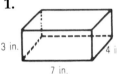
3 in.
4 in.
7 in.

2.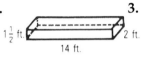
$1\frac{1}{2}$ ft.
2 ft.
14 ft.

3.
10 cm
8 cm

4.
5 m
5 m
5 m

5. Cube
$s = 8.5$ m

6. Cube
$s = 14$ cm

7. Prism
$l = 3$ ft.
$w = 3$ ft.
$h = 4$ ft.

8. Pyramid
$s = 5$ m
$a = 7$ m

9. Cube
$s = 30$ in.

10. Prism
$l = 9$ ft.
$w = 7$ ft.
$h = 20$ ft.

11. Pyramid
$s = 11$ cm
$a = 8$ cm

12. Prism
$l = 0.3$ m
$w = 0.6$ m
$h = 0.8$ m

13. Pyramid
$s = 25$ cm
$a = 22$ cm

14. Cube
$s = 6.4$ cm

15. Prism
$l = 8$ in.
$w = 2$ in.
$h = 14$ in.

16. Prism
$l = 48$ in.
$w = 12$ in.
$h = 2$ in.

Lesson 15.3 (continued)
14. 3750 square inches
15. 318 square inches
16. 893.04 square centimeters

Extra Practice Answers
Lesson 15.4
1. 96 square inches
2. ≈169.56 square meters
3. ≈602.88 square centimeters
4. 1188 square centimeters
5. ≈188.4 square centimeters
6. 48 square meters
7. ≈533.8 square meters
8. ≈1456.96 square meters
9. ≈1256 square feet
10. 160 square feet
11. ≈1193.2 square meters
12. ≈200.96 square centimeters
13. 96 square inches
14. ≈7724.4 square meters
15. 339.25 square centimeters
16. ≈100.48 square meters

Extra Practice Answers
Lesson 15.5
1. 84 cubic inches
2. 42 cubic feet
3. $213\frac{1}{3}$ or ≈213.3 cubic centimeters
4. 125 cubic meters
5. 614.125 cubic meters
6. 2744 cubic centimeters
7. 36 cubic feet
8. $58\frac{1}{3}$ or ≈58.3 cubic meters
9. 27,000 cubic inches
10. 1260 cubic feet
11. $322\frac{2}{3}$ or ≈322.7 cubic centimeters
12. 0.144 cubic meters
13. $4583\frac{1}{3}$ or ≈4583.3 cubic centimeters
14. 262.144 cubic centimeters
15. 224 cubic inches
16. 1152 cubic inches

▶ **Lesson 15.7**

Find the volume of each figure.

1.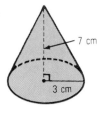
24 cm
6 cm

2.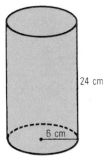
7 cm
3 cm

3.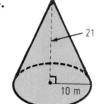
21 m
10 m

4.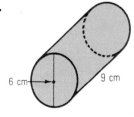
6 cm
9 cm

5. Cone
$r = 2$ cm
$a = 6$ cm

6. Cylinder
$r = 5$ cm
$h = 8$ cm

7. Cylinder
$d = 18$ m
$h = 7$ m

8. Cone
$r = 1.5$ m
$a = 5$ m

9. Cone
$d = 10$ cm
$a = 10$ cm

10. Cone
$r = 1.5$ m
$a = 1.5$ m

11. Cylinder
$r = 8$ cm
$h = 21$ cm

12. Cylinder
$r = 3$ cm
$h = 7$ cm

13. Cone
$d = 10.4$ cm
$a = 4$ cm

14. Cylinder
$r = 3$ m
$h = 12$ m

15. Cone
$r = 10$ cm
$a = 5$ cm

16. Cylinder
$d = 5$ m
$h = 3.7$ m

▶ **Lesson 16.2**

Write as an algebraic expression.

1. two times some number plus eight
$2n + 8$

2. six times some number
$6n$

3. some number more than thirteen
$13 + n$

4. ten less than forty-three
$43 - 10$

5. fifty minus three
$50 - 3$

6. the sum of some number and forty
$n + 40$

7. sixty-five minus some number
$65 - n$

8. twenty-eight times some number
$28n$

9. five times four
5×4

10. the sum of three and some number $3 + n$

11. ninety divided by some number $90 \div n$ or $\frac{90}{n}$

12. fourteen less than some number
$n - 14$

13. fifteen more than twenty-five
$25 + 15$

14. nine minus six
$9 - 6$

15. ten divided by five $10 \div 5$ or $\frac{10}{5}$

16. thirteen minus seven
$13 - 7$

17. seven times nine
7×9

18. the sum of seven and twenty
$7 + 20$

Write in words.

19. $5d - 6$

20. $12 + 3e$

21. $\frac{40}{c} - 7$

22. $11 + b$

23. $100 - z$

24. $6 + \frac{a}{9}$

25. $\frac{y}{30}$

26. $6t + 10$

▶ Lesson 16.3

Find the value of each expression.

1. $8 + e$ when $e = 37$
45

2. $\frac{x}{4} - 3$ when $x = 40$
7

3. $9a + 5$ when $a = 2$
23

4. $5y$ when $y = 15$
75

5. $f - 12$ when $f = 68$
56

6. $\frac{77}{7} - b$ when $b = 5$
6

7. $\frac{169}{c}$ when $c = 13$
13

8. $a + \frac{45}{a}$ when $a = 9$
14

9. $187 - r$ when $r = 49$
138

10. $8g + g$ when $g = 7$
63

11. $s + 35$ when $s = 18$
53

12. $\frac{65}{n}$ when $n = 5$
13

13. $\frac{86}{q} + q$ when $q = 2$
45

14. $\frac{16}{x} + 3$ when $x = 1$
19

15. $50r + r$ when $r = 10$
510

16. $a + 12a$ when $a = 12$
156

17. $129 - b$ when $b = 17$
112

18. $2c + 42$ when $c = 7$
56

19. $\frac{64}{t} - t$ when $t = 8$
0

20. $\frac{x}{3}$ when $x = 96$
32

21. $\frac{84}{r} + 3$ when $r = 2$
45

22. $4f + 9$ when $f = 3$
21

23. $91 - b$ when $b = 54$
37

24. $c + \frac{c}{8}$ when $c = 32$
36

▶ Lesson 16.4

Write as an equation.

1. Three times seven is some number. $3 \times 7 = n$

2. The quotient of twelve and some number is two. $12 \div n = 2$

3. Some number less than thirteen is five. $13 - n = 5$

4. The difference between fifty-eight and some number is four. $58 - n = 4$

5. The product of some number and nine minus twenty is fifty-two. $9n - 20 = 52$

6. The sum of thirty-eight and some number is ninety-four. $38 + n = 94$

7. Sixteen minus some number is eleven. $16 - n = 11$

8. Forty-eight divided by some number is three. $48 \div n = 3$

9. Some number divided by five plus twenty is thirty-eight. $n \div 5 + 20 = 38$

10. Thirty-one less than some number is fifty-two. $n - 31 = 52$

11. Five plus five times some number is seventy. $5 + 5n = 70$

12. The sum of six and some number is twenty-six. $6 + n = 26$

► Lesson 16.6

Solve.

1. $b + 6 = 18$
$b = 12$
2. $n - 9 = 15$
$n = 24$
3. $z + 12 = 61$
$z = 49$
4. $a - 2 = 50$
$a = 52$
5. $b - 5 = 42$
$b = 47$
6. $m - 3 = 19$
$m = 22$
7. $c + 16 = 30$
$c = 14$
8. $a - 17 = 3$
$a = 20$
9. $y - 34 = 9$
$y = 43$
10. $m + 18 = 54$
$m = 36$
11. $n - 23 = 2$
$n = 25$
12. $s + 26 = 53$
$s = 27$
13. $y - 30 = 12$
$y = 42$
14. $h + 55 = 65$
$h = 10$
15. $b + 4 = 19$
$b = 15$
16. $n + 12 = 20$
$n = 8$
17. $s + 7 = 16$
$s = 9$
18. $c + 21 = 29$
$c = 8$
19. $a - 32 = 14$
$a = 46$
20. $q + 14 = 28$
$q = 14$
21. $y - 13 = 23$
$y = 36$
22. $d + 19 = 38$
$d = 19$
23. $t - 25 = 55$
$t = 80$
24. $w - 59 = 31$
$w = 90$
25. $r - 12 = 48$
$r = 60$
26. $e + 75 = 100$
$e = 25$
27. $c - 15 = 40$
$c = 55$
28. $s - 9 = 35$
$s = 44$
29. $f - 8 = 42$
$f = 50$
30. $p + 44 = 66$
$p = 22$
31. $q + 5 = 35$
$q = 30$
32. $w - 16 = 32$
$w = 48$
33. $a - 33 = 11$
$a = 44$
34. $r + 21 = 46$
$r = 25$
35. $d + 9 = 54$
$d = 45$
36. $c - 6 = 24$
$c = 30$
37. $m - 25 = 8$
$m = 33$
38. $n + 13 = 39$
$n = 26$
39. $f - 11 = 88$
$f = 99$
40. $g + 42 = 80$
$g = 38$

► Lesson 16.7

Solve.

1. $25t = 125$ $t = 5$
2. $\frac{r}{12} = 12$ $r = 144$
3. $13x = 169$ $x = 13$
4. $\frac{b}{4} = 24$ $b = 96$

5. $\frac{x}{9} = 7$ $x = 63$
6. $\frac{m}{50} = 9$ $m = 450$
7. $6y = 72$ $y = 12$
8. $9s = 162$ $s = 18$

9. $\frac{r}{3} = 37$ $r = 111$
10. $7n = 105$ $n = 15$
11. $\frac{p}{8} = 32$ $p = 256$
12. $12w = 240$ $w = 20$

13. $\frac{y}{5} = 19$ $y = 95$
14. $10x = 440$ $x = 44$
15. $\frac{s}{6} = 90$ $s = 540$
16. $2c = 38$ $c = 19$

17. $3n = 45$ $n = 15$
18. $\frac{t}{2} = 75$ $t = 150$
19. $4x = 64$ $x = 16$
20. $\frac{y}{15} = 5$ $y = 75$

21. $\frac{z}{18} = 2$ $z = 36$
22. $9n = 216$ $n = 24$
23. $7r = 119$ $r = 17$
24. $\frac{q}{11} = 11$ $q = 121$

25. $8y = 120$ $y = 15$
26. $\frac{b}{14} = 5$ $b = 70$
27. $\frac{c}{22} = 30$ $c = 660$
28. $35r = 105$ $r = 3$

29. $16s = 96$ $s = 6$
30. $\frac{y}{8} = 18$ $y = 144$
31. $25d = 625$ $d = 25$
32. $\frac{c}{2} = 57$ $c = 114$

33. $40m = 280$ $m = 7$
34. $16b = 80$ $b = 5$
35. $\frac{r}{90} = 8$ $r = 720$
36. $\frac{q}{19} = 5$ $q = 95$

37. $\frac{y}{25} = 9$ $y = 225$
38. $12n = 600$ $n = 50$
39. $\frac{x}{18} = 4$ $x = 72$
40. $45p = 90$ $p = 2$

▶ Lesson 16.8

Solve.

1. $4x - 80 = 40$ $x = 30$
2. $8a + 55 = 127$ $a = 9$
3. $\frac{c}{10} - 3 = 9$ $c = 120$

4. $\frac{d}{5} - 8 = 1$ $d = 45$
5. $3e - 4 = 23$ $e = 9$
6. $\frac{p}{6} - 2 = 6$ $p = 48$

7. $4s - 2 = 26$ $s = 7$
8. $8x - 10 = 54$ $x = 8$
9. $\frac{a}{7} + 8 = 15$ $a = 49$

10. $2d + 6 = 16$ $d = 5$
11. $\frac{w}{2} + 13 = 88$ $w = 150$
12. $6y + 27 = 99$ $y = 12$

13. $\frac{b}{9} - 5 = 7$ $b = 108$
14. $\frac{m}{3} + 5 = 25$ $m = 30$
15. $\frac{q}{4} + 27 = 47$ $q = 80$

16. $3c - 5 = 7$ $c = 4$
17. $\frac{r}{2} + 5 = 19$ $r = 28$
18. $5a - 8 = 12$ $a = 4$

19. $8c - 13 = 43$ $c = 7$
20. $\frac{x}{11} + 10 = 15$ $x = 55$
21. $7n + 4 = 46$ $n = 6$

22. $10t + 9 = 129$ $t = 12$
23. $\frac{y}{5} - 5 = 5$ $y = 50$
24. $13s + 7 = 72$ $s = 5$

25. $\frac{a}{8} - 12 = 38$ $a = 400$
26. $9x + 23 = 104$ $x = 9$
27. $\frac{e}{2} + 47 = 71$ $e = 48$

28. $14r - 19 = 65$ $r = 6$
29. $25a + 15 = 240$ $a = 9$
30. $\frac{s}{3} - 41 = 17$ $s = 74$

▶ Lesson 17.2

Add.

1. $^{+}9 + {}^{-}4$ $+5$
2. $^{-}8 + {}^{-}13$ -21
3. $^{-}6 + {}^{+}15$ $+9$
4. $^{+}7 + {}^{+}23$ $+30$

5. $^{-}9 + {}^{-}12$ -21
6. $^{+}15 + {}^{+}35$ $+50$
7. $^{+}17 + {}^{-}11$ $+6$
8. $^{-}4 + {}^{+}4$ 0

9. $^{-}31 + {}^{+}37$ $+6$
10. $^{+}55 + {}^{+}20$ $+75$
11. $^{+}14 + {}^{-}28$ -14
12. $^{-}18 + {}^{-}19$ -37

13. $^{+}63 + {}^{-}63$ 0
14. $^{-}20 + {}^{-}38$ -58
15. $^{+}22 + {}^{-}74$ -52
16. $^{-}42 + {}^{-}16$ -58

17. $^{+}36 + {}^{+}54$ $+90$
18. $^{+}88 + {}^{-}11$ $+77$
19. $^{-}51 + {}^{+}69$ $+18$
20. $^{-}75 + {}^{-}150$ -225

21. $^{-}29 + {}^{+}29$ 0
22. $^{-}80 + {}^{-}46$ -126
23. $^{+}92 + {}^{+}33$ $+125$
24. $^{-}48 + {}^{+}17$ -31

25. $^{-}95 + {}^{-}67$ -162
26. $^{+}37 + {}^{-}66$ -29
27. $^{+}11 + {}^{+}72$ $+83$
28. $^{-}31 + {}^{-}52$ -83

29. $^{-}79 + {}^{-}49$ -128
30. $^{-}65 + {}^{+}13$ -52
31. $^{+}83 + {}^{-}14$ $+69$
32. $^{+}25 + {}^{+}56$ $+81$

33. $^{+}94 + {}^{-}87$ $+7$
34. $^{-}62 + {}^{+}17$ -45
35. $^{+}51 + {}^{-}51$ 0
36. $^{-}24 + {}^{-}74$ -98

37. $^{+}57 + {}^{+}39$ $+96$
38. $^{-}76 + {}^{+}42$ -34
39. $^{-}35 + {}^{-}85$ -120
40. $^{+}71 + {}^{-}66$ $+5$

▶ Lesson 17.3

Subtract.

1. +6 − −12 +18
2. −5 − −20 +15
3. +8 − +17 −9
4. −4 − +11 −15

5. −13 − +9 −22
6. +10 − −25 +35
7. −3 − −2 −1
8. +6 − −6 +12

9. +30 − +24 +6
10. −23 − −18 −5
11. +5 − −17 +22
12. −8 − +19 −27

13. +16 − −4 +20
14. +21 − −9 +30
15. −14 − −14 0
16. +31 − +35 −4

17. −45 − +35 −80
18. +21 − +21 0
19. +19 − +12 +7
20. −26 − +13 −39

21. +50 − −25 +75
22. −33 − −11 −22
23. +10 − −40 +50
24. −12 − +24 −36

25. −95 − −10 −85
26. −95 − +10 −105
27. +95 − +10 +85
28. +95 − −10 +105

29. +4 − −18 +22
30. −72 − +28 −100
31. +5 − −25 +30
32. −16 − −64 +48

33. −7 − +30 −37
34. +50 − +25 +25
35. −33 − −99 +66
36. +12 − +36 −24

37. +35 − +6 +29
38. −51 − −17 −34
39. −75 − +25 −100
40. +21 − −7 +28

▶ Lesson 17.4

Use the graph at the right. Write the ordered pair for each point.

1. E (4, 2)
2. A (−2, −2)
3. H (3, −5)

4. C (1, 6)
5. G (−5, 4)
6. B (−5, −4)

7. D (6, 0)
8. F (−3, 6)
9. K (1, −1)

10. M (3, 3)
11. P (−4, −6)
12. T (6, −6)

Name the point for each ordered pair.

13. (−4, 0) L
14. (5, 4) I
15. (−2, 1) J

16. (−6, −3) N
17. (5, −1) Q
18. (−5, 6) S

19. (0, −3) W
20. (4, 5) Z
21. (3, −3) X

22. (−2, 4) V
23. (2, −5) Y
24. (−6, 2) R

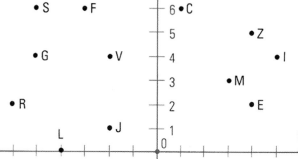

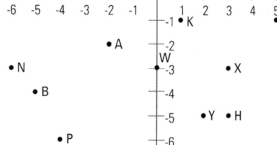

▶ Lesson 17.5

Multiply.

1. -9×-10 +90
2. $+15 \times +4$ +60
3. $+13 \times -13$ -169
4. $-25 \times +5$ -125

5. $+14 \times -2$ -28
6. -8×-20 +160
7. $+5 \times +60$ +300
8. -12×-3 +36

9. $+10 \times -40$ -400
10. -33×-2 +66
11. -16×-6 +96
12. $-3 \times +15$ -45

13. $+18 \times +2$ +36
14. -6×-40 +240
15. $+19 \times -4$ -76
16. -8×-21 +168

17. -29×-5 +145
18. $-66 \times +2$ -132
19. $+37 \times 0$ 0
20. -1×-99 +99

21. $+44 \times -7$ -308
22. $+17 \times -6$ -102
23. $+88 \times +3$ +264
24. $-36 \times +3$ -108

25. $-21 \times +8$ -168
26. $+50 \times -4$ -200
27. -42×-10 +420
28. $+93 \times -6$ -558

29. -38×-5 +190
30. $+18 \times -7$ -126
31. $-9 \times +24$ -216
32. $+34 \times +9$ +306

33. $+28 \times -4$ -112
34. -67×-1 +67
35. 0×-89 0
36. $-95 \times +5$ -475

37. -8×-26 +208
38. $+4 \times -49$ -196
39. $+12 \times -20$ -240
40. $+15 \times +15$ +225

▶ Lesson 17.6

Divide.

1. $-88 \div -11$ +8
2. $+40 \div -4$ -10
3. $+48 \div +12$ +4
4. $-65 \div +5$ -13

5. $-50 \div +25$ -2
6. $-84 \div -2$ +42
7. $+39 \div -13$ -3
8. $+93 \div +3$ +31

9. $+100 \div +10$ +10
10. $-66 \div +33$ -2
11. $-42 \div -3$ +14
12. $+81 \div -3$ -27

13. $-125 \div +5$ -25
14. $-60 \div -4$ +15
15. $+96 \div +16$ +6
16. $+108 \div -9$ -12

17. $-400 \div -50$ +8
18. $+320 \div +80$ +4
19. $+280 \div -70$ -4
20. $-630 \div +90$ -7

21. $+128 \div -2$ -64
22. $-195 \div -5$ +39
23. $-90 \div +9$ -10
24. $+121 \div +11$ +11

25. $-84 \div -4$ +21
26. $+120 \div -6$ -20
27. $-168 \div +8$ -21
28. $+225 \div +25$ +9

29. $+444 \div -4$ -111
30. $-98 \div +2$ -49
31. $-75 \div -1$ +75
32. $+169 \div -13$ -13

33. $-130 \div -10$ +13
34. $+225 \div -15$ -15
35. $-300 \div +30$ -10
36. $+96 \div +3$ +32

37. $+70 \div -5$ -14
38. $-55 \div +5$ -11
39. $-200 \div -4$ +50
40. $+99 \div +9$ +11

▶ Lesson 17.7

Solve. Check your answers.

1. $m + {}^-8 = {}^-4$
$m = {}^+4$

2. $n - {}^-7 = {}^+28$
$n = {}^+21$

3. $c + {}^+15 = {}^-45$
$c = {}^-60$

4. $d - {}^+6 = {}^-26$
$d = {}^-20$

5. $x - {}^-10 = {}^+25$
$x = {}^+15$

6. $b + {}^+13 = {}^-3$
$b = {}^-16$

7. $e - {}^-7 = {}^+38$
$e = {}^+31$

8. $r + {}^-21 = {}^+15$
$r = {}^+36$

9. $y + {}^+5 = {}^-62$
$y = {}^-67$

10. $w - {}^-12 = {}^+6$
$w = {}^-6$

11. $f + {}^-30 = {}^-9$
$f = {}^+21$

12. $b - {}^+4 = {}^+48$
$b = {}^+52$

13. $s + {}^-3 = {}^-13$
$s = {}^-10$

14. $d - {}^-25 = {}^+7$
$d = {}^-18$

15. $m - {}^+54 = {}^-1$
$m = {}^+53$

16. $c + {}^+12 = {}^+36$
$c = {}^+24$

17. $c - {}^+17 = {}^-8$
$c = {}^+9$

18. $n + {}^-38 = {}^-5$
$n = {}^+33$

19. $e - {}^-27 = {}^+2$
$e = {}^-25$

20. $r + {}^-33 = {}^-44$
$r = {}^-11$

21. $a + {}^-23 = {}^-9$
$a = {}^+14$

22. $r - {}^-51 = {}^-8$
$r = {}^-59$

23. $m - {}^+27 = {}^-3$
$m = {}^+24$

24. $z + {}^+48 = {}^+75$
$z = {}^+27$

25. $b - {}^+16 = {}^+4$
$b = {}^+20$

26. $x + {}^-57 = {}^-1$
$x = {}^+56$

27. $n - {}^-12 = {}^+3$
$n = {}^-9$

28. $c + {}^-66 = {}^-17$
$c = {}^+49$

29. $e + {}^+25 = {}^+2$
$e = {}^-23$

30. $t - {}^+11 = {}^-8$
$t = {}^+3$

31. $s + {}^-8 = {}^+72$
$s = {}^+80$

32. $m - {}^-8 = {}^-40$
$m = {}^-48$

33. $y - {}^-13 = {}^+9$
$y = {}^-4$

34. $b + {}^+7 = {}^-30$
$b = {}^-37$

35. $c - {}^+16 = {}^+9$
$c = {}^+25$

36. $n + {}^-7 = {}^+24$
$n = {}^+31$

37. $t + {}^-45 = {}^-6$
$t = {}^+39$

38. $r - {}^-90 = {}^+8$
$r = {}^-82$

39. $b + {}^+64 = {}^-3$
$b = {}^-67$

40. $r - {}^+53 = {}^-58$
$r = {}^-5$

▶ Lesson 17.8

Solve.

1. $-6n = -36$
$n = {}^+6$

2. $\dfrac{x}{-4} = {}^+7$
$x = {}^-28$

3. $+3b = -39$
$b = -13$

4. $\dfrac{r}{+8} = -10$
$r = -80$

5. $\dfrac{c}{+2} = {}^+34$
$c = {}^+68$

6. $\dfrac{d}{-12} = -5$
$d = {}^+60$

7. $-5s = -65$
$s = {}^+13$

8. $-7w = {}^+105$
$w = -15$

9. $-9t = -90$
$t = {}^+10$

10. $\dfrac{b}{+5} = -20$
$b = -100$

11. $\dfrac{m}{+8} = {}^+9$
$m = {}^+72$

12. $-6b = {}^+96$
$b = -16$

13. $-4r = {}^+120$
$r = -30$

14. $\dfrac{n}{-12} = -12$
$n = {}^+144$

15. $-9e = -81$
$e = {}^+9$

16. $\dfrac{y}{+2} = -38$
$y = -76$

17. $\dfrac{w}{-30} = {}^+5$
$w = -150$

18. $-14f = {}^+56$
$f = {}^-4$

19. $\dfrac{d}{-15} = -6$
$d = {}^+90$

20. $-4s = -60$
$s = {}^+15$

21. $+11b = {}^+121$
$b = {}^+11$

22. $+20c = -180$
$c = {}^-9$

23. $\dfrac{s}{+70} = -7$
$s = -490$

24. $\dfrac{w}{-8} = -100$
$w = {}^+800$

25. $-33a = {}^+99$
$a = {}^-3$

26. $\dfrac{t}{-60} = -2$
$t = {}^+120$

27. $\dfrac{r}{+80} = -10$
$r = -800$

28. $-6b = {}^+90$
$b = -15$

29. $\dfrac{x}{+13} = {}^+13$
$x = {}^+169$

30. $\dfrac{y}{-25} = {}^+8$
$y = -200$

31. $-19c = -95$
$c = {}^+5$

32. $-41a = -123$
$a = {}^+3$

33. $+50c = -600$
$c = -12$

34. $-18d = -54$
$d = {}^+3$

35. $\dfrac{e}{-75} = {}^+4$
$e = -300$

36. $\dfrac{f}{+12} = {}^+9$
$f = {}^+108$

37. $\dfrac{t}{-11} = -11$
$t = {}^+121$

38. $\dfrac{w}{+2} = -44$
$w = -88$

39. $-4s = -48$
$s = {}^+12$

40. $-8n = -32$
$n = {}^+4$

Solve.

1. $\dfrac{r}{+3} - {}^-8 = {}^+18$
$r = {}^+30$

2. $^-8s + {}^+9 = {}^+73$
$s = {}^-8$

3. $^+12y - {}^+7 = {}^-79$
$y = {}^-6$

4. $^-5w + {}^-3 = {}^-33$
$w = {}^+6$

5. $\dfrac{c}{-4} + {}^+6 = {}^+26$
$c = {}^-80$

6. $\dfrac{d}{-10} - {}^-15 = {}^+8$
$d = {}^+70$

7. $^-6t - {}^-13 = {}^-5$
$t = {}^+3$

8. $^-9y + {}^-25 = {}^-7$
$y = {}^-2$

9. $\dfrac{a}{-2} - {}^+25 = {}^-75$
$a = {}^+100$

10. $\dfrac{b}{+8} + {}^-15 = {}^-22$
$b = {}^-56$

11. $\dfrac{f}{-15} - {}^-30 = {}^+27$
$f = {}^+45$

12. $^-13r + {}^+14 = {}^-12$
$r = {}^+2$

13. $^-10a - {}^-27 = {}^+67$
$a = {}^-4$

14. $^+12t + {}^-18 = {}^-78$
$t = {}^-5$

15. $\dfrac{x}{-50} + {}^+6 = {}^-4$
$x = {}^+500$

16. $^+4c - {}^+3 = {}^-51$
$c = {}^-12$

17. $^-8b + {}^-4 = {}^-28$
$b = {}^+3$

18. $\dfrac{w}{-42} - {}^-15 = {}^+13$
$w = {}^+84$

19. $\dfrac{e}{-75} - {}^+9 = {}^-11$
$e = {}^+150$

20. $^-3d + {}^-66 = {}^-33$
$d = {}^-11$

21. $^-8x - {}^-1 = {}^-63$
$x = {}^+8$

22. $\dfrac{m}{-4} + {}^-15 = {}^-20$
$m = {}^+20$

23. $\dfrac{r}{+6} - {}^+9 = {}^+1$
$r = {}^+60$

24. $^-5w + {}^+25 = 0$
$w = {}^+5$

25. $^+9s - {}^-50 = {}^-22$
$s = {}^-8$

26. $\dfrac{y}{-10} + {}^-27 = {}^-18$
$y = {}^-90$

27. $^+14t - {}^+4 = {}^-32$
$t = {}^-2$

28. $^-3x + {}^+24 = {}^-12$
$x = {}^+12$

29. $^+7a - {}^-5 = {}^+54$
$a = {}^+7$

30. $\dfrac{b}{-6} - {}^+11 = {}^-16$
$b = {}^+30$

Appendix

Calculator Applications

▶ Basic Calculator Operations

All calculators have standard keys that allow you to perform the basic mathematical operations of addition $\boxed{+}$, subtraction $\boxed{-}$, multiplication $\boxed{\times}$, and division $\boxed{\div}$. Just enter the problem in the order you would solve it using a pencil and paper, and then press $\boxed{=}$ to get the answer.

Whenever you begin a problem, clear the calculator. Not all calculators clear in the same way, but two common clear keys are $\boxed{c}$ and $\boxed{\text{AC}}$. If you make a mistake in the middle of a problem, you can correct the last step by pushing the clear error key, either $\boxed{\text{CE}}$ or $\boxed{c}$.

One Operation		Two Operations		Correcting An Error	
275 + 319 + 481		57.1 + 473.9 ÷ 0.5		149 × 3.5	
Enter	**Display**	**Enter**	**Display**	**Enter**	**Display**
$\boxed{c}$ or $\boxed{\text{AC}}$	0.	$\boxed{c}$ or $\boxed{\text{AC}}$	0.	$\boxed{c}$ or $\boxed{\text{AC}}$	0.
275	275.	473.9	473.9	149	149.
$\boxed{+}$	275.	$\boxed{\div}$	473.9	$\boxed{\times}$	149.
319	319.	0.5	0.5	2.5	2.5
$\boxed{+}$	594.	$\boxed{+}$	947.8	$\boxed{\text{CE}}$ or $\boxed{c}$	0.
481	481.	57.1	57.1	3.5	3.5
$\boxed{=}$	1075.	$\boxed{=}$	1004.9	$\boxed{=}$	521.5

275 + 319 + 481   57.1 + 473.9 ÷ 0.5   149 × 3.5 = 521.5
     = 1075   = 1004.9

Estimation is a valuable skill in calculator use, since it is easy to make mistakes when entering numbers on the calculator. Always check the answers the calculator gives to make sure that they are reasonable.

For each of the following problems, estimate the answer mentally. Then use your calculator to solve. If an estimated answer and a calculated answer are very different, recompute. Remember to use order of operations. Round each answer to the nearest hundredth.

1. 6791 + 22,372 + 47
29,210

2. 23.9 × 73.8 − 467.5
1296.32

3. 0.11336 ÷ 0.11336
1.00

4. 8899 ÷ 47.3 × 2.005
377.22

5. 7.136 × 35 − 329.4
⁻79.64

6. 5872 + 2.7 ÷ 3.234
5872.83

7. 7 × 37,037 × 3
777,777

8. 201 − 47.3 × 2.01
105.93

9. 55 − 5.13 × 6.7 + 1.2
21.83

10. 374 + 8194 − 92 × 5
8108

11. 4592 ÷ 61 − 43
32.28

12. 1.993 + 4.505 × 1.993
10.97

▶ Interpreting Quotients

When you divide to solve a problem and the answer is not a whole number, you have to interpret the quotient. Read the Example and Questions A and B below.

Example. 194 students are going on a field trip. They will travel on buses that hold 40 passengers.

A How many buses can be completely filled?
B How many buses will be needed to hold all the students?

For both questions, enter 194 ÷ 40 = on your calculator. The answer should be 4.85.

Answer to Question A: The whole-number part of 4.85 shows that 4 buses can be completely filled.

Answer to Question B: The decimal part of 4.85 shows that 1 bus will be partially filled. Thus, 5 buses will be needed in all.

Use your calculator to solve each problem below.

1. 1 case holds 24 bottles; you have 844 bottles. How many full cases will you have? 35

2. 1 pencil box holds 12 pencils; you have 72 pencils. How many pencil boxes will you need? 6

3. Every classroom has seats for 35 students; there are 187 freshmen. How many freshman homerooms are needed? 6

4. The population of the Boston metropolitan area is 5,563,000. Fenway Park, home of the Boston Red Sox, has a seating capacity of 33,871. How many times must Fenway Park be filled to hold the entire Boston area population? 165

5. 1 bus token costs $0.35. Anne has $8.92. How many bus tokens can she buy? How much money will she have left over? 25; $0.17

6. Maxwell builds toolboxes. It takes him 45 minutes to finish one box. How many boxes does he complete in an 8-hour day? 10

7. Mar Vista Cleaners charges $1.45 for each 8-pound load of laundry. Gregor has 37 pounds of laundry. How much will it cost him to have his laundry done? $7.25

8. Tamara must cut as many 5-inch strips as she can out of $6\frac{1}{2}$ yards of fabric. How many strips will she end up with? 46

▶ Using Percents

The calculator's ⊠ key, in combination with the operation keys, can make some mathematical tasks easier. Even if your calculator doesn't have a ⊠ key, you can still calculate percents. Simply change the percents to decimals.

Example A. Calculate a 15% tip on a meal tab of $18. Without a ⊠ key, enter as follows: 18 ⊠ .15 🟰. With a ⊠ key, enter as follows: 18 ⊠ 15 ⊠. The answer is $2.70.

Find the tip, at a rate of 15%, on the following amounts. Round to the nearest ten cents.

   1. $26.89 $4.00 **2.** $46.27 $6.90 **3.** $8.12 $1.20 **4.** $3.50 $0.50 **5.** $19.75 $3.00

Since not all calculators use the same method to calculate percents, four methods are presented below for finding a total price with tax. Method 1 shows how to calculate a total price without a ⊠ key. Methods 2, 3, and 4 are for calculators with a ⊠ key. Try all that your calculator allows. Then use the quickest one that gives the correct answer.

Example B. Find the total price of a $17.99 item with $6\frac{1}{2}$% tax.

Method 1		Method 2		Method 3		Method 4	
Enter	**Display**	**Enter**	**Display**	**Enter**	**Display**	**Enter**	**Display**
17.99	17.99	17.99	17.99	17.99	17.99	17.99	17.99
✕	17.99	✕	17.99	+	17.99	+	17.99
.065	0.065	6.5	6.5	6.5	6.5	6.5	6.5
+	1.16935	%	1.16935	%	1.16935	%	19.15935
17.99	17.99	+	1.16935	=	19.15935	**Round to $19.16**	
=	19.15935	17.99	17.99	**Round to $19.16**			
Round to $19.16		=	19.15935				
		Round to $19.16					

Use your calculator to find the total price of each item.

  6. A $24.99 sweater; sales tax is 5% $26.24

  7. A $6.99 record and a $5.79 cassette; sales tax is 7% $13.67

  8. 3 pounds of cashews at $5.89 a pound; sales tax is 4% $18.38

  9. A $120 coat marked down 50%; sales tax is $6\frac{1}{2}$% $63.90

10. A $33 bookbag selling for $\frac{1}{3}$ off; sales tax is $4\frac{1}{2}$% $22.99

▶ Pythagorean Theorem

When a variable n is multiplied by itself we refer to it as n^2 (stated as "n squared" or "n to the second power").

$$n^2 = n \times n$$

For example, $3^2 = 3 \times 3 = 9$, and
$$12^2 = 12 \times 12 = 144.$$
To find 12^2 using a calculator, press 12 ⊠ 12 ⊟ or 12 ⊠⊟.

All right triangles obey a special relationship called the *Pythagorean Theorem*. The theorem is represented by the equation $a^2 + b^2 = c^2$.

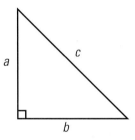

You can determine if a triangle is a right triangle by substituting the lengths of the sides given for a, b, and c in the equation. The longest measure must be substituted for c.

Use the Pythagorean Theorem to determine if the given sides form right triangles.

1. $(3, 4, 5)$ yes **2.** $(6, 7, 8)$ no **3.** $(7, 24, 25)$ yes **4.** $(6, 8, 10)$ yes

5. $(16, 63, 65)$ yes **6.** $(5, 10, 15)$ no **7.** $(30, 40, 50)$ yes **8.** $(48, 55, 73)$ yes

To find the longest side of a right triangle when the other two sides are given, find $a^2 + b^2$. Then press √ (called the "square root key").

Find the longest side of each right triangle with the known given sides.

9. $(5, 12, \underline{\quad})$ 13 **10.** $(9, 12, \underline{\quad})$ 15 **11.** $(20, 21, \underline{\quad})$ 29 **12.** $(8, 15, \underline{\quad})$ 17

13. $(12, 35, \underline{\quad})$ 37 **14.** $(33, 56, \underline{\quad})$ 65 **15.** $(39, 80, \underline{\quad})$ 89 **16.** $(65, 72, \underline{\quad})$ 97

To find a third side when the longest side is given, find $c^2 - a^2$ (or $c^2 - b^2$). Then press √.

Find the unknown side for each right triangle.

17. $(\underline{\underset{12}{\quad}}, 16, 20)$ **18.** $(20, \underline{\underset{99}{\quad}}, 101)$ **19.** $(28, \underline{\underset{45}{\quad}}, 53)$ **20.** $(\underline{\underset{36}{\quad}}, 77, 85)$

Real-Life Applications

▶ Paychecks

Often when you receive a paycheck, you will find that **deductions** have been taken by your employer. These deductions cover such obligatory payments as federal income tax (FIT), state income tax, and Social Security tax (or FICA, Federal Insurance Contributions Act). In addition, voluntary payments into a health insurance plan or charities may be deducted from your paycheck.

The amount of money that you actually receive is called your **net pay**. The amount of money that you earn (hours worked × hourly wage) is called your **gross pay**.

Net pay = Gross pay − Deductions

| | | | | Amount earned | Gross pay − Deductions |
Dept.	Employee	Check No.	Pay Period	Gross Pay	Net Pay
Sales	Martin, H.	60783	3/7–3/13/88	$340.40	$235.36

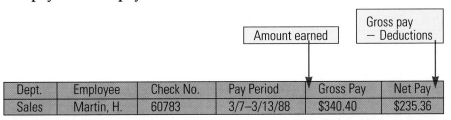

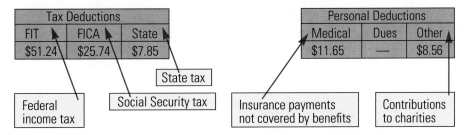

Use the pay statement above to answer the following questions.

1. How long is the pay period covered by this check? One week

2. Henry Martin earns $7.40 an hour for a regular 40-hour week and time and a half for overtime. Use Henry's gross pay to determine how many hours he worked in the pay period covered by this check. 44 hours

3. Calculate the total taxes paid. $84.83

4. Calculate the total deductions for health insurance ("Medical") and charities ("Other"). $20.21

5. What are the total deductions listed on this pay statement? $105.04

6. Show how Henry's net pay was determined. $340.40 − $105.40 = $235.36

▶ Sales Receipts

When you go shopping, you usually receive a sales receipt as proof of purchase. The receipt may be a cash register tape listing amounts only, a computer slip listing both items purchased and amounts, or a sales slip such as the one shown below. A receipt indicates the price of each item you bought, the sales tax (if any), and the total amount you paid.

Total purchase price = Sum of items bought + Sales tax

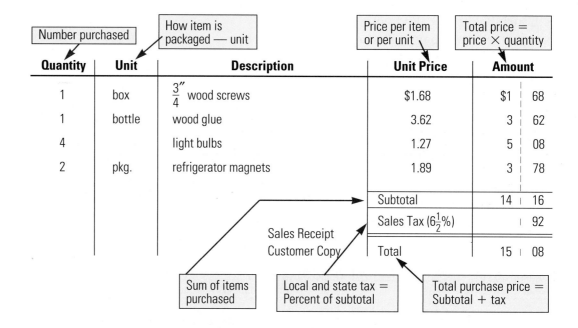

Use the sales receipt above to answer the following questions.

1. What is the sales tax rate (percent) on the items purchased? $6\frac{1}{2}\%$

2. Calculate the amount of sales tax on the original order at a rate of $4\frac{1}{2}\%$. What would the total purchase price be? $0.64; $14.80

3. How much does 1 light bulb cost? What would the total purchase price be if 6 light bulbs were bought, instead of 4? $1.27; $17.79

4. What would the sales tax on the original order be if, in addition, 2 extension cords costing $2.98 each were purchased? $1.31

5. Suppose that, instead of $0.92, the sales tax on the original order is $0.57. What is the tax rate? 4%

▶ Checking Accounts

When you write checks, make deposits into your checking account, or use an automatic teller machine to withdraw cash from your account, it is important that you write down the amount of your transaction. Check registers are designed to help you keep track of your account. One column is for withdrawals, and another column is for deposits. The **balance** column shows how much money you have in your account.

New balance = Previous balance − Check amount
New balance = Previous balance + Deposit amount

Balance brought forward from previous page

Check No.	Date	Description	Amount of Check	Amount of Deposit	Balance
					$429.02
	3/14	Paycheck deposit		$125.53	554.55
583	3/17	Fox's Sporting Goods	$73.92		480.63
584	3/19	Marcy's Clothing Store	59.45		421.18
	3/20	Deposit of birthday money		25.00	446.18

Previous balance + Deposit amount

Previous balance − Check amount

Use the check register above for the following problems.

1. Write the calculation that gives the second balance. $429.02 + $125.53 = $554.55

2. Write the calculation that gives the third balance. $554.55 − $73.92 = $480.63

3. Write the calculation that gives the fourth balance. $480.63 − $59.45 = $421.18

4. What will the new balance be if a check is written for $27.92? $418.26

Complete the balance column in the check register below.

	Check No.	Date	Description	Amount of Check	Amount of Deposit	Balance	
						$261.39	
5.	954	7/1	Lions baseball tickets	$23.75		?	$237.64
6.		7/5	Refund		$19.99	?	$257.63
7.	955	7/5	Eatery Grocery Store	42.81		?	$214.82
8.		7/7	Paycheck deposit		$172.64	?	$387.46

Stock Market

Investing in the Stock Market allows people to buy an "interest" in a corporation. This interest is called a *share*. If the company is successful, then the value of each share increases and the shareholders earn money. On the other hand, if the company is not successful, then the shares you own go down in value, and shareholders lose money.

Here is an example of how math is used by people who invest in the stock market. Suppose a person buys 10 shares of a corporation for $85 per share. The shares would cost $850. What if in six months the stock value rises to $105 per share? The ten shares are now worth $1050. The person has earned $200 by investing in this corporation's stock.

The newspaper gives many facts about a stock. This table shows how stocks are reported in the newspaper. Some of the key information you can find is the total amount of shares bought and sold that day (volume), the high and low price for the year, the latest price (last), and if the stock went up (+) or down (−) that day.

	High	Low	Last	Change	Volume (× 100)
Sip Stores	$4\frac{7}{16}$	$26\frac{3}{4}$	42	$-\frac{11}{16}$	31675
Good Motors	$78\frac{3}{8}$	$38\frac{7}{8}$	$62\frac{13}{16}$	$-1\frac{5}{16}$	34990
Fun Park	$40\frac{5}{16}$	$22\frac{1}{2}$	$30\frac{1}{2}$	$+\frac{1}{2}$	71386
Disco Donut	$53\frac{3}{8}$	$26\frac{1}{4}$	$43\frac{3}{4}$	$+\frac{1}{8}$	101035
Tons of Toys	$44\frac{1}{2}$	$21\frac{1}{4}$	$23\frac{7}{16}$	$+\frac{9}{16}$	56913

Use the stock report to answer these questions.

1. How much did one share of Sip Stores cost at the end of the day? Did the value of the stock go up or down? $42; down, the change is $\frac{11}{16}$
2. What is Fun Park's high for the year? $40\frac{5}{16}$ Low? $22\frac{1}{2}$
3. Which stock did the best today? Tons of Toys, up $\frac{9}{16}$
4. Which stock has the highest value? Good Motors
5. Which stock had the highest volume of trading on this day? Disco Donut
6. Which stock is closest to its high for the year? Sip Stores

Table of Measures

Time

60 seconds (sec.) = 1 minute (min.)
60 minutes (min.) = 1 hour (hr.)
24 hours = 1 day
7 days = 1 week

$$\left.\begin{array}{l} 365 \text{ days} \\ 12 \text{ months (mo.)} \end{array}\right\} = 1 \text{ year (yr.)}$$

366 days = 1 leap year
10 years = 1 decade
100 years = 1 century

Metric System of Measurement

Length
10 millimeters (mm) = 1 centimeter (cm)

$$\left.\begin{array}{l} 1000 \text{ millimeters} \\ 100 \text{ centimeters} \end{array}\right\} = 1 \text{ meter (m)}$$

1000 meters = 1 kilometer (km)

Capacity
1000 milliliters (mL) = 1 liter (L)
1000 liters = 1 kiloliter (kL)

Mass
1000 milligrams (mg) = 1 gram (g)
1000 grams = 1 kilogram (kg)
1000 kilograms = 1 metric ton (T)

Temperature
Water freezes at 0 degrees Celsius (0° C).
Water boils at 100 degrees Celsius (100° C).

Customary System of Measurement

Length
12 inches (in.) = 1 foot (ft.)

$$\left.\begin{array}{l} 36 \text{ inches} \\ 3 \text{ feet} \end{array}\right\} = 1 \text{ yard (yd.)}$$

$$\left.\begin{array}{l} 1760 \text{ yards} \\ 5280 \text{ feet} \end{array}\right\} = 1 \text{ mile (mi.)}$$

Capacity
8 fluid ounces (fl. oz.) = 1 cup (c.)

$$\left.\begin{array}{l} 16 \text{ fluid ounces} \\ 2 \text{ cups} \end{array}\right\} = 1 \text{ pint (pt.)}$$

$$\left.\begin{array}{l} 32 \text{ fluid ounces} \\ 2 \text{ pints} \end{array}\right\} = 1 \text{ quart (qt.)}$$

4 quarts = 1 gallon (gal.)

Mass
16 ounces (oz.) = 1 pound (lb.)
2000 pounds = 1 ton (T.)

Temperature
Water freezes at 32 degrees Fahrenheit (32° F).
Water boils at 212 degrees Fahrenheit (212° F).

Glossary

Numbers in parentheses refer to chapter and lesson numbers.

altitude (AL-tuh-tood)   In geometry, the shortest segment from a vertex to the opposite base. (15.1)

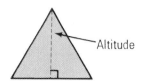

Altitude

area   The measure of the region inside a polygon or other figure. Area is measured in square units. (14.5)

average   Mean. (10.1)

balance column   In a check register, the column that shows how much money is left in an account. (Appendix)

bar graph   A diagram in which parallel bars represent quantities. (9.1)

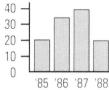

capacity (kuh-PAS-uh-tee)   The amount of space that can be filled. (8.1)

chance   The likelihood that a particular event will occur; also called *probability*. (13.1)

circle   A figure in which each point is an equal distance from its center. (14.1)

circle graph   A circular diagram divided into regions that represent data. (9.1)

circumference (sir-KUM-fer-ence) The distance around a circle. (14.4)

cone   a three-dimensional figure, as pictured below. (15.7)

cube   A three-dimensional figure with square surfaces. (15.3)

customary measurement   The system used in the United States for nonscientific measurement. Examples: feet, yards, quarts. (8.1)

cylinder (SIL-ihn-dur)   A three-dimensional figure with equal circular bases that are parallel. (15.4)

data   Facts and figures. (10.1)

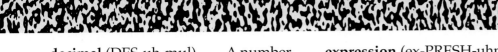

decimal (DES-uh-mul)   A number in which quantities less than 1 are expressed by place values based on 10. Example: 1.13, 9.7, 0.004. (1.2)

deductions   Obligatory and/or voluntary payments deducted from a paycheck. (Appendix)

denominator (dih-NOM-uh-nay-ter) In the fraction $\frac{3}{4}$, the denominator is 4. (5.1)

diameter (dy-AM-ih-tur)   A line segment passing through the center of a circle, with endpoints on the circle. (14.4)

Diameter

difference   The result of subtraction. (1.10)

dividend (DIV-uh-dend)   In $600 \div 15 = 40$, 600 is the dividend. (3.1)

divisor (dih-VY-zur)   In $600 \div 15 = 40$, 15 is the divisor. (3.1)

equally likely outcomes   Results with the same changes of occurring. (13.2)

equation (ee-KWAY-zhun)   A statement that two expressions are equal. Example: $2n + 5 = 15$. (16.1)

equivalent fractions   Fractions that represent the sane number. Example: $\frac{2}{3}$ and $\frac{4}{6}$. (5.3)

equivalent ratio   A ratio that represents the same comparison as a given ratio. Example: 1 : 2 and 2 : 4. (11.1)

event   In probability, an outcome or a group of outcomes. (13.1)

expression (ex-PRESH-uhn)   A mathematical phrase. Examples: x, $4x$, $n + 12$. (16.1)

factors   Numbers being multiplied; also called *multipliers*. (2.1)

favorable outcome   A desired result. (13.1)

Fermi (FER-mee) **problem**   A problem in which you must estimate an answer, using only common sense and commonly known information. (17.9)

formula (FORM-yuh-luh)   A statement of a mathematical rule. Example: The formula for the area of a rectangle is Area = length × width, or $A = l \times w$. (14.2)

fraction   A number that names part of a whole or part of a group. (5.1)

frequency (FREE-kwen-see)   The number of times an event occurs. (10.1)

frequency table   A table that tells how many times a group of events occurs. (10.2)

gram (g)   In the metric system, the basic unit used to measure mass. (4.1)

graph   A drawing or diagram that provides information. (9.1)

greatest common factor (GCF) The greatest factor shared by each number in a given set. Example: 4 is the GCF of 12 and 16. (5.5)

gross pay   The amount of pay earned before deductions are subtracted. (Appendix)

height The length of an altitude. (14.1)

hexagon (HEX-uh-gon) A polygon with six sides. (14.1)

histogram (HIS-tuh-gram) A bar graph that shows frequency. (10.6)

horizontal scale The line running across the bottom of a graph, giving information about what is represented on the graph. (9.1)

hypotenuse The side opposite the right angle in a right triangle (Appendix)

identity property Rule stating that any number multiplied by 1 equals that number. (2.1)

improper fraction A fraction with a numerator that is greater than or equal to the denominator. Examples: $\frac{3}{2}; \frac{6}{6}$. (5.1)

integer (IN-tih-jur) A whole number or its opposite. (17.1)

line graph A graph that uses an unbroken line to show trends or changes over time. (9.1)

liter (L) In the metric system, the basic unit used to measure volume, or capacity. (4.1)

lowest common denominator (LCD) The smallest number that can be divided by each denominator in a given set of fractions. Example: 20 is the lowest common denominator of $\frac{3}{4}$ and $\frac{1}{10}$. (7.2)

lowest terms A fraction is in lowest terms when 1 is the GCF of the numerator and the denominator. Examples: $\frac{1}{2}, \frac{7}{13}$, and $\frac{15}{4}$ are in lowest terms. (5.6)

mean The value obtained by dividing the sum of a set of numbers by the number of items in the set. Example: the mean of 3, 4, and 8 is $15 \div 3 = 5$. (10.1)

median The middle number in an ordered set of numbers. (10.3)

11
14
17   Median
19
20

meter (m) In the metric system, the basic unit used to measure length or distance. (4.1)

mixed number A number that consists of a whole number and a fraction. Example: $3\frac{5}{8}$. (5.1)

mode The number that occurs most frequently in a set of numbers. (10.3)

7
7
9
9   Mode
9
11
13

multiple A multiple of a given number is obtained by multiplying that number by any whole number. Example: Multiples of 4 are 4, 8, 12, etc. (2.3)

multiple event In probability, a situation involving more than one outcome. Example: A coin tossed twice. (13.5)

multipliers Numbers being multiplied; also called *factors*. (2.1)

negative integer An integer less than zero. (17.1)

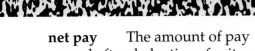

net pay The amount of pay earned after deductions for items such as income tax. (Appendix)

numerator (NOO-mer-ay-tur) In the fraction $\frac{3}{4}$, the numerator is 3. (5.1)

odds A ratio used in mathematics to express the chance of an outcome occurring. (13.3)

opposite integers Two integers the same distance from zero on the number line. Example: +5 and −5. (17.1)

ordered pair A pair of numbers that corresponds to a location on a grid. (17.4)

origin (OR-ih-jun) In mathematics, the point where the horizontal and vertical number lines meet on a grid. (17.4)

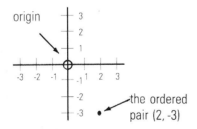

outcome In probability, the result of an experiment. (13.1)

parallel (PAR-uh-lel) **lines** Two lines that are the same distance apart and that never meet. (14.1)

parallelogram A four-sided polygon whose opposite sides are parallel. (14.5)

pentagon (PEN-tuh-gon) A polygon with five sides. (14.1)

percent Per hundred. Example: 12% means 0.12, or $\frac{12}{100}$. (12.1)

perimeter (puh-RIM-uh-tur) The distance around a shape or a figure. (14.1)

pi (py) The ratio of the circumference of a circle to its diameter, written as π. π is ≈3.14, or $\frac{22}{7}$. (14.4)

pictograph A graph in which pictures represent quantities. (9.1)

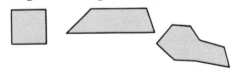

Pictograph
Test Score Distribution

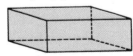

= 2 Students

polygon (POL-ee-gon) A two-dimensional figure such as a square, triangle, or octagon. (14.1)

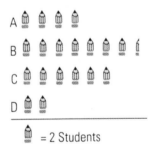

polyhedron (pol-ee-HEE-drun) A three-dimensional figure with faces that are polygons. (15.1)

positive integer A whole number greater than zero. (17.1)

power   A number obtained by multiplying a given number by itself. Examples: Powers of 10 are 100 (10 × 10), 1000 (10 × 10 × 10), etc. (2.3)

prism (PRIZ-uhm)   A three-dimensional figure with two parallel, identical faces. (15.3)

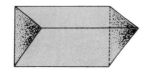

probability (prob-uh-BIL-uh-tee) The likelihood that a particular event will occur; also called *chance*. (13.1)

product   The result of multiplication. In 6 × 7 = 42, the product is 42. (2.1)

proper fraction   A fraction with a numerator that is less than the denominator. Example $\frac{3}{5}$. (5.1)

property   A characteristic or rule. (2.1)

proportion   A mathematical statement that two ratios are equal. Example: $\frac{3}{6} = \frac{1}{2}$. (11.2)

pyramid (PIR-uh-mid)   A three-dimensional figure with a base that is a polygon and triangular sides. (15.4)

Pythagorean (puh-thag-uh-REE-uhn) **Theorem**   A rule stating that the square of the hypotenuse of a right triangle is equal to the sum of the squares of the two other sides. (Appendix)

quotient (KWOH-shunt)   The result of division. In 600 ÷ 15 = 40, 40 is the quotient. (3.1)

radius (RAY-dee-uhs)   A line segment with endpoints at the center of a circle and at a point on the circle. (14.4)

Radius

range   The difference between the largest and the smallest number in a set of numbers. (10.3)

ratio   A comparison of two numbers by division. Example: A ratio of 4 : 2 would represent 4 books for 2 people. (11.1)

reciprocal (ruh-SIP-ruh-cuhl)   A number formed by exchanging a fraction's numerator and denominator. When reciprocals are multiplied, the product is 1. Example: $\frac{3}{2}$ is the reciprocal of $\frac{2}{3}$; $\frac{3}{2} \times \frac{2}{3} = 1$. (6.6)

rectangle (REK-tan-guhl)   A four-sided polygon with four right angles. (14.5)

rectangular prism   a three-dimensional figure with rectangular faces. (15.3)

regular polygon   In a regular polygon, all sides have equal length and all angles are equal. (14.1)

remainder　When 14 is divided by 3, 2 is left and is the remainder. (3.2)

right angle　An angle as pictured below. (14.5)

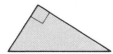

right triangle　A triangle containing a right angle. (Appendix)

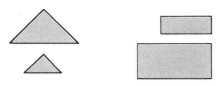

scale drawing　A drawing of an object with dimensions proportional to those of the actual object. (11.5)

similar figures　Figures that have the same shape and are proportional in size. (11.7)

square　A polygon with four right angles and four sides of equal length. (14.1)

square root　The square root of a given number is a number which, when multiplied by itself, gives the original number. Example: The square root of 9 is 3 because $3 \times 3 = 9$. (Appendix)

statistics　Numerical data organized and analyzed to give information. (10.1)

subtotal　A partial sum. (12.11)

sum　The result of addition. In $12 + 24 = 36$, 36 is the sum. (1.9)

surface area　The total area of all the faces of a three-dimensional figure. (15.1)

times　Multiplied by. (2.1)

trapezoid (TRAP-uh-zoid)　A four-sided polygon that has exactly one pair of parallel sides. (14.7)

tree diagram　A diagram showing all possible outcomes of a series of events. (13.5)

triangle　A three-sided polygon. (14.1)

unit price　The cost of one unit of a product. (11.4)

unknown　In algebra, a symbol, such as x, used to represent a quantity; also called *variable*. (16.1)

variable (VAR-ee-uh-buhl)　In algebra, a symbol, such as x, used to represent a quantity; also called *unknown*. (16.1)

vertical scale　The line running up and down at the left of a graph, giving information about what is represented on the graph. (9.1)

volume　The amount of space inside a three-dimensional figure. (15.1)

whole number　Any counting number or zero. Examples: 7, 99, 1376. (1.1)

zero property　Rule stating that any number multiplied by 0 equals 0. (2.1)

Index

Feet, 176
Fermi problems, 388–389
Fluid ounces, 184
Formula, using a, 392–393
Fractions, 110
  adding and subtracting, with like
    denominators, 150–151
  adding, with unlike denominators,
    154–155
  career application of, 144–145
  comparing, 116–117
  different strategy for working
    with, 160–161
  dividing, 140–141
  estimating with, 168–169
  estimating products of, 138–139
  factoring to find GCF, 118–119
  finding equivalent, 112–113
  finding patterns with, 124–125
  improper, 111
  multiplying, 130–131
  proper, 111
  simplifying problems with,
    164–165
  subtracting, with unlike
    denominators, 158–159
  understanding, 110–111
  writing as decimals, 122–123
  writing as percents, 266–267
  writing in lowest terms, 120–121
  writing mixed numbers as,
    114–115
  writing percents as, 268–269
Frequency table, 226–227

G

Gallons, 184
GCF, 118–119
Geography, 267, 355
  computing odds in, 293
  integers in, 372, 373
  mapping and coordinate graphing,
    378–379
  measuring mass in, 95
  scale maps, 256–257
  statistics in, 237
Geometry
  analyzing diagrams, 326–327
  areas of circle, 324–325
  areas of rectangles and other
    parallelograms, 318–319
  areas of trapezoid, 322–323

  area of triangle, 320–321
  career application of, 346–347
  circumference, 316–317
  constructing polyhedron models,
    334–335
  estimating lengths and
    perimeters, 314–315
  perimeters of polygons, 312–313
  surface areas of cubes and
    prisms, 336–337
  surface areas of pyramids and
    cylinders, 338–339
  three-dimensional figures,
    332–333
  two-dimensional figures, 310–311
  volumes of cubes, prisms, and
    pyramids, 340–341
  volumes of cylinders and cones,
    344–345
Grams, 86, 94
Graphs, 202
  bar, 202, 204–209
  choosing appropriate, 218–219
  circle, 202, 216–217, 270–271
  coordinate, 378–379
  double bar, 206–207
  intervals on, 203
  introduction to, 202–203
  line, 202, 210–213
  percents in, 270–271
  pictographs, 202, 214–215
  single bar, 204–205
  statistics in, 236–237
  vertical and horizontal scales of,
    203
Greater than, 10
Greatest common factor (GCF),
  118–119
Gross earnings, 192–193, 461
Guess and check, 134–135,
  360–361

H

Harmonious sevenths, 125
Height
  of cylinders, 338–339, 344–345
  of prisms, 336–337
  of pyramids, 338–339
  of trapezoid, 322–323
  of triangle, 320–321
Histograms, 234–235

History applications, 212–213,
  275, 341
Horizontal scale, 203
Hour, 190

I

Identity property, 31
Improper fraction, 111
Inches, 176
  cubic, 333
Increase, percent of, 280–281
Independent events, 301
Integers, 372
  adding, 374–375
  addition and subtraction
    equations with, 384–385
  dividing, 382–383
  introduction to, 372–373
  multiplication and division
    equations with, 386–387
  multiplying, 380–381
  negative, 373
  opposite, 373
  positive, 373
  subtracting, 376–377
  two-step equations with negative,
    390–391
Intervals, on graph, 203
Isolation, of variable, 364

K

Kilo-, 87
Kilogram, 94

L

LCD, 152–153
Length
  converting customary units of,
    176–177
  converting metric units of, 88–89
  estimating perimeter and,
    314–315
  measuring with customary units
    of, 178–179, 465
  measuring with metric units of,
    90–91, 465
Less than, 10
Line graphs, 202
  constructing, 212–213

Prism, 336
surface area of, 336–337
volume of, 340–341
Probability, 288
computing odds, 292–293
counting principle, 298–299
dependent and independent
events, 301
finding simple, 290–291
introduction to, 288–289
investigating, 300–301
of multiple event, 298–299
relating odds to, 294–295
tree diagram, 296–297
Problem solving
break a problem into parts,
342–343, 389
choose the appropriate graph,
218–219, 236–237, 271
choose the operation, 30–31,
70–71
choosing ways to compute, 50–51
construct models, 334–335
estimate, 92–93, 314–315,
388–389
four-step process for, 6–9, 38–39,
68–69
guess and check, 134–135,
360–361
look for patterns, 124–125
make a chart, 38–39
make a drawing, 252–253
make a table, 100–101, 145,
173, 241
read a map, 256–257, 378–379
read a table, 98–99, 144–145,
182–183, 367
simplifying the problem, 164–165
use alternate strategies, 160–161,
190–191, 282–283
use a diagram, 250–253,
296–297, 326–327
use a formula, 392–393
use a graph, 270, 378–379
Product, 30
cross, 244
estimating, 40–41
of fractions and mixed numbers,
estimating, 138–139
Proper fractions, 111
Proportions, 244
finding, 244–245
in problem solving, 256–257

in scale drawings, 250–253
in similar figures, 254–255
solving, 246–247
in unit pricing, 248–249
Pyramid, 338
surface area of, 338–339
volume of, 340–341
Pythagorean theorem, 460

Q

Quadrants, 378
Quarts, 184
Quotients, 57
estimating, 62–63
interpreting, 458
rounding, 76–77

R

Radius, 316–317, 324–325
Range, 228–229
Rates, 242–243
Ratios, 242–243
Receipts, sales, 462
Reciprocals, 140–141
Rectangle, 318
area of, 318–319
perimeter of, 312
Rectangular prism, 336–337
surface area of, 336–337
volume of, 340–341
Reduction
price, 6–7
size, 246
Regular polygon, 311
Repeating decimals, 124–125
Right angle, 310
Right triangles, 460
Rounding
with customary units of length,
178–179
decimals, 16–17
quotients, 76–77, 458
whole numbers, 14–15

S

Sales receipts, 462
Scale, horizontal and vertical
203
Scale drawings, 250–253

Science
adding fractions with unlike
denominator in, 154
application, 317, 363
averages in, 233
gravity table, 182–183
line graphs in, 210–211
measuring in, 92–93
temperature scales, 188
Short ton, 180
Similar figures, 254–255
Social studies applications,
207, 388–389
Sociology application, 206–207
Sports, 205, 265
adding integers in, 374
adding mixed numbers in, 156
application, 205, 265, 355, 359
comparing decimals in, 13
constructing bar graphs in,
208–209
converting customary units of
length in, 177
division in, 55
dividing mixed numbers in, 142
estimating with fractions and
mixed numbers in, 168
estimating lengths and perimeters
in, 314
finding lowest common
denominator in, 152
finding mean in, 230–231
percentages in, 266
rounding whole numbers in, 14
subtracting mixed numbers in,
162
subtracting whole numbers in, 22
tree diagram in, 297
using a formula in, 392–393
Square pyramid, 338
surface area of, 338–339
volume of, 340–341
Square root key, 460
Squaring, 460
Standard numeral, 2–3
Statistics
career application of, 224,
236–237
frequency table, 226–227
histograms, 234–235
introduction to, 224–225
mean, 230–231
range, mode, and median, 228–229

Photo/Art Credits

Cover John Payne/Stefano Carbini
Title Page John Payne/Stefano Carbini
Chapter Opener Design Design Five, Inc.

Assignment Photography
Ralph Brunke: 1, *r* 2, 9, 10, 11, 12, 14, 15, 18, 19, 20, 21, 23, 25, 29, *t* 30, 31, 32, 33, *r* 34, 36, 40, 44, 45, 46, 48, 49, 58, 59, 62, 64, *r* 76, 77, 78, 80, 85, *b* 88, *b* 92, *l* 94, 95, 96, 97, *l* 99, *t* 100, 109, *l* 112, 113, 114, 116, 117, 129, 130, *r* 132, 133, *l* 144, 145, 149, 150, 151, 160, 175, *l* 218, 223, *tr,b* 226, 228, 229, 241, 243, 250, 251, 252, 253, 255, *r* 266, 270, 273, *r,l* 274, 280, 282, 287, *t* 288, *r* 290, 291, 293, 297, 302, 303, 309, 314, 315, 316, 317, 331, 338, 342, 347, 351, *l* 352, 354, 356, 357, 365, *l* 366, 371, *l* 374, *l* 378, 380, *b* 386, 389, 391, *b* 392; Charles Shotwell: *l* 2, 4, *b* 30, *l* 34, 56, 60, 72, *l* 76, *t* 88, 90, *br* 92, *r* 94, *r* 112, 120, 122, *l* 132, 134, 136, 138, 140, 142, *r* 144, 156, 164, *r* 218, *tl* 226, 230, 232, *in* 242, 244, 248, *l* 266, *c* 274, 276, *l* 290, 292, 296, 298, 300, 310, *in* 317, 322, 344, *r* 352, 360, *l* 364, *r* 366, *r* 374, 376, *r* 378, *l* 382, *t* 386; Simone Studios: 16, 66, 79, 87, 272; 22 Robert Beck, Focus West; 50 David K. Crow/PhotoEdit; 91 Stephen Earley; 92 *t* Bettmann Archive; 93 Michael Melford, Wheeler Pictures; 98 Georgine Knoll; 99 Fritz Bronzel, Peter Arnold; 100 *b* Peter Hendrie, Image Bank; 101 Robert Frerck, Click/Chicago; 164 John Beykin/PhotoEdit; 166 J Sohm/The Image Works; 174 ©MONKMEYER/Siteman; 201 Frithfoto, Bruce Coleman; 202 Steve Satushek, Image Bank; 204 Myrleen Ferguson/PhotoEdit; 212 Bettmann Archive; 218 James L. Shaffer©; 226 Frans Lanting; 233 NASA; 242 H. Armstrong Roberts; 254 Suzanne Murphy, Click/Chicago; 257 *l* FPG; *r* FPG; 264 Focus on Sports; 270 *t* Frank Loose; *b* Thomas Craig, FPG; 288 *bl* William Warren, Click/Chicago; *br* Steve Meltzer, West Stock; 301 Marc Pokempner, Click/Chicago; 309 Aram Gesar, Image Bank; 326 Chuck O'Rear, West Light; 346 *l* Robert Perron; *c* Robert Perron; *r* Robert Perron; 358 Terry Murphy, Animals, Animals; 363 JPL; 364 *r* Walter Chandoha; 372 *b* Stock Photos, Image Bank; *t* T. Mareschal, Image Bank; 382 Frank Loose; 384 ©Will Hart/ PhotoEdit; 388 *t* Eric Meola, Image Bank; *b* Fermilab; 392 Robert Soltis, Nawrocki Stock Photo; Hutchings Photography: facing 1, 28, 54, 84, 108, 128, 148, 172, 200, 222, 240, 260, 286, 308, 330, 350, 370.

Illustrators
Martin Austin: 92, 130, 139, 157, 165, 169, 177, 189, 194, 261, 310, 353, 358, 377, 383; Steven Boswick: 29, 40, 46, 51, 66, 70, 71, 72, 90, 98, 100, 113, 134, 185, 190, 194, 223, 234, 253, 334, 340, 373, 386, 399; David Lee Csicsko: 2, 24, 176, 287, 360; Steve George: 12; Linda Kelen: 56, 57, 110, 188, 294, 351; Ligature: 3, 4, 6, 8, 13, 20, 30, 37, 38, 45, 47, 48, 55, 63, 68, 85, 88, 90, 98, 100, 109, 110, 111, 124, 125, 126, 127, 129, 137, 138, 139, 149, 165, 173, 174, 178, 187, 192, 202, 203, 204, 205, 206, 207, 210, 211, 212, 213, 214, 215, 217, 220, 221, 225, 226, 229, 230, 231, 234, 249, 250, 252, 255, 263, 264, 265, 268, 270, 271, 272, 275, 277, 281, 289, 291, 307, 309, 311, 312, 313, 315, 316, 317, 318, 319, 320, 321, 322, 323, 324, 325, 326, 327, 328, 329, 332, 333, 334, 336, 337, 339, 340, 341, 342, 344, 346, 347, 348, 349, 360, 372, 378, 379, 381, 392, 399; Tim McWilliams: 6, 60, 74, 158, 199, 224, 258, 262, 263, 290, 291, 343, 390; Precision Graphics: 9, 56, 98, 119, 140, 154, 155, 168, 182, 210, 236, 237, 312, 332, 343, 344, 353, 356, 372; William Rieser: 124, 250, 292, 293, 346, 362; Slug Signorino: 118, 162, 163, 324; Dave Stuckey: 216, 218, 246, 300; Paul Vaccarello: 107, 109, 129, 140, 149, 159, 224, 232, 248, 278, 279, 280, 296, 336, 376.